Skills & Knowledge of Cost Engineering

Fifth Edition Revised
With New Appendix Listings

Edited by Dr. Scott J. Amos, PE

2007

A Special Publication
of
AACE International – the Association for the Advancement of Cost Engineering

SKILLS & KNOWLEDGE
OF
COST ENGINEERING

Fifth Edition, Revised
With New Appendix Listings

Edited by Dr. Scott Amos, PE

A continuing project of the AACE International Education Board

Education Board Members:

Mark T. Chen, PE CCE, Chair
Dr. Scott J. Amos, PE, Co-Chair and Editor
William R. Barry, CCE
Lawrence J. Bloch, ECCE
Brian D. Dunfield
M. Steven Franklin, CCE
Donald F. McDonald, Jr. PE CCE
Franklin D. Postula, PE CCE
Dr. Parviz F. Rad, PE CCE
Rohit Singh, CCE
Dr. George Stukhart, PE
Michael B. Pritchett, CCE
Sean T. Regan, CCE
Harry W. Jarnagan, PE CCE

Technical Production Staff:

Charla Miller, Staff Director Education and Administration
Marvin Gelhausen, Managing Editor
Cathie Falvey, Production Editor
Noah Kinderknecht, Graphic Designer
Robin Donley, IT/IM/Graphics Specialist

Support the AACE Education Fund

Net proceeds from the sale of this book go to the AACE Education Fund and support scholarship grants at many colleges and universities in the U.S. and Canada. Your tax-deductible donations to the AACE Education Fund are also welcome in any amount. Donations are tax deductible in both the U.S. and Canada. Please make your checks payable to AACE and mail them to:

AACE Education Fund
209 Prairie Avenue
Suite 100
Morgantown, WV 26501 USA

Printing by:

ISBN: 1-885517-49-1

CONTENTS

DEPRECIATION-
CHAPTERS 7 & 10.14

PREFACE

Cost Engineers: Who are they and what do they do?

So just what is cost engineering and who are the people we call cost engineers? The first place to seek an answer is the *AACE International Constitution and Bylaws*, which states the following:

> **Section 2**. The Association is dedicated to the tenets of furthering the concepts of Total Cost Management and Cost Engineering. Total Cost Management is the effective application of professional and technical expertise to plan and control resources, costs, profitability and risk. Simply stated, it is a systematic approach to managing cost throughout the life cycle of any enterprise, program, facility, project, product or service. This is accomplished through the application of cost engineering and cost management principles, proven methodologies and the latest technology in support of the management process.

> **Section 3**. Total Cost Management is that area of engineering practice where engineering judgment and experience are utilized in the application of scientific principles and techniques to problems of business and program planning; cost estimating; economic and financial analysis; cost engineering; program and project management; planning and scheduling; and cost and schedule performance measurement and change control.

What this says is that the list of practice areas in Section 3 are collectively called *cost engineering*; while the "process" through which these practices are applied is called *total cost management* or *TCM*. Let's elaborate a bit more.

TCM and its subprocesses (strategic asset management and project control) are defined in the "integration" chapter that follows this preface. However, we can summarize that chapter by saying that TCM is a management process focused on coming up with ideas for creating things (i.e., a strategic assets), analyzing and deciding upon the best idea, and finally planning and creating the selected thing (i.e., by doing projects) in a controlled way (i.e., project control). So, that's the process; but who performs the process?

Many people would say that "engineers" and engineering are most often responsible for creating functional things (or strategic assets as we call them). They are correct. However, there are multiple elements to engineering. Most look at engineering and see the element of physical "design" and the calculation and analysis tasks that are done to support that physical design (e.g., design a bridge). Again they are correct. However, many people don't see that beyond the physical dimension of the design (e.g., the bridge structure), there are less tangible dimensions of money, time, and other resources that are invested in the creation of the asset. We refer to these investments collectively as "costs". Someone needs to estimate what the bridge might cost, determine the activities needed to design and build it, estimate how long these activities will take, and so on. Furthermore, someone needs to continually monitor and assess the progress of the bridge design and construction (in relation to the expenditure of money and time) to ensure that the completed bridge meets the owner's objectives. This is a lot of work. It requires special skills and knowledge.

The cost dimension requires calculation, analysis, planning, and control. No bridge has ever been built without dealing with both the physical and cost dimensions. However, the engineering skills and knowledge required to deal with "costs" are quite different from those required to deal with the physical design dimension. From that difference, the field of cost engineering was born. So, cost engineers work alongside of and are peers with engineers (or software analysts, play producers, architects, and other creative fields) to handle the cost dimension. And, returning to the Constitution and Bylaws definition, the skills and knowledge needed by that dimension are "business and program planning; cost estimating; economic and financial analysis; cost engineering; program and project management; planning and scheduling; and cost and schedule performance measurement and change control." All these functions are performed in an integrated way through the process of TCM.

Cost engineers often specialize in one function with a focus on one side of the asset and project business. They may have titles such as cost estimator, parametric analyst, strategic planner, scheduler, cost/schedule engineer, project manager, or project control lead. They may work for the business that owns and operates the asset (emphasis on economics and analysis), or they may work for the contractor that executes the projects (emphasis on planning and control). But, no matter what their job title or business environment, a general knowledge of, and skills in, all areas of cost engineering are required to perform their job effectively.

The History of this Publication

This AACE International publication had its beginnings in 1985, when the Education Board started work on the AACE Recommended Practice: *Required Skills & Knowledge of a Cost Engineer*. Board members included Brian D. Dunfield (Chair), Dr. Brisbane H. Brown Jr., Frank J. Kelly Jr., CCE, James M. Neil, PE CCE, and Gord Zwaigenbaum, CCE. The AACE staff administrator supporting the Education Board was Barry G. McMillan, our current AACE International executive director.

The document *Required Skills & Knowledge of a Cost Engineer* was published in August 1986 in *Cost Engineering* magazine. Then in 1987, a 13-session workshop was organized and presented at the AACE Annual Meeting in Atlanta. The presenters prepared instructional materials for the workshop, and Dr. James M. Neil, PE CCE, served as editor for a new AACE publication containing all of the instructional materials. The publication, *Special Supplement-1987 Transactions*, was the 1st edition of this publication. Similar sessions have been presented at AACE annual meetings every year since that first effort in 1987.

The following year (1987), the 2nd edition was published with its present title, *Skills & Knowledge of Cost Engineering*. Dr. James M. Neil, PE CCE, again served as editor. The content was increased to 17 chapters, and a consistent style was adopted.

Five years later (1992), the 3rd edition was published with Donald F. McDonald Jr., PE CCE, and Dr. James M. Neil, PE CCE, serving as co-editors. A large number of AACE International members became involved in the updating and revising of the published materials. The 18 chapters in this edition were presented as the basis of a system for teaching the basic skills and knowledge any cost engineer should possess.

The 4th edition—published in 1999 with Dr. Richard E. Larew, PE, CCE serving as editor—added new chapters, problems, and solutions, while grouping closely-related chapters into eight parts. The AACE International Canon of Ethics was also included as an appendix.

This Edition

The 5th edition, with 31 Chapters organized into seven sections, is the first step in aligning the content of educational materials within the Association to improve their value in the certification preparation process. Special attention is given to the need to have a good match between materials in this *Skills & Knowledge of Cost Engineering* and the *AACE International Certification Study Guide*.

New chapters include:

Introduction – Integration of Skills and Knowledge of Cost Engineering
Chapter 1 – Cost Elements
Chapter 2 - Pricing
Chapter 3 - Materials
Chapter 4 - Labor
Chapter 5 – Engineering
Chapter 6 – Equipment, Parts, Tools
Chapter 7 – Economic Costs
Chapter 8 – Activity Based Cost Management
Chapter 9 – Estimating
Chapter 21 – Project Labor Cost Control
Chapter 22 – Managing Project People
Chapter 23 – Quality Management
Chapter 24 – Value Analysis
Chapter 25 – Contracts
Chapter 26 – Strategic Asset Management
Chapter 29 – Statistics and Probability
Chapter 31 - Risk

As in past editions, all new materials have been subjected to independent reviews by professional cost engineers and other subject area experts.

The Next Edition

The Education Board will begin to review this 5th edition a short time after it has been published. It will begin to ask:

What technical corrections are needed?
Which chapters need to be updated or rewritten?
Which chapters need to be converted to SI units?
How can chapters best be grouped?
Are there chapters that should be eliminated or combined with others?
Should more multiproject and enterprise level chapters be included?

In addition, the Education Board will be considering needed changes in other AACE International publications. You, the reader and user of this publication, can be of great help to the Education Board and AACE International. You can make note of changes you believe should be made in the next edition. You can offer to help write or edit the next edition. Please take the time to send your suggestions to the Education Board chair. If your present objective is to become certified as a CCE or CCC, we hope this publication will be helpful to you.

A final reminder: net income from this publication goes into the fund for competitive scholarships offered by AACE International.

A special thanks to John Hollman and Dr. Richard E. Larew who contributed significantly to this preface.

Dr. Scott J. Amos, PE
Springfield, MO
January 2004

Dedication to Dr. James M. Neil, PE

1927 - 2003

AACE International Education Board Member 1982 – 1990

This 5th edition of the *Skills & Knowledge of Cost Engineering* is dedicated to the memory of Dr. James M. Neil, PE who was the editor of the first and second editions of this Education Board publication. Jim was much more than an editor and contributor to the early editions. He was an accomplished author, teacher, leader, and mentor to many AACE members and countless others in the profession.

It is through Jim's collective works and mentoring efforts that the first edition of the "S&K" text was an instant success that allowed future expanded editions to build on that success. This is the most popular book that AACE International has ever produced.

The original scope of cost engineering skills was a product of a survey developed by Jim Neil to ascertain what was important to working professionals. It listed hundreds of topics of relevant areas of technical expertise. Jim compiled an index of the most important and most used technical areas and, based on the response from AACE's membership, determined what was relevant and what was not. This led to the identification of the skills and knowledge of cost engineering standard criteria, and subsequently to the publication of the book, *Skills and Knowledge of Cost Engineering*, of which he was editor and author of nearly 50 percent of the material included in the first edition.

While Jim's mentoring and quiet advice has led many AACE members to become polished cost engineers, Jim and his wife Delores, became a part of the Association's extended family. Jim and Delores have helped many members learn how to combine and balance our social and professional lives.

The editor and authors of the 5th edition, along with AACE's Education Board, are dedicated to continually improving on Jim Neil's great start to the Skills & Knowledge series. We would encourage you to embrace the positive spirit Jim Neil embodied and use it to improve your knowledge of cost engineering.

by Donald F. McDonald, Jr. PE CCE – Education Board Member

ACKNOWLEDGMENTS

AACE International wishes to thank all contributors to the publication and to thank their employers for their support in making this most important project possible. Special thanks to AACE International staff members: Barry G. McMillan, Executive Director; Charla Miller, Staff Director Education and Administration; Marvin Gelhausen, Managing Editor; and Noah Kinderknecht, Graphic Designer. Thanks also to the Production Editor, Cathie Falvey. The following are persons who contributed to the development of this edition:

Introduction
John K. Hollmann, PE CCE

Cost Elements
Franklin D. Postula, PE CCE

Pricing
Rohit Singh, PEng CCE

Materials
Neil D. Opfer, CCE

Labor
Morris E. Fleishman, PE CCE

Engineering
Neil D. Opfer, CCE

Equipment, Parts and Tools
Dr. Carl C. Chrappa

Economic Costs
Neil D. Opfer, CCE

Activity-Based Cost Management
Gary Cokins

Estimating
Larry R. Dysert, CCC

Process Product Manufacturing
Dr. Kenneth K. Humphreys, PE CCE

Discrete Product Manufacturing
Dr. Robert C. Creese, PE CCE

Planning
Jennifer Bates, CCE

Scheduling
Anthony J. Werderitsch, PE CCE

Progress Measurement and Earned Value
Dr. Joseph J. Orczyk, PE

Earned Value for Variable Budgets
Dr. Joseph J. Orczyk, PE

Tracking Cost & Schedule Performance
Dr. Joseph J. Orczyk, PE

Performance and Productivity Management
Dr. James M. Neil, PE CCE

Project Management Fundamentals
James A. Bent, CCC

Project Organization Structure
James A. Bent, CCC

Project Planning
James A. Bent, CCC

Project Labor Cost Control
Dr. Joseph J. Orczyk, PE

Leadership and Management of Project People
Dr. Ginger Levin

Quality Management
Gary Cokins

Value Analysis
Del L. Younker, CCC

Contracting for Capital Projects
James G. Zack, Jr.

Strategic Asset Management
John K. Hollmann, PE CCE

Basic Engineering Economics
Dr. Scott J. Amos, PE

Applied Engineering Economics
Dr. Scott J. Amos, PE

Statistics and Probability
Mark T. Chen, PE CCE
Dr. Elizabeth Y. Chen

Basic Concepts in Descriptive Statistics
Dr. Frederick B. Muehlhausen

Risk Management
Allen C. Hamilton, CCE

Editor
Dr. Scott J. Amos, PE

Production of Skills & Knowledge, 5th Edition
Charla Miller
Marvin Gelhausen
Cathie Falvey
Noah Kinderknecht

These individuals contributed to the development of the first four editions:

Introduction
Dr. Richard E. Larew, PE CCE
Donald F. McDonald, Jr. PE CCE
Brian D. Dunfield

Cost Estimating Basics
Charles P. Woodward, PE CCE
Mark T. Chen, PE CCE
Duane R. Meyer, PE CCE
Donald F. McDonald, Jr. PE CCE
Dr. Kweku K. Bentil
Franklin D. Postula, PE CCE
Raymond A. Cobb

Order-of-Magnitude Estimating
Charles P. Woodward, PE CCE
Mark T. Chen, PE CCE
Duane R. Meyer, PE CCE
Donald F. McDonald, Jr. PE CCE
Dr. Kweku K. Bentil
Franklin D. Postula, PE CCE
Raymond A. Cobb

Definitive Estimates
Charles P. Woodward, PE CCE
Mark T. Chen, PE CCE
Duane R. Meyer, PE CCE
Donald F. McDonald, Jr. PE CCE
Dr. Kweku K. Bentil
Franklin D. Postula, PE CCE
Raymond A. Cobb

Manufacturing & Operating Costs
Dr. Robert C. Creese, PE CCE
Dr. Kenneth K. Humphreys, PE CCE

Cost Estimating Methods for Machining Operations
Dr. Robert C. Creese, PE CCE

Planning
Jennifer Bates, CCE
Remo J. Silvestrini, PE
Dr. James M. Neil, PE CCE
David L. Freidl, PE CCE

Scheduling Basics
Jennifer Bates, CCE
Dr. James M. Neil, PE CCE
Dr. Brisbane H. Brown, Jr.
David L. Freidl, PE CCE

James A. Bent, CCC
Dr. Gui Ponce de Leon, PE
Donald J. Fredlund, Jr.

Project Management Fundamentals
James A. Bent, CCC

Project Organization Structure
James A. Bent, CCC

Project Planning
James A. Bent, CCC

Contract Packages; Contracting Arrangements
James A. Bent, CCC

Basic Concepts in Descriptive Statistics
Dr. Frederick B. Muehlhausen

The International System of Units (SI)
Kurt G. R. Heinze, CCE

Communication
Dr. George Stukhart, PE

Change Control and Risk Analysis
James A. Bent, CCC

Word Processing & Graphics
LaQuita Caraway

Consulting Technical Editor
Judith Harris Bart

Scheduling Techniques
Jennifer Bates, CCE
Dr. James M. Neil, PE CCE
Dr. Brisbane H. Brown, Jr.
David L. Freidl, PE CCE

Progress & Cost Control I
Dr. Joseph J. Orczyk, PE
Dr. James M. Neil, PE CCE
F. Fred Rahbar

Project & Cost Control II
Dr. Joseph J. Orczyk, PE
T. Lynn Hyvonen
Dr. James M. Neil, PE CCE
F. Fred Rahbar

Project & Cost Control II
Dr. Joseph J. Orczyk, PE
Dr. James M. Neil, PE CCE
F. Fred Rahbar

Progress Measurement and Earned Value
Dr. Joseph J. Orczyk, PE

Earned Value for Variable Budgets
Dr. Joseph J. Orczyk, PE

Tracking Cost and Schedule Performance
Dr. Joseph J. Orczyk, PE

Basic Engineering Economics
Dr. Scott J. Amos, PE
Julian Piekarski, PE CCE

Applied Engineering Economics
Dr. Scott J. Amos, PE
Julian Piekarski, PE CCE

Performance & Productivity Management
Dr. James M. Neil, PE CCE
Dorothy J. Burton

Constructability
Dr. James M. Neil, PE CCE
Dorothy J. Burton

Value Engineering
Dr. James M. Neil, PE CCE
Dr. Brisbane H. Brown, Jr.
Dorothy J. Burton

Managing Contracts
James A. Bent, CCC
Dr. Gui Ponce de Leon, PE
Donald J. Fredlund, Jr.

Project Management Fundamentals
James A. Bent, CCC

Project Organization Structure
James A. Bent, CCC

Project Planning
James A. Bent, CCC

Contract Packages; Contracting Arrangements
James A. Bent, CCC

Basic Concepts in Descriptive Statistics
Dr. Frederick B. Muehlhausen

The International System of Units (SI)
Kurt G. R. Heinze, CCE

Communication
Dr. George Stukhart, PE

Change Control and Risk Analysis
James A. Bent, CCC

Word Processing & Graphics
LaQuita Caraway

Consulting Technical Editor
Judith Harris Bart

Editor
Dr. Richard E. Larew, PE CCE
Donald F. McDonald, Jr. PE CCE
Dr. James M. Neil, PE CCE

INTEGRATION OF THE SKILLS AND KNOWLEDGE OF COST ENGINEERING

John K. Hollmann, PE CCE

LEARNING OBJECTIVES

The objective of this chapter is show how the various skills and knowledge of cost engineering are integrated or brought together into a whole. There are three ways to view or model integration: from a work process or application perspective, from a human or organizational competency perspective, or from a physical perspective. This chapter examines the skills and knowledge of cost engineering from all three perspectives. It also serves as an adjunct to the text index, by showing how the various chapters are integrated in accordance with the integrative models.

At the end of the chapter, the reader should understand the following concepts:

- how cost engineering skills and knowledge can be integrated through a work process, specifically the total cost management (TCM) process;
- how cost engineering skills and knowledge can be integrated within the competency of a cost engineering professional and the collective competencies of an organization;
- how cost engineering skills and knowledge about individual resource types are integrated through creation of an asset;
- challenges to successful integration (e.g., bureaucracy, complacency, and lack of vision); and
- how the chapters of this text come together as a whole.

The reader of this chapter is expected to gain a conceptual understanding of how the skills and knowledge of cost engineering come together as a whole, not to learn the details of any particular integration model (e.g., TCM) or any particular skill or knowledge area.

CONCEPTS

Integration

Integration is broadly defined as bringing things together as a whole. However, this definition begs the question of a whole *what?*. In this chapter, "what" is defined a whole process (the activities cost engineers do), a whole person and organization (what cost engineers know and skills they have), and a whole asset (things that firms that employ cost engineers own). One author has referred to these three dimensions as the "strategic resources" of an organization [2].

As an integrative process model, AACE International is developing the Total Cost Management Framework [3]. The Framework defines TCM as the sum of the practices and processes that an enterprise uses to manage the total life cycle cost investment in its portfolio of strategic assets. The practices are called cost engineering; the process through which the practices are applied is called TCM.

By its nature, the TCM process is integrative. However, it is the people in organizations that make processes work. Only when an enterprise integrates its process with people that have the right set of skills and knowledge for the right tasks at the right time (i.e., the right personal and organizational competencies) will a process give an enterprise a competitive advantage.

Furthermore, there is a physical or resource dimension to integration. The objective of TCM is to manage the investment of resources through projects or programs in strategic assets. The asset is the physical end result of the integration of resources. So, integration can be thought of as the combination of process plus competency plus resources as brought together in projects to create competitive strategic assets.

There are factors that impede integration (i.e., that lead to disintegration). From a process and organizational perspective, bureaucracy is a major impediment. In a bureaucracy, the steps of a process are viewed as ends in themselves, and competency in an organization is viewed as skill in performing a particular step without regard for skill in facilitating the process. Bureaucracy works against successful team development. On an individual level, complacency is an impediment because integration requires that individuals renew their skills and knowledge to match the changes that occur in the work environment and process. Finally, a lack of vision of the objective of the TCM process impedes integration because failure to understand how all the resources come together in a project or asset risks project performance and/or asset quality. Lacking vision, the project or asset will not come together as a "whole" to meet the owner's needs and expectations.

Effective integration then is the dynamic combination of process, competency, and resources with an eye on project and asset objectives. By "dynamic," we mean that the people in an enterprise know when to modify their processes, renew their skills, and leverage shared resources in a way that yields projects, programs, and assets that collectively meet the owner's changing needs and expectations and give the enterprise a competitive advantage.

Integration from a TCM Process Perceptive

We will start our discussion of how the skills and knowledge of cost engineering and the chapters in this text are integrated by first examining the process perspective. TCM is a process map that by its nature is integrative. The TCM process model is based upon the "PDCA" management or control cycle (also known as the Deming or Shewhart cycle). The PDCA cycle is a generally accepted, quality driven, continuous improvement management model. PDCA stands for plan, do, check, and assess, with the word *check* being generally synonymous with *measure*. The word *assess* is sometimes substituted with the word *act* as in "to take corrective action". Figure 1 shows the TCM process map at an abstract level. In TCM, the PDCA model is applied in a nested manner, where-

by the basic PDCA process is applied for each asset and group of assets, and then again for each project being performed to create, modify, maintain, or retire those assets.

The two levels of the TCM process in Figure 1 are called the strategic asset management and project control processes. Project control is a process nested within the project implementation step of strategic asset management. An enterprise will have a portfolio of assets in various stages of their life cycles, and during each asset's life cycle, many projects will be performed (often as a program) to create, modify, or terminate that asset.

Chapter 26 covers how the steps and activities of cost engineering come together in the strategic asset management process (left side of Figure 1). The four chapters in section 4 (chapters 14 to 17) then describe how various cost engineering activities, and tools come together in project control (right side of Figure 1).

Products, in terms of the owner's technology, design, and knowledge of the product manufacturing process, are assets to an enterprise. As such, TCM also applies to the design and manufacturing of products. Chapters 10 and 11 describe how various activities and tools of cost engineering come together in process product and discrete product manufacturing applications respectively. Manufacturing applications such as materials requirement planning (MRP) are covered in these chapters.

Below the general application level, a more detailed process map is needed to understand how the individual skills and knowledge of cost engineering are integrated. The process maps in Figure 2 and Figure 3 provide the additional detail. The next few paragraphs briefly describe the TCM sub-process maps shown in these two figures, and then show how the *other*

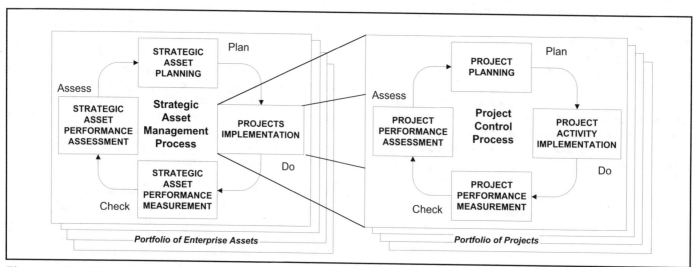

Figure 1—Total Cost Management Process Map [3]

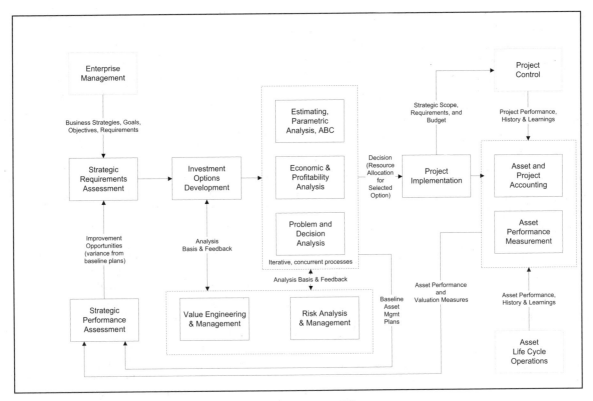

Figure 2. The TCM Strategic Asset Management Process [3]

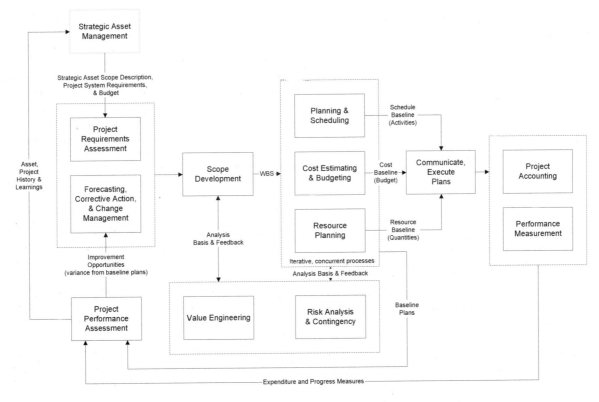

Figure 3. The TCM Project Control Process [3]

text chapters are linked using these process maps.

The strategic asset management process is detailed in Figure 2. This subprocess starts on the left with assessing the enterprise's objectives, requirements, and resource constraints. Benchmarking and other methods are also used to identify performance improvement opportunities for new or existing assets. The information from these steps is used in formulating strategic asset performance requirements. Considering the requirements and opportunities (and moving towards the center of the figure), asset investment options are identified and developed, and then evaluated and decided upon using a wide variety of asset planning and decision making techniques that should be familiar to cost engineers. The investment decisions that are made become part of the enterprise's integrated asset portfolio management plan. Asset investment plans and requirements are then communicated to and executed by project teams. The project teams return completed assets to the owner.

Moving to the right side of Figure 2, performance of assets and the project system that creates those assets are measured. A key measure is profitability, but there are many other measures such as quality. Coming back around to the left of the figure, asset performance is assessed to determine if the profitability, quality, and other measures vary from asset management plans and objectives. Also, trends or changes in performance are evaluated. If everything is according to plan, the strategic management process continues its cycle.

If there are performance deviations noted, action should be taken to correct or improve the trend. If performance corrections will affect asset portfolio investment plans, or changes to enterprise requirements or resource availability occur, then asset portfolio investment plans must be managed to incorporate the changes.

On the right of Figure 2, there is project implementation step. The project control process is nested within that project implementation step. Project control, as detailed in Figure 3, is a process for controlling the investment of resources in an asset.

On the left side of Figure 3, a project starts with assessing the enterprise's strategic asset requirements and aligning them with project performance requirements. Based upon the project requirements, the project technical scope and integrated plans for cost, schedule, and resource management are developed. The various planning steps in the middle of Figure 3 should again be familiar to cost engineers. Project performance is measured against these plan baselines.

Moving to the right side of Figure 3, the project plans are communicated to and executed by the project team. Teams usually include both owner and contractor personnel; therefore, contracting is integral to this step. The performance of project activities is then measured. Measurement steps

---

include accounting for cost expenditures and commitments, as well as physical progressing that includes measures of the work and resource quantities that have been completed. Moving back around to the left of Figure 3, activity performance is assessed. Assessment determines if the expenditures and progress vary from the plans and if there are trends in performance. If everything is according to plan, the project control process cycle continues on with more measurements.

If performance deviations or trends are noted in assessments, action is taken to correct or improve the performance trend. Forecasting techniques (scheduling, estimating, and resource planning) are used to determine if corrective actions will achieve plan targets. If performance corrections will affect the project scope (or changes to the requirements or scope are initiated by the owner), the project baseline plans must be managed to incorporate the changes.

The process maps in Figures 2 and 3 give a general idea of how the various skills and knowledge areas come together as a whole. However, the figures fail to show how truly integrated the process steps are. For example, the project planning and scheduling, estimating, and resource steps are closely tied. Estimators help determine activities for the schedule; schedulers determine activity duration that affects the estimated productivity; estimators provide resource quantities, that when loaded in a schedule, support resource planning, and so on. It is beyond the scope of this chapter to describe the myriad interconnections—however, readers must not view each step of the process map as independent (i.e., the bureaucratic view).

Having laid out the more detailed process maps, the following paragraphs describe how some of the text chapters are integrated from a process perspective.

Chapters 12 and 20 deal with planning both from a strategic and a project perspective. Chapter 12 describes high level activities and tools that roughly correspond to the asset planning process steps in Figure 2 (i.e., from requirements assessment through project plan implementation). Chapter 20 covers the corresponding project planning steps in Figure 3 (i.e., from requirements assessment through executing plans).

Chapter 2 and 7 on price and economic costs respectively delve into the basic concepts of the strategic economic and profitability analysis step shown in Figure 2 (e.g., discount rates, present value, and so on). These chapters also touch on the strategic assessment step (e.g., competition, markets, and so on) that precedes economic analysis. Chapters 27 and 28 cover the practices of engineering economics where the basic concepts of price and economic costs are pulled together into techniques for analyzing asset and project investment decision options.

Chapter 8 on activity-based costing (ABC) covers cost analysis methods that ensure that "activities" are properly recognized and addressed as causal drivers of cost. In other words, ABC helps ensure that when a decision is made to pursue or eliminate an activity, you truly know what the decision is going to cost because the causal link has been established.

Chapter 9 on estimating covers the specific activities and tools of this critical cost engineering planning step shown in both Figure 2 and Figure 3. It covers topics such as the various types of estimates, estimating techniques, contingency, and so on.

Chapter 13 on scheduling covers the specific activities and tools of this planning process step as shown in Figure 3. It covers topics such as work breakdown, scheduling techniques, and so on.

Chapter 21 on project labor cost control covers tools for analyzing labor cost performance, which is part of the "performance assessment" step in Figure 3. Labor costs are typically a major cost element of asset and project investments. Labor costs are also often the most variable (i.e., risky) element of cost.

A number of the text's chapters cover cost engineering "tools" that can also be viewed from a process integration perspective.

Chapter 31 on risk covers the specific activities and tools of this planning step shown in both Figure 2 and Figure 3. It covers topics such as the risk analysis process steps, risk analysis techniques, and contingency for both cost and schedule.

Chapter 23 on quality management covers topics such as the quality assurance and control, continuous improvement, and benchmarking. As was discussed, the TCM process map itself is based on a quality management model (i.e., the PDCA model). As such, Chapter 23 touches on all activities and tools in TCM.

Chapter 24 on value analysis covers the specific activities and tools of the value engineering and value management steps shown in both Figure 2 and Figure 3. It covers general topics such objective setting and team development, but also specific value engineering steps such as functional analysis.

Finally, Chapter 25 on contracts recognizes that there are multiple parties involved in implementing assets and projects. The roles and relationships of these parties are legally defined by contracts. Done well, contracting contributes to strong process and organizational integration and team development. Done poorly, contracting is a disintegrating factor. From a process perspective, contracting can be viewed as helping to define the links between any activity or step in the TCM process when parties other than the asset owner are involved. Contracting plays a very significant role in the "project implementation step" shown in Figure 2 and the "communicate and execute plans" step in Figure 3. These steps often involve a hand-off in roles and responsibilities for the asset or project.

There are other text chapters that cover basic concepts and knowledge areas that are more appropriately viewed from a competency integration perspective.

Integration from a Competency Perspective
As an integrated whole, the cost engineering skills and knowledge competency of an enterprise resides in the organization of the enterprise, not in any single individual. However, for an organization or team to function effectively, each individual needs to understand what the skills and knowledge competency of other individuals are and when to bring these personal competencies to bear in the asset or project life cycle. This text includes chapters that cover aspects of both personal as well as organizational competency.

Depending on its mission and scope, and enterprise will have a set of "core" competencies that are retained and fostered in-house. Other competencies will be considered non-core (i.e., not contributing to competitive advantage) and these will typically be out-sourced or contracted to other parties with strengths in those areas. One cost engineering competency that owners should never outsource is the basic cost knowledge of their asset base.

Some competencies are brought to bear in, or are central to, most if not all of the cost engineering skill areas and TCM process steps. For example, the concepts of statistics and probabilities are applied in cost estimating, scheduling, risk assessment, economic analysis, contract strategy development, forecasting, and many other areas. Much of cost engineering (as opposed to accounting) is predictive in nature; therefore, it is important that every cost engineer be competent in basic statistics and probabilities. However, some competencies are not as generically applicable. For example, a cost engineer whose role and responsibility is to perform strategic economic analysis is unlikely to make use of project scheduling tools (though understanding the concept of the critical path is useful in understanding project drivers and risks that affect economic analysis).

Figures 4 and 5 provide examples of how the importance of various skills and knowledge or competency areas of cost engineering increase and decrease over the course of asset

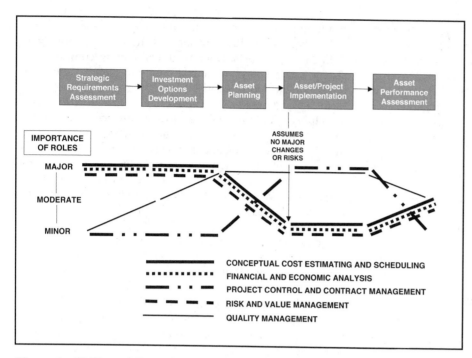

Figure 4—Skills and Knowledge Importance in the Asset Life Cycle

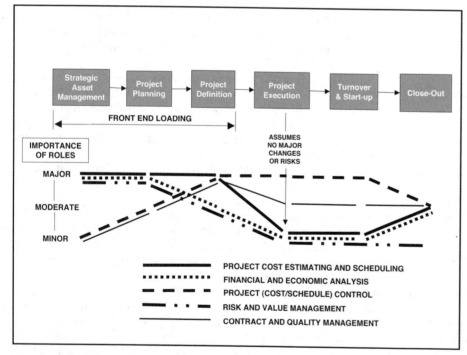

Figure 5—Skills and Knowledge Importance in the Project Life Cycle

and project life cycles respectively. The figures are only examples; the relative importance of each competency will be different for each enterprise, asset, or project. However, the point of the examples is to show that the competency of an enterprise cannot reside in any single individual. No one person can be the best at every skill and as asset and project life cycles progress, cost engineers with different competencies will be included on the team. Only with assets of the most limited scope or projects of the smallest size can one person do all the cost engineering tasks.

For example, Figure 4 shows that conceptual cost estimating competency is very important early in asset planning stages as asset options are evaluated. Later, as the asset is implemented (and assuming no changes in scope), the importance of conceptual cost estimating diminishes while the importance of cost/schedule control increases.

The competency related chapters of the text can be categorized in one of two groups; either general competencies or functional competencies. The importance of general competencies does not increase and decrease much over the course of asset or project life cycles. Each cost engineer needs excellent skills and knowledge in the general competencies. On the other hand, the importance of various functional competencies does change, and it is less important that each individual be strong in every functional competency.

The general competency areas start with Chapter 1 on cost elements. This chapter describes all the different types of cost. Topics such as fixed and variable costs, capital and expense, life cycle costs and other cost element concepts are covered. Understanding the concept of cost elements is critical to the competency of every cost engineer.

Chapters 18 and 19 cover project management fundamentals and project organization structure, respectively. The "fundamentals" chapter covers management knowledge that is critical to a cost engineer's personal competency in managing projects, while the "structure" chapter covers the organizational competencies needed for project management.

Chapter 22 on management of project people describes how people and organizations work together. It also covers topics such as leadership and ethical considerations. Whether or not a cost engineer is a manager, understanding management concepts is critical to their competency.

Chapters 29 and 30 on statistics and probability and descriptive statistics cover concepts such as distributions, confidence, accuracy, and simulation and modeling. As was discussed the concepts of statistics and probabilities are applied in cost estimating, scheduling, risk assessment, economic analysis, contract strategy development, and many other areas.

Many of thechapters described earlier from a "process integration" perspectivecan also be viewed from a competency perspective. For example, chapter 31 on risk covers a process step (risk management), general competency (risk concepts), and functional competency (quantitative risk analysis). .

Integration from a Resource Perspective

In this last section, we examine how some skills and knowledge of cost engineering and the chapters in this text are integrated from a resource or physical perspective. As was discussed, the objective of TCM is to manage the investment of resources through projects in strategic assets. The resources are integrated as a whole in the form of an asset. The primary resources that go into most assets are materials and labor. Equipment and tools are resources used by labor to manipulate the material resources. Labor includes labor to evaluate, design and manage an asset or project (e.g., engineering labor), as well as labor to build or create the asset (e.g., construction or fabrication labor), and later to operate or maintain the asset.

The chapters of the resources section of the text are best viewed from a resource integration perspective.

Chapter 3 on materials covers material types such as bulk, fabricated, and enginecred materials, as well as practices for managing materials such as purchasing, expediting, and inventory management.

Chapter 4 on labor covers labor types such as direct and indirect labor, but also labor issues such as productivity and the learning curve.

Chapter 5 on engineering focuses on one particular type of labor. Cost engineers often work as partners with other engineering discipline leads; the cost engineer's strong cost management competency compliments the design competency of the other engineers. Topics in this chapter include system and product design, engineering tools (CAD/CAM), and other engineering issues.

Chapter 6 on equipment parts and tools covers the resources that are used by labor to manipulate materials. Topics include the use, rental and lease of equipment are covered, as well as testing, operating and maintenance, and other issues.

PRACTICE PROBLEMS AND QUESTIONS

1. What does AACE International call the integrative process through which cost engineering skills and knowledge are practiced?

   Answer: Total Cost Management

2. What distinguishes competencies that an enterprise will keep in-house versus those that are typically outsourced?

   Answer: Something along the lines of competencies kept in house are those that do not contribute to competitive advantage.

3. When might it be reasonable to expect that one individual can do most of the cost engineering activities on a project?

   Answer: Something along the lines of only when an asset or project is of limited size and or scope.

DISCUSSION CASES

1. Assume you are responsible for cost estimating on a project. Discuss why it is important that you understand project scheduling practices.

   Answer: Along the lines of how cost/schedule integration supports resource planning, how you need to know durations and activity logic in order to understand crewing, supervision, and equipment needs, how time and money are related, how the cost and schedule work breakdown should be related to support resource loading and progressing, etc, etc .

2. Assume you are assigned cost engineering responsibilities on an ongoing project that has a bureaucratic project organization in place and poor cost and schedule performance. From various integration perspectives, discuss some actions you might recommend to project management to improve project performance.

   Answer: Along the lines of establishing an integrative project process or system, consider cross-training, ensure asset and project mission and objectives (vision) are communicated in a workshop, etc.

REFERENCES

1. AACE International. *Cost Engineering Terminology.* Recommended Practice No. 10S-90,
2. Hamel, Gary. *Leading the Revolution.* Harvard Business School Press.
3. AACE International. *Total Cost Management Framework.* www.aacei.org/technical.

Section 1

Cost

Chapter 1

Cost Elements

Franklin D. Postula, PE CCE

INTRODUCTION

Cost is a basic "yard stick" by which activities and assets are measured and compared. Because the word *cost* is so commonly used and generally related to monetary value, we may lose sight of its true meaning and importance as a cost engineering concept. This chapter is strategically located first in this *Skills & Knowledge* (S&K) textbook for the very reason that cost is a fundamental attribute of activities and assets.

Cost is one of the three fundamental attributes associated with performing an activity or the acquisition of an asset. These are (1) price (cost), (2) features (performance), and (3) availability (schedule).

The need to understand and quantify the attribute of cost spawned the engineering discipline of cost engineering. Cost engineering is the application of scientific principles and techniques to problems of estimation, cost control, business planning and management science, profitability analysis, project management, and planning and scheduling [3]. While this definition seemingly addresses non-cost areas, it lists key engineering activities that either generate cost when they are performed or define plans and processes that cause (or influence) cost to be generated in other activities and/or assets.

What are the elements that make up cost? How are these cost elements categorized and how do they relate to one another? Why is it important to collect and account for costs as they relate to specific activities and assets? And, finally, how do we apply these cost elements and categories to the insight for managing activities and assets? This chapter will provide you with a basic understanding of these cost fundamentals

and will give you the insight and background you will need as you study the following chapters in this S&K textbook.

LEARNING OBJECTIVES

After completing this chapter, the reader should be able to

- understand what makes up cost—i.e. the basic resources (material, labor, etc.) that are needed to perform an activity or create an asset;
- understand the distinction between cost elements that are directly applied to an asset and those that are indirectly applied;
- relate the cost elements to the life cycle of the asset: acquisition, use, and disposal;
- use the understanding of cost elements to further understand how cost is measured, applied, and recorded to arrive at the total activity and/or asset cost; and
- apply the knowledge gained to solve problems related to cost element source and definition.

CONCEPTS

Cost is the value of an activity or asset. Generally, this value is determined by the cost of the resources that are expended to complete the activity or produce the asset. Resources utilized are categorized as material, labor, and "other." Although money and time are sometimes thought of as resources, they only implement and/or constrain the use of the physical resources just listed. The path by which resources are converted (via a "project") to activities and assets is illustrated in Figure 1.1. The final activity or asset produced depends on what can be

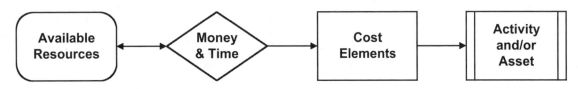

Figure 1.1— Conversion of Resources to Project Results

"afforded" given the money and time allocated to the project. Normally you think of material as the physical composition of the asset. However, the value of the asset may also include the cost elements of scrap material or manufacturing spares, construction form work and expendable safety items, and the cost of transporting the material to the work site.

Often, we think of labor as the value of the work needed to complete the activity or asset; i.e. the worker's labor in painting the building or soldering an electrical contact. Labor also includes the work of the engineer who prepares the design, the foreman supervising the field work, or the technician that maintains the wave soldering equipment.

The "other" cost category consists of resources needed to support the activity and/or asset. An example would be the facilities needed to produce an activity or asset, which would include the tooling, electricity, taxes, and maintenance, etc., necessary to keep the facility available for use. Other costs might be office supplies, communication costs, travel costs, and security costs.

Another important aspect of cost relates to whether one is the producer or consumer of an activity or asset. The cost categories just listed are those associated with the producer. The consumer has additional costs that add to the value of the activity or asset being acquired. A fundamental addition is profit for the producer. Generally, profit is established by market competition, although the law limits profit on certain government procurements.

The value of an asset or activity also may be related to intangible costs. The value of an art object is often related to the name of the artist. When evaluating alternatives, the value of each alternative should be assessed in terms of the benefits that can be expected if selected and the consequences that might be suffered if not selected [10]. An intangible benefit might be an avoided cost if the alternative is selected. For example, incorporating a spell checker into word processing software saves (avoids) the labor of manual checking.

An intangible negative consequence might be the cost of missing an opportunity because resources were invested in another alternative instead of the more beneficial one.

The following example illustrates the resource cost categories:

Example 1—John decides to build a deck on the back of his house. He draws up plans for the project, gets the building permit from the city, buys the material, hauls it home, and constructs the deck. The cost elements and categories associated with building this asset are shown in Table 1.1. Notice that some of these cost elements are not part of the physical deck, but are necessary in order to complete the project. Furthermore, some of the cost elements are not part of the

Table 1.1—Costs Associated with John's Deck

Category	Cost Elements
Materials	drafting paper/pencil, concrete, nails, lumber, deck screws, paint, brushes, turpentine, drop cloth
Labor	draw plans, get permit, get materials, construct footings, erect deck, paint deck, wife's support in making lunch
Other	building permit fee, use of house to draw plans, shovel, power saw, power drill, electricity; pickup truck, gasoline

work activity needed to get the deck built, but are essential to support the project. In the next section, we will see how these cost categories are structured.

COST STRUCTURING

It is important to further structure the cost elements within the material, labor, and other resource categories in order to understand how they influence the total cost of the activity or asset and to get a better understanding of how they can be controlled. This structuring sorts the cost elements into direct costs, indirect costs, fixed costs, and variable costs. In practice, some costs may fall in more than one of these groupings. This will be shown through an extension of the previous example.

Direct Costs
Direct costs are those resources that are expended solely to complete the activity or asset. In other words, "Any cost that is specifically identified with a particular final cost objective, but not necessarily limited to items that are incorporated in the end product as material or labor" [1]. Thus, the direct cost of a foundation for a house includes trenching for the footings, the wooden forms (if not reusable), the concrete, and the labor to place and finish the concrete. Direct costs for making a metal bowl would be the metal sheet stock and the stamping machine operator labor cost. The material cost for manufacturing the bowl would include the scrap from the stamping process less any salvage value.

Indirect Costs
Indirect costs are those resources that need to be expended to support the activity or asset but that are also associated with other activities and assets. In other words, "Any cost not directly identified with a single final cost objective but identified with two or more final cost objectives ..." [1]. Consequently, indirect costs are allocated to an activity or asset based upon some direct cost element, such as labor hours, material cost or both. Indirect costs also may be referred to as "overhead costs" or "burden costs." Indirect costs are general administrative activities associated with operating the business, costs for providing and maintaining field equipment or a manufacturing facility, and expenses for

utilities, taxes, legal services, etc.

Fixed Costs

Fixed costs are those cost elements that must be provided independent of the volume of work activity or asset production that they support. These can be either direct or indirect costs. The tool used to stamp the metal bowl is a direct fixed cost that is incurred whether 100 or 1,000 items are produced. The tools used to finish the concrete foundation are an indirect fixed cost since they can be reused on other concrete finishing work.

Variable Costs

Variable costs are those cost elements that must be provided and are dependent on the volume of work activity or asset production that they support. Again, these can be either direct or indirect costs. An example of a direct variable cost is the material used to form the metal bowl since the amount varies with the quantity produced. An indirect variable cost would be the electricity used to operate the stamping machine since it also varies with the quantity produced but is considered to be an overhead cost.

In business practice, cost element information may be

grouped in a variety of ways to provide the basis for management decisions. Some of these groupings are listed in Table 1-2. Bear in mind that this table only shows a representative list of cost groupings. Any set of cost groupings should be tailored to the individual company's method of doing business.

Let's see how the cost elements of Example 1 can be structured.

Example 2—John tries to better understand the costs associate with building the deck. He structures the costs as shown in Table 1.3 on page 1.4.

Table 1.2—Example Cost Element Groupings

Cost Center	Cost centers are groups of activities within a project that provide a convenient point for collecting and measuring costs. This could be a department in an engineering organization such as a structural design group. Or it could be process related such as a metal stamping operation.
Labor Craft	It may be convenient to group types of labor such as electricians, plumbers, etc. on a construction site. Or machinists, tool & die technicians, etc. in a manufacturing operation.
Material Type	These groups could be raw material, purchased parts, etc. in a manufacturing company. Or could be concrete, 1.5-inch and smaller pipe, etc. for a construction project.
Inventory	This could be the value of purchased material and equipment waiting to be used in manufacturing or installed in a facility under construction. This could also be the cost of finished goods waiting to be sold.
Overhead	As discussed previously, these are indirect costs that are allocated to labor and material cost elements. Examples are the cost of maintaining a manufacturing facility or the cost of the home office of a construction company that has several projects underway.
Equipment	This is the value of all machines, tools, and other equipment needed to support a manufacturing operation or a construction project.
Subcontracts	It is important to separately collect and report work that is contracted out to others in support of the project. This could be labor or material, direct or indirect work.
Other Direct Costs	Sometimes it is convenient to charge directly a cost that may also be treated as an indirect cost. Examples are travel expenses, start-up costs, plant protection, etc.
Commitments	This is a group of future costs that are represented by obligations to obtain subcontracted/purchased material and services. It's extremely important to have this information available when changes to production or construction plans occur.

Table 1.3—Costs Associated with John's Deck

Direct	
Material:	drafting paper, concrete, nails, lumber, deck screws, paint, turpentine
Labor:	draw plans, get permit, get materials, construct footings, erect deck, paint deck
Other:	building permit fee
Indirect	
Material:	pencil, brushes, drop cloth
Labor:	wife's support in making lunch
Other:	use of house to draw plans, shovel, power saw, power drill, electricity, pickup truck, gasoline
Fixed	
Direct:	get permit
Indirect:	use of house to draw plans, shovel, power saw, power drill, pickup truck, pencil, brushes, drop cloth
Variable	
Direct:	drafting paper, building permit fee, concrete, nails, lumber, deck screws, paint, turpentine, draw plans, get materials, construct footings, erect deck, paint deck
Indirect:	wife's support in making lunch, electricity, gasoline

As you consider these groupings of cost elements, you may realize that the variable direct cost elements are those that depend on the size of the deck. Although you might think of them as being "fixed" for this specific project, their value would change if the deck design were to change. Also, if a second identical deck were to be built, the value of these cost elements may go down due to efficiencies (learning) in performing the job.

In the next section, we will investigate the purpose for collecting and reporting cost elements and how these elements might be organized to provide information for management decision making.

COST ACCOUNTING

What is the purpose of cost accounting and why is it important? Cost accounting is defined as the historical reporting of disbursements and costs and expenditures on a project. When used in conjunction with a current working estimate, cost accounting can assist in giving the precise status of the project to date [7]. Historical costs can also provide a sound basis for forecasting and budgeting costs of future activities and assets.

While detailed methods used for cost accounting may vary from business to business or from project to project, all accounting systems include the three basic steps of recording, classifying, and summarizing cost element data in terms of money expended with time [5]. The recording of cost information is nothing more than the mechanical gathering of data in a routine manner. There are a variety of methods to achieve this. Generally, it's accomplished with time sheets for labor and invoices for subcontracts and procured items. Other costs are gathered from utility bills, expense reports, tax bills, etc.

Every business enterprise has an established approach for classifying and summarizing costs that is organized around their business practices. This approach is called a "code of accounts" by which all recorded cost elements are classified. A code of accounts (sometimes referred to as a chart of accounts) is a systematic numeric method of classifying various categories of costs incurred in the progress of a job; the segregation of engineering, procurement, fabrication, construction, and associated project costs for accounting purposes [3].

A company's code of accounts is configured to support the recording of cost data in the general ledger. An example of summary-level accounts is shown in Table 1.4.

While classifying costs in accordance with the general ledger breakout is a common practice, this approach does not generally provide the visibility needed to manage the work or to make informed forecasts of the cost of new jobs. An alternate method of cost element classification is called activity-based costing (ABC). In the ABC approach, resources that are used are assigned to activities that are required to accomplish a cost objective [9]. ABC makes cost accounts understandable and logical, and much more useful for the cost engineer [4]. This method of collecting and summarizing cost elements reveals which resources and activities are the most significant contributors (drivers) to the cost of the cost objective.

Another approach to classifying costs that is similar to ABC accounting is using a work breakdown structure (WBS) to group cost elements. It has become a common practice for a WBS to be a required project management tool on most contracts. Not only does a WBS provide a framework for planning and controlling the resources needed to perform the technical objectives, but it facilitates a summary of project data regarding the cost and schedule performance. Table 1.5 shows an example WBS for a study project wherein the deliverable item is an intellectual product documented in technical publications.

When used to classify and record costs, the WBS becomes the cost element structure (CES), as well. The general format, however, is applicable for the CES of a manufactured product or construction project [8].

While there is no universal WBS/CES standard, some have

Table 1.4— Typical Code of Accounts (after Jelen [6])

2000 Assets	6000 Expenses
2100 Cash	6100 Cost of goods sold
2200 Accounts Receivable	6200 Salaries and wages
2300 Notes Receivable	6300 Heat, light, and power
2400 Inventory - materials and supplies	6400 Communications expense
2500 Inventory – finished products	6500 Reproduction expense
2600 Work-in-progress	6600 Insurance
2700 Equipment	6700 Taxes
2800 Buildings and fixtures	6800 Depreciation
2900 Land	6900 Interest expense
3000 Liabilities	7000 Construction work in progress
3100 Accounts payable	7100 Site preparation
3200 Notes payable	7200 Concrete work
3300 Taxes payable	7300 Structural steel
3400 Accrued liabilities	7400 Heavy equipment
3500 Reserve accounts	7500 Buildings
	7600 Electrical systems
4000 Equity	7700 Piping systems
4100 Capital stock issued and out-standing	
4200 Retained earnings	8000 Manufactured goods in progress
	8100 Direct materials
5000 Revenues	8200 Direct labor
5100 Sales of finished goods	8300 Overhead
5200 Other revenues	

Table 1.5—Typical WBS Format

Level 1	Level 2	Level 3
1.0 Research Project	1.1 Concept Study	1.1.1 State-of-Art Research
		1.1.2 Concept Definition
		1.1.3 Data Analysis
	1.2 Mathematical Model	1.2.1 Equation Formulation
		1.2.2 Computer Programming
		1.2.3 Test and Evaluation
	1.3 Deliverable Data	1.3.1 Technical Documents
		1.3.2 Engineering Data
		1.3.3 Management Data
	1.4 Project Support	1.4.1 Project Management
		1.4.2 Review Meetings

been developed for government acquisition. One comprehensive example is the U.S. Army Cost Element Structure [11] (www.asafm.army.mil/ceac/ceac.asp). This CES provides a definition of each cost element within the structure. It also provides structure for cost elements in all procurement phases: development, production, and operation and support.

Sometimes the code of accounts to be used is determined by law. For example, the Federal Energy Regulatory Commission (FERC) has established a Uniform System of Accounts for the electrical power generation industry (www.ferc.fed.us). The account numbering plan used consists of a system of three-digit whole numbers as shown in Table 1.6.

Regardless of how cost elements are classified and grouped, it is important that this is done in a manner that is consistent with the way future work is estimated and budgeted. Historical cost records represent the way a company conducts its business and can be analyzed to determine whether improvements have been made and how costs may trend in the future. Therefore, the integrity of the cost

Table 1.6— FERC Uniform System of Accounts

100-199	Assets and other debits.
200-299	Liabilities and other credits.
300-399	Plant accounts.
400-432, & 434-435	Income accounts.
433, 436-439	Retained earnings accounts.
440-459	Revenue accounts.
500-599	Production, transmission and distribution expenses.
900-949	Customer accounts, customer service and informational, sales, and general and administrative expenses.

accounting system is essential to developing a project cost baseline.

Example 3—John recognizes that the deck he is building is an improvement to his home that would be considered a capital investment. He decides that he needs to structure his cost accounts to provide data for future maintenance estimates. Here is the code of accounts he develops:

Table 1.7—John's New Code of Accounts

1.0 Material	1.1 Footing form lumber, nails, and concrete
	1.2 Deck lumber and screws
	1.3 Paint and turpentine
2.0 Labor	2.1 Draw plans (self)
	2.2 Get permit (self)
	2.3 Get materials (self)
	2.4 Construct footings—Sam's Handyman Service
	2.5 Erect deck—Sam's Handyman Service
	2.6 Paint deck - Sam's Handyman Service
3.0 Other	3.1 Permit fee

Notice that John hired some of the labor and has cost records (invoices) for the work. For the labor he performed, John might use a fair market value to account for the cost of these activities. Also, values of indirect cost elements are not shown in this list. For, example, John could have included the rental value of the tools used in the construction. This valuation approach would have allowed him to get a better understanding of the total value of the deck.

John's code of accounts allows him to group material and labor costs to find the total cost of the footings, deck structure, and painting. Table 1.8 shows how he rearranges the cost elements to get this visibility:

Cost element allocation would be ratioed to the cost of the material and labor in each component of the asset. This arrangement of cost elements is similar to the ABC or WBS approach.

COST MANAGEMENT

There are many ways that cost elements and cost structure can be displayed to provide information for cost management. We will consider four of the most common methods of how cost information is applied to cost management. These are: cost estimating, cost trending, cost forecasting, and life-cycle costing. Although these methods will be discussed in more detail in later chapters, it is important to see how they relate to cost elements and structure.

Table 1.8—Cost Elements of John's Deck Project

1.0 Footings

    1.1 Allocation, in part, of:
- Draw plans (self)
- Get permit (self)
- Permit fee
- Get material (self)

    1.2 Form lumber, nails, and concrete

    1.3 Construct footings—Sam's Handyman Service

2.0 Deck Structure

    2.1 Allocation, in part, of:
- Draw plans (self)
- Get permit (self)
- Permit fee
- Get material (self)

    2.2 Lumber and screws

    2.3 Erect deck—Sam's Handyman Service

3.0 Painting

    3.1 Allocation, in part, of:
- Draw plans
- Get permit
- Permit fee
- Get material

    3.2 Paint and Turpentine

    3.3 Paint deck—Sam's Handyman Service

Cost Estimating

Cost Estimating predicts the quantity and cost of resources needed to accomplish an activity or create an asset. The building blocks of a cost estimate are

- a well-defined scope (what we are trying to estimate),
- a cost element structure (how we organize the information), and
- historical cost data (data from cost accounting records and/or "experience" of knowledgeable people).

Key questions to ask regarding a cost estimate always include "What cost data was used?" and "How can we reduce the cost of x?" Therefore, cost element data and its structure are paramount ingredients of a sound cost estimate.

Cost Trending *Forecast based on history*

Cost trends are established from historical cost accounting information. Cost management questions may focus on how expenditures are trending relative to physical accomplishments. "How much are we spending for pipe fitters and how much piping has been installed during the last six months?" or "What has been our monthly cost for steel this last year and how many bowls have we produced?" Again, having access to cost history in the structure needed is key to providing the required information.

Cost Forecasting

Forecasts are much like estimates. Whereas an estimate is always for future activities and assets, forecasts are predictions of the cost at completion for cost elements in progress. Therefore, a sound cost forecast will be based on cost element data from inception of the work to the date of the forecast, the cost trend of that data compared to accomplishments, and a cost estimate of the work remaining to be completed. Cost element history in the proper activity structure is essential for realistic cost forecasts.

Life-Cycle Costing

Life-cycle costs (LCC) are associated with an asset and extend the cost management information beyond the acquisition (creation) of the asset to the use and disposal of the asset. Asset acquisition consists of the design/development phase and the production/construction phase. Generally, cost elements are segregated into these phases because design/development costs are often recovered over more than one asset. For example, design and development cost of a new airplane is amortized over the production. The design of a housing project is recovered through sales of the houses built.

Once the asset is created, it enters the operation and support (O&S) phase, sometimes called operations and maintenance (O&M). A new set of cost elements and CES is applicable to this phase and cost data must be collected to support cost management efforts. The final phase is disposal of the asset with another unique set of cost elements.

Refer to Table 1.9 to see how John might group cost elements of the deck project to reflect its LCC.

Example 4—John rearranges the project cost elements to understand what it cost to design and construct the deck and to get a perspective on what it might cost to maintain and eventually remove the deck. If John wants to, he can develop a cost estimates for the maintenance and disposal phases. As a first cut at the estimate, he can refer to the construction cost element history for most of the information and add estimates for termite inspection and replanting the grass.

SUMMARY

In this chapter, we have studied some of the fundamental aspects of cost. We started with an understanding of resources and cost elements and how they relate to the performance of activities and the creation of an asset. Money and time we introduced as both enablers of and constraints on the execution of a project. Cost elements were illustrated by an example of building a wood deck at a house.

Table 1.9—Life-Cycle Cost Elements of John's Deck

1.0 Design	
	1.1 Draw plans
	1.2 Get permit
	1.3 Permit fee
2.0 Construction	
	2.1 Get materials
	2.2 Form lumber, nails, concrete
	2.3 Construct footings
	2.4 Deck lumber and screws
	2.5 Erect deck
	2.6 Paint and turpentine
	2.7 Paint deck
3.0 Maintenance	
	3.1 Repaint deck every 5 years
	3.2 Termite inspection every 2 years
4.0 Disposal	
	4.1 Tear-down deck after 25 years
	4.2 Remove footings
	4.3 Haul demolition material to dump
	4.4 Replant grass

Next we considered how cost elements are structured into direct, indirect, fixed, and variable cost groups. The purpose for organizing costs into groups is to determine which cost elements are used in performing the activity or creating the asset and which are in support of the work. Other possible groupings were introduced to illustrate how cost elements can be arranged to provide visibility on the cost of specific activities or resources. The deck example was extended by structuring the cost elements into cost groups.

The importance of cost accounting in establishing a database for cost management was discussed. Several methods of classifying and summarizing cost elements were introduced: code of accounts, activity based costing, and work breakdown structure (WBS). The cost elements of the deck example were organized into a code of accounts and WBS to illustrate these methods.

Finally, the topic of cost management was introduced. Four common methods for providing cost information were discussed as they apply to cost management. This illustrated the importance of having sound cost history that is structured in a usable format. The deck example was extended further to demonstrate the four phases of life-cycle costing.

PRACTICE PROBLEMS AND QUESTIONS

Problem 1: A manufacturing company is producing furniture and buys the hardwood lumber from a supplier who make daily deliveries. Consequently, when the wood is inspected some is not useable and is returned to the supplier. Of the wood used, some ends up as chips and scrap pieces.

Questions: Is the returned material a manufacturing cost element? How about the scrap? Would these be direct, indirect, fixed, or variable costs?

Answers: The returned material is not a cost to the manufacturer but would be a handling cost to the supplier that could show up in the price of the hardwood. The scrap is a direct manufacturing cost that is also a variable cost since it depends on the number of units produced.

Problem 2 : A shopping mall is under construction. The general contractor owns some construction equipment but needs to rent a crane for the steel placement.

Questions: Is the crane rental a direct cost or indirect cost? How about the equipment that is owned by the contractor?

Answers: The crane rental is a direct cost to the project. However, the use of the equipment that is owned would be part of the overhead and considered an indirect cost.

Problem 3 : A company develops computer programs for children's game machines. The product (the game software) is an intellectual property that is transferred to CDs and marketed. Consider the cost elements that make up the CDs.

Questions: What are some of the direct cost elements in the CD? How is the cost to develop the game software recovered?

Answers: The direct costs associated with the production of the CD are the raw material, the operators labor, the label, crystal case, and packaging. Game software development costs would be amortized to production and recovered in the CD price.

Problem 4 : Mary has been assigned the task of estimating the cost of a new product that is a redesign of one currently in production. She needs to get historical costs records from the company's accounting system.

Questions: Does the company's code of accounts (refer to Table 1.4) provide the information Mary needs? What type of accounting would have provided better cost visibility.

Answers: There is not much detail available, however, an approximation can be made of the proportion of material, labor, and overhead by looking at the Manufactured goods in progress accounts. Better visibility would result from application of activity based cost accounting.

Problem 5 : An electric utility operates a natural gas-fired turbine generating station. It is necessary to shut down operation for one week each year for preventive maintenance. During this time, extra work crews are assigned and repair parts are purchased.

Questions: The asset is now in what life-cycle phase? Are the station operating costs part of the cost elements in this phase? How do the operating and maintenance costs relate to the cost of the electricity produced?

Answers: The asset is in the O&S phase. Yes, the operating costs and maintenance costs are part of the O&S phase costs. In addition, there would be some indirect costs. Since this asset is used to produce a product, electricity, all the O&S costs along with the cost of the natural gas make up the cost of the electricity produced.

REFERENCES

1. U.S. Dept. of Defense. *Armed Services Pricing Manual.* Commerce Clearing House, Inc. (latest revision).
2. Merriam-Webster On-Line Dictionary. www.merriam-webster.com
3. AACE International. Standard Cost Engineering Terminology. Recommended Practice No. 10S-90. Morgantown, WV.
4. Cokins, Gary. 2002. Activity-Based Costing: Optional or Required.; *2002 AACE International Transactions.* RISK.03.1
5. Humphreys, K. K. 1984. *Project and Cost Engineers' Handbook.* Marcel Dekker, Inc.
6. Jelen, Frederic C. and James H. Black. 1983. *Cost and Optimization Engineering.* McGraw-Hill, Inc. 1983.
7. Meigs, Walter B., Charles E. Johnson, and Robert F. Meigs. 1977. *Accounting: The Basis for Business Decisions.* McGraw-Hill, Inc.
8. Postula, Frank D. 1991. WBS Criteria for Effective Project Control. *AACE International Transactions.* I.6.1
9. Player, Steve, and David Keys. 1995. *Activity-Based Management: Arthur Andersen's Lessons from the ABM Battlefield.* MasterMedia Limited.
10. Souder, William E. 1980. *Management Decision Methods for Managers of Engineering and Research.* Van Nostrand Reinhold Company.
11. U.S. Army. 2001. *Army Cost Analysis Manual.* Appendix E.

Chapter 2

Pricing

Rohit Singh, PEng CCE

INTRODUCTION

The goal of this chapter on pricing is to serve as "a guide to the subject matter in which a cost engineer and a cost manager should be both knowledgeable and competent" [1]. In the following pages, pricing is established as a set of management processes (tools and techniques) required to establish the cost of an endeavor (project, business). These tools and techniques include the following:

- pricing strategies,
- sales and revenues,
- return on investment (ROI),
- return on sales (ROS), and
- break-even analysis.

With the complexities involved, it should not come as a surprise that pricing is considered to be an art by many cost managers [2]. Establishing the right information on customer cost budgets and competitive pricing is an essential element in this art of pricing. The unreliability of the information base can lead to wrong or misleading information in many cases. However a disciplined approach derived from combining the art of pricing and science is very beneficial.

LEARNING OBJECTIVES

After completing this chapter, the reader should be able to

- differentiate between costing and pricing,
- establish a framework for the comparison of pricing strategies on projects,
- analyze profitability and establish return on investments (ROI) and return on analysis (ROA),
- establish the return on sales (ROS) parameters, and
- understand the concept of break-even analysis for any business situation.

COST AND PRICING—IS THERE A DIFFERENCE?

Price refers to "the cost at which something is bought or sold" [5]. Therefore, pricing is the process of establishing the cost of a project/business. Pricing refers to a set of tools and techniques used to establish an output-cost. The difference is subtle, and in real-world applications, it is not incorrect to use these terms interchangeably, as long as there are terms of reference. In this chapter the terms of references for pricing are based on the tools and techniques used to establish cost; i.e., pricing strategies, sales and revenues, ROI, ROS, and break-even analysis.

PRICE – COST = GROSS PROFIT

TOOLS AND TECHNIQUES OF PRICING

Analysis of the Pricing Process

In Figure 2.1 on page 2.2, the process of pricing is described in terms of its inputs, tools and techniques, and output. These are described separately in this chapter with the focus being on the tools and techniques. The inputs are the documentable items that will be acted upon and include, but are not limited to: work breakdown structure (WBS), historical records, cost estimation and cost management system. The tools and techniques are the mechanisms applied to the inputs to produce the outputs and include pricing strategies, sales and revenues, ROI, ROS, and break-even analysis. Tools and techniques of the pricing process is the focus of this section.

Pricing Strategies

Pricing Strategies must be developed for each individual situation. Essentially two situations frequently appear when one is pursuing a project. These situations that often occur in competitive acquisitions are referred to as Types I and II [2]. In each case there are specific but different business objectives.

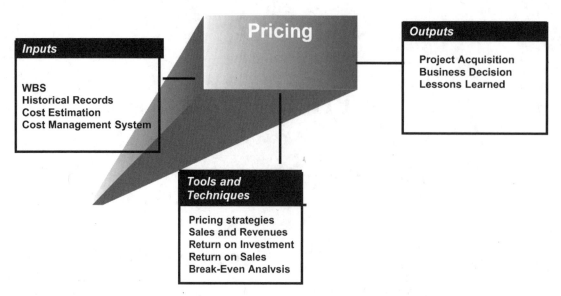

Figure 2.1—Analysis of the Pricing Process

The objective for Type I acquisitions is to win the project and execute it profitably and satisfactorily according to contractual agreements. The same applies to Type II acquisitions; however, Type II refers to a new industry that a company is trying to get a foothold into. In such cases, the profit may not be as important as obtaining the new business acquisition.

A Type II acquistion is an example of a "must win" situation where the price is determined by the market forces. Thus the fundamental difference is that for a Type I profitable new business acquisition, the bid price is determined according to the actual project cost; whereas in a "must-win" Type II situation, the price is determined by the market forces. This is the basis of pricing strategies as applied in cost management.

BUSINESS AND ECONOMIC RATIOS:
AN OVERVIEW

A business can normally forecast its outgoings, but incomings can be more difficult to predict. Even a business that appears to be successful can flounder if it does not generate enough cash to pay its obligations.

The following ratios provide the necessary guidance to assist in the successful planning of a business:

*   ROI,
*   ROS, and
*   break-even analysis.

A business begins with a the following set of inputs or resources:

*   **Natural resources**—These form the basic ingredients of the product or assist in its manufacture. This includes such resources as coal and steel, which one day will be exhausted, and assets, such as buildings, that help in the production process.
*   **Capital**—This includes the assets through which business is done or the cash that makes this possible. Therefore, a shop is capital, as is an oil refinery.
*   **People**—Normally referred to as the most important assets a business has, the abilities of its employees are vital to the success of any business. The attitudes shown by both employees and managers will shape much of what happens within any business. Managers or entrepreneurs will be called upon to lead, and workers/employees will be responsible for making the goods/services that the customers want. If any member of this process gets it seriously wrong, then the livelihoods of all can be threatened.

Obviously, these inputs vary in nature and importance from one business to another. However they offer a background to understanding these business economic ratios. All ratios must be taken in context. The reason to look at them on a monthly basis is to make sure that you spot trends as they develop, not afterward. If you are doing something exceedingly well, you need to know it. And if something is wrong, it's better to find out sooner than later.

ROI is one of several approaches to building a financial business case. The term means that decision makers evaluate the investment potential by comparing the magnitude and timing of expected gains to the investment costs. In the last few decades, this approach has been applied to asset purchase decisions (computer systems or maintenance vehicles, for example), "go/no-go" decisions for programs of all kinds (including marketing programs, recruiting programs, and training programs), and to more traditional investment decisions (such as the management of stock portfolios or the use of venture capital).

Simple ROI

ROI is frequently derived as the return (incremental gain) from an action divided by the cost of that action—that is simple ROI. For example, what would be the ROI for a new marketing program that is expected to cost $500,000 over the next five years and deliver an additional $700,000 in increased profits during the same time?

Simple ROI = (Gains – Investment Costs)/Investment Costs = ($700,000 – 500,000)/$500,000 = 40%

Simple ROI works well in situations where both the gains and the costs of an investment are easily known and where they clearly result from the action. Other things being equal, the investment with the higher ROI is the better investment. The return on investment metric itself, however, says nothing about the magnitude of returns or risks in the investment.

Complex ROI

In complex business settings, ROI, also called the Dupont or engineer's method, is the percentage relationship of the average annual profit to the original investment, including non-depreciable items such as working capital:

ROI = (average yearly profit during earning life)/(original fixed investment + working capital) expressed as a percentage.

Let's look at an example. Based on Table 2.1 below calculate the ROI.

The average profit = (275 + 200 + 130 + 70 + 0)/5 = 135 k$/year

By the equation above, the ROI = (135)/(1000+0) = 13.5%.

Return on Average Investment (RAI)

Table 2.1-Project Cash Flow [4]

Time, end year	After Tax Profit, K$	Depreciation, K$	Cash Flow, K$
0	-1,000	0	-1,000
1	275	200	475
2	200	200	400
3	130	200	330
4	70	200	270
5	0	200	200

> ### GLOSSARY TERMS IN THIS CHAPTER
>
> capital ◆ cash flow ◆ competitive advantage
> cost ◆ inputs ◆ opportunity ◆ price
> production ◆ work breakdown structure (WBS)

On the other hand, return on average investment (RAI) is similar to ROI except that the divisor is the average outstanding investment.

RAI = (average yearly profit during earning life)/(average Outstanding investment) expressed as a percentage.

Other ROI Metrics

Other "financial ratios" are sometimes treated as ROI figures, including return on capital, return on total assets, return on equity, and return on net worth. In still other cases, the term refers simply to the cumulative cash flow results of an investment over time.

In brief, several different ROI metrics are in common use and the term itself does not have a single, universally understood definition. When reviewing ROI figures, or when asked to produce one, it is a good idea to be sure that everyone involved does the following:

- defines ROI the same way, and
- understands the limits of the concept when used to support business decisions

Return on Sales (ROS)

What it is—This ratio compares after tax profit to sales. It can help you determine if you are making enough of a return on your sales effort.

When to use it—If your company is experiencing a cash flow crunch, it could be because its mark-up is not enough to cover expenses. Return on sales can help point this out and allow you to adjust prices for an adequate profit. Also, be sure to look for trends in this figure. If it appears to be dropping over time, it could be a signal that you will soon be experiencing financial problems.

The formula—Net profit divided by sales.

Return on Assets (ROA)

What it is—This number tells you how effective your business has been at putting its assets to work. The ROA is a test of capital utilization—how much profit (before interest and income tax) a business earned on the total capital used to make that profit. This ratio is most useful when compared

2.3

Net Operating Income = Net profit

Price
- costs
Gross Profit (margin) – OH = NOI

with the interest rate paid on the company's debt. For example, if the ROA is 15 percent and the interest rate paid on its debt was 10 percent, the business's profit is 5 percentage points more than it paid in interest.

When to use it—Return on assets is an indicator of how profitable a company is. Use this ratio annually to compare your business' performance to your industry's norms.

The formula—Earnings before interest and taxes (EBIT) divided by net operating assets.

Gross Profit Margin Ratio

What it is—The gross profit margin ratio indicates how efficiently a business is using its materials and labor in the production process. It shows the percentage of net sales remaining after subtracting cost of goods sold. A high gross profit margin indicates that a business can make a reasonable profit on sales, as long as it keeps overhead costs in control.

When to use it—This figure answers the question, "Am I pricing my goods or services properly?" A low margin—especially in relation to industry norms— could indicate you are underpricing. A high margin could indicate overpricing if business is slow and profits are weak.

The formula—Gross profit divided by total sales.

Break-Even Analysis

Break-even analysis involves finding the level of sales necessary to operate a business on a break-even basis. At break-even, total costs equal total revenue; i.e., you don't make any money, but you don't lose any money either. If you produce more units than at the break-even level, you will be generating a profit. Conversely, if you produce less than the break-even level, you will be losing money.

The following are typical terms that are used in performing a break-even analysis:

- **Selling Price (SP)**—This is the price that each unit will sell or retail for. The SP is generally expressed as revenue in dollars per unit.
- **Variable Costs (VC)**—These consist of costs that vary in proportion to sales levels. They can include direct material and labor costs, the variable part of manufacturing overhead, and transportation and sales commission expenses. The VC are usually expressed as a cost in dollars per unit.
- **Contribution Margin (CM)**—This is equal to sales revenues less variable costs or SP − VC.
- **Fixed Costs (FC)**—These costs remain constant (or nearly so) within the projected range of sales levels. These can include facilities costs, certain general and administrative costs, and interest and depreciation expenses. The FC are usually expressed as a lump-sum cost in dollars.

- **Units (X)**—The unit is another way to say number of items sold or produced. For the purpose of a break-even calculation, it is assumed that the number of units produced during a period is equal to the number of units sold during the same period.

The following steps are involved in calculating the break-even point for a business. Remember, at break-even, the total sales revenue is equal to total costs (fixed and variable).

Determine the variables: FC, SP, and VC. Occasionally, the selling price and variable costs are not identified separately; instead, a contribution margin (CM) is given. The CM can still be used in the break-even calculation, replacing the SP and VC.

Calculate the number of units produced or sold at break-even.

$$SP(X) = VC(X) + FC$$

Rearranging the formula to solve for X, the number of units at break-even will give you:

$$X = FC / (SP - VC) \text{ or } X = FC / CM$$

Calculate the break-even revenue in dollars as follows:

break-even revenue ($) = (break-even units) x (selling price)

For example, let's say you manufacture widgets. Each unit retails at $5. It costs you $2 to make each one, and the fixed costs for the period are $750. What is the break-even point in units and in sales revenue?

SP = $5
VC = $2
FC = $750

Break-even units:
$$X = FC / (SP - VC)$$
$$= \$750 / (\$5 - \$2)$$
$$= \$750 / \$3$$
$$= 250 \text{ units}$$

Break-even sales revenue = break-even units x SP
$$= 250 \times \$5$$
$$= \$1,250$$

In other words, you would have to manufacture 250 widgets to break-even, which results in a revenue of $1,250.

OUTPUTS

These are the documentable items that result from the pricing process and include

* project acquisition,
* business decision, and
* lessons-learned.

A project is acquired as a result of the application of a financial analysis on the scope and work breakdown structure (WBS) on the preliminary information. A decision is made on a business proposition based on the tools and techniques (financial ratios) being applied to the information in order to make a decision on the business. Lessons are learned from any process and the pricing process is no exception.

SUMMARY

In reviewing the following tools and techniques, it is obvious why pricing is considered to be an art by many cost managers:

* differentiating between costing and pricing;
* establishing a framework for the comparison of pricing strategies on projects;
* analyzing profitability and establishing ROI, RAI, and ROA;
* establishing ROS parameters; and
* understanding the concept of break-even analysis for any business situation.

However, the pricing tools, techniques, and processes presented in this chapter combine art and science will result in a disciplined process when properly applied. Finally, it must be remembered that in reviewing all financial ratio figures, it is a good idea to be sure that everyone involved does the following:

* defines the ratios the same way, and
* understands the limits of the concept when used to support business/project decisions

PRACTICE PROBLEMS AND QUESTIONS

1. Why is it correct to use cost and pricing interchangeably in the real world?

2. How does cost and price differ?

3. Explain the differences between Type I and II objectives for the acquisition of a business/project.

4. Based on the table below, calculate the cash flow and ROI.

Time, end year	After Tax Profit, K$	Depreciation, K$	Cash Flow, K$
0	-5,000	0	
1	750	400	
2	500	400	
3	300	400	
4	200	400	
5	0	400	

5. Let's say you manufacture widgets. Each unit retails at $5. It costs you $2 to make each one, and the fixed costs for the period are $750. What is the break-even point in units and in sales revenue?

6. Define ROS, and RAI.

REFERENCES

1. AACE International. 2002. *Skills and Knowledge of Cost Engineering*. 4th ed. Morgantown, West Virginia.
2. Kerzner, Harold. 1998. *Project Management: A systems Approach to Planning, Scheduling and Controlling*. New York: John Wiley and Sons.
3. Project Management Institute (PMI). 2000. *The Project Management Body of Knowledge*. (PMBOK 2000)
4. Jelen, F. C. and J. H. Black. 1983. *Cost and Optimization Engineering*. New York: McGraw Hill.
5. Funk and Wagnalls. 1975. *Standard Encyclopedic Dictionary*. Funk and Wagnall Publishing Co.

Chapter 3

Materials

Neil D. Opfer, CCE

INTRODUCTION

Materials are a key element in most projects and production endeavors. There may be isolated instances, such as a service call for the adjustment of a component, where no materials are required. However, in most cases, materials and their related issues must be addressed by those responsible for the project.

Materials have the quality of being purchased by those utilizing them, rather than being manufactured by the subject entity. Thus a tree log is material to the lumber mill that manufactures it into dimension lumber (product), which is material to the roof truss plant that fabricates it into a roof truss (product), which is material to the home builder that incorporates the roof trusses into a finished house.

Materials are a key resource in almost any economic endeavor. Materials range from the simplest of raw materials to the most complex fabricated materials with a large range in between. The simplest of raw materials may be silica sand from a pit that is mined in order to manufacture glass. On the other end of the spectrum, an electronic components manufacturer may require complex fabricated materials such as a printed circuit board containing millions of transistors. While both the glass and the printed circuit boards rely on a form of silica, there are vast differences in the degree of complexity between the two.

Besides the issues of materials type, materials must be procured in proper amounts at the right time and at the right cost in order to lead to an efficient production process. In addition to materials shaped in the particular production process, those machines and related equipment that perform the work also need maintenance materials, again, ranging from the simple to the complex. Simple materials may consist of grease and oil whereas complex materials may again consist of fabricated items.

LEARNING OBJECTIVES

After completing this chapter, the reader should be able to

- identify types of project materials;
- understand the issues involved in selecting and handling materials;
- understand the principles of materials purchasing and management, including maintaining the proper amount of stock to save money and avoid waste and production delays; and
- understand possible safety hazards associated with materials and be aware of regulations governing worker and materials safety.

MATERIALS COMPETITION

Practical selection of materials for a given application must always take into account materials competition issues. Materials compete on a number of characteristics including cost, availability, service life, weight, corrosion/wear resistance, machinability, weldability, and other ease-of-fabrication criteria. A standard phrase used in industry is "there are no bad materials just bad applications of materials." The strong performance of materials in one application does not guarantee success in a differing application and sometimes the differences may be difficult to ascertain.

The automotive industry is a prime example of continued competition among materials due to various factors, such as weight with its attendant impact on fuel economy. Steel has been replaced in numerous applications in autos by the advent of high performance plastics and aluminum. At first, targets were nonstructural auto applications, such as interior panels and interior trim items. These plastic and aluminum components through further engineering have migrated into structural auto components, such as tanks and body parts. Steel auto applications have also witnessed significant changes through the advent and improvements of high-strength, low-alloy steels. Galvanized steels in auto body fabrication have seen increased use through the advent of two-sided galvanized steels, with a mini-spangle spray application of zinc galvanizing that permits smooth-finish painting.

MATERIALS HANDLING

In the materials area, the materials handling issue is a significant concern regarding cost structure and system efficiencies. Materials handling is a requirement of the production process, but inefficiencies in this area create plant-wide problems. Poor materials handling can result in damage to either raw materials or the finished product. An inefficient materials handling system can slow production operations creating other excessive costs due to production delays.

Materials Handling Principles
All materials manufacturing situations are somewhat different. However, there are some basic principles in this area that find wide application. These basic principles include

- material movement should be over the shortest distance possible;
- terminal time should be in the shortest time possible, since the objective is to move materials;
- eliminate manual material handling when mechanized methods are feasible;
- avoid partial transport loads since full loads are more economical; and, finally,
- materials should be readily identifiable and retrievable.

Some of these above principles always apply whereas others are situation specific. Mechanized material handling methods are most cost-effective in high wage countries. In a lesser-developed country, the capital/labor trade-off given low wages will tend to emphasize manual methods as compared to equipment-intensive operations. In virtually all situations, it is uneconomical to delay material handling equipment at terminal points for materials loading and unloading. Thus, materials can be loaded onto containers or pallets that are quickly transferred on and off materials handling platforms.

Materials Handling Decision Factors
There are four basic decision factors that affect materials handling. These four factors are

1. material to be handled,
2. production system type,
3. facility type; and
4. materials handling system costs.

The material to be handled will impact numerous other decisions. A brick manufacturing plant will be dependent upon a source of clay material. In part, this clay can be handled much as other earthen products are handled with similar equipment, including front-end loaders and conveyors. A paint production facility will handle numerous raw materials through pipelines, thus requiring other criteria. Such materials as pipe or structural steel in a fabrication facility will require overhead cranes and forklifts for their movement.

The production system type will be divided into job shop or batch process and continuous process types. Continuous processes, such as seen in a petrochemical plant or a steel mill, will find fixed-path equipment, including conveyor lines and pipelines. Job shop or batch processes need more flexibility in their material handling requirements. Many job shops perform unique jobs, and large investments in single-application equipment are often not economical.

The facility type will govern materials handling decisions. A facility with low-ceiling heights and barely adequate structural system will not be a candidate for installation of overhead cranes. Rectangular facilities versus other facility shapes will govern production layout and hence material handling decisions.

Material handling system costs and their economic feasibility will be dependent on labor costs in the capital/labor trade-off equation. Predicted demand for a facility can help in the economic and practical evaluation of alternatives. Facilities with high levels of demand over several years can better justify more expensive materials handling systems. Comparisons between alternative materials handling systems is difficult and must include not only initial costs but life-cycle costs as well, such as labor, maintenance, repair, energy, and disposal costs.

TYPES OF MATERIALS AND RELATED INFORMATION

Materials, for purposes of differentiation, can be segregated into four basic categories:

1. raw materials,
2. bulk materials,
3. fabricated materials, and
4. engineered or designed materials.

These categories are differentiated on the criteria of the amount of processing required for the material to be useful for its intended purpose.

Raw Materials
Raw materials are those materials utilized in a production or fabrication process that require a minimum amount of processing to be useful. The most basic example of this might be

natural gravel from a river deposit that, combined with some screening for size separation, is then used as a subbase material for a roadway or foundation slab. The gravel can further be processed into materials for a concrete mix. In the steel-making process, certain raw materials such as coal, limestone, and iron ore are mined for eventual combination and utilization for producing steel.

Bulk Materials

The steel product can be considered to be a bulk material in all of its various forms, including sheet steel, steel bars, steel pipe, and structural steel shapes, such as wide-flange beams and angles. The bulk materials category is distinguished by its availability. A customer desiring a bulk material such as steel pipe can call a distributor and achieve delivery of this pipe as soon as the next day, depending on transport distance. Bulk materials in common sizes are typically readily available with minimal lead times for order and delivery.

Fabricated Materials

Fabricated materials are bulk materials transformed into custom-fit items for a particular product or project. As an example, the bulk material of steel pipe is transformed by fabrication operations into custom dimensions for a particular use, such as in a petroleum refinery. If the particular use is a welded piping system with flanged fittings, the pipe will be cut to dimension with welded flanges added where necessary based on shop drawings.

In the shop drawing phase, data from design drawings, which have been prepared by the project's or product's design professionals, is used to develop detailed shop drawings. These shop drawings need to convey all information necessary for the fabrication of the given item. In some cases, the shop drawings will also provide information for field assembly and erection of the fabricated items. The design professionals typically require review shop drawings prior to fabrication for acceptance. The design professional's review of shop drawings is undertaken to ensure conformance with original design intent. The historical separation between design drawings and shop drawings is due to the fact that fabricators are more familiar with economies of fabrication. Therefore, as long as design intent is met, the fabricator has a significant degree of flexibility, thus leading to lower costs in the fabrication process.

Engineered/Designed Materials

Engineered or designed materials constitute a category requiring substantial working in order to attain their final form. Design or engineered materials are also based on shop drawings. These engineered materials may consist of many components and subcomponents that end with a completed product. They consist of such diverse items as pumps, motors, boilers, chillers, fans, compressors, transformers, and motor control centers. The engineered materials producer, in some cases, will be producing these items as off-the-shelf

---

GLOSSARY TERMS IN THIS CHAPTER

bill of materials ◆ bulk materials ◆ cycle stock
engineered or designed materials ◆ expiditing
fabricated materials ◆ inventory ◆ production
purchasing ◆ raw materials ◆ safety stock ◆ surplus

---

products, and in other instances as custom products. An engineered item, such as a fan, will consist of such components as a fan housing, impeller, shaft, bearings, motor, and support base. Items such as the impeller, shaft, and fan housing may be manufactured directly by the subject vendor from various materials. Bearings and motor may come from other manufacturers to be added as components of the final product. The degree of capabilities possessed by the particular manufacturer will often be the deciding factor concerning what items in the final product are self-performed and which are subcontracted out.

The issue of custom or off-the-shelf products will have an impact to the potential customer on availability. The manufacturer will often produce standard sizes and maintain these in inventory. Unusual sizes will require special designs and often lengthy lead times. In materials procurement and selection, those responsible will want to analyze these issues for value-added benefits. In certain cases, the cost- and time-effective alternatives may be to attempt to standardize as much as possible to allow purchase of off-the-shelf components rather than custom items.

PRODUCTION MATERIALS PURCHASE AND MANAGEMENT

Materials procurement is an important business function because it has a key role on the organization's ability to offer products at a competitive price. Purchasing can be defined as the acquisition of necessary materials of the correct quality at the correct time for a competitive price, from the selected vendor or supplier. Sufficient stocks of materials must be acquired to prevent delays in production operations. Thus the concept of safety stocks are important whereby ensuring the critical amount on hand when a replenishment quantity is received. The safety stock's purpose is to protect against the uncertainty in demand and in the length of the replenishment lead time.

On the other hand excessive materials supplies create additional costs and problems for the organization. Excess materials beyond reasonable quantities require an investment in operating capital to finance this inventory and require storage space. Moreover, excess material quantities can lead to damage and theft.

Materials Quality

Materials procurement must focus on the proper quality of the required materials. This implies the existence of predetermined standards and specifications to measure materials acceptance. Over-specifying on higher-quality materials in excess of requirements will lead to excessive costs and customers may not appreciate these benefits. Similarly, the usage of poor quality materials can result in product defects leading to increased costs and potential litigation problems.

Materials Vendor Surveillance and Materials Traceability

In certain situations, the criticality of materials in a given application is such that vendor surveillance is an important requirement. Vendor surveillance may require periodic inspection by purchasers at the vendors' location(s) to ensure conformance with performance standards and specifications. Depending on volume and criticality, this periodic inspection may need to be conducted on a full-time basis at the subject vendor facility. Materials traceability is accomplished by means of mill certifications. Before a material is utilized in a given application, mill certifications ensure that the material used meets the purchasing specifications. Thus, a mill certification will verify that a material, such as cross-linked polyethylene tubing, is in fact as it has been represented before incorporation into a finished product.

Materials traceability is a key issue, because the improper substitution of one improper type of material for the specified material can lead to significant in-service problems and defects. A railroad car manufacturer that utilizes the improper lower grade of steel of mixed steel in fabricating railroad car axles will witness a significant number of service failures resulting in expensive call-backs and repairs.

Materials Quantity

Funds spent to acquire materials are a cost to the firm until these same materials can be sold as part of the completed product. Firms in industries where materials obsolescence is a factor encounter special problems in holding excess material quantities. As an example, a large inventory of printed circuit boards may have to be discarded or drastically discounted as technology changes thus creating obsolescence.

Materials storage is a further burden that can sometimes exceed the value of the materials. The simple example of storing some bags of cement proves this point. If the inside storage space costs $100 per square meter per year, and the storage of an excess of 20 bags of cement valued at $5 per bag takes up 1 square meter of space, any storage beyond one year, therefore, exceeds the actual value of the stored cement. On the other hand, maintaining insufficient materials inventories may create dangers of "stock-outs" interrupting the production process. Ordering too-small materials quantities

may create higher costs through missing the economies of volume discounts. The organization needs to balance these competing issues involving materials quantity.

Economic Order Quantity

As aforementioned, there must be sufficient materials inventory to meet production requirements while still avoiding excessive inventory carrying costs and storage costs. In order to balance these competing demands, the firm must determine its economic order quantity (EOQ) number. This EOQ number is determined based upon materials costs, storage costs, order costs, and annual demand. A garden tractor manufacturer has a requirement for 15,000 engines per year. The engines each cost $75. The order cost for a purchase order is $250. The storage costs for the engine are $12 per year which includes space costs and financing costs. The standard formula for EOQ is

$$EOQ = [\sqrt{(2 \times D \times O) / S}]$$

where
   D = annual demand,
   P = purchase order costs, and
   S = storage/carrying costs.

Thus, in this example:

$$EOQ = [\sqrt{(2 \times 15,000 \times \$250) / \$12}] = 790$$

Therefore, in this case, the manufacturer should order 790 engines at a time which is the EOQ value.

The formula for computing reorder point (RP) is:

$$RP = (O \times R) + I$$

where

   RP = reorder point,
   O = order time,
   R = production rate, and
   I = minimum inventory level or safety stock.

Assume that the production process uses 60 engines per day for the 60 garden tractors produced per day. If the lead time for an order is 5 days, and the safety stock level is 180 engines (minimum level), then the reorder formula in this example yields:

$$RP = (5 \text{ days} \times 60 \text{ units/day}) + 180 \text{ units} = 480 \text{ units}$$

Thus the EOQ value of 790 engines should be ordered whenever inventory drops to 480 units. Cycle stock levels maintained at very low levels can almost ensure the potential for production delays.

Just-In-Time Inventory Techniques

Recent years have seen the widespread introduction of just-in-time techniques for materials procurement across various industries. The just-in-time concept implies that the exact materials quantities needed are delivered at the exact time needed. The goal is to reduce inventories. Traditional practices that focus on safety stocks can mask unprofitable variations in the production process. By removing these safety stocks, the goal of just-in-time systems is a lean production process and an enhanced competitive position.

Individual Purchasing Orders and Systems Contracts

Nonstandard and costly items may be procured by the purchasing function through a system of plans/specifications requirements and competitive bidding. For items that the organization utilizes on a continual basis, a systems contract may be the best solution. At the start of every year, the organization estimates potential quantities of required materials and places these out for bid on a systems contract. Thus, a fabricator during a year may require x thousand pounds of various types of welding wire and welding rod for their operations. This is bid on a systems contract with periodic deliveries throughout the year as usage demands based on actual production. If quantities vary significantly higher or lower, there may be additional provisions for price adjustments in the systems contract or for inflationary upstream price increases not controllable by the vendor. The advantage of the systems contract is reduced purchasing work load and improved pricing based on economies of scale.

Expediting

Expediting involves the monitoring of all steps in the procurement cycle to ensure on-time delivery of the necessary materials. This monitoring includes checking design status, material status, production status, and shipping status. Analysis of potential delays is a key element in the expediting process. If shipping delays take place, alternative forms of delivery may be necessary to avoid production delays. By continually reviewing status, the expediting process helps to avoid unpleasant interruptions of the production process. Expediting communication is conducted through telephone, fax, and e-mail methods. Personal visits to vendors as part and parcel of vendor surveillance efforts can also be helpful.

The author remembers one site visit to a manufacturer of motor control centers for a wastewater treatment plant. The week before surprise site visit, the manufacturer had promised over the telephone that the motor control centers were almost ready to ship. Instead, it was found upon a site visit that this manufacturer had not even started construction on these units.

Global Materials Decisions

Materials fabrication decisions as to locations and methods are being made on a global basis. An example may assist in illustrating this concept.

A large East-coast hotel in the United States wanted a series of simulated trees and canopies created inside the hotel areas with beads simulating the tree and canopy cover. These beads would be strung such that there were 9,000 beads per square meter, and there were almost 200 square meters of area to cover. A West-coast interior theming firm won the contract. The quantities meant that nearly 1.8 million beads would need to be strung on the canopies and trees at a competitive price. The trees and canopies were fabricated out of structural steel at the firm's West-coast fabrication shop. To be cost-competitive, the beads and the bead stringing work were subcontracted to a firm in India. In India, skilled craftspeople strung the beads. The steel frames were shipped to India, strung with beads, and then transshipped to the U.S. East-coast hotel for final installation.

PLANT MATERIALS MANAGEMENT

Plant materials are a special category of materials. These are materials that are not associated with incorporation into any particular product or project. Instead these are materials that assist the plant in completing materials fabrication and production operations. Examples range from oils, greases, solvents, and cutting bits to parts, such as spare motors or cylinders for a production machine.

These plant materials assist in the production, maintenance, and repair of the facilities. Commodity plant materials such as oils, greases, solvents, and cutting bits, are typically low-cost items with predictable usage patterns. Moreover, sources of supply are readily available and order/procurement lead times are minimal.

Specialized Plant Materials

Specialized plant materials such as production equipment replacement parts can pose more difficult problems. A particular replacement part may be available only from the original equipment manufacturer (OEM) and require significant lead time. Those responsible for this area will want to maintain an inventory of critical replacement parts. Supplementing replacement parts inventory is networking with other manufacturers or fabricators owning the same type of equipment that may be willing to "loan" out a replacement part item in an emergency. A secondary strategy is to have a backup plan in place to procure replacement parts through other manufacturers if there are difficulties with the OEM.

Plant Materials Benchmarking

Plant materials usage and longevity should be tracked through such measures as benchmarking. Benchmarking involves the examination of other organizations as to their practices. The benchmarking organizations do not need to be competitors but merely similar organizations. Therefore, a structural steel fabricator may examine the operations of a steel pipe fabricator for comparison of operational practices.

Often it becomes easier to study the actions and practices of another organization than your own because it is easier to be objective. Studying your own organizations' materials management practices brings with it a certain degree of defensiveness and rationalization of poor practices. Benchmarking can, in turn, invite others from various organizations into the subject organization for an evaluation of practices.

MATERIALS WASTE PRODUCT AND HAZARD ISSUES

Users and producers of materials deemed as hazardous to humans are required to comply with government regulations concerning hazard communication. The purpose of these regulations is to ensure that potential hazards are properly evaluated and hazard information is properly communicated to employers and employees. These requirements include labels, warnings, material safety data sheets, information, and training.

A fabricator, for example, may be utilizing a solvent for cleaning parts prior to a welding operation necessary to join the parts. The potential effects of the solvent on employees from fumes or direct contact must be properly evaluated prior to use. Moreover, some employees may have special allergic reactions to this particular cleaning solvent.

Material Safety Data Sheets and Hazard Communication

Materials safety is always an important issue in the safe handling, fabrication, and transport of materials. In the United States, material safety data sheets (MSDS) must be readily available and accessible to those dealing with the particular hazardous materials as required by Occupational Safety & Health Administration (OSHA). Other countries may have similar regulations. An organization with multiple work locations must have complete files on these MSDS sheets for review and inspection. The MSDS requirements can force a re-examination of various issues in terms of the use and application of hazardous materials. The organization may find that they are using four different types of cleaning solvent for the same application, each with its own attendant MSDS issues. Based on an evaluation, these four solvent types may be narrowed to one type, promoting standardization and, thus, reducing potential problems. With the widespread advent of the Internet, Web publishing of this MSDS information may be a viable alternative. Web publishing ensures current up-to-date information is available anywhere in the organization through computer access.

These MSDS sheets contain information on chemical and common names of ingredients including substances that may be carcinogenic along with physical and chemical material characteristics such as vapor pressure and flash point. Other MSDS information includes physical hazards, such as fire and explosion potentials. Health hazards listed in MSDS information include primary routes of entry, exposure symptoms, and medical conditions which may be aggravated by exposure.

Environmental Regulations

Materials production operations involving potential hazards to the environment must pay attention to environmental regulations. As an example, in the United States, solid waste is regulated from "cradle to grave" through the Resource Conservation And Recovery Act (RCRA). RCRA regulates three categories of hazardous waste handlers: (1) generators, (2) transporters, and (3) owners and operators of treatment, storage, and disposal (TSD) facilities. Hazardous waste generators must keep accurate records, store waste in approved containers, label the waste, and utilize a manifest system to track the waste until delivery to a TSD facility. Violations of RCRA can result in civil and criminal penalties including fines of up to $25,000 per day assessed by the U.S. Environmental Protection Agency.

Waste Materials and Surplus Materials

Production operations on materials frequently result in the production of significant quantities of waste materials. This production of waste materials or scrap is a significant cost in numerous production processes. This cost comprises the original materials' cost plus waste material handling and disposal costs. Reduction in materials waste thus provides a cost reduction potential in these three areas. Some waste materials can be reused in the production process. A grade of steel not meeting requirements in one use may be reutilized for a product not requiring a premium steel grade. A steel manufacturer can take scrap steel from downstream production processes and transfer the scrap upstream to re-melt the scrap as a raw material component.

Surplus materials result from either mistakes due to excessive ordering, changes in material requirements, and/or incorrect original quantity information. The production of an order for a job shop production process may have specified a given number of pieces of steel plate. The original take-off regarding material requirements was incorrect. Mistakes may have taken place in development of the bill of materials. If this is material for which there is a continuing use, it may make sense to return the materials to inventory with a credit to the job shop order. Purchasing may have incorrectly processed the order with an incorrect quantity requirement. With a fast-track fabrication job, the requirements for the steel plate may have been a late design change where the materials procurement function could not act soon enough to cancel the order. In any case, the existence of surplus materials points to inefficiencies in the materials process. Returning the materials to the original vendor may be possible, although, in most cases, a restocking fee of 15 to 20 percent or more may be charged to the organization. However, unless, as noted above, the materials have a continuing use in fabrication operations, this may be the most economical course of action. The prevalence of surplus materials should be tracked with the goal of minimization of this expensive practice.

SUMMARY

Users and producers of materials must recognize potential areas for practice improvement. The recognition of the impact and potential of materials issues will lead to more rational decision processes by those responsible. This will result in an improved cost structure for the organization better able to achieve competitive advantage. The general objective of materials procurement is to minimize total costs through reduction in purchase costs, material handling costs, storage costs, and shortage costs. Tools such as the EOQ formula can lead to more rational decision processes in this area. In recent years, techniques such as just-in-time inventory methods have seen widespread introduction in materials-intensive applications.

PRACTICE PROBLEMS AND QUESTIONS

Questions: What materials handling method would be most appropriate for each choice? What factors must be considered for each of these alternatives?

> **Problem 1**: You are planning a materials production process that utilizes cement as a raw material. You can have the cement (1) received in bags, (2) received through a dry-transfer piping system from a rail head located one mile from your plant, (3) receiving the cement in bulk container bins, or (4) receiving the cement via a hopper truck.

Problem 2: What is meant by the concept of materials lead time? Outline the procedure through a flow chart for determining the reorder point for a given material.

Problem 3: Survey the methods at a supermarket used for merchandizing liquids in approximately one liter containers. Describe at least five different products, identifying the materials of construction and probable production processes.

Problem 4: Take a site visit to a large construction project. Survey the methods used for material handling on the project and suggest potential feasible alternatives.

REFERENCES

1. Azadivar, Farhad. 1984. *Design And Engineering of Production Systems.* San Jose, California: Engineering Press, Inc.
2. Hayes, Robert H., Steven C. Wheelwright, and Kim B. Clark. 1988. D*ynamic Manufacturing: Creating the Learning Organization.* New York: The Free Press.
3. Kalpakjian, Serope. 1991. *Manufacturing Processes for Engineering Materials.* 2nd ed. Reading, Massachusetts: Addison-Wesley Publishing Company.

Chapter 4

Labor

Morris E. Fleishman, PE CCE

INTRODUCTION

As an owner, employer, project manager, and estimator, I have a given set of work tasks that I need a worker to complete. As such, I need to know how much this will cost me. I also need to know how to set up and monitor the effort, so that I can be assured that I am getting the desired work product in the timeframe required and for a price that I can afford. In order to do this, I need to understand the cost factors that go into this work and the techniques to monitor progress to ensure that I will achieve my goals.

LEARNING OBJECTIVES

After completing this chapter, the reader should be able to

- identify different classifications of labor and how each contributes to the final completed project;
- develop labor rates for estimating, and develop and use weighted average rates/composite crew rates;
- include indirect and overhead labor and other costs;
- estimate work hours for a given work scope at a given location; and
- use labor hours to monitor work progress.

LABOR CLASSIFICATIONS

The following definitions were taken or adapted from AACE International's *Cost Engineer's Notebook* [1].

- **Direct Labor**—The labor involved in the work activities that directly produce the product or complete the installation being built.
- **Indirect Labor**—The labor needed for activities that do not become part of the final installation, product, or goods produced, but that are required to complete the project.
- **Overhead Labor**—The labor portion of costs inherent in the performing of a task (such as engineering, construction, operating, or manufacturing), which cannot be charged to or identified with a part of the work, and, therefore, must be allocated on some arbitrary basis believed to be equitable, or handled as a business expense independent of the volume of production.

Table 4.1 provides examples of different labor classifications and costs. The examples are not all-inclusive and only serve to illustrate the elements of each type of labor.

Table 4.1—Examples of Labor Costs

Cost Type	Direct Labor	Indirect Labor	Overhead labor
Construction	Carpenters, Electricians, Ironworkers, etc. and Foremen working on the project	General Foremen, Construction Management, Field Purchasing, Field Warehouse personnel, Payroll Personnel, Jobsite Computer Support, Project Cost Engineers and Schedulers etc.	Home Office Support such as; Legal Assistance, Procurement, Human Resources, Senior Management review, Corporate Computer Support, Estimating and Business Development, etc.
Manufacturing	Plant Equipment Operators, First Line Foreman, and Supervisors, etc.	Plant Accountants, Maintenance Personnel, Purchasing Personnel, Security, Plant Supervision, Warehouse Personnel, Production Planning and Cost Personnel, On-site Computer Support	Corporate support: Legal, Human Resources, Computer Support, Corporate Finance and Accounting Support, Sales, etc.
Engineering	Civil, Mechanical, Electrical, Instrumentation and Controls Engineering and first line supervision	Documentation Support – duplicating and record keeping, Engineering Cost and Scheduling Personnel, Project Supervision	Corporate Support: Human Resources, Computer Support, Corporate Accounting Support, Estimating, Business Development, etc.

The difference between indirect and overhead labor appears to be somewhat vague. Depending upon the size of a project, plant, or office and its location, some elements could shift from indirects to overheads, and there may be instances where direct labor moves to indirects and overheads as well.

For example, if the construction project is small, payroll and accounting may be located offsite and may be composed of personnel who are splitting their time between several projects at different locations. In this instance, this function could be an indirect or an overhead. Therefore, it is *imperative* that the estimator and/or cost engineer understand where within his project, industry, and company each of these costs are included, so that they can be correctly estimated and included in the estimate and budget.

DEVELOPING LABOR RATES

Base Wages

The base wage is the amount that will go directly to the employee. The source of these wage structures can be found in databases from previous projects, labor contracts, unit rates supplied by contracting and engineering firms, local chamber of commerce data, government labor statistics, published labor databases, and standardized estimating publications, such as Means and Richardson [2–5].

Base wages are usually calculated on a per hour basis. However, it can also be a breakdown of weekly or monthly base salary prorated to a daily or hourly rate. The reason for an hourly breakdown is that estimates are usually based upon the amount of work hours to complete. Therefore, the labor cost rates need to be developed on a comparable basis.

If one is costing out craft labor, their pay rate is usually given in hourly increments. Supervision, support staff, and engineering, etc., often are paid on a weekly, bi-weekly, or monthly rate. This rate can also be broken down to an hourly rate for estimating and payroll purposes.

The following are examples of base wages:

- craft personnel—$25.00 per hour,
- supervision—$1,200 per week divided by 40 hours per week = $30.00 per hour, and
- engineering—$ 60,000 per year divided by 2,080 hours per year = $ 28.85 per hour (2,080 hours = 5 days per week at 8 hours per day for 52 weeks).

The examples above can be used to calculate the direct amount that each employee will earn and be paid for each hour that they work.

Fringe Benefits

Paid time off (PTO)—Most employees have additional benefits of time off for local and national holidays, vacation, and sick time. Therefore, in developing a unit cost for labor, a factor is added to increase the estimated and booked cost per hour worked each week to cover PTO. Most companies transfer this money to special fund to be used when an employee takes paid time off.

In the case of construction craft that may work for many employers during a given period, wages are usually paid into a fund managed by their union or trade organization who distributes the salary for PTO.

For example, an engineer gets 5 days of sick time, 10 days of vacation, and 10 holidays per year. His base salary is $28.85 per hour. Adders are

- sick time: 5 days at 8 hours /day @ $28.85 = $1,154 per year
- vacation: 10 days at 8 hours /day @ $28.85 = $2,308 per year
- holiday: 10 days at 8 hours /day @ $28.85 = $2,308 per year
- total: $5,770 per year

This Engineer is now working 2,080 hours (52 weeks x 40 hours per week) less 25 days at 8 hours or 200 hours for PTO. So his productive time is 1,880 hours.

His hourly cost is

> $28.85 base wage + 3.07 PTO adder ($5,770 divided by 1,880 hours) = $31.92 total.

Medical & Life Insurance Benefits—Some firms and labor contracts include contributions to a medical and life insurance program. These costs are usually can be calculated on an hourly, weekly, or monthly cost basis and added to the per hour work cost.

If the firm that employs the engineer in the previous example contributes $400 per month for medical and other insurances, the following should be added to the hourly costs:

> $400/month x 12 months = $4,800/year divided by 1,880 hours = $2.55 per hour

If the company contributes to 401ks and other retirement plans for the engineer, the following should be added:

> $300/month x 12 months = $ 3,600/year divided by 1,880 hours = $1.91 per hour

Government Mandated Benefits

These benefits include such items as government retirement funds, unemployment insurance, retirement healthcare insurance, etc. In the United States, these funds are federal old age insurance (Social Security), Medicare, state unemployment insurance, etc.

These costs are usually calculated on a straight percent of the worked hours. Continuing with our example engineer, we will add the following:

- retirement (6.2%) = .062 x $28.85 = $ 1.79
- retirement medical (1.35%) = .0135 x $28.85 = $ 0.39
- state unemployment (1.0%) = .01 x $28.85 = $0.29
  total government mandated benefits = $ 2.47

Summary of Engineer's Wages Example

The cost basis for an engineer who makes $60,000 is summarized in Table 4.2:

Table 4.2—Example Labor Costs for Engineer

	Per Hour	
Base Salary Working Fringe Benefits:	1,880 hrs/yr	= $28.85
company retirement contributions		= $1.91
PTO (holidays, vacation, sick time)		= $3.07
company medical and life insurance		= $2.55
government mandadted benefits (retirement, etc.)		= $2.47
Total Cost Per Hour Benefits Adder	= ($38.85 - $28.85)	= $10.00
	= $10.00/28.85	= $34.7%

Engineer/Contractor Overhead and Profit

The above calculations will apply for the direct hire of individual workers. When hiring contract employees, or estimating an engineer or contractor's costs, labor rates are usually broken down differently:

- base wages including fringes,
- worker's compensation (if applicable),
- overhead, and
- profit (if applicable for time and material situations).

In these instances, the vacation, sick time, retirement contributions, and medical contributions are included in the fringes. Worker's compensation is a direct government rate. Overhead will apply to the home office cost of administration, payroll, and billing, etc. Profit usually only applies to approved time and material changes. All of these costs are dependent upon what type of contract is negotiated.

GLOSSARY TERMS IN THIS CHAPTER

base wages ◆ direct labor
indirect labor ◆ overhead labor

R.S. Means, for example, includes a table of average rates for various types of contractor personnel including overhead and profit in their manual *Concrete & Masonry Cost Data 2001* [5]. These labor rates are based upon a survey of union rates in 30 cities.

Fully-Loaded or Billing Rate

A fully-loaded rate is the base salary plus adders that will be paid for an hours work on the job. An owner employing a contractor on time and material basis only pays for the workers time when he is on the job. If he is sick, on vacation, or holiday, the contractor cannot bill the owner. However, the payment rate charged usually includes funds to cover this paid time off. The contractor either places the funds in a separate account for use when the worker is off or, if the worker is in a union, the union may get the funds to disburse when the worker is off. All estimates relating cost of labor to work performed are usually calculated using the fully-loaded rates.

Overtime Wages

There are many different overtime wage situations and there are several aspects that need to be evaluated in developing an overtime wage structure. Overtime can range from straight time pay for the additional hours beyond the standard workweek of 40 hours or 8 hours per day, to 1.5 and 2.0 times the regular pay.

When developing the overtime formula the estimator needs to take into account that some benefits are calculated on an 8-hour day or 40-hour week and are not added to overtime hours. Benefits such as PTO, some insurance, and some government funding programs may be included in this category. Government funded retirements, such as Social Security and Medicare, are calculated as a percentage of the wage and are usually added to the overtime rate. The estimator needs to confirm what needs to be added for the specific work area that the project is located in order to develop the correct rate.

For example, a craft worker earning $25.00 per hours is working overtime at 1.5 times his base rate at $ 37.50. PTO adders, company insurance adders, and state unemployment are not included. Federal retirement and medical is included at 7.55 percent, which equals $2.83. The total cost per hour for 1.5 overtime is $40.33.

WEIGHTED AVERAGE RATES/CREW COMPOSITION RATES

Most estimates are for groups of workers who have a variety of backgrounds, years of experience, etc. In the craft area, within each craft you could have a range of apprentices to journeymen at the top step of the salary ladder based upon their training and years of experience. The same applies in the engineering ranks as your team mix will have beginning engineers right out of school, engineering aides, registered engineers, senior engineers, etc. Since you don't know who will be part of the actual team, you must make some assumptions in order to develop a comparable base wage rate to use. In most cases you will build a weighted average team.

Table 4.3—Weighted Average Example

Civil Engineering Design Team

No.	Classification	Hourly Base Wage	Extension
2	Engineering Aides	$14.00	$28.00
2	Junior Engineers	$20.00	$40.00
4	Engineers	$25.00	$100.00
2	Senior Engineers	$30.00	$60.00
1	Eng. Supervisor	$35.00	$35.00
11	Total		$263.00*

*Average cost for the group = $263.00/ 11 = $23.91/hour with benefits adder of 34.7% = $32.21/hour.

Composite Concrete Crew– Normal Time (40 hours per week)

No.	Classification	Hourly Base Wage	Extension
2	Laborers	$14.00	$28.00
4	Carpenters	$18.00	$72.00
2	Cement Masons	$20.00	$40.00
1	Foreman	$25.00	$25.00
9	Total		$165.00*

*Average cost for the group = $165.00/ 9 = $18.33/hour with benefits adder of 30.0% (assumed) = $23.83/hour

Composite Concrete Crew—Overtime (1.5 times Normal wages over 40 hours per week)

No.	Classification	Hourly Base Wage	Extension
2	Laborers	$14.00 x 1.5	$42.00
4	Carpenters	$18.00 x 1.5	$108.00
2	Cement Masons	$20.00 x 1.5	$60.00
1	Foreman	$25.00 x 1.5	$37.50
9	Total		$247.50*

*Average cost for the group = $247.00/ 9 = $27.50/hour with benefits adder of 7.55% (assumed) = $29.58/hour

Composite Concrete Crew—Double Time (2 times Normal wages)

No.	Classification	Hourly Base Wage	Extension
2	Laborers	$14.00 x 2	$56.00
4	Carpenters	$18.00 x 2	$144.00
2	Cement Masons	$20.00 x 2	$80.00
1	Foreman	$25.00 x 2	$50.50
9	Total		$330.50*

*Average cost for the group = $330.00/ 9 = $36.67/hour with benefits adder of 7.55% = $39.44/hour

Example Calculation:

A contractor needs to make up time in his schedule. If he works the concrete crew shown in Table 4.3 10 hours per day for two weeks and 10 hours a day on two Saturdays, how much extra will it cost him?

Overtime is paid for all hours over eight, Monday thru Friday and the first eight hours on Saturday. Double-time is paid for hours greater than eight on Saturday and all Sunday work.

Monday thru Friday = 2 hours per day = 10 hours of 1.5 time

Saturday	= 8 hours of 1.5 time
Total 1.5 time	= 18 hours
Saturday Double time	= 2 hours
Crew Cost (1.5 time) x 18 hours x 2 weeks	= $29.58/hour x 9 workers = $9,584
Crew Cost (2 time) x 2 hours x 2 weeks	= $ 39.44/hour x 9 workers = $1,420
Total	= $11,004

Normal time cost if no OT worked = $23.83/hour x 9 workers x 40 hours x 2 weeks =$17,158. Additional cost to work overtime $11,004.

INDIRECT AND OVERHEAD LABOR

The examples above have shown how to determine wage rates and how to use them to develop an estimate for the direct portion of the work. However, a complete estimate needs to include indirect and overhead labor and other costs as well. Overhead and indirect positions were discussed at the beginning of this chapter and were illustrated in Table 4.1.

There are two methods of determining these costs that will be addressed here. The first method is to do a direct estimate of the indirect staff required and cost them out the same way as the direct work crews.

For example, if we were building a manufacturing facility that will take a year, the indirect support could consist of the personnel listed in Table 4.4 using wage rates determined by methods explained earlier:

As was shown in Table 4.1 on page 4.1, a manufacturing facility or power plant will have the same kinds of functions that will be included in their list of indirect labor positions.

Table 4.4—Example Indirect Labor for Facility Project

Indirect Positions	Duration On-Site (months)	No. of Positions	Worker Months	Monthly Rate*	Estimate
warehouse workers	12	2	24	$3,500	$84,000
	6	2	12	$3,500	$42,000
accounting clerks	12	1	12	$3,800	$45,600
	6	1	6	$3,800	$22,800
payroll supervisor	8	1	8	$4,500	$36,000
first aid person	12	1	12	$4,000	$48,000
safety engineer	10	1	10	$4,600	$46,000
office manager	12	1	12	$5,200	$62,400
clerical support	12	1	12	$3,000	$36,000
	6	1	6	$3,000	$18,000
On-site computer support	11	1	11	$5,000	$55,000
Project Manager	10	1	10	$8,000	$80,000
Total Indirect Labor					**$575,800**

    * monthly rate includes benefits

The second method will be to use historical job percentages to determine an appropriate allowance for indirect labor. Typical examples would include applying a percentage of direct labor, based upon historical data, or applying a percentage of the total direct costs for both indirect labor, material, and other costs.

For example,

> Estimated Direct Costs = $360, 000
> Indirect Costs at 25% = $90,000 (25% is from
> company historical data)

or

> Estimated Direct Labor = $250,000
> Indirect Labor at 30% = $ 75,000

In the second example, material and other indirect costs would have to be estimated separately.

The choice of methods will depend upon how much detailed information is available for the estimator to use in developing his estimate.

Overhead Labor

While indirect costs are often located at the plant or jobsite, overhead personnel are more likely to be located at a corporate facility, which is physically separate from the manufacturing facility or construction site. These personnel usually work on many different projects for their company at the same time, or just spend short periods, days or weeks, on each project. Examples of theses kinds of positions were included in Table 4.1.

For early estimates, the general methodology is to apply a percentage factor to either direct costs, direct labor costs, etc. as determined by corporate historical data to develop your overhead estimate. This method can be used for more detailed estimates as well. A detailed estimate for overhead labor also can be developed using number of persons similar to the indirect labor estimate already illustrated. It is up to management and the estimators involved to determine which method will supply them with the estimate accuracy they need.

ESTIMATING WORK HOURS TO COMPLETE A GIVEN WORK SCOPE

Estimating work hours is usually not done in detail until enough scope information is available to do at least a Class 3 estimate. A Class 3 estimate, as defined by AACE International[1], is a project on which the major equipment has been identified, layout drawings are available, and rough quantities are available for many of the major elements (such as cubic yards of concrete, linear feet of pipe, etc.). (Class 2 or Class 1 estimates would have more detailed unit information, as more of the final drawings would be available). With this kind of information available, the estimators will group these quantities into appropriate work packages, and working with the schedulers, start to develop the work package sequence. They can then estimate the labor costs by multiplying work hours, from their databases, times the identified quantities. It is critical to do this so that overall staffing requirements over the project duration can be used to confirm the sum of the individual work package requirements.

---

[1]The AACEI classification starts with the least detail, a Class 5 estimate, going to the most detailed, a Class 1 estimate, in which all of the drawings and specifications are completed. *AACE International Recommended Practice 18R-97: Cost Estimate Classification System for Process Industries.*

Work Packaging/Work Breakdown Structure (WBS)

The first step is to review the project and develop meaningful work packages. Often several summary level estimates are completed before enough of the project is designed to provide the estimator with detailed quantities of material so that a detailed labor estimate can be developed. An example of a WBS is shown below for a small manufacturing facility consisting of a main building, warehouse and office building, site work area including entrance roads and utilities.

The WBS for this project is shown in Table 4.5:

Table 4.5—Example WBS for Small Facility

Level 1 - ABC Manufacturing Plant		
Level 2 - Site Development	**Main Building**	**Warehouse**
Roads	Foundation	Foundation
Utilities	Excavation	Excavation
Water	Base Fill (gravel)	Base fill (gravel)
Gas/Electrical	Concrete	Concrete
Sewerage	Structural Steel	Structural Steel
Lighting	Building walls	Building walls
Parking Lot	Building roof	Building roof
	Building interior	Building interior
	Building lighting	Building lighting
	Building utilities	Building utilities
	Equipment (installation)	Office furniture
	Equipment (cost)	Warehouse equipment
	Electrical	
	Piping	

In the above example, the work hour estimates will be done at the level 3. We will use the main building concrete foundation as an example [5, p. 89]:

- the building is 300 ft/m x 100 ft/m;
- the concrete foundation consists of wall footings, foundation walls, and a slab;
- the slab will be our example, and it is 1 foot/meter thick; and
- the quantity of concrete in the slab is; 200 ft/m x 100 ft/m x 1 ft/m = 20,000 cubic ft/cubic meters = 741 CY/CM.

Determination of the work hours required is done by consulting a reference database to determine how many hours it has taken historically to complete a foundation slab of this type. There are multiple places to obtain this data including company historical data for projects on this site or in the area, a commercial estimating database, Means, Richardson, etc.

For example, using Means[2] to place this slab will take

.026 labor hours per sf/sm. This equals
20,000 sf/sm x .026 = 520 labor hours.

Costs to Support the Worker

The costs above include only the direct work required to place the slab. The assumption is that all of the material is on hand, the site is prepared, and the crew is ready to start work. The reality is that the costs need to include many items and support personnel that allow the worker to perform his/her task. In addition to indirect and overhead labor, the following examples further illustrate indirect and overhead costs.

Construction indirects and overheads can include items, such as storage and fabrication facilities, lunch and restroom facilities, and tool rooms, etc. Manufacturing indirects could include warehouse space, administrative offices, rest rooms, lunchrooms, locker rooms, and raw material loading and unloading facilities. Engineering indirects could include duplicating facilities, computer facilities, administrative offices, and personnel. When doing a conceptual or Level 1 estimate, these will normally be added as a percentage or allowance. When doing a definitive or Level 5 estimate, these costs will be estimated in detail. If you are doing a less detailed estimate, often these support costs are estimated by adding a historical factor to the direct work estimate to provide for these necessary personnel and activities.

Factors Affecting Productivity

Most estimates are developed from a common database that equates so much work done for so many work hours expended. In the petrochemical industry, common indices are based upon "Houston-Gulf Coast" production. These rates are then adjusted for conditions at the jobsite. The following is a typical, but not all-inclusive, list of items that each estimator needs to review to determine if they affect the job and the estimate:

- Will union or non-union craft labor be used?
- Is sufficient labor available locally, or will workers have to come from a long distance away?
- If the area is remote, do workers have to be bused in?
- What will the weather conditions be like (hot, cold, rainy, etc.)?
- Are there any local holidays?
- Are temporary living quarters needed?
- Is overtime necessary to attract workers?
- What are the standard work hours and work days?

---

[2] In this example, measurements are in feet or meters and are designated by ft/m (feet/meters), sf/sm (square feet/square meters), etc.

The Richardson Estimating System suggests adjustments to their rates for the following [3, p. 1–2]:

Jobsite Conditions

Good	+ 3% to 5%
Average	+ 6% to 8%
Poor	+ 9% to 15%

Worker Skill Level

High	+ 2% to 5%
Average	+ 6% to 10%
Poor	+ 11% to 20%

Temperature
Below 40 degrees or above 85 degrees add 1% per degree of variance

Work Weeks in excess of 40 hours

40 to 48 hours	+ 5%b to 10%
49 to 50 hours	+ 11% to 15%
51 to 54 hours	+ 16% to 20%
55 to 59 hours	+ 21% to 25%
60 to 65 hours	+ 26% to 30%
66 to 72 Hours	+ 31% to 40%

Example Calculation:

The standard labor cost for 100 LF of footing 8 inches by 12 inches = $130.90 [3, p. 3–1].

The jobsite conditions are as follows

Adders

Jobsite conditions	Good	+ 4%
Worker Skill	Average	+ 8%
Temperature	95 degrees	+10%
Work week = 40 hours		+ 0 %
Total adders =		+22%

Unit Rate = $130.90 x 1.22   =$159.70

Productivity Improvements
The discussion above was meant to make the reader aware of various conditions that affected both the cost and schedule of the project.

Learning Curve—One of the most important items affecting learning curve is the productivity improvement that results from a crew performing repetitive type operations. In a manufacturing environment or a construction project where similar kinds of work are done, the more the crew does the work, the faster and more efficient they become as they become familiar with working together, using the tools, possibly fabricating special tooling to make the work easier and faster, etc. This needs to be encouraged and factored into any budget or estimate made.

Examples of other types of productivity improvements— While it is one thing to recognize existing factors, there is also the opportunity to put in place procedures or make changes to improve productivity and minimize the cost of some of these factors. For example, to shorten waiting time for a crew, material may be prestaged at the work location, stored on trailers which can be easily moved to the work site, fabricated in sections, and assembled at the work site. To minimize the impact of adverse weather, temporary shelters can be built which provide shelter from the elements. Using portable tool sheds, which can be moved around to various locations as the work progresses, can shorten the time required to pick up tools. In addition to these physical actions, there is a whole series of actions, including training and team building, which can be used to improve communications and working relations between the various crews and personnel on a site. A manufacturing plant has the added benefit of more permanent personnel and the same physical location at which all of these ideas can be used to improve the worker's efficiency. There are many books and programs dealing with ways to improve productivity, and these should be consulted for a complete list of options available. The cost of these types of programs can be more than offset by the savings.

Using Commercially Available Data for Location Estimating and Comparisons
In addition to your own company database, sources for comparison data include R.S. Means and Richardson Estimating Systems [2–5].

R.S. Means publishes a city-by-city comparison that is also broken down by material and installation costs as by cost division (concrete, masonry, etc.). Their system involves comparing the ratio of the different city indices to develop a multiplier to apply to your labor cost estimates. Since they also publish unit rates, they offer comparison factors by states by zip code, which can then be adjusted to determine a factor to apply to their unit rate extensions.

An example of R.S. Means comparison data for two cities is given in Table 4.6 on page 4.8.

The comparisons listed in Means are comparisons to a national average. Therefore, in order to compare one city to another, you need to calculate the ratio difference, not the numerical difference.

The city index number = $\dfrac{\text{Specific City Cost}}{\text{National Average Cost}}$ x 100

Table 4.6—Comparison Data for Two Cities as per R.S. Means 2001[4].

		Chicago, Illinois[1]			Los Angeles, California[2]		
		Matl	Inst	Total	Matl	Inst	Total
02	Site Construction	86.0	91.0	89.8	89.5	109.0	104.5
03	Concrete (Summary)	100.6	134.6	117.6	108.2	115.6	111.9
04	Masonry	93.9	131.5	117.0	97.8	116.5	109.3
05	Metals	96.4	123.7	106.3	111.2	99.3	106
06	Woods & Plastics	103.3	128.9	116.5	99.6	117.3	108.7
07	Thermal & Moisture Protection	99.3	128.7	113.3	114.2	114.6	114.4
08	Doors & Windows	104.1	136.4	111.9	99.1	114.8	102.9
09	Finishes	89.4	129.9	110.1	108.5	116.6	112.7
Total (10-14) *(Define)*		100.0	123.7	105.0	100.0	114.5	103.1
15	Mechanical	100.0	124.5	111.3	100.2	114.0	106.6
16	Electrical	101.1	130.7	121.4	109.8	113.6	112.4
	Weighted Average	98.2	125.4	111.4	104.3	112.9	108.5

1. R.S. Means 2001, *Concrete & Masonry Cost Data*, page 436
2. R.S. Means 2001, *Concrete & Masonry Cost Data*, page 433

For example, a building in Chicago was erected for $1,540,000. I want to estimate the cost of the same building in Los Angeles.

$$\frac{\text{Index of LA}}{\text{Index of Chicago}} \times \text{cost of Chicago} = \text{Cost in LA}$$

$$\frac{108.5}{111.4} \times \$1,540,000 = \$1,500,000 \text{ (rounded)}$$

Note: Explanation from R.S. Means *Concrete & Masonry Cost Data 2001* [5, p. 430].

PERFORMANCE MONITORING

Work Packaging/Work Breakdown Structure (WBS)

An estimate is usually assembled in work packages. Work packages should be clearly identified. Items that determine what makes up a work package include portions of the job that complete a specific portion, building, or area, or are assigned to one subcontractor, can clearly be designed and scheduled, etc. Construction activity has been fairly standard for years.

However, manufacturing, power plants, and other portions of industry also utilize labor estimating and control. In their situations, work output and their organizations are more complicated than the labor craft versus work activities on the construction site. In order to better address their situations, activity-based cost (ABC) methodology has been developed to aid in organizing, analyzing, and setting up labor monitoring systems within these industries. This methodology gives some guidelines and suggests procedures that can be used to clearly define

appropriate work packages. While there is not sufficient time to discuss this methodology here, a discussion of ABC is included in Chapter 8.

For purposes of this presentation, we will start with a simple construction-related WBS for a project to install a new boiler at an existing manufacturing facility.

1. mobilization
2. excavation
3. subfoundation
4. slab placement
5. support steel
6. piping
7. boiler installation
8. utilities
9. startup
10. cleanup
11. demobilization

The labor estimate is usually the basis for project performance monitoring. The comparison of actual work hours expended, versus the estimated work hours and the development of a relationship between milestone goals, is a key tool in determining how much of the project is completed, how much effort has been expended to get to the current point, if there are problems, what has to be worked on to overcome these problems, and how this will affect the completion date and final costs.

The estimate is shown in Table 4.8:

Table 4.8—Boiler Project Labor Estimate

Work	Quantities	Units	Work hrs
Mobilization	1	Lot	50
Excavation	300	CF/CM	100
Sub Foundation	100	CF/CM	50
Slab Placemen	100	CY/MY	270
Support Steel	2	Tons	60
Piping	30	LF/LM	90
Boiler Installation	1	Lot	50
Utilities	1	Lot	80
Startup	1	Lot	100
Cleanup	1	Lot	50
Demobilization	1	Lot	50
		Total Work Hours =	950

Table 4.10—Slab Placement Percent Complete

Slab Placement	Estimated Work hrs.	% Complete	Work hrs. Earned
Formwork	25%/67.5	100 %	67.5/ 25%
Reinforcing Steel	25%/67.5	100%	67.5/25%
Concrete Placed	40%/108.0	0%	0.0/ 0%
Cured	10%/27.0	0%	0.0/0%
Total	100%/270.0		135.0/50%

Since each of these activities have different units of work, you cannot add the units for each piece together. However, you can add the work hours together. So, if you have done 100 CY/MY of the slab to place and you are 50 percent completed, you have earned 135 work hours (50% x 270 estimated work hours). Adding the earned hours up for each of the work packages will then allow a composite percent complete for the entire project to be determined.

A more detailed example is shown in Table 4.9:

It is important when reporting percent complete that the milestones and the credit for each are as clearly defined as possible. This will build credibility with your system in that everyone reporting progress will do it the same way and the data collected will stand up to Management scrutiny.

For an example, refer to Table 4.10.

For some activities, such as cleanup or mobilization and demobilization, it may be very difficult to define the mile-

stones. Progress for these activities may be monitored using a duration scale. In other words, if these are to take 4 days to complete, and 2 days have gone by, then this portion of the work is 50 percent complete (see Table 4.11). This is a subjective approximation and is one of many ways to obtain an earned value when a mathematical calculation is not practical. For these activities, it is imperative that management understand and agree to the methodology used prior to the start of the project.

Table 4.11—Example Slab Placement Work Progress

Activity	Est. Work hrs.	Day 1	Day 2	Day 3	Day 4	Day 5
Formwork	67.5	67.50				
Reinforcing Steel	67.5	12.50	55.0			
Concrete Placed	108.0			54.0	54.0	
Cured	27.0					27.0
Total	270.0	80.0	55.0	54.0	54.0	27.0
Cumulative Hours (Plan)		80.0	135.0	189.0	243.0	270.0

Table 4.9—Detailed Boiler Project Labor Estimate

Work	Quantities	Units	Work hrs	%Complete	Earned hrs.
Mobilization	1	Lot	50	100%	50
Excavation	300	CF/CM	100	100%	100
Sub Foundation	100	CF/CM	50	100%	50
Slab Placemen	100	CY/MY	270	50%	135
Support Steel	2	Tons	60	10%	6
Piping	30	LF/LM	90	10%	9
Boiler Installation	1	Lot	50	0%	0
Utilities	1	Lot	80	0%	0
Startup	1	Lot	100	0%	0
Cleanup	1	Lot	50	0%	0
Demobilization	1	Lot	50	0%	0
Total Work Hours =			950	35%	335

Graphic Presentation of Earned Value Data

The project status data for Example 1 is shown in Figure 4.1 on page 4.10. Reviewing this work package in graphic form, it appears that this work will finish ahead of schedule and under budget. The differences on the graph between the plan, earned, and expended lines provide a visual analysis of this example.

The addition of the cost performance indicator (CPI) and schedule performance indicator (SPI) calculations provides a numerical calculation to further define the status:

CPI = hours earned/hours expended = 243/200 = 1.22

SPI = hours earned/hours planned = 243/189 = 1.29

If the indicators are equal to or above 1, then the project is generally on or ahead. If the project, or elements of the project, is below 1, then these activities need to be reviewed to determine if

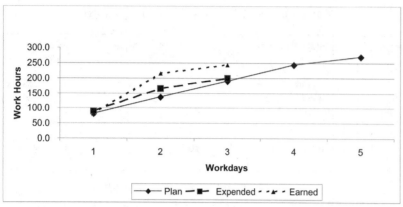

Figure 4.1—Earned Value Example 1

So, the work package appears to be overrunning the budget and behind schedule as well.

Example 3—Work Package Status

In Example 3 (Figure 4.3, Table 4.13, p 4.11), the costs are less than the plan. This would normally be OK. However, the earned is less than the plan, and it looks like there are some schedule problems. Confirming that there are schedule problems, the CPI (cost) is 1.03 (greater than 1.0), and the SPI (schedule) is 0.93 (less than 1.0). So, the work package appears to be underrunning the budget at a

action is required to improve their performance, as they are not progressing as planned. (Note: If more work is completed on noncritical activities, it is mathematically possible for the indicators to be above 1, and the project still to be in trouble. That would be because the critical path activities are behind schedule.)

Example 1 — Work Package Status

In Example 1 (Figure 4.1, Table 4.11), the costs are higher than the plan. This is normally not good, except when the schedule is also ahead of the plan. Since the project is ahead of schedule, and the CPI (Cost) is less than the SPI (schedule), this indicates that this portion of the project will finish early and may finish less than budgeted.

Example 2 — Work Package Status

In Example 2 (Figure 2, Table 4.12), the costs (work hours expended) are higher than the plan. This is normally not good, and since the earned is less than the plan, it looks like there are some problems. Confirming that there are problems, the CPI (cost) and the SPI (schedule) are less than 1.0.

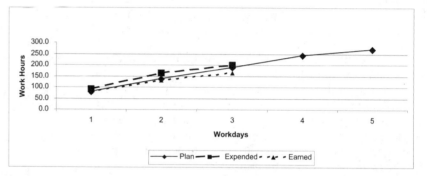

Figure 4.2—Earned Value Example 2

greater rate than the work package is behind schedule. If the schedule slippage is allowed to remain, then the budget may still be OK.

Work Sampling

Work sampling is a method that can be used to determine production or unit rates for specific work activities. These rates are to be used in setting up a company database, or determining the relationship between work at an individual site and labor standards, which have been or may be used for estimating projects in the future.

The process involves picking a sample work item or items and having personnel record all activities and labor hours associated with those activities so that unit rates per production measure can be determined. Personnel who witness and record the activities and the labor hours worked on each activity can collect from timesheets, or create their own database based upon their observation of the work activities. Comparisons can then be made against existing experience or databases to determine the most reasonable data to use

Table 4.11—Example 1 Work Package Status

Activity Estimated Work Hours	Day 1	Day 2	Day 3	Day 4	Day 5	CPI	SPI
cumulative hours (plan)	80.0	135.0	189.0	243.0	270.0		
actual hours expended	90.0	165.0	200.0			1.22	
actual hours earned	80.0	135.0	243.0				1.29

Table 4.12—Example 2 Work Package Status

Activity Estimated Work Hours	Day 1	Day 2	Day 3	Day 4	Day 5	CPI	SPI
cumulative hours (plan)	80.0	135.0	189.0	243.0	270.0		
actual hours expended	90.0	165.0	200.0			0.83	
actual hours earned	80.0	135.0	243.0				0.87

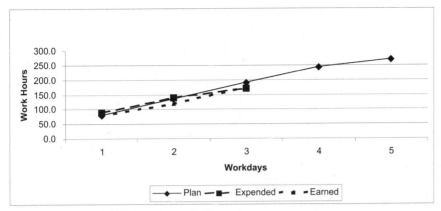

Figure 4.3—Earned Value Example 3

as the standard. Or, the data can be used to determine how the actual work is deviating from the standard.

Table 4.13—Example 3 Work Package Status

Activity Estimated Work Hours	Day 1	Day 2	Day 3	Day 4	Day 5	CPI	SPI
cumulative hours (plan)	80.0	135.0	189.0	243.0	270.0		
actual hours expended	90.0	140.0	170.0			1.03	
actual hours earned	80.0	120.0	175.0				0.93

CONCLUSION

In this chapter, the basics of labor cost development and progress monitoring have been discussed. In all instances, it is imperative that the estimator /cost engineer understand the basics in order to make sure that all of the areas impacting the estimate are thoroughly investigated and that the correct data is used in a consistent manner.

PRACTICE PROBLEMS AND QUESTIONS

Question: What is the composite rate per hour for this crew?

Problem 1: The following personnel run a production line:

Crew Mix	Base Wage/Hr
1 foreman	$20.00
2 operators	$16.00
2 assistant operators	$12.00
1 material handler	$13.00
1 material handler helper	$10.00

Questions: What is the fully loaded rate per hour for this

Problem 2: The following adders are given:

PTO	= 10%
Government Programs	= 8%
Benefits	=15%

crew? How much would it cost to have this crew work 8 hours on Saturday at time and one- half? (Assume that the only adder included in overtime is the government programs.)

Problem 3: A building was completed in Chicago for $2,755,000.

Question: How much will it cost to build that same building in Los Angeles? (Refer to page 4.8.)

Question: Which of the above are factors that could affect

Problem 4:

- union or non-union craft labor,
- Super Bowl week,
- labor availability,
- a supermarket strike,
- number of shopping days to Christmas,
- weather conditions,
- erection of temporary living quarters,
- several large projects being built concurrently within 5 miles of the jobsite.

productivity?

Questions: Calculate the SPI and the CPI. What is the status

Problem 5: The following data is provided for a production run of plastic bottles

Activity	Estimated Work Hours	Day 1	Day 2	Day 3	Day 4	Day 5
Setup	24.0	24.0				
Material handling	20.0	4.0	4.0	4.0	4.0	4.0
Production run	64.0		16.0	16.0	16.0	16.0
QC Check	12.0			4.0	4.0	4.0
Packaging	24.0			8.0	8.0	8.0
Loading & Shipping	12.0					12.0
Total	156.0	28.0	20.0	32.0	32.0	44.0
Cumulative Hours (Plan)		28.0	48.0	80.0	112.0	156.0

Thru Day 3 the following data is given:

		Day 1	Day 2	Day 3		
Actual work hours expended		32.0	60.0	95.0		
Earned		28.0	52.0	90.0		

of the production run? Draw the earned value graph.

Sample Problem Answers

Answer: The composite rate per hour for this crew is

Answers Problem 1: The following personnel run a production line:

Crew Mix	Base Wage/Hr	No.	Extension
	(1)	(2)	(3) = 1 x 2
1 foreman	$20.00	1	$20.00
2 operators	$16.00	2	$32.00
2 assistant operators	$12.00	2	$34.00
1 material handler	$13.00	1	$13.00
1 material handler helper	$10.00	1	$10.00

$99.00/7 =$14.14.

Answers: The fully loaded rate per hour for this crew is

Answers Problem 2: The following adders are given:

PTO	= 10%
Government Programs	= 8%
Benefits	=15%
Total	**= 33%**

$14.14 x 1+.33 = $ 18.81. The following equation solves how much would it cost to have this crew work 8 hours on Saturday at time and one- half, assuming that the only adder included in overtime is the government programs:

$14.14 x 1.5 = $21.21 x 1.08 (govt. programs) =
$22.91 x 7 workers x 8 hrs = $1282.96

Answers Problem 3: A building was completed in Chicago for $2,755,000. How much will it cost to build that same building in Los Angeles?

Answer: $\dfrac{108.5}{111.4}$ x $2,755,000 = $2,683,000 (rounded)

Answers Problem 4:

- union or non-union craft labor—**Yes**
- Super Bowl week—**No**
- labor availability—**Yes**
- a supermarket strike—**No**
- number of shopping days to Christmas—**No**
- weather conditions—**Yes**
- erection of temporary living quarters—**Yes**
- several large projects being built concurrently within 5 miles of the jobsite—**Yes**

Answers Problem 5:

SPI = Earned/Planned = 90.0/80.0 = 1.13
CPI = Earned/Expended = 90.0/95.0 = 0.95

What is the status of the production run? Ahead of schedule but over budget.

Draw the earned value graph:

REFERENCES

1. AACE International. *Cost Engineer's Notebook.* Morgantown, West Virginia.
2. Richardson Engineering Services, Inc. 2001. *Rapid Construction Cost Estimating System.* Mesa, Arizona.
3. Richardson Engineering Services, Inc. 2001. *Process Plant Construction Estimating Standards.*
4. R.S. Means Co., Inc. 2001. *Construction Cost Data 2001.* Kingston, Massachusetts.
5. R.S. Means Co., Inc. 2001. *Concrete and Masonry Cost Data 2001.* Kingston, Massachusetts.

The following is a partial list of companies (by no means all available) that provide estimating data

ARES Corporation
Building Systems Design, Inc.
Icarus/Richardson – Aspen Technology, Inc.
R.S Means
Win Estimator

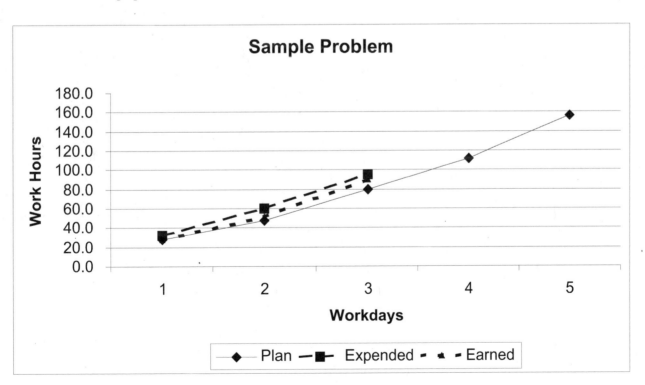

Chapter 5

Engineering

Neil D. Opfer, CCE

INTRODUCTION

The success of many products and projects is predicated upon an effective and efficient engineering effort. Improved engineering is essential in many applications given globalized competition and product/project liability issues among other concerns. Globalization has meant that countries around the world are now competitors. Adequate engineering is no longer sufficient as previous trade barriers have fallen or seen substantial reductions.

Where not offset by advantages in materials and transportation costs, labor-intensive tasks are exported around the world. Labor-intensive engineering tasks have, in some instances, followed the same pattern. Businesses out-source engineering tasks off-shore to lesser-developed countries, where an educated engineering workforce environment yields competitive advantage. In some cases, the engineering itself may be componentized, with various elements of a design done in many countries and eventually integrated into a unified whole.

Traditional product and project engineering has been revolutionized iby the advent of computer-aided design and manufacturing (CAD/CAM), which enable the rapid development and prototyping of design concepts. Businesses realize they must automate many heretofore manual engineering practices to compete in a globalized environment. Practitioners in this area must understand the potential of CAD/CAM and business reengineering for maintaining a competitive advantage. One must be able to relate engineering decisions on product selection to their impact on process selection.

LEARNING OBJECTIVES

After completing this chapter, the reader should be able to

- identify engineering issues involved in product, project, and process development, including research, the use of CAD/CAE/CAM, product liability, patents, trade secrets, and developing prototypes;
- understand product and process design and production issues, including process selection, standardization, manufacturability, constructability, and "make" or "buy" decisions;
- identify production health and safety issues;
- know issues involved in planning facility layout;
- design assembly and flow process charts; and
- understand other engineering production/construction concepts, such as reengineering, and relate engineering decisions on product selection to their impact on process selection.

PRODUCT, PROJECT, AND PROCESS DEVELOPMENT

Development of products, projects, and processes ranges from the simple to the incredibly complex. Similarly, time-frames for their development can range from days, weeks, and months to several years or more. In addition, development may depend upon concurrent and predecessor development of other items. The advent of low-cost functional microprocessors has enabled control on a real-time basis of processes that were previously only imagined.

Pure and Applied Research

Organizations conduct research in the development of products. The research can be divided into two types: pure research and applied research. Pure or basic research involves work without a specific particular end product or use in mind. A common example might be a researcher in a lab examining the interactions of different chemical compounds. Pure research functions most often take place at universities or foundations and may be financed from government grants or private sector grants. On the other hand, applied research is the attempt to develop usable products or add new feature-sets to existing products. Applied research is more specific than pure research and is typically carried out by the organization producing the product.

Product, Project, and Process Life Cycles

The life cycle of a particular product/project will have a significant influence on all design decisions, including producing plant and equipment. Some products such as automobiles have long lives while seeing significant changes in feature sets over their history. Civil infrastructure projects often have lives of many decades and should be designed for easy maintenance and upgrade. Other products may have a life cycle measured in a handful of years or less.

With short life-cycle items, time to market is essential requiring both rapid design and production to avoid missing windows of opportunity. It makes no sense to build a factory and its associated equipment with a 30 year life cycle for a product that will be obsolete in five years.

There is, of course, a prediction problem inherent in life cycles and forecasting demand. In the era of large mainframe computers, who could have foreseen the era when computers would be prevalent on desktops in both homes and offices? Phonograph records were a viable product for decades until supplanted by superior compact disc technology. Videotapes are now being replaced by digital video discs, while other technologies, such as laser discs, have fallen by the wayside.

Computer-Aided Design (CAD)/Computer-Aided Engineering (CAE)

In product, project, and process development, designers have been aided significantly by the advent of computer-aided design (CAD) and computer-aided engineering (CAE) software. CAD/CAE software involves the utilization of computerized work stations and software, including databases and computer graphics, to quickly develop and analyze a product, project, or process design. Combined with the Internet revolution with high bandwidth connections, designers and engineers around the world can work on a single design.

For example, electrical engineers in Germany may be working with mechanical engineers in India to develop a new product that will actually be produced in China. The Indian mechanical engineer can call up a part in a database, such as a motorcycle strut on a suspension system. The part then can be automatically generated as a finite model and run in a mechanical design optimizer package for a certain number of cycles. At the same time, the Indian mechanical engineer can be engaged in an on-line conversation with the German electrical engineer on a key mechanical/electrical interface issue for routing of a wiring harness. In a half-hour, the conversation ends, and the results of the mechanical design optimizer software are now available. The optimizer software has continually refined the design through numerous iterations. The engineer can now review the results including color graphic views of stress/strain diagrams. The mechanical engineer can then bring this strut into the complete design and perform analysis on this design as well.

Once designs are finalized, design data can then be ported to the manufacturing process through the interface between CAD/CAE software and CAM software.

Computer-Aided Manufacturing (CAM)

Computer-aided manufacturing (CAM) provides the counterpart advantages of CAD/CAE software to the factory floor. Design information from CAD/CAE software can be ported directly into CAM software. Design dimensional information then can directly be sent to machines to control their actions in producing parts and products. This degree of automation can range from the simple to the complex, as previously noted.

A fabricator of wood roof trusses for residential and light commercial structures can take its designs and port them to its CAM software. The CAM software aggregates the design information for computer-controlled cutting of wood roof truss members. The software package calculates member's dimensional requirements against lumber piece length to optimize production and minimize waste. Truss designs are stored on computer diskette, and when time comes to actually produce the truss, the truss layout is projected onto a laser layout table. Therefore, truss assembly personnel do not have to measure truss chord and web locations with the computer laser table projection. Thus the CAM process is faster with fewer mistakes.

In more complex cases, computer-numerically controlled (CNC) machines are linked with design and receive tooling/machining instructions. Design information can be sent separately to various machines for production with final assembly to take place later. These CNC tools are typically multi-function for operations, such as machining, with numerous operations being accomplished automatically at one workstation.

Prototypes

For a variety of reasons, organizations will typically develop prototypes prior to large-scale production. Prototypes are developed to test designs and also to test customer reaction. An equipment manufacturer planning a new type of equipment may place prototypes in the hands of customers for real-world testing and demonstration. Design concepts may be uncertain, or user reaction may be a key element in downstream product success. Prototype development is expensive, but is less expensive than producing an unwanted item or an item with a key flaw that otherwise may only be discovered after numerous units are in customer hands. Prototype development may mean the actual construction of a small-scale pilot plant to test concepts, such as is done in the petrochemical business.

The advent of CAD/CAE has led to the development of virtual prototypes on computer. Organizations, at a fraction of the cost of physical prototypes, can produce computer simulations of a prototype for testing by operators and designers.

These computer simulations mean that operator mistakes will not cause real physical damage, further reducing testing costs. Changes to a computer simulation can be readily accomplished far faster than with a physical prototype. This is important anywhere time-based competition is an issue.

Whether the prototypes be actual physical models or computer simulations, their use and application provides significant benefits for the organization. Customers may be exposed to both physical and computer-simulation prototypes. This also provides for interaction of the design team with customers that can provide important feedback. This one-on-one interaction gathers information far better than simple survey form methods. Physical or computer prototypes represent a significant financial and time outlay by the organization, but eliminating this development step has typically proven to be a short-sighted measure.

Patents and Trade Secrets

Investing in new products and their research is usually both expensive and time-consuming. This investment must be protected. Typically, organizations can protect their investments through either patents or trade secrets. In the United States, a patent's duration is 17 years. In return for publishing the information underlying the patent, protection is granted to the inventor(s) for an exclusive period of 17 years. Those organizations wishing to emulate the patent's provisions will either have to develop a creative approach different from the patented design or pay royalties to the patent holder. Copying patented features before the 17-year patent expiration date will result in a case of patent infringement.

Trade secrets also serve as protection for intellectual property. Trade secrets can be somewhat broader than patent protection in that they protect both commercial and technical information from disclosure. Organizations producing a popular soft drink, a fried chicken recipe, or services, such as a particular business method, have all successfully protected these through the trade secret route. The advantage of trade secrets is their perpetual nature, as long as disclosure can be prevented. Employees are prohibited from disclosure of trade secrets through employment contracts. In addition, organizations may subdivide processes to prevent the repository of total information with one or two employees.

Product Liability

In today's increasingly litigious society, product liability is gaining importance in engineering design and production. In some cases, the product liability issue can act as a drag on engineering innovation, retarding the advancement of design due to these concerns.

Product liability provides a means by which those injured by a product can seek compensation for their damage. The tort law in this area has evolved over decades from a concept of "buyer beware" to a concept of "seller beware." In part, this is due to the increasing complexity of today's products. The

---

GLOSSARY TERMS IN THIS CHAPTER
computer-aided design (CAD) ◆ computer-aided manufacturing (CAM) ◆ constructability manufacturability ◆ patent ◆ product design reengineering ◆ robot ◆ system design variance analysis ◆

old concept of buyer beware was more applicable in days of peddlers selling bolts of cloth. The buyer could reasonably examine a bolt of cloth as to quality. Compare this with the purchase of a rotary lawnmower at a store. The variety of pieces and parts on the lawnmower make it more difficult to examine, and certain defects in design may only become apparent after extended use of this unit.

PRODUCT, PROJECT, AND PROCESS DESIGN

Standardization

Design engineers must pay close attention to standardization concepts. Standardization is the attempt to base product designs, in whole or in part, on existing product items and tooling. The advantages of standardization are readily apparent in that by incorporating existing elements into new products, overall product development costs will be lower and time to market will be shorter. An example of design standardization may be through utilization of common parts, such as an automotive frame. One automotive frame system may provide the basis for several automobile types. The same principles would apply to engines as one powerplant is utilized in a number of applications. Engine horsepower may be varied by use of turbochargers versus naturally aspirated engines. Engine displacement can be varied by changing the stroke and holding the cylinder bore constant.

There are economic benefits to standardization not only for the producer, but for the customer as well. Product standardization means less investment in spare parts inventory and lower general maintenance costs. Maintenance personnel are able to become more familiar with fewer equipment components resulting in faster repairs and fewer mistakes.

However, standardization can pose a problem concerning product defects. If there is a product flaw, the flaw will be spread over a wide variety of products. These general product flaws can be costly from a repair/recall standpoint in addition to harming the organizations' overall image and reputation.

Process Selection

Part and parcel of product engineering design will be process selection. Process selection relates to the production methods chosen to produce the product. There are two basic types of production methods:

- continuous production, and
- discrete production.

Examples of continuous production methods would be petrochemical plants, power plants and manufacturers with assembly-line methods, such as wire/cable manufacturers and automotive manufacturers. Examples of discrete production would be manufacturers of any type of custom product, such as a pre cast concrete plant, structural steel fabrication shop, or machine shop. Some products will envelope both methods sometimes by the same firm. A structural steel fabrication shop will take basic steel products from a steel manufacturer engaged in a continuous process method, such as continuous casting, and turn them into customized "one-off" structural steel fabrications for a particular project.

Continuous production method systems are less expensive in the long run because the high fixed costs of extensive production machinery can be amortized over many units of production. The determining factor in deciding in favor of continuous production is whether demand is such that production volumes can justify the investments required for this method. In general, continuous production methods use specialized equipment including conveyor lines and specialized machinery.

Discrete production methods use general-purpose equipment. Production equipment, such as forklifts, welders, fabrication tables, and machining centers can be utilized for a wide variety of items. Discrete production methods will have a higher labor factor versus continuous methods. In regions of the world where labor costs are less expensive relative to capital equipment, discrete methods may be favored due to their more favorable capital/labor tradeoff ratios.

Manufacturability

Engineering design methods must focus not only on issues of product design, but also on issues of manufacturing the design [3]. A design may work perfectly in terms of function, but if it is unnecessarily complicated to produce, problems may ensue. Design tolerances may be specified that are unnecessary for product function yet create substantial problems in production.

Designs, where possible, should be

- forgiving of minor inaccuracies,
- easy to fabricate, and
- based on efficient utilization of labor, materials, and equipment.

Slight changes or modifications in a design that don't affect the product but instead promote ease of assembly of the product are referred to as manufacturability. During the design and development process, experienced manufacturing personnel should view products from the manufacturability perspective. These reviews can pinpoint problems before designs are developed to the point where changes create significant delays and associated costs.

Constructability

Constructability is the counterpart of manufacturability applied to constructed projects and their elements. The same issues apply to the realm of constructability. Designs can be developed on paper and in the computer that may make sense from the designer's viewpoint but present significant problems in their construction. The Construction Industry Institute has defined constructability as the optimum use of construction knowledge and experience in planning, design, procurement, and field operations to achieve overall project objectives [1]. The same precepts of manufacturability apply to constructability. Early preconstruction implementation of these techniques can pinpoint problems before designs are developed to the point where changes create significant delays and associated costs.

Make or Buy Decisions

Product, project, and process development must concern decision-makers with "make" or "buy" decisions. That is to say, which items should be subcontracted out to others and which should be made in-house. Decision-makers must question whether their organization's quality and cost on an item can compete with outside suppliers. If trade secrets are involved, the decision will typically be to make the item, unless the trade secret is the result of certain combinations of widely-sourced ingredients. For example, if a commodity such as sugar is part of a fermentation trade secret process, the organization will not find it practical to produce its own sugar unless it is already in that line of business.

The overarching goal with make or buy decisions is making the best selections to enhance overall quality at a lower cost. If a manufacturer is producing 100,000 units of a piece of equipment on an annual basis, it will usually make far more sense to purchase motors from another manufacturer specializing in motors. The motor manufacturer may be making 1,000,000 of these motors for their own use and as OEM-sourced equipment for others. There is no practical way to achieve these kinds of economies-of-scale benefits at the relatively low 100,000 units per year. Therefore, the motor selection will be a buy decision.

ENGINEERING
PRODUCTION/CONSTRUCTION

Numerous decisions must be made with regards to engineering production/construction. These decisions will naturally occur based on decisions reached in other areas as discussed previously.

Production Health And Safety

Personnel health and safety is paramount in any production situation. Health and safety is important from both a humanitarian and an economic standpoint. Developed countries place a premium on human health and safety. From the economic viewpoint, health and safety lapses are expensive. An accident, for example, results in the loss of a trained worker and an interruption in the process.

Systems must be selected that reduce and/or eliminate the potential of accidents. Health issues are more difficult to ascertain because usually they are not immediate as opposed to a safety-related accident. Health issues include exposures to fumes, dust, noise, and heat. Fumes from a production process may cause long-term health problems for personnel. The exposure risk may require a change to eliminate fumes or robotic operation so that human exposure is unnecessary.

Facility Layout

Facility layout involves decisions as to arrangement, including equipment location, labor location, and services location. The facility may be existing requiring renovation or one that is being built from the ground up on a "greenfield" basis. Layout decisions should always consider the potential impact of additional demand therefore considering future expansion and additions to the base layout.

Assembly And Flow Process Charts

Assembly and flow process charts assist in planning the facility layout. They help to analyze production operations in terms of operations sequences performed, distances between operations, and operation time requirements [4].

Process charts are developed based on standard symbols for studying operations. The symbol O represents an operation. An operation occurs when any change takes place whether of a physical nature or when new information is received. The symbol ∇ represents storage of an item. Storage is when any item is kept or held in the process. The symbol ⇒ represents transportation or movement in the process as when items are moved from one location to another. The symbol ▯ represents inspection. An inspection occurs when an object is examined for conformance as to quality or quantity. The symbol D represents delay. Delays occur with interruptions to the process that prohibit the next operation or item from taking place.

A production operation might entail the cutting of steel beams to length and drilling holes in the beams. Flow charting of this operation would be as shown in Table 5.1 below:

Flow charts offer the advantage of mapping product flow, which helps in spotting inefficiencies in the production process. Steps can be changed and rearranged to promote higher productivity and lower costs. Therefore, these charts can be a powerful tool.

Quantitative Analysis In Facility Layout

Techniques such as linear programming and Monte Carlo can significantly assist in facility layout and production decisions.

Linear programming is a mathematical technique that is widely used in finding optimal solutions to problems. Linear programming techniques are designed to either minimize or maximize some objective function. Thus, material distances in a facility can be minimized or space available may be maximized. These linear programming decisions are also bounded by parameters, which are limitations or restraints. There may only be a limited amount of space available or limited milling machines available for a certain production operation. Detailed linear programming techniques are beyond the scope of this chapter since entire books have been written on these topics.

Monte Carlo techniques provide for simulation. Queuing problems, such as wait time for a crane in a plant, can be analyzed with Monte Carlo techniques. Data can be generated via computer programs with random number generators. Information, such as wait time costs, are factored into the equation and simulations are conducted on this basis. Again, these techniques are beyond the scope of this chapter. Practitioners in this area are encouraged to consult the many books published on these techniques for further information.

Table 5.1—Flow Chart of Steel Beam Production

Symbol	Operation
∇	Beams In Storage
⇒	Transport Beam To Saw
O	Cut Beam To Length At Saw
∇	Place On Pallet
⇒	Transport By Forklift To Vertical Drill
O	Drill Beam
▯	Inspect Beam To Verify Quality
D	Store On Pallet Until Needed
⇒	Transport To Paint Booth
O	Prime Beam

Reengineering

Reengineering is the fundamental rethinking and radical redesign of business processes to achieve dramatic improvements in critical contemporary measures of performance, such as cost, quality, service, and speed. Some of these steps include combining two or more jobs into one and enabling workers to make decisions with work being performed where it makes most sense. An example of reengineering might have your supplier monitoring your inventory of their supplied item since they are better able to accomplish this task. This then frees the organization to focus on its own mission-critical work.

Reengineering focuses on the optimization of the total organization, rather than suboptimization of individual departments or units. In the context of this section, disparate units, such as design, manufacturing, sales/marketing, and customer service are brought together to deliver optimal solutions that benefit the entire organization as opposed to the individual unit. Moreover, reengineering focuses on the "whys" of an action or process as opposed to the "hows." An appliance manufacturer may be concerned with welding spatter on new appliances and how to control this. However, a change in the steel purchased from a smooth pattern to an embossed pattern on steel sheet may make the welding spatter not noticeable in the finished product. Here, a focus on why the welding spatter needs to be controlled is more important than the how and results in a simple purchasing specifications change. Reengineering focuses on these global issues.

SUMMARY

The recognition of the impact and potential of engineering issues will lead to more rational decision processes by those responsible. Traditional product and project engineering has been revolutionized in many cases by the advent of CAD/CAE/CAM concepts, which enable the rapid development and prototyping of design concepts. Businesses are realizing that they must automate many heretofore manual engineering practices in order to compete in a globalized environment. Individuals practicing in this area must understand the potential of CAD/CAM and business reengineering for competitive advantage. One must be able to relate engineering decisions on product selection to their impact on process selection.

REFERENCES

1. Construction Industry Institute. 1986. *Constructability Primer Publication 3-1*. University of Texas, Austin.

2. Hammer, M., and J. Champy. 1993. *Reengineering The Corporation*. New York: HarperBusiness.

3. Mazda, F. 1998. *Engineering Management*. Addison-Wesley. Harlow, England.

4. Meyer, C. 1993. *Fast Cycle Time*. New York: The Free Press.

Chapter 6

Equipment, Parts, and Tools

Dr. Carl C. Chrappa

INTRODUCTION

Selecting, purchasing, tracking, storing, maintaining, and selling equipment, parts, and tools is an important project management function that can greatly impact project schedules and costs. This chapter outlines current issues and industry practices regarding equipment for the cost engineer.

LEARNING OBJECTIVES

After completing this chapter, the reader should be able to

- establish an equipment valuation database and identify the different equipment value categories and subcategories;
- research equipment cost information; and
- understand the factors that affect current and residual values for new and used equipment.

ESTABLISHING AN EQUIPMENT VALUATION DATABASE

In order to establish a reliable equipment valuation database upon which to base estimates or appraisals, emphasis must be placed on the quality and level of trade data being cataloged so that the values contained in the database are appropriate for their intended use. Such data can be used to establish reliable current value appraisals and residual value estimates (future values) for equipment needed on a project.

Equipment Value Categories

Equipment values can be divided into two major categories: (1) Replacement Cost New (new equipment cost), and (2) Market Value (used equipment, secondary market value). Within each category are subcategories.

The first catagory, **Replacement Cost New**, has the following subcategories:

- **Reproduction Cost** is the cost new of an identical item.
- **Replacement Cost** is the cost new of an item having the same or similar utility.
- **Fair Value** is the adjusted cost new of an item, giving consideration for the cost of similar items, and taking into account utility and all standard adjustments and discounts to list price.

The second category, **Market Value,** also contains several subcategories:

- **Fair Market Value-in-Place** is the amount expressed in terms of money that may reasonably be expected to exchange between a willing buyer and a willing seller with equity to both, neither under any compulsion to buy or sell, and both fully aware of all relevant facts as of a certain date, and taking into account installation and the contribution of the item to the operating facility. This value presupposes continued utilization of the item in connection with all other installed items.
- **Fair Market Value-in-Exchange** is the value of equipment in terms of the money that can be expected to be exchanged in a third-party transaction between a willing buyer, who is under no compulsion to buy, and a willing seller, who is under no compulsion to sell, both being fully aware of all relevant facts (also referred to as retail value).
- **Orderly Liquidation Value** is the probable price for all capital assets and equipment in terms of money that could be realized from a properly executed orderly liquidation type of sale, given a maximum time of six months to conduct such sale and adequate funds available for the remarketing campaign. This value further assumes that all assets will be sold upon completion of the allotted time period (also referred to as wholesale value).
- **Forced Liquidation Value** is the value of equipment in terms of money that can be derived from a properly advertised and conducted auction where time is of the

essence (also referred to as "under the hammer" or "blow-out" value).

- **Salvage Value/Part-Out Value** is the value of equipment in terms of money that a buyer will pay to a seller, recognizing the component value of parts of the equipment that can be used or resold to end-users, usually for repair or replacement purposes.
- **Scrap Value** is the value of equipment in terms of money that relates to the equipment's basic commodity value. For example, dollars per ton of steel or pound of copper.

Valuation Examples/Subcategories of Value

The Table 6.1 is an example of market value subcategories for the sale of a certain four-year-old CNC machining center (original cost new $350,000):

This example illustrates the relative meaning and weight of some of the valuation terms previously discussed. It is based on these terms and definitions that valuation data should be collected and cataloged.

Table 6.1—Market Value Subcategories for CNC Machining Center

Type of Value	Sales Price	% of Highest Price
Fair Market Value-in-Place	$275,000	100%
Fair Market Value-in-Exchange	$200,000	73%
Orderly Liquidation Value	$175,000	64%
Forced Liquidation Value	$150,000	55%
Salvage/Part-Out Value	$15,000	5%
Scrap Value	$2,000	1%

Replacement Cost New, Sources of Data

Replacement Cost New is the highest value that can be attributable to a piece of equipment. Thus, it can be considered 100 percent of value (new). Several source are available for collecting and monitoring equipment replacement cost (new) data. several sources are available. Among these are prices and data obtained from the following sources:

- manufacturers price lists,
- data obtained verbally from sales representatives and new equipment dealers,
- published prices from technical and trade journals,
- literature obtained at trade shows,
- invoices containing cost data relating to past transactions;
- purchase orders from past transactions,
- equipment quotations from manufacturers or dealers, and
- appraised values obtained from replacement value (new) or insurance appraisals, which typically list replacement cost (new).

By cataloging valuation data obtained through the various sources listed above, the estimator/appraiser can establish a sizeable and meaningful database from which to plot value trends for a specific piece of equipment over time, or to validate the fair value of a similar item in the future.

Market Value, Sources of Data

An equipment valuation database can also be established for market values. Sources of this data (for the various subcategories already mentioned) include the following:

- trade publications listing sales advertisements for used equipment,
- retail prices obtained from used equipment dealers or brokers,
- equipment price quotations for the purchase of used equipment documented in previous transactions,
- values from "market data publications" available for purchase,
- auction "sales catalogs" available from auction companies at a nominal cost ($20 to $50),
- regulatory filings, and
- past remarketing and sales results from one's own firm.

Market Valuation Example

To better illustrate the basis for some of the subcategories of market value (how equipment is bought and sold), an example is given in Table 6.2 involving a 10-year-old metal lathe. It is followed by an example summary (Table 6.3), which shows the relationship of subcategories of market value to one another.

Table 6.2—Market Value Subcategories for Metal Lathe

Event	Cost/Value
a. **purchase price** as-is at auction	$5,500 (orderly liquidation sale)
b. **sales tax**	exempt (equipment dealer)
c. **deinstallation**, rigging, shipping, and delivery to warehouse	$600
d. **cost of money** (estimated) time to sell: 90 days, 10% annual rate x 3 months x $6,100 purchase and deinstall	$154
e. **overhead** (20% of purchase price, includes some preparation and advertising	$1,100
f. **profit** (15%–20%: use 20% of purchase price plus deinstallation	$1,220
g. **subtotal** (a+c+d+e+f)	$8,574 (min. desired selling price)
h. **ask** (advertise for sale)	$9,800 (retail asking)
i. **take** (sale to end user)	$8,600 (fair market value-in-exchange)
j. **buyer** (end user) pays sales tax (6%)	$516
k. **delivery**	$600
l. **installation and debugging**	$1,400
Total installed cost to end user (i+j+k+l)	$11,116 (fair market value-in-place)

Table 6.3—Metal Lathe Example Summary

Type of Market Value	% of Value
Fair Market Value-in-Place ($11,116)	100%
Fair Market Value-in-Exchange ($8,600)	77%
Orderly Liquidation Value ($5,500)	49%

GLOSSARY TERMS IN THIS CHAPTER

fair market value-in-exchange ◆ fair market value-in-place
fair value ◆ forced liquidation value
orderly liquidation value ◆ replacement cost
reproduction cost ◆ salvage value
scrap value ◆

Trade Data/Cost Adjustments

Used equipment sales data is often inconsistent for the same or similar pieces of equipment. In order to adjust or normalize this data, the following considerations should be addressed and value added or deducted as appropriate. These adjustments include the following:

- the same equipment, but with different years of manufacture (normally adding value for newer equipment);
- the same equipment, but with different attachments, drive motors, etc.;
- the location of the sale (i.e., equipment sold in a prime geographic market area will usually achieve a higher sales price than equipment sold in a remote area);
- utilization (amount of wear/use); and/or
- condition (one of the most important considerations).

Condition alone in some instances can cause considerable value swings for identical pieces of equipment. It is extremely important that the condition of a piece of equipment be noted at the time of sale to ensure that equipment sold in excellent condition for a relatively high price will not later be used to anticipate the price of a piece of equipment expected to be in average or fair condition at the end of the lease. Once again, this is one of the most important parts of any database and should not be overlooked.

Equipment Condition Terms and Definitions

Following is a sample selection of condition terms and definitions used to describe equipment.

Example 1:

- **Very Good (VG)**—This term describes an equipment item in excellent appearance and being used to its full design specifications without being modified and without requiring any repairs or abnormal maintenance at the time of inspection or within the foreseeable future.

- **Good (G)**—This term describes equipment that was modified or repaired and is being used at or near its fully specified utilization.
- **Fair (F)**—This term describes equipment used at some point below its fully specified utilization because of the effects of age and/or application and that will require general repairs and some replacement of minor elements in the foreseeable future to raise the level of utilization to or near its original specifications.
- **Poor (P)**—This term describes equipment being used at some point well below the fully specified utilization and that will require extensive repairs and/or the replacement of major elements in the near future to realize full capacity.
- **Scrap (X)**—This term describes equipment that is no longer serviceable and cannot be utilized to any practical degree regardless of the extent of the repairs or modifications that may be undertaken. This condition applies to equipment that has been used for 100 percent of its useful life or that is 100 percent technologically or functionally obsolete.

Another variation is **Example 2:**

- **Excellent (E)**—This term describes equipment that is new or in practically new condition, with extremely low utilization, no defects, and that may still be under warranty.
- **Good (G)**—This term describes equipment that has good appearance, may have just recently been completely overhauled or rebuilt with new materials, and/or has had such use and maintenance that no repairs or worn part replacement is necessary. This equipment shows no deferred maintenance.
- **Average (A)**—This term describes equipment that is in 100 percent operating condition with no known major mechanical defects but may have some worn parts that will need repair or replacement in the future. This equipment may have high utilization, but any defects are not obvious.
- **Fair (F)**—This term describes equipment that shows high utilization; defects are obvious and will require repair or a general overhaul or rebuild soon. This equipment is operational but questionable and may exhibit deferred maintenance.
- **Poor (P)**—This term describes equipment that has seen severe and long hours of service. It requires rebuild, repair, or overhaul before it can be profitably used and is not operational.

In summary, the logging of raw data and condition, along with the cost adjustments previously mentioned, will permit a fine tuning of market data, yielding a more reliable and meaningful value.

Data Filing Systems

Once data is obtained in sufficient quantities, a decision can be made on how to record it. Most valuation and research firms file data using one of four methods:

1. The first is by Standard Industrial Classification (SIC) code where data is stored in broad industry category codes, such as #34-machine tools, #44-marine, etc. This method is quite effective when utilizing an electronic database, since a numerical method of encoding each piece of data lends itself to an SIC type of listing.
2. Another method of filing is to list data by equipment class and type, such as machine tools-lathes, aircraft-commuter, construction-crawler crane, trailers-dry van, barges-covered hopper, or railcar-center beam flat.
3. A third method lists equipment by industry category, such as machine shop equipment, construction, mining equipment, aircraft, or marine vessels.
4. Finally, another filing system is based strictly on the equipment manufacturer's name, such as Freuhauf -trailers, Warner and Swasey-machine tools, Caterpillar-construction equipment, Boeing-commercial aircraft, and IBM-computers, etc.

By using any one of the above methods of filing, a workable cataloging system can be created that will enable the user to obtain valuation data in a minimal amount of time. The larger the database, however, the more complex the filing system must be for prompt retrievals.

Data Storage

Data can be stored via several methods. The system most widely used is electronic data storage. Here, systems can be developed utilizing hardware ranging from PCs to servers that file (log) everything from individual equipment specifications to a manufacturer's total equipment production run, listing all pertinent data and serial numbers for each piece of equipment studied. When establishing an electronic data filing system, sufficient time should be devoted to selecting appropriate software that is user-friendly and can be adapted to listings and searches by whatever method of retrieval the user desires. Also, numerous sites on the Internet have databases that can be easily accessed when needed. Such use of third-party information can augment or support an in-house (proprietary) database.

Additionally, estimators/appraisers may wish to consider purchasing certain trade data available in the public domain. There is no substitute for actual trade data.

Equipment Valuations

One of an estimator/appraiser's most difficult tasks is the analysis and calculation of equipment residual values (future values) for leases or life cycle costing. Unfortunately, there are no magic formulas or short cuts, and no college to teach how to properly calculate residuals—the only way to gain this knowledge is through hard work and years of experience.

Because industry and business place such an importance on (future) residual values, the role of the estimator/appraiser has become vital. One key component of estimating residual values is the appraiser's understanding of the equipment and the industry in which it operates.

The analyst must have access to trade (sales) data. There are no substitutes for facts. Sometimes unqualified opinions can cause serious financial damage to a company. Although the determination of residual values using trade data does not guarantee the future value of equipment, it nonetheless provides a sound basis upon which to predicate future values. In addition, there are many variables the analyst should consider in arriving at a realistic residual value estimate.

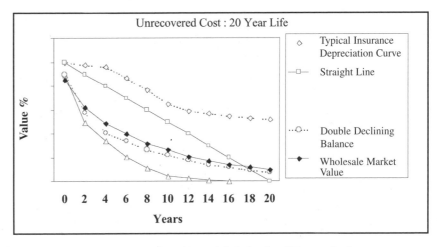

Figure 6.1—Executive Aircraft Methods of Depreciation

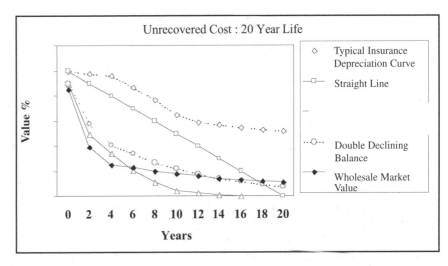

Figure 6.2—Machine Tools Methods of Depreciation

Residual Value Curves

Residual value is the expected future amount of money an owner/lessor will realize from an asset at a specified future date, such as the end of a lease term or project, from any and all sources, including sale, re-lease, holdover rent, penalties, damage, litigation, and payments for noncompliance to the lease documentation (such as return and maintenance provisions).

Figures 6.1 and 6.2 illustrate that wholesale market value (Orderly Liquidation Value) of equipment does not follow predefined curves or formulas. In fact, the shape of a residual curve may change on an annual or even monthly basis, depending on circumstances. It is important to remember that the market is constantly changing. The variables that cause this change will be discussed later.

Figure 6.3 on page 6.6 illustrates some of the classic, as well as unusual, residual value curves for used equipment.

The "normal" residual value curve of long-lived equipment usually follows an L-shaped curve that is illustrated in Figures 6.1–6.3. Another shape is the disrupted market curve, which is a deviation from the normal curve and is usually in the shape of a U. This curve is typically results from excess supply or regulatory pressures causing the market value for a piece of equipment to suddenly plunge or deviate from normal for a period of time. Past examples include the "U" curves for covered hopper railcars and intercostal barges during the mid-1980s.

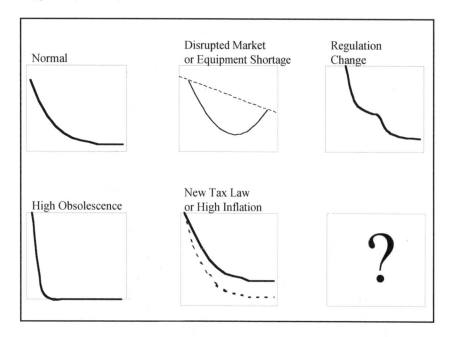

Figure 6.3—Residual Value Curves for Used Equipment

Another curve that can be studied is the regulatory change curve, which illustrates the sudden impact on market value that regulation can cause, such as the effect of FAA Part 36 Stage 3 on the values of Boeing 727s and 737–100s, 200s, etc.

The high obsolescence curve is a truncated shape that illustrates the impact of technological obsolescence. This curve is particularly prevalent among items such as computers and certain other types of high-tech equipment.

Another deviation from the normal shape is the (new) tax law/high inflation residual curve. Tax laws and inflation can, in some cases, cause a normal residual curve to rise dramatically in a short time. Although this pattern is quite appealing to the lessor when selling in a strong market, it should also be recognized that an elevated curve will sooner or later likely fall back to its "normal" shape.

Variables That Affect Residual Value

In general, there are twelve items that should be considered in estimating residual values:

1. initial cost,
2. maintenance,
3. use/wear and tear,
4. population,
5. age,
6. economy,
7. changes in technology,
8. foreign exchange,
9. tax laws,
10. legislation/regulation,
11. location of equipment
12. method of sales.

1. Initial Cost—One of the most frequently overlooked items in any transaction is the initial cost of equipment. Many times, the owner/lender/lessor is presented with a funding containing indirect costs that it may not be aware are included in the price. For residual purposes, the estimator/appraiser should consider basing his or her residual estimate on 'hard costs' only for individual items. The hard cost of an asset includes the cost new of the basic machine and the cost of any additional items necessary to make it operate, including drives, motors, electricals, and controls. Items referred to as "soft costs" that should not be included are as follows:

*   foundations (which some large machines may require due to their size or overall sensitivity),
*   freight,
*   debugging,
*   taxes (which may include federal, state, and local taxes, as well as duty on foreign imports), and
*   installation (which includes fastening the equipment to a foundation, piping, and electrical wiring from a main distribution system, and other items necessary to the machine's operation).

The following is an example of an actual situation involving a transfer stamping press line in an automotive facility. A leasing company was presented with a transaction valued at $2.1 million. Subsequent investigation found the following:

*   the basic cost of the machine was $1.5 million,
*   the cost of foundations was about $400,000,
*   the cost of freight was $40,000,
*   taxes were $60,000, and
*   installation was estimated at $100,000 (all totaling $2.1 million).

In this instance, if a leasing company's historical "residual curve" for this equipment indicated 30 percent of the new cost at the end of the term, the difference between calculating the residual on a value-in-exchange basis for the hard asset only versus the value-in-place including soft costs would equal $180,000 at lease term.

Total Cost: $2.1 million x 30% =	$630,000
Hard Cost: $1.5 million x 30% =	$450,000
Difference =	$180,000

This difference could present a future shortfall if the asset were sold on a value-in-exchange basis. It should be understood that in some instances—such as a facility lease or financing or life-cycle costing—soft costs should be considered in determining residual values.

2. Maintenance—The next consideration is maintenance. The difference in value received from a well-maintained versus a poorly maintained piece of equipment can be substantial. Maintenance can also affect the useful life of equipment. In calculating a residual value, estimators/appraisers must consider how the equipment will be maintained and/or the maintenance language in the lease. Maintenance provisions in leases can be relied upon by the lessor as a future condition statement and also for future claims for damage, abuse, or deferred maintenance. If the lease contains strong maintenance provisions, a higher residual usually can be assumed strictly on the basis of the condition in which the equipment is expected to be returned at the end of the lease.

3. Use/Wear and Tear—Use/wear and tear is another important consideration that should be understood by the estimator/appraiser in estimating residual values. The difference between equipment in harsh service versus mild service can be substantial and, in some instances, can affect the equipment's useful life. An example is covered hopper railcars. Used in grain service, they can have useful lives of approximately 40 to 50 years. However, if used in salt service, their useful lives can be as short as 15 years. Other examples include construction equipment used in sand pits, which subject the undercarriage to excessive wear. Thus, the analyst should be aware of all such conditions when estimating residual values.

Some types of equipment, such as aircraft, define use in hours of utilization and cycles (takeoffs and landings); other transportation equipment defines use in miles or kilometers per year. Mechanical equipment utilization is usually recorded by the hour. Typically, most mechanicals tend to wear out at around 10,000 to 20,000 hours. At these milestones, usually some form of rebuild or refurbishing is required.

For analysis purposes, 1,700 to 2,000 hours per year utilization is usually considered one shift; 3,000 to 4,000 hours is considered two shifts; and 5,000+ hours per year is considered three shifts. Leasing terms for equipment that will be utilized 5,000+ hours per year (as frequently happens in the mining industry) usually contain strong return and maintenance provisions in order to ensure the future condition of the equipment. The appraiser may then base his or her residual value estimates on this assumption.

An example of the effects of high utilization and wear and tear is the partial disintegration, in flight, of a commercial jet that had approximately 80,000 cycles of use in addition to high time. Besides the high utilization rate in this example, the geographic area of use, which was tropical, could have also played a part in the incident, since it may have caused the aircraft to be subjected to further wear and tear from the corrosion caused by the moist, tropical, salty air.

4. Population—Another important consideration is the overall population of the subject equipment. Typically, the larger the population of equipment, the more data can be obtained. This gives statistical significance to the residual value, because the value will be based on a large sample referred to as a commodity. Residual valuations are particularly difficult and oftentimes meaningless for prototype equipment. When valuing a prototype, the equipment analyst can only attempt to compare the item being valued to another item having similar utility. Technology could be a large risk in such a transaction, as well as a very limited secondary market.

Many times estimators/appraisers are able to obtain information on annual production runs of certain equipment. A review of this data may reveal a sizeable increase in the manufacture of the product during a certain year, which may have an impact on the future residuals; e.g., if much of the equipment produced in a boom year comes off lease all at once.

Boom years for particular types of equipment are generally related to the overall health of the economy, or, in particular market segments, to regulatory mandates and/or special tax incentives. One illustration of this is the chassis industry, which had production rates during the 1950s and 1960s in the area of 4,000 units per year. In the 1970s, this average increased to about 10,000 units per year, while in 1984 the number jumped to about 24,000, then in 1985 to almost 29,000 units. In such instances, the estimator/appraiser should have considered the potential downward impact of boom years on future residual values. (This, however, was mitigated by the explosion of the intermodal industry in the 1990's.) These production spikes have also recently occurred in the truck and trailer markets. What drives the primary market today may not drive the secondary market in five to eight years.

5. Age—Another item that is often overlooked is the actual age of date of manufacture of a piece of equipment. Equipment presented as new in January 2003 could have a 2001 or 2002 build date. This is particularly important for transportation equipment. If, for example, the equipment comes off of a lease or project in 2006, which truck will sell for more: the 2001 or 2002 model? The answer is obvious. The estimator/appraiser should verify model years and serial numbers on each transaction.

The following example is given to illustrate the different sales tiers that should be considered when estimating residual values. Recently, an 8-year-old insulated trailer fleet was sold to an end-user. The equipment manager surveyed the market at all levels. The results of this survey are shown in Table 6.4 on page 6.8.

Table 6.4—The Transaction: 195 trailers, 8 years old, original cost $3,510,000

Sales Tier	% of Highest Sales Price	Comments
retail sales level	100%	actual sales price $1,040,00
wholesale	76%	offers received to purchase trailers by wholesalers
auction	63%	estimated proceeds from the sale at auction received from several auctioneers
end of economic useful life	7%	estimate of the value of trailers to be used as storage units only

The difference in the values above for the same equipment illustrates the importance of an appraiser recognizing at what level or sales tier the equipment typically sells, and then adjusting its residuals to reflect this level.

6. Economy—The equipment appraiser must also consider the overall shape of the economy. For instance, the U.S. economy usually performs at 4-to 7-year business cycles. A used truck that sells for $25,000 in a robust economy may sell for $17,000 in a recession. Further, the sale of equipment in a robust economy might take from 1 to 30 days, while in a recession it could take 60 to 90 days. The additional time it takes to sell should also be calculated in the overall cost of the sale (cost of money).

7. Changes in Technology—Changes in technology can also affect residual values. These changes occur in every type of equipment. However, some changes have a more profound impact on value. An analysis of technological changes occurring over the past 20 years shows that future advances in technology were generally known at the time of lease origination. The astute analyst may choose to make an adjustment in the residual of a piece of equipment that is subject to such obsolescence.

Some recent changes can be found in the computer microprocessor as reflected in the Pentium 4 chip. Big ticket medical imaging equipment, such as CT Scanners, are currently utilizing fourth- and fifth-generation scanners that have reduced the time necessary to "fix" an image from minutes to seconds.

Even the railcar industry now shows examples of obsolescence, such as the impact the container and chassis, along with the piggy-back trailer have had on the 50-foot boxcar. Locomotives have also undergone significant changes in technology affect-ing the levels of tractive horsepower and mode of power; i.e., AC versus DC.

Trailers have also experienced changes in technology based on the "maximizing of cubes." Trailers with a length of 53 feet conform to state regulations for length, height, and weight, plus can carry more volume (cubic feet). Thus, in today's market, 53-foot trailers hold an advantage over 48-foot trailers, and 48-foot trailers hold an advantage over the older and more obsolete 45-foot trailers, and 45-foot trailers hold an advantage over the yet older and more obsolete 40-foot trailers.

8. Foreign Exchange—Foreign exchange is also a consideration that may enter into a residual calculation. Factors that influence foreign exchange include international trade relations and the international political environment, which can cause trade wars, embargoes and thus higher or lower duties. Consider the following example (which actually occurred during the mid-1980's to 1990's):

A Japanese tractor manufacturer produces a tractor which sells for 10 million yen. At an exchange rate of 250 yen to the dollar, the tractor would cost U.S. $40,000; however, at 100 yen to the dollar, that same tractor would cost U.S. $100,000. This increase of 2.5 times is strictly due to currency.

Thus, the value of foreign exchange, such as the yen or euro, can increase or decrease quite rapidly. Such changes could put pressure on selling prices (and residual values), causing them to suddenly drop or increase. The analyst should attempt to compare the cost of foreign manufactured equipment to that of similar domestically manufactured equipment in order to calculate a realistic base value on which to predicate the residual analysis. Strong foreign currency may cause the price of foreign equipment to rise in the U.S., which, in turn, may pull residuals up. However, it should also be understood that the reverse can also occur.

9. Tax Law—Tax law is another concern that leasing companies deal with regularly. Tax law can affect such things as build rates (when incentives are given), and thus the secondary market.

As a result of 1990 tax laws, depreciation rates have been extended. The net effect is that, in many instances, it is more appealing for an end-user to buy used equipment rather than new equipment. Currently, the federal government is studying bonus depreciation rates in order to spur new equipment sales.

It is imperative that the equipment appraiser consider the true economics of a transaction and not simply the tax ramifications. The following two classic examples illustrate the impact of certain tax legislation and regulation.

In the early 1980s, because of tax incentives, the cost of new hopper barges suddenly increased from $220,000 to about $330,000. Between 1978 and 1981, approximately 3,000 hopper barges were built, increasing the existing capacity by 33 percent. Further, because of certain tax incentives, two-thirds of the new barges were owned by private investors (limited partnerships, etc.). Many of these investors participated in leasing transactions for tax purposes. Most residuals were set without considering that the cost of the barges had increased almost 50 percent in only two to three years. In addition to the sudden jump in prices, the early 1980s also signaled the end of the U.S. coal export boom, and the end of the Polish and Australian coal strikes.

Investors found themselves in a situation where too many barges were built for artificial purposes (i.e., tax benefits). The supply/demand balance was drastically altered. Charter rates for hopper barges fell from $130 per day to $35 per day, and the value of the $330,000 barge plummeted to about $80,000 for a five-year-old asset with a 25+ year useful life (see Figure 6.4). After a few years, many barge manufacturers went out of

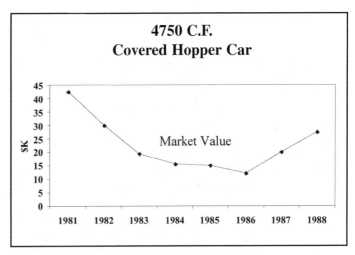

Figure 6.5—Covered Hopper Car Market Values

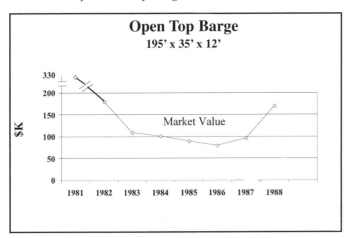

Figure 6.4—1981 Open-Top Barge Market Values

business. No new barges were built, and since there were a great number of barges laid up, up to 25 percent of the older barges were scrapped over a five-year period. This soaked up some of the glut.

At that time, the dollar weakened 60 to 80 percent against foreign currencies, and exports once again started to flow from the U.S. Increased exports, coupled with a sharp decrease in the production of new hopper barges, and the ongoing scrapping of the excess fleet, caused a barge shortage. The price of barges suddenly escalated in 1988 to approximately $175,000 (for the same 1981-built equipment). This example illustrates the disrupted U curve.

Figure 6.5 illustrates an almost identical situation that occurred with covered hopper railcars, which were likewise over-built in

the early 1980s because of tax incentives, and were owned to a great extent by private investors not familiar with the industry. An imbalance in the supply/demand curve resulted, causing the price of five-year-old equipment with a useful life of 50 years to plummet to the point where covered hopper railcars manufactured new in 1981 for $44,000 were selling a few years later for about $14,000, if at all.

Once again, this scenario caused many railcar builders to cease operations. This situation was further aggravated by the Russian grain embargo and the Railroad Deregulation Act of 1980 (Stagger's Act), which deregulated the rail industry and caused downward pressure on shipping rates.

For five years, the rail industry had essentially not built any new railcars and had scrapped a significant portion of the older covered hopper car fleet. When the dollar weakened and exports started to flow, there was once again an equipment shortage that caused the price of the asset to suddenly rise, once again illustrating the disrupted U curve. Several operating lessors that followed this situation, correctly predicted when the demand curve would pass above supply, and made tens of millions of dollars overnight.

10. Legislation/Regulation—Another important variable is legislation/regulation. Although it can't be predicted, a sense of future legislation can be recognized, such as current talk about increased regulation related to commercial aircraft, or the impact of the CAFE or Clean Air Act on engine technology. Regulations sometimes impact values in positive ways, such as the effect of the Jones Act on U.S. hulled marine vessels. However, more often than not, the impact of legislation and regulation on the equipment market is a negative one.

11. Equipment Location—Another factor to be considered is the location of equipment at the end of the lease. Does the lessee require that the equipment be delivered to a prime market location or will it have to be sold in a remote area? To illustrate this point, consider the sale of seven off-highway rock trucks. Ideally, these trucks should have been marketed in prime mining areas of the country, such as Wyoming, Arizona, Minnesota, the Southeast, or the Appalachian area, where they had an estimated value of $130,000 each. However, since the owner could find no buyer in the immediate geographic area, each truck had to be physically cut in half, matchmarked, disassembled, and shipped on nine flatbeds to buyer out of the area. The incremental cost of performing this work and reassembly amounted to a reduction in the sales price of approximately 35 percent. As a result, the owner/lessor was able to realize only $85,000 per truck. Thus, because the equipment was not delivered to a prime geographic marketing area, the owner/lessor lost $315,000 in residual value for the trucks. This illustrates the importance of recognizing the location of prime geographic equipment markets.

12. Method of Sale—In general, if the equipment analyst considers all of these factors, along with the method of sale and current and historical trade data, the lessor should be well positioned to meet or exceed its estimated or booked residual at lease termination.

Calculating Residual Values

The calculation of residual values is more art than science. It has been said that economists only give major predictions on the economy every six months, the reason being that someone might remember. The same can be said for the calculation of residual values. Professional economists sometimes miss short-term predictions by 100 percent or more, so a lessor might wonder what degree of accuracy a residual value calculation might have in ten years! However, if an analyst performs a thorough and proper analysis based on available market data, a high degree of accuracy is possible.

In fact, during the 1980s, when the residual value guarantee industry was in its heyday, such values were typically calculated for equipment with terms of 3 to 8 years. Based on available information, it was found that guarantee companies annually experienced losses (on their guarantees) in the area of only 1.5 percent of the total values guaranteed. This is a somewhat startling statistic, but once again shows that if estimators/appraisers are thorough and perform a proper analysis, a high degree of accuracy is possible.

Residual Valuation Formats

Residual analysis formats differ from company to company, but should contain the same basic elements. Shown below are two of the more popular formats used in the industry:

Example Format 1:
- **Marketplace**—a general description of the marketplace in which the equipment is used;
- **Manufacturer**—background on the manufacturer and

the part in which the equipment plays in the overall sales and marketing of the manufacturer;
- **Model Run**—the number of years the equipment has been manufactured;
- **U.S. Market**—the number of units of the subject equipment in the U.S. market;
- **Installation**—the estimated time to install a subject machine and estimated cost;
- **Software**—a brief discussion of software, such as used in controls;
- **Versatility**—the number of uses for the subject equipment;
- **Life Expectancy**—the estimated economic useful life of the equipment, allowing for proper maintenance;
- **Residual Value**—the analyst's estimate of residual values as of a given future date(s);
- **Manufacturer Name**—a listing of the complete manufacturer's name, address of corporate headquarters, and phone number;
- **Type of Equipment**—a complete description of the equipment being analyzed;
- **Manufacturing/Marketplace**—a general discussion of the manufacturer's future marketing plans and outlook;
- **Future Improvements**—any technological breakthroughs on the horizon;
- **Price Increases**—a listing of any price increases that are planned in the future, as well as an analysis of past increases;
- **Deinstallation**—the estimated time and cost to deinstall the equipment; and
- **Conclusion**—a narrative summary of the entire analysis.

Example Format 2:
- **Equipment Description**—a detailed narrative on the piece of equipment being analyzed;
- **Transaction Price**—the cost of equipment listed in the lease transaction (lessor's cost);
- **Fair Value**—the adjusted transaction price on which the residual is based, including only hard costs, those adjusted for discounts, and the prices of competitor's equipment of similar quality and utility;
- **Estimated Residuals**—the numerical estimate of residual value given in terms of dollars as of a specified future date(s); and
- **Comments (Discussion)**—a narrative description of the analysis, including a brief description of the equipment being analyzed with comments on the equipment's desirability in the secondary market, what makes it better than a competitor's, the manufacturer's reputation in the industry, the amount of time the manufacturer has been in existence, the manufacturer's estimated current marketshare, a list of market competitors, the equipment's estimated useful life, obsolescence considerations (planned introductions of new models, etc.), and estimated time and cost to remarket the equipment, etc.

As stated previously, appraisers may develop their own style or format, but regardless of which format is used, all of the items shown in the two previous examples should be addressed somewhere within the analysis.

Residual Curves

Estimators/appraisers who have been studying equipment values over a number of years should save their work. Since these analyses are based on actual market data, it is felt that similar equipment being valued over a period of years will start to develop a standard shape or residual curve as a percentage of fair value (standard discounted price new).

To illustrate the fair value of an item, consider a heavy-duty over-the-road truck tractor. The truck carries a list price of $115,000, yet can be readily purchased on a fleet basis for $65,000. Thus, the fair value is $65,000, and not the $115,000 list price. Using fair value will help the analyst avoid the trap of applying a "standard curve" (for conceptual purposes) against a list price that is inflated for whatever reason, yielding a residual curve that is also inflated and most likely in error.

From time to time, equipment manufacturers raise prices for no apparent reason other than perhaps not to be caught in case the government someday applies price controls. The same manufacturers routinely apply large discounts to their equipment, showing the importance of using a fair value as a benchmark for a realistic discounted selling price.

"Standard curves" for indicative purposes can be developed through constant residual analysis over many years. Table 6.5 shows some residual curves that are used from time to time on a conceptual basis only.

A study of these curves can be made to determine which curves may be applicable to "rusty iron" and which may apply to high-tech equipment. The higher the obsolescence factor, the shorter the equipment's life, and the lower the residual curve. In some cases, the curve becomes almost truncated after a short period of time. Unless absolutely necessary, residual curves should not be used to determine actual residual values, but only for conceptual "order of magnitude" purposes. They can, however, be useful in an analysis method called curve fitting, when only several points of data are obtained and the appraiser is left with information gaps at certain years. (This concept will be explained later in this chapter.)

Methodology

Estimators/appraisers have various methods available to use in determining residual values, including the cost approach, the income approach, and the market data (or trade data) approach to value. From a practical standpoint, the market approach is oftentimes felt to be the most accurate, because of its reliance on sales and trade data. A market approach analysis involves the following steps:

1. A complete market analysis and technical review of the subject piece of equipment is undertaken. Once that is finished, the appraiser collects all available sales trade data relating to the same or similar equipment, noting manufacturer, model, capacity, equipment age at the time of trade, trade level, condition and sales price. If different trade levels are found, notations should be made next to the price noting levels, such as auction (liquidation value), retail (fair market value-in-exchange), and retail asking (fair market value-in-exchange/asking).

2. The current list price (new) is obtained for each piece of equipment analyzed and all standard discounts are applied. The discounted list price of the subject equipment is then compared to other equipment of similar quality and utility to arrive at a fair value. The fair value new represents a reference point of 100 percent that is the basis of the residual calculation. From this absolute dollar value, a residual curve in the form of a percentage (of fair value) can be determined.

3. After the fair value is determined, and all available trade data is collected, an equipment valuation history is compiled (see Figure 6.6). This form is used to compile available residual information (in raw form) characterized by the age of the equipment sale. The example notes the fair

Table 6.5—Sample Residual Curves

Curve #	Years (% of Fair Value)								
	1	2	3	4	5	6	7	8	9
1	76%	63%	51%	43%	45%	30%	24%	17%	14%
2	60%	55%	50%	45%	40%	35%	30%	25%	20%
3	55%	50%	45%	42%	39%	36%	32%	30%	25%
4	50%	45%	35%	30%	25%	22%	20%	18%	15%
5	45%	33%	27%	22%	20%	18%	17%	16%	15%
6	45%	32%	20%	15%	10%	5%	4%	3%	2%
7	35%	30%	25%	20%	15%	10%	7%	5%	3%
8	31%	27%	23%	19%	16%	12%	9%	3%	1%
9	45%	25%	10%	5%	3%	0%	0%	0%	0%

value (100 percent) and various trades (auction) for the same or similar piece of equipment at different ages up to six years. The trade data shown represents equipment sold in average condition with normal wear and tear.

(All Amounts in $1,000s)							
	Fair Value Adjusted Price	1 yr.	2 yr.	3 yr.	4 yr.	5 yr.	6 yr.
Residual Value Actual, $	200.0	--	130.0	122.5	101.6	85.0	72.5
			130.0				
				120.0			
				125.0			
					110.0		
					100.0		
					95.0		
TRADE DATA						90.0	
						80.0	
						85.0	
							75.0
							70.0

Figure 6.6—Equipment Valuation History

4. After the trade data is documented, an average is determined and entered onto the residual analysis line. When a wide discrepancy exists in the values, the high and low may be discarded, or simple common sense can be used to determine what looks like the average.

5. The residual value in a percentage form is then calculated from the available data (see Figure 6.7). This data now represents the historical relationship between the current secondary market and the current fair value new. If this historical analysis is turned around, it can also be used in a conservative way to represent the residual value of equipment of the same age carried into the future. This type of analysis is based on zero inflation. For equipment where no trade data is available, data is obtained on the most comparable machine and applied.

In instances where available trade data is limited, "curve fitting" (Figure 6.8) will fill the voids. Analysts who routinely log residual curves will, over time, accumulate a large number of these curves. Each curve is based on actual equipment trades and rep-

resents how certain types of equipment tend to depreciate in trade value over a period of years.

Thus, an analyst can complete the residual curve presented in Figure 6.8 by matching the known percentages with a standard curve having the same or similar percentage at a given age (see Figure 6.7), and then filling in the unknown "gaps" on the curve with the known corresponding percentages of the fitted curve.

6. After the final curve is completed, it should be reviewed by the analyst and adjusted up or down accordingly for factors such as maintenance, use, location, regulation, technology, and other relevant elements that could affect residual values.

7. After a final review and adjustment, the residual curve should be cross-checked with other curves of similar equipment. The analyst should notice a similarity in shape to the known curve. If not, then it should be re-analyzed to determine if an error was made. Additional research may be required to increase the sample of trade data, etc. An increase in sample size and additional research may lead to a change in the curve or confirm the original shape.

In any event, the analyst should review the final results and base the findings on the body of knowledge as well as experience. This will lead the analyst to the selection of the final curve and appropriate residual values.

(All Amounts in $1,000s)							
	Fair Value Adjusted Price	1 yr.	2 yr.	3 yr.	4 yr.	5 yr.	6 yr.
Residual Value Actual, $	200.0	--	130.0	122.5	101.6	85.0	72.5
Residual Value Curve, %	100%	--	65%	61%	51%	43%	36%

Figure 6.7—Residual Value Curves

Curve Fitting

	Fair Value Adjusted Price	1 yr.	2 yr.	3 yr.	4 yr.	5 yr.	6 yr.
Residual Value Actual, $	200.0	--	130.0	122.5	101.6	85.0	72.5
Subject Curve, %	100%	--	65%	?	51%	?	36%

Figure 6.8—Curve Fitting

In summary, the residual valuation method described above is basic. It is also noninflated, and based on actual historical sales, trades, and in some instances the use of curve fitting to fill voids in certain curves. Finally, and most importantly, the analyst must review the curve and make subjective adjustments based on personal experience and variables that affect value.

Inflation Factors

The trade data method of residual value analysis described here does not use inflation factors. However, many owners/leasing companies routinely apply an inflation factor to residual values. Care must be taken in selecting an index. Several types of indices are published and are available for purchase by trade associations, insurance companies, appraisal companies, and/or the government.

If an inflation factor is used, it should be based on a "machine-specific" index, that is, an index devoted strictly to that type of equipment being valued (e.g., a "handy-size" bulk carrier index, a Class 7 over-the-road truck/tractor index, a locomotive index, a plastic injection molding machine index, etc.)

The use of machine-specific indices for equipment of a similar type provides much greater reliability than the use of "industry-specific" indices. Industry-specific indices are based on a basket of goods felt to be representative of a typical manufacturing plant or operation in a certain industry. For example, a machine shop index, reflective of the typical machine shop, may include milling machines, lathes, drilling machines, machining centers, turning centers, grinder, welders, cranes, measuring machines, and other related items. In reality, each type of equipment will escalate at its own rate. It is not uncommon to see one type of equipment escalating at one percent per year, while another type may be escalating at five percent per year.

Thus, a blending of weighting of the index can yield an answer that is half right (also half wrong). If the error is com-

pounded over a number of years, the deviation from the actual inflation rate can be significant.

This principle also applies to leasing companies that use governmental indices, such as the consumer price index (CPI). An analysis of the CPI would probably startle most leasing company executives. Not too many lessors would care to have the inflated value of their truck fleet or aircraft based on the cost of a loaf of bread, a pound of butter, or one month's home rent.

The analyst should take particular care and exercise caution when applying inflation factors to non-inflated residual values. Each owner/leasing company will have its own philosophy regarding the use of inflation factors, which the analyst should follow in a responsible way.

Chapter 7

Economic Costs

Neil D. Opfer, CCE

INTRODUCTION

Economic costs is a wide-ranging area of importance for cost engineers and cost managers. Ultimately, there is an owner or client, public or private, supplying the funds for the project. The project must be economically feasible to construct. The same principle applies to producing a product. The price of the product must be in a range that is affordable for its target market.

With globalization, the area of economic costs is complicated by the production of product components in various countries. These countries have their own unique set of economic cost factors, including currency issues, inflation rates, and taxation rates. Cost engineers and cost managers thus need to be informed of economic cost concepts and their potential applications to their work. Often, one is faced with comparing alternatives, and the cost implications may not be immediately apparent. Economic analysis techniques, properly applied, can pinpoint the alternative with the most favorable cost aspects.

LEARNING OBJECTIVES

After completing this chapter, the reader should be able to

- evaluate, on an economic analysis basis, the differences between two or more alternative courses of action; and
- understand such concepts and techniques as net present value, annual cash flow analysis, rate of return analysis, benefit-cost analysis, and payback periods.

CONCEPTS

Cost engineering professionals must make sensible decisions in the arena of economic costs. Often this task is complicated by the fact that certain elements of these decisions, such as costs, revenues, and benefits, occur at different times in the life cycle of a project. For example, manufacturing processes that proved

economical over a lengthy period of time may end up at a net negative cost when the downstream costs of hazardous waste cleanup are factored into the equation. While no one can peer unerringly into the future, the more effective the analysis of the totality of economic costs is, the better the resulting decisions will be. Recognition of the impact of various factors of economic costs leads to more rational decision processes by cost engineers.

Elements of economic costs may be outside the ability of the cost engineering professional to control. Taxation policies and the respective rates of taxation are set by political entities responding to their often-diverse constituencies. Depreciation rules, again, are enacted by political entities. Currency variations may be outside even the control of the particular political entity and, instead, are influenced by the actions and inactions of governments and currency traders around the world. Some aspects of inflation may be the result of government actions as the government expands the money supply with the result that too much money chases too few goods and services. While some elements of economic costs may be outside the control of any one decision maker, one still cannot ignore their potential impact on investment decisions.

TYPES OF COSTS

Opportunity Costs
Economic decision makers need to consider the impact of opportunity costs. An opportunity cost represents the foregone benefit by choosing one alternative over another. A student upon graduation from high school has many choices including work, military service, and further education. If the student decides to pursue further education, the costs of this endeavor represent not only tuition, books, and living costs, but also wages or salary foregone from work opportunities. Thus, a total cost calculation will include the lost salary or wages given up in favor of the further education decision. Similarly, other economic decisions need to consider foregone benefits for an accurate analysis.

Sunk Costs

Sunk costs represent funds already spent by virtue of past decisions. Since these expenditures are in the past, by definition, they should not influence current decisions. While a past investment may still be yielding benefits from an income stream, these current and future benefits are relevant. The past expenditure, however, is considered to be a sunk cost and is ignored in current and future decision-making.

Book Costs

Assets are carried on the firm's books at original cost less any depreciation. Book costs represent the value of an item as reflected in the firm's books. Books costs do not represent cash flows and thus are not taken into account for economic analysis decisions except for potential depreciation impacts for tax consequences. Conservative accounting principles dictate that if the market price for financial assets, such as a stock, is lower than the original price, this asset will be carried at the lower of cost or market value. The underlying land values may have significantly escalated over a period of years; however, the asset will still be carried at its original or book costs. For the firm to be a going concern, the sale of the land at a higher market price would not make sense unless this was part of a strategy to dispose of surplus assets.

Incremental Costs

In economic analysis decisions, focus must be on incremental costs or those cost differences between alternatives. As an example, in the comparison between two alternative pieces of processing equipment, if both units have the same yearly annual maintenance costs of $2,500 each, there is no incremental difference. Therefore, maintenance costs can be excluded from the analysis. On the other hand, if a third piece of processing equipment has annual maintenance costs of $1,500, then there is an obvious incremental cost difference of $1,000, which then must be considered in the analysis between the three alternative units.

CHANGES IN COSTS

Changes in costs occur for a number of reasons in the economy. Cost professionals must be conversant with the potential for cost changes and their implications. The most common cost changes concepts are

- inflation,
- deflation,
- escalation, and
- currency variation.

Cost changes are usually measured by price indexes, which represent relative prices for either a single good or service or a market basket of goods and services. Generally, indexes are used over time to measure the relative price changes in goods and services. Price indexes can be inaccurate barometers of price changes in certain contexts. If the quality of a good or service changes for better or worse, price indexes do not account for this change in quality. Comparing a 1970-era car to a 2000-era car will find not only a change in relative price but in quality as well. Price indexes lose relevancy when the items being compared are not the same. A factory built in one country in 1995 of a given size with its own price index could be compared to a factory built in another country in 2005 only if adjustments are made for relevant differences. If the 1995 factory construction included several miles of additional utility lines for services, these differences must be considered in the analysis along with currency translation issues.

Inflation

Inflation is a rise in the price level of a good or service or market basket of goods and/or services. Inflation does not occur by itself but must have a driving force behind it. There are four effects that can result in inflation either by themselves or in combination with other effects. These four effects are

- money supply,
- exchange rates,
- demand-pull inflation, and
- cost-push inflation.

Money supply is influenced by the central bank of a country. Most countries' governments are able to operate by selling and buying bonds and setting certain internal interest rates. These central bank operations will, therefore, have an impact on monetary policy, which thus can impact inflation. A loosening of monetary policy will increase the flow of money in the system, which means the increased money supply will be chasing the same amount of goods and services. This bids up the price of the goods and services resulting in inflation.

Exchange rates can impact inflation by influencing the price of imported goods and services. If the currency of Country A falls in relation to the currency of Country B, imports from Country A are relatively less expensive. On the other hand, a rising Country A currency relative to Country B currency will make those same imports more expensive. If the import is a basic industrial commodity, such as copper, utilized in a wide range of products, the rise in relative price will lead to inflationary price ripples throughout the economy of Country A.

Demand-pull inflation is when excessive quantities of money are chasing a limited amount of goods and services resulting in what is essentially a "seller's market" as sellers receive premium prices. Examples of this can be anything from autos to real estate. An auto in short supply commands prices above list invoice. The same demand-pull inflation would apply to real estate in a popular location.

Cost-push inflation takes place when product producers encounter higher costs and then push these costs along to others in the production chain through higher prices. These higher costs may be for labor, material, or any other item with a significant cost element. A labor contract with workers may dictate 10 percent wage increases in a given year, and, if not offset by productivity gains, in a product with 50 percent labor content, these wage increases will be passed on to purchasers of the product.

Deflation

Deflation is the opposite of inflation with a fall in the general price level for goods and services or a representative market basket of goods and services. The same aforementioned factors of money supply, exchange rates, demand-pull, and cost-push factors operate but in the opposite direction with a resultant decrease in prices. If costs for producers of goods and services fall in competitive industries, this cost decrease will be passed onto purchasers. For example, prices for personal computers have fallen across the board since their large-scale introduction in the 1980s even while features have increased in the units. Complete personal computers can now be purchased twenty years later for a fraction of their original cost. A contracting money supply can result in price deflation. Exchange rates that rise in one country, giving that country a stronger currency relative to those countries from which it imports goods and services, will result in deflationary price decreases for those same imports.

Escalation

Escalation is a technique to accommodate price increases or decreases during the life of the contract. An escalation or de-escalation clause is incorporated into the contract so that the purchaser will compensate the supplier in the event of price changes. For instance, an aircraft maintenance firm may sign a five-year contract for the maintenance and fueling of a firm's aviation fleet. If aviation fuel increases in cost during the contract, the escalation will be paid for by the purchaser as an additional contract amount. Similarly, if the price of fuel declines or de-escalates during the contract, the supplier will rebate a like amount to the purchaser. These escalation and de-escalation clauses help to shield both the supplier and the purchaser from unpredictable cost changes. Without such clauses, suppliers would include contingency amounts that might later be found to be unrealistically high. The supplier would gain from this windfall while the purchaser would be the loser. Similarly, excessive price increases in a commodity, such as aircraft fuel, might force a supplier into contractual default depending on magnitude.

Currency Variation

Currency changes can have a significant cost impact both on those inside the country as well as those outside the country. Currency prices are set in markets around the world and change on a constant basis as the result of daily trading fluctu-

---

GLOSSARY TERMS IN THIS CHAPTER

benefit/cost ◆ currency variation
depreciation ◆ discount rate ◆ economic life
escalation ◆ future value ◆ inflation
opportunity cost ◆ present value ◆ price index
price variation ◆ profitability ◆ sunk cost
taxation ◆ taxes ◆ time value of money

---

ations and moves by central banks. Many organizations operate on a multinational basis. Therefore, the currency fluctuations in one country or many countries can have an overall impact on earnings. A contract for work or to supply products to one country if set in that countries' currency can make the value of that contract go up or down when those earnings are repatriated to the home country of the firm. Financial assets held in one country can witness a significant decline in value if that countries' currency is devalued by the central bank. Protecting against currency variation is complicated and can be accomplished through currency futures hedging or valuing contracts against very stable currencies, to cite two examples.

GOVERNMENTAL COST IMPACTS

The actions of governmental units and jurisdictions can impose significant cost impacts on the firm. In some cases, the cost impacts of governmental units are direct, such as in the case of imposed taxes. In other cases, such as in governmental regulations that require or prohibit certain action, governmental cost impacts may be more difficult to measure. Whether direct or indirect, an accounting of costs must recognize these governmental actions.

Taxes

Governments are most often maintained by the taxes they impose. These taxes take many forms, such as income taxes, property taxes, inventory taxes, employment taxes, gross receipts taxes, and sales taxes. In the case of such taxes as sales taxes, the firm merely acts as the tax collector for the government adding the sales tax and collecting it from customers. While the firm does not pay the sales tax itself, excepting sales tax on items it may purchase for its own use, there are costs involved for the firm in administering these tax types. Other taxes, such as income taxes, directly impact the firm in terms of profitability as they tax the net income of the firm. Some countries have a value-added tax (VAT). The VAT is applied to the added value applied by the firm. Therefore, if a firm took $100 worth of raw materials and produced a product valued at $250, the value-added tax (VAT) would be applied to the $150 difference or value added by the firm. Similarly, another firm taking the same product and incorporating it in an assembly would be assessed the VAT based, again, only on the added value.

Effective Tax Rates and Marginal Tax Rates

Effective tax rates, also termed average tax rates, are calculated for income taxation purposes by the percentage of total taxable income paid in taxes. The effective tax rate results from dividing the tax liability by the total taxable income. The marginal tax rate is the tax rate on the next dollar of taxable income. For financial decision-making, the marginal tax rate is a key element because the firm is concerned with the tax impact of additional income or income deductions.

Investment Tax Credits

To encourage economic activity, governments may give firms tax credits based on their investments in a given location. Governments may want to encourage the location of new plants in economically depressed areas and, therefore, promote this through investment tax credits including abeyance on certain taxes such as property taxes. In other cases, tax credits may be granted for certain types of investments in plant and equipment. The investment tax credits may be tied to certain public policy goals. Thus, a firm installing more energy efficient equipment that reduces energy consumption may be able to avail it of energy investment tax credits.

Depreciation and Depletion

In order to encourage firms to invest in new plants and equipment, governmental entities often allow firms to depreciate their investments over time. This investment depreciation allows the firm to reduce its income by a set proportion per year with a depreciation write-off until the investment is fully depreciated. The limits on investment depreciation write-off are proscribed by the governmental tax code. It must be realized that depreciation itself is not a cash flow. Depreciation instead is a non-cash expense that reduces taxable income. Depreciation therefore provides an incentive for firms to invest in new plant and equipment. However, firms are only allowed to depreciate based on original plant and equipment costs. Therefore, current and future inflation during the asset's depreciation cannot be taken into account for these purposes. The rationale underlying depreciation concepts is that physical assets lose value over time due to such factors as deterioration, wear, and obsolescence.

Depletion is analogous to depreciation but for natural resources. Thus, owners of a stone quarry, an oil well, or standing timber as examples can take depletion allowances based on the percentage of the resource used up in a given time period.

Depreciation Techniques

Given that governments allow firms to depreciate their investments, there are numerous methods to accomplish the depreciation process. These standard methods simplify accounting for the depreciation expenses. Some of the more common depreciation techniques are

- straight-line (SL) method,
- double-declining balance (DDB) method,
- sum-of-years digits (SOYD) method,
- modified accelerated cost recovery system (MACRS), and (5) units of production (UOP) method.

Straight-Line Depreciation

Straight-line (SL) methods take an equal amount of depreciation every year. The SL method takes the original cost less the salvage value divided by the number of years of life by the formula

$$D = (C-S)/N$$

Where

D = depreciation charge,
C = asset original cost,
S = salvage value, and
N = asset depreciable life (years).

Therefore, an asset with a $5,000 original cost, 5-year life, and $1,000 residual salvage value would have SL depreciation of $800 per year: ($5,000 - $1,000)/5 years = $800.

Double-Declining Balance Depreciation

Double-declining balance depreciation applies a constant depreciation rate to the assets' declining value. The DDB formula is:

$$D = (2/N)(C-BV_{t-1})$$

Where

D = depreciation charge,
C = asset original cost,
BV = Book value at given year, and
N = asset depreciable life (years).

Note: Book value includes deduction for depreciation charges to date.

In the SL example above, the similar DDB amounts would be as follows in Table 7.1 for an asset with a $5,000 original cost, 5-year life, and $1,000 residual salvage value:

Sum-of-Years Digits Depreciation

Sum-of-years digits (SOYD) method allows depreciation to be taken at a faster rate than SL. This SOYD method takes depreciation in any one year as the product of a fractional value times the total original depreciable value. The fractional value for any given year has as numerator the years of asset life remaining, while the denominator is the sum of digits including 1 through the last year of the asset's life. The

Table 7.1—DDB Amounts for an Asset with a $5,000 Original Cost, 5-Year Life, and $1,000 Residual Salvage Value

Year	DDB Formula	DDB Calculated Amount	DDB Allowable Depreciation
1	(2/5)($5,000 – 0) =	$2,000	$2,000
2	(2/5)($5,000 – $2,000) =	$1,200	$1,200
3	(2/5)($5,000 – $3,200) =	$720	$720
4	(2/5)($5,000 – $3,920) =	$432	$80*
5	(2/5)($5,000 – $4,352) =	$259.20	$0*
	Total =	$4,611.20	$4,000

*****Note**: An asset cannot be depreciated below its salvage value thus depreciation totals under the DDB method for Years 4 and 5 total $80. In the comparison between SL and DDB methods, DDB allows faster write-offs of the asset value. A general economic cost principle given the time value of money is that early money is of greater importance.

SOYD formula is:

$$D_r = (C – S)*[(2(N-r+1))/(N(N + 1))]$$

Where:

D_r = depreciation charge for the rth year

C = asset original cost

S = salvage value

N = remaining asset depreciable life (years)

r = rth year

From the SL and DDB examples above, the similar SOYD amounts would be as follows in Table 7.2 for an asset with a $5,000 original cost, 5-year life, and $1,000 residual salvage value:

$$SOYD = [(N/2)(N + 1)] = [(5/2)(5 + 1)] = 15$$

In the comparison between SL and SOYD methods, SOYD is similar to DDB in that it allows faster write-offs of the asset value in the early years. Again, as noted above, a general economic cost principle given the time value of money is that early money is of greater importance.

Modified Accelerated Cost Recovery System Depreciation

The modified accelerated cost recovery system (MACRS) method is unique to the United States Tax Code. Depreciation under this MACRS method is based on original asset cost, asset class, asset recovery period, and asset in-service date. Asset classes are differentiated based on 3-year,

Table 7.2—SOYD Amounts for an Asset with a $5,000 Original Cost, 5-Year Life, and $1,000 Residual Salvage Value

Year	SOYD Formula	SOYD Calculated Amount
1	(5/15)($5,000 - $1,000) =	$1,333
2	(4/15)($5,000 - $1,000) =	$1,067
3	(3/15)($5,000 - $1,000) =	$800
4	(2/15)($5,000 - $1,000) =	$533
5	(1/15)($5,000 - $1,000) =	$267
	Total =	$4,000

5-year, 7-year, 10-year and other property lives, depending on asset type. Depreciation rates are set by percentages allowed under the U.S. Tax Code.

Units of Production Depreciation

The units of production (UOP) method is utilized when depreciation is more accurately based on usage instead of time. The UOP Method is particularly useful when an asset encounters variable demand. A piece of construction equipment may be utilized 1,200 hours in one year, 1,600 hours the next, and 900 hours the third year. The UOP method recognizes that the equipment wears out based on use and, therefore, is a more accurate barometer than years.

ECONOMIC ANALYSIS TECHNIQUES

There are a variety of economic analysis techniques available to enable accurate choices between competing alternatives. The general principle is that there are competing alternatives and the goal is to choose the alternative with the highest return. In order to analyze returns from alternative choices, there are a number of techniques including

- net present worth,
- capitalized cost,
- annual cash flow analysis,
- rate of return analysis,
- benefit-cost ratio analysis, and
- payback period.

Except for the payback period method, these analysis techniques deal with a concept commonly referred to as the time value of money.

Time Value of Money

The time value of money is a key area in economic cost analysis. Different alternatives will have differing amounts of cash income and cash expenses over their lifetime. In order to compare these different alternatives on the same basis, these cash amounts of income and expenditure must be set to equivalent terms.

There is a common unit of measure set in a currency whether it be dollars, euros, pesos, yen or some other measure. There will also be an interest rate set that provides the common basis for calculations. In order to perform this analysis, certain information will be available with other information requiring calculation. The problem must be expressed in quantitative terms. A problem of whether it is best to paint a building blue or green cannot be judged on a quantitative basis. But if one type of building paint has a life of 10 years with its own cost structure, and another paint type has a life of 7 years with a separate cost structure, this is a problem suitable for quantitative analysis.

Common language terms and their symbols for time value of money problems are as follows:

P = present value or present worth
F = future value or future worth
A = annual amount or annuity
G = uniform gradient amount
n = number of compounding periods or asset life
I = interest rate
S = salvage value

The standard formulas for economic analysis are shown in Table 7.3.

Net Present Worth Method

A common basis is needed when comparing alternatives. Alternatives typically will have different costs and benefits over the analysis period. The net present worth (NPW) method provides the platform to resolve alternatives into equivalent present consequences.

Example NPW Problem: A firm is evaluating the potential purchase of one of two pieces of equipment. Unit A has a purchase price of $10,000 with a four-year life and zero salvage value. Annual maintenance costs are $500 per year. Unit B has a purchase price of $20,000 with a twelve-year life and $5,000 salvage value. In Year 1, maintenance costs are zero. In Year 2 maintenance costs are $100 and increase by $100 per year thereafter. The firm's cost of capital is 8 percent.

Example NPW Problem Solution: This problem illustrates two common issues faced in comparison of alternatives. Units A and B have unequal lives of four years and twelve years respectively. Therefore, a common multiple of the respective unit lives must be selected, which, in this case, will be twelve years. Economic analysis problems view repurchase of the same unit at four-year intervals at original cost unless there is concrete information to the contrary. The second issue this problem illustrates is that of a gradient where

Table 7.3—Standard Formulas for Economic Analysis

Formula Name	Operation	Symbol	Formula
Single-Payment Compound Amount	P to F	(F/P, I%, n)	$F = P(1+I)^n$
Present Worth	F to P	(P/F,I%, n)	$P = F(1+I)^{-n}$
Uniform Series Sinking Fund	F to A	(A/F,I%, n)	$A = F[I/((1+I)^n - 1)]$
Capital Recovery	P to A	(A/P,I%, n)	$A = P[(I(1 + I)^n))/(1 + I)^n - 1]$
Compound Amount	A to F	(F/A,I%, n)	$F = A[((1 + I)^n - 1)/ I]$
Equal Series Present Worth	A to P	(P/A,I%, n)	$P = A[((1 + I)^n - 1) / I(1 + I)^n]$
Arithmetic Uniform Gradient Present Worth	G to P	(P/G,I%, n)	$P = G[((1 + I)^n - In - 1)/ (I^2(1+I)^n]$

maintenance costs for Unit B are increasing on a year-to-year basis as opposed to steady costs.

NPW Unit A:

$$
\begin{aligned}
NPW &= \$10,000 + \$10,000(P/F,8\%,4) + \$10,000(P/F,8\%,8) + \$500(P/A,8\%,12) \\
&= \$10,000 + \$10,000(0.7350) + \$10,000(0.5403) + \$500(7.536) \\
&= \$26,521
\end{aligned}
$$

NPW Unit B:

$$
\begin{aligned}
NPW &= \$20,000 + \$100(P/G,8\%,12) - \$5000(P/F,8\%,12) - \$100 \\
&= \$20,000 + \$100(34.634) - \$5000(0.3971) - \$100 \\
&= \$21,347
\end{aligned}
$$

Since in this example problem we are analyzing costs and not benefits, the unit with the lower NPW cost structure is preferable, which is Unit B since $21,478 < $26,521. If the calculation involved benefits greater than costs, then Unit A with the higher benefit NPW would be preferable.

Capitalized Cost Method

In some cases, problems have an infinite analysis period. The need for a structure such as a road or a bridge, for example, is perpetual. With these types of situations, the capitalized cost method is chosen. Capitalized cost (CC) represents the present sum of money that needs to be set aside now, at some interest rate, to yield the funds required to provide the service indefinitely. The capitalized cost formula is A = PI.

Example CC Problem: A bridge is built for $5,000,000 and will have maintenance costs of $100,000 per year. At 6 percent interest, what is the capitalized cost of perpetual service?

Example CC Problem Solution: The $5,000,000 is a present cost with the $100,000 per year maintenance costs as ongoing. Therefore,

Capitalized Cost = $5,000,000 + ($100,000) / 0.06
                 = $5,000,000 + $1,666,667 = $6,666,667

Equivalent Uniform Annual Cost or Benefit

For some types of analysis, it may be preferable to resolve the comparison to annual cash flow analysis. The comparison may be made on the basis of equivalent uniform annual cost (EUAC), equivalent uniform annual benefit (EUAB) or on the EUAB-EUAC difference.

Example EUAC Problem: Assume that the two units, Unit A and Unit B, are compared on the basis of EUAC. Unit A has an initial cost of $20,000 and $3,000 salvage value, while Unit B has an initial cost of $15,000 and $2,000 salvage value. Unit A has a life of 10 years, whereas Unit B has a 5-year life. Cost of capital is 10 percent.

Example EUAC Solution: The relevant EUAC formula is
$(P-S)(A/P,I,n) + SI$.

EUAC Unit A:

$EUAC_A$ = ($20,000-$3,000)(A/P,10%,10) + $3,000(0.10)
        = ($17,000)(0.1627) + $300
        = $2765.90 + $300   = $3065.90

EUAC Unit B:

$EUAC_B$ = ($15,000-$2,000)(A/P,10%,5) + $2,000(.10)
        = ($13,000)(0.2638) + $200
        = $3429.40 + $200   = $3629.40

On the basis of the EUAC comparison between Unit A and Unit B, Unit A has the lower EUAC by $563.50 ($3629.40 - $3065.90) and would be the choice.

Rate of Return Analysis

Many organizations in making investment choices often set hurdle rates. The hurdle rate is the benchmark rate of return that a capital investment decision must achieve to be acceptable. A rate of return (ROR) is computed from the projected cash flows of the project. ROR values provide a ready basis for the comparison of alternatives. In the case where capital investment funds are limited, projects with the highest ROR values can be selected for the organization.

Example ROR Problem: Assume that in the comparison between Unit A and Unit B (each with a 1-year life) that the cost of $20,000 for Unit A versus a $10,000 cost for Unit B also results in an incremental benefit of $15,000 for Unit A as compared to Unit B. If the organization has a hurdle rate of 20 percent for capital projects, which alternative is a better choice?

Example ROR Solution: The NPW of the cost is set equal to the NPW of the benefit. The NPW Cost of Unit A versus Unit B is $10,000 ($20,000 - $10,000). The NPW of the Unit A – Unit B Benefit is $15,000.

ROR   NPW Cost = NPW Benefit
           $10,000 = $15,000(P/F,I,1)

           $10,000 / $15,000 = 0.6667

By inspection, if $10,000 cost difference increases benefits by $15,000 in one year, the ROR must be 50 percent. Consulting either compound interest factor tables or calculation by the P/F formula for 1 year at a 50 percent, ROR confirms this fact. Since the organizations' hurdle rate is 20 percent, the additional investment in Unit A meets the criteria.

Benefit-Cost Ratio Analysis Method

Benefit Cost (B/C) Ratio Analysis involves the simple comparison between benefits and costs of a proposed action. Benefits are placed in the numerator and costs are placed in the denominator. If the ratio of benefits to costs is greater than one, the project is viable. Comparisons can be made between projects to select those projects with the highest B/C ratio.

Example B/C Problem: Project A with the NPW of Benefits of $1,500,000 and NPW Of Costs of $1,200,000 is being compared to Project B with NPW Benefits of $2,000,000 and NPW Costs Of $1,700,000. Which is the preferred project on a B/C analysis basis?

Example B/C Solution:
Project A:

B/C   = $1,500,000 NPW Benefits/$1,200,000 NPW Costs
            = 1.25 B/C Ratio

Project B:
B/C   = $2,000,000 NPW Benefits / $1,700,000 NPW Costs
            = 1.17 B/C Ratio

On the basis of the above B/C analysis, both Projects A and B have a positive B/C ratio, but Project A would be selected as its 1.25 Ratio is greater than the Project B 1.17 ratio.

Payback Period Method

Payback period is the period of time necessary for the benefits of the project to pay back the associated costs for the project. This is a very simple method and can prove inaccurate. A project with a payback period of three years may be selected over a similar project with a five-year payback period. Differences in the timing of cash flows are not considered nor are benefits and costs beyond the payback period. Payback period analysis is approximate and may not yield the same result as with other more precise methods such as NPW or EUAC criteria.

As an example, an investment of $4,000 with benefits of $800 per year would have a payback period of 5 years ($4,000/$800 = 5 years).

CONCLUSION

The area of economic costs presents problems ranging from the simple to the complex. In this era of intense global competition, economic cost decisions must be made by gathering as much relevant information as possible and then applying the most appropriate analysis technique. Enhanced knowledge of these economic cost analysis tools will lead to improved decisions for an organization.

RECOMMENDED READING

1. DeGarmo, E. P., W. G. Sullivan, J. A. Bontadelli, and E.M Wicks. 1997. *Engineering Economy, Tenth Edition.* Upper Saddle River, New Jersey: Prentice Hall.
2. Humphreys. K. K. 1991. *Jelen's Cost And Optimization Engineering.* Third Edition. New York: McGraw-Hill.
3. Newnan, D. G., J. P. Lavelle, and T. G. Eschenbach. 2002. *Engineering Economic Analysis, Eighth Edition.* New York: Oxford University Press.

Chapter 8

Activity-Based Cost Management

Gary Cokins

INTRODUCTION

Growing Discontent with Traditional Cost Calculation

Why do managers shake their heads in disbelief when they think about their company's cost accounting system? I once heard an operations manager complain, "You know what we think of our cost accounting system? It is a bunch of fictitious lies—but we all agree to them." It is sad to see users of accounting data resign themselves to hopelessness. Unfortunately, many accountants are comfortable when the numbers all "foot-and-tie" in total and could care less if the parts making up the total are correct. The total is all that matters, and any arbitrary cost allocation can tie out to the total.

The sad truth is that when employees and managers are provided with reports that have accounting data in them, they use that information regardless of its validity or their skepticism of its integrity. Mind you, they are using the data to draw conclusions and make decisions. This is risky.

Activity-Based Cost Management to the Rescue

How can traditional accounting, which has been around for so many years, suddenly be considered so bad? This chapter on activity-based cost management (ABC/M) systems explains the reasons leading to the interest and acceptance of ABC/M, as well as how to construct an ABC/M cost assignment model.

LEARNING OBJECTIVES

After completing this chapter, the reader should be able to

- understand why managers and employees are misled by arbitrary cost "allocations;"
- understand how ABC/M transforms spending expenses on resources (e.g., salaries) into "calculated" costs of work activities and processes and then into products, service-lines, channels, and customers;

- learn how cost "drivers" cause costs to occur;
- understand how "attributes" are tags or scores that attached to activities to suggest actions; and
- understand how ABC/M is used in addition to strategic purposes, such as profit margin analysis, but also for cost management, productivity, and asset utilization.

OVERHEAD EXPENSES ARE DISPLACING DIRECT COSTS

The direct laborers in organizations are the employees who perform the frontline, repeated work that is closest to the products and customers. However, numerous other employees behind the frontline also do recurring work on a daily or weekly basis. These employees' work is highly repeatable at some level, for example, a teller in a bank. Figure 8.1 on page 8.2 is a chart that includes this type of expense plus the other two major expense components of any organization's cost structure, its purchased materials and its overhead.

Most organizations are experienced at monitoring and measuring the work of some of the laborers who do recurring work by using cost rates and standard costs. In the bottom layer of the chart is cost information that also reveals performance-related costs other than the period's spending, such as labor variance reporting. It is in this area of the chart, for example, that manufacturers use labor routings and process sheets to measure efficiency. These costs are well known by the name *standard costs*. Service organizations also measure this type of output-related information. For example, many banks know their standard cost for each deposit, each wire transfer, and so forth.

Problems occur in the overhead expense area appearing at the top portion of Figure 8.1. The chart reveals that over the last few decades, the support overhead expenses have been displacing the recurring costs. The organization already has substantial visibility of its recurring costs, but it does not have any insights into its overhead or what is causing the

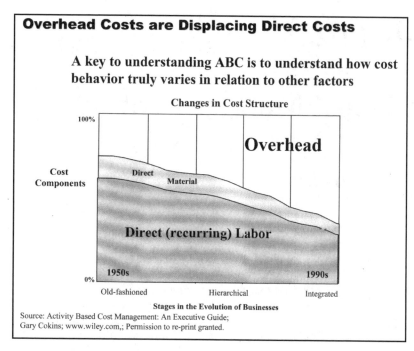

Figure 8.1—Overhead Costs Are Displacing Direct Costs

level of spending of its overhead. ABC/M can help provide for insights and learning.

(Note: Organizations often refer to this support-related work as overhead. Overhead is also referred to as indirect costs. The two terms can be used interchangeably; however the term "overhead" can be misleading and often has a negative connotation. In many cases overhead is a crucial and is a very positive thing to have.)

In a bank, for example, managers and employee teams do not get the same robustness of financial information about the vice presidents working on the second floor and higher up in the building as they do about tellers. The only financial information available to analyze the expenses of the vice presidents and other support overhead is the annual financial budget data. These levels of expenses are annually negotiated. The focus is on spending levels, not on the various cost rates. The expense spending is monitored after the budget is published. Spending is only monitored for each department or function for each period to see if the managers' spending performance is under or over their budget or plan.

ABC/M extends to the overhead the understanding and visibility of spending that is already applied to the recurring laborers. ABC/M can then become an organization-wide method of understanding work activity costs as well as the standard costs of outputs.

Impact of Diversity in Products, Service Lines, Channels, and Customers

When you ask people why they believe indirect and overhead expenses are displacing direct costs, most answer that it is because of technology, equipment, automation, or computers. In other words, organizations are automating what previously were manual jobs. However, this is only a secondary factor in the shift in organizational expense components.

The primary cause for the shift is the gradual proliferation in products and service lines. Over the last few decades, organizations have been increasingly offering a greater variety of products and services as well as using more types of distribution and sales channels. In addition, organizations have been servicing more and different types of customers. Introducing greater variation and diversity (i.e., heterogeneity) into an organization creates complexity, and increasing complexity results in more overhead expenses to manage it. So the fact that the overhead component of expense is displacing the recurring labor expense does not automatically mean that an organization is becoming inefficient or bureaucratic. It simply means that the company is offering more variety to different types of customers.

In short, the shift to overhead displacing direct labor reveals the cost of complexity. ABC/M does not fix or simplify complexity; the complexity is a result of other things. But what ABC/M does do is point out where the complexity is and where it comes from.

ACTIVITIES ARE EXPRESSED WITH ACTION VERBS AND TRACE EXPENSES TO OUTPUTS

Figure 8.2 begins to reveal the explanation as to why traditional cost allocations of expenses are flawed and, therefore, misleading. The left side shows the classic monthly responsibility-center statement report that managers receive. Note that the example used is the back office of an insurance company. This is to demonstrate that, despite misconceptions, indirect white-collar workers produce outputs no differently than do factory workers.

If you ask managers who routinely receive this report questions such as, "How much of these expenses can you control or influence? How much insight do you get into the content of work of your employees?" they will likely answer both questions with, "Not much!" This is because the salary and fringe benefit costs usually make up the most sizable portion of controllable costs, and all that the manager sees are those expenses reported as lump-sum amounts.

When you translate those "chart-of-account" expenses into the work activities that consume the financial general ledger's expenses, a manager's insights from viewing the activity costs begin to increase. The right side of Figure 8.2 is the ABC/M view that is used for analysis and as the starting point for calculating the costs for both processes and diverse outputs. In effect, the ABC/M view resolves the deficiencies of traditional financial accounting by focusing on work activities. ABC/M is work-centric, whereas the general ledger is transaction-centric.

"Expenses" must be distinguished from "costs." They are not the same thing. All costs are *calculated* costs. It is important to recognize that assumptions are always involved in the conversion and translation of expenses into costs. The assumptions stipulate the basis for the calculation. Expenses occur at the point of acquisition with third parties, including employee wages. This is when money (or its obligation) exits the company. At that special moment, "value" does not fluctuate; it is permanently recorded as part of a legal exchange. From the expenses, all costs are *calculated* representations of how those expenses flow through work activities and into outputs of work.

A key difference between ABC/M and the general ledger and traditional techniques of cost allocation (i.e., absorption costing) is that ABC/M describes activities using an "action-verb-adjective-noun" grammar convention, such as *inspect*

defective products, open new customer accounts, or *process customer claims.* This gives ABC/M its flexibility. Such wording is powerful because managers and employee teams can better relate to these phrases, and the wording implies that the work activities can be favorably affected, changed, improved, or eliminated. The general ledger uses a chart of accounts, whereas ABC/M uses a chart of activities. In translating general ledger data to activities and processes, ABC/M preserves the total reported revenues and costs but allows the revenues, budgeted funding, and costs to be viewed differently.

Also, notice how inadequate the data in the chart of accounts view are for reporting business process costs that run cross-functionally, penetrating the vertical and artificial boundaries of the organization chart. The general ledger is organized around separate departments or cost centers. This presents a reporting problem. As a result of the general ledger's structure of cost center mapping to the hierarchical organization chart, its information drives vertical behavior—not the much more desirable process behavior. The general ledger is a wonderful instrument for what it was designed to do—to "bucketize" and accumulate spending transactions into their accounts. But the data in that format is structurally deficient for decision support other than the most primitive form of control, budget variances.

In effect, using traditional cost systems, managers are denied visibility of the costs that belong to the end-to-end business processes. This is particularly apparent in the stocking, distribution, marketing, and selling costs that traditional accounting "expenses to the month's period." With traditional cost allocations, these sales and general and administrative expenses (SG&A) are not proportionately traced to the costs of the unique products, containers, services, channels, or customers that cause those costs to occur.

In summary, the general ledger view describes "what was spent," whereas the activity-based view describes "what it was spent for." The ledger records the expenses,

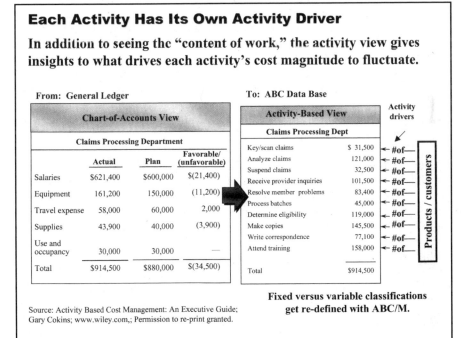

Each Activity Has Its Own Activity Driver

In addition to seeing the "content of work," the activity view gives insights to what drives each activity's cost magnitude to fluctuate.

From: General Ledger

Chart-of-Accounts View

Claims Processing Department

	Actual	Plan	Favorable/ (unfavorable)
Salaries	$621,400	$600,000	$(21,400)
Equipment	161,200	150,000	(11,200)
Travel expense	58,000	60,000	2,000
Supplies	43,900	40,000	(3,900)
Use and occupancy	30,000	30,000	—
Total	$914,500	$880,000	$(34,500)

To: ABC Data Base

Activity-Based View

Claims Processing Dept

		Activity drivers
Key/scan claims	$ 31,500	← #of—
Analyze claims	121,000	← #of—
Suspend claims	32,500	← #of—
Receive provider inquiries	101,500	← #of—
Resolve member problems	83,400	← #of—
Process batches	45,000	← #of—
Determine eligibility	119,000	← #of—
Make copies	145,500	← #of—
Write correspondence	77,100	← #of—
Attend training	158,000	← #of—
Total	$914,500	

Products / customers

Fixed versus variable classifications get re-defined with ABC/M.

Source: Activity Based Cost Management: An Executive Guide; Gary Cokins; www.wiley.com,; Permission to re-print granted.

Figure 8.2—Each Activity Has Its Own Driver

and the activity view calculates the costs of work activities, processes, and all outputs, such as products. Intermediate output costs, such as the unit cost to process a transaction are also calculated in the activity view. When employees have reliable and relevant information, managers can manage less and lead more.

DRIVERS TRIGGER THE WORKLOAD

Revisit Figure 8.2. Much more information can be gleaned from the right-side view. Look at the second activity, "analyze claims" for $121,000, and ask, "What would make that cost significantly increase or decrease?" The answer is the number of claims analyzed. That is that work's activity driver. It shows that each activity on a stand-alone basis has its own activity driver. At this stage the costing is no longer recognizing the organizational chart and its artificial boundaries. The focus is now on the work that the organization performs and what affects the level of that workload.

There is additional information. Let's assume there were 1,000 claims analyzed during that period for the department shown in Figures 8.2. The unit cost per each analyzed claim is $121 per claim. If a specific group of senior citizens over the age of 60 were responsible for half those claims, we would know more about a specific customer or beneficiary of that work. The senior citizens would have caused $60,500 of that work (i.e., 500 claims times $121 per claim). If married couples with small children required another fraction, married couples with grown children a different fraction, and so forth, ABC/M would trace all of the $121,000. If each of the other work activities were similarly traced using the unique activity driver for each activity, ABC/M would pile up the entire $914,500 into each group of beneficiary. This reassignment of the resource expenses would be much more accurate than any broad-brush cost allocation applied in traditional costing procedures and their broad averages.

In the past, calculating costs using volume-based allocations may have been acceptable and may not have introduced excessive error. But most organizations' cost structures began to change in the 1970s. With greater overhead costs relying on a basis for cost allocations that were tied to unrelated volumes of usage, the traditional costing method had become invalid relative to how the rich variation of products and services consumed costs. Therefore, the unfavorable impact of the costing errors was becoming much more intense than in the past. ABC/M resolves the problem of poor indirect and overhead cost allocations, but it also provides additional information for analysis to suggest what positive actions, strategic or operational, can be taken based on the new data.

To sum up Figure 8.2, when managers receive the left-side responsibility center report, they are either happy or sad, but rarely any smarter.

The cost assignment network is one of the major reasons that ABC/M calculates more accurate costs of outputs. The assignment of the resource expenses also demonstrates that all costs actually originate with the customer or beneficiary of the work. This is at the opposite extreme of where people who perform "cost allocations" think about costs. Cost allocations are structured as a one source-to-many destinations redistribution of cost. But the destinations are actually the origin for the costs. The destinations, usually outputs or people, place demands on work, and the costs then "measure the effect" by reflecting backward through the ABC/M cost assignment network.

ABC/M IS A COST RE-ASSIGNMENT NETWORK

In complex support-intensive organizations, there can be a substantial chain of indirect activities prior to the work activities that eventually trace into the final cost objects. These chains result in activity-to-activity assignments, and they rely on intermediate activity drivers in the same way that final cost objects rely on activity drivers to re-assign costs into them based on their diversity and variation.

The direct costing of indirect costs is no longer, as it was in the past, an insurmountable problem given the existence of integrated ABC/M software. ABC allows intermediate direct costing to a local process or to an internal customer or required component that is causing the demand for work. That is, ABC cost-flow networks no longer have to "hit the wall" from limited spreadsheet software that is restricted by columns-to-rows math. ABC/M software is arterial in design. Eventually, via this expense assignment and tracing network, ABC re-assigns 100 percent of the costs into the final products, service lines, channels, customers, and business sustaining costs. In short, ABC connects customers to the unique resources they consume—and in proportion to their consumption.

Let's review the ABC cost re-assignment network in Figure 8.3, which consists of the three modules connected by cost assignment paths. This network calculates the cost of cost objects (e.g., outputs, product lines, service lines, or customers). It is basically a snap-shot view of the business conducted during a specific time period.

Resources, at the top of the cost assignment network, are the capacity to perform work because they represent all the available means that work activities can draw upon. Resources can be thought of as the organization's checkbook; this is where all the period's expenditure transactions are accumulated into buckets of spending. Examples of resources are salaries, operating supplies, or electrical power. These are the period's cash outlays and amortized cash outlays, such as

ABC/M Cost Re-Assignment Network

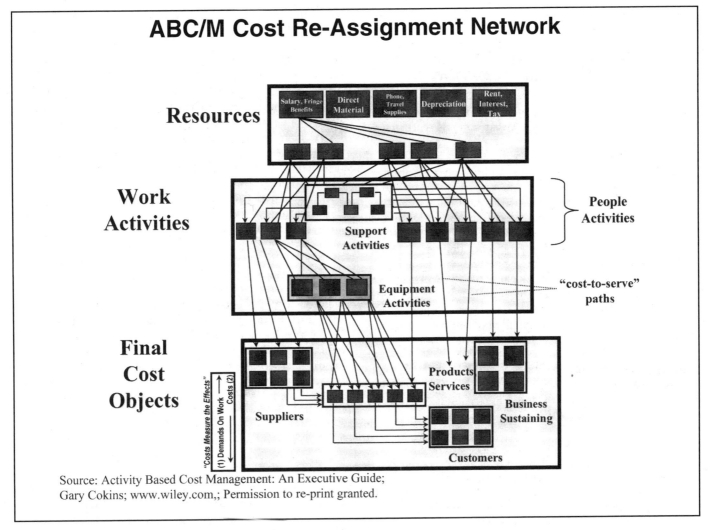

Source: Activity Based Cost Management: An Executive Guide;
Gary Cokins; www.wiley.com,; Permission to re-print granted.

Figure 8.3—ABC/M Cost Assignment Network

for depreciation, from a prior period. It is during this step that the applicable resource drivers are developed as the mechanism to convey resource costs to the activity.

In sum, resources are traced to work activities. It is during this step that the applicable resource drivers are developed as the mechanism to convey resource expenses into the activity costs.

A popular basis for tracing or assigning resource expenses is the time (e.g., number of minutes) that people or equipment spend performing activities. Note that the terms *tracing* or *assigning* are preferable to the term *allocation*. This is because many people associate the *allocation* with a redistribution of costs that have little to no correlation between source and destinations; hence to some organizations, overhead cost allocations are felt to be arbitrary and are viewed cynically.

The activity module is where work is performed. It is where

resources are converted into some type of output. The activity cost assignment step contains the structure to assign activity costs to cost objects (or to other activities), utilizing activity drivers as the mechanism to accomplish this assignment.

Cost objects, at the bottom of the cost assignment network, represent the broad variety of outputs and services where costs accumulate. The customers are the final-final cost objects; their existence ultimately creates the need for a cost structure in the first place. Cost objects are the persons or things that benefit from incurring work activities. Examples of cost objects are products, service lines, distribution channels, customers, and outputs of internal processes. Cost objects can be thought of as the for what or for whom that the work is done.

Once established, the cost assignment network is useful in determining how the diversity and variation of things, such as different products or various types of customers, can be detected and translated into how they uniquely consume activity costs.

USING THE ATTRIBUTES OF ACTIVITY-BASED COSTING

One role for calculating costs is to help suppliers and service-providers identify which of their organization's work activities are as follows:

- not required at all and can be eliminated (e.g., a duplication of effort);
- ineffectively accomplished and can be reduced or redesigned (e.g., due to outdated policies or procedures);
- required to sustain the organization (i.e., the work is not directly caused by making product or delivering services through channels to customers), and, therefore, it may not be possible to reduce or eliminate the work activity (e.g., provide plant security, compliance with government regulations, etc.); and
- discretionary and can potentially be eliminated (e.g., the annual employees' picnic).

Activity-based cost management (ABC/M) systems provide for distinguishing these work activities either by including them in a cost assignment structure (i.e., sustaining cost objects) or by tagging their costs as an overlay (i.e., attributes).

Organizations have very little insight about how their individual costs—whether in products, customers, or business processes—vary among themselves aside from the amount of the cost. Traditional cost accounting methods do not provide any way for individual costs to be tagged or highlighted with a separate dimension of cost other than the amount that was spent. An example of a range of a tag that can be scored for activities is as "very important" versus "required" versus "postponable." These are popular ways of measuring how much value-added costs exist and where they are located. What this introduces is visibility to the colors of money.

In short, traditional accounting simply provides racked-and-stacked numbers; aside from the cost amount or emphasis in the appearance of the numbers, one cannot differentiate one cost from another. This is true whether one is examining resource expenditures or their calculated costs of activities, processes, and final cost objects (i.e., workflow outputs, products, or customers). Attributes solve this money-level-only limitation of traditional costing. One can think of attributes as offering many other dimensions to segment costs that are different from absorption costing's single dimension, which only reflects variation and diversity consumption of cost objects like outputs, products, service lines, and customers. Attributes can be used as a grading method to evaluate the individual activities that contribute to a process output's goods or services. ABC/M attributes allow managers to

differentiate activities from one another even if they are equal in amount.

Advanced, mature users are masters at employing ABC/M attributes. A popular attribute involves scoring activities along their "high- versus low-value-adding" scale. The idea is to eliminate low-value-adding activities and optimize higher-value-adding activities, thus enabling employees to focus on the worth of their organization's work. Employees can see how work really serves customers and which activities may be considered wasteful. Focus and visibility are enhanced because people can more easily see where costs are big or small and also which costs can be managed in the near-term. Scoring costs with attributes invokes action beyond just gazing at and analyzing costs.

In the early days of ABC/M, the scoring choices for value-adding were limited to either value-added (VA) or nonvalue-added (NVA). This either-or choice created problems. First, it was considered a personal insult to employees to tell them that part or all of what they do is nonvalue-adding. Employees are not real happy to hear that. But even more restrictive is the ambiguity of scoring value that can lead to unsolvable debates. For example, take the activity "expedite order" to prevent a late shipment to an important customer. Is this VA or NVA work? A solid argument can support either case. It is better to simply discard the VA versus NVA dichotomy with a different set of words that scale along a continuum and better describe levels of importance (e.g., critical, necessary, regulatory, or postponable.)

Regardless of what type of scale you use to score or grade value, the objective is to determine the relation of work or its output to meeting customer and shareholder requirements. The goal is to optimize those activities that add value and minimize or eliminate those that do not. Following are some tips, but by no means hard rules, for classifying value attributes. High-value-adding activities are those

- required to meet customer requirements;
- that modify or enhance purchased material of a product;
- that, if more of them are accomplished, the customer might pay more for the product or service;
- that are critical steps that cannot be eliminated in a business process;
- that are performed to resolve or eliminate quality problems;
- that are performed due to a request or expectation of a satisfied customer; and
- that, in general, if time permitted, you would do more of.

Low-value-adding activities are those that

- can be eliminated without affecting the form, fit, or function of the product;
- begin with the prefix "re" (such as rework or returned

goods);

- result in waste and add no value to the product or service;
- are performed due to inefficiencies or errors in the process stream;
- are duplicated in another department or add unnecessary steps to the business process;
- are performed to monitor quality problems;
- are performed due to a request of an unhappy or dissatisfied customer;
- produce an unnecessary or unwanted output; and
- if given the option, you would prefer to do less of.

Another popular attribute scores how well each activity is performed, such as "exceeds" "meets," or "below customer expectation." This reveals the level of performance. Multiple activities can be simultaneously tagged with these grades from two or more different attributes. As an option, activities can be summarized into the processes the activities belong to. Using two different attributes along the process view, organizations can see, for example, that they are spending a lot of money doing things they are good at but that they have judged to be unimportant. Attributes are very suggestive. In this example, it is obvious the organization should scale back and spend less on that kind of work. Figure 8.4 illustrates the four quadrants that result from combining the two attributes for performance (vertical axis) and importance (horizontal axis). The activity costs for such unimportant activities would be in the upper-left quadrant.

Although most attributes are subjectively scored or graded

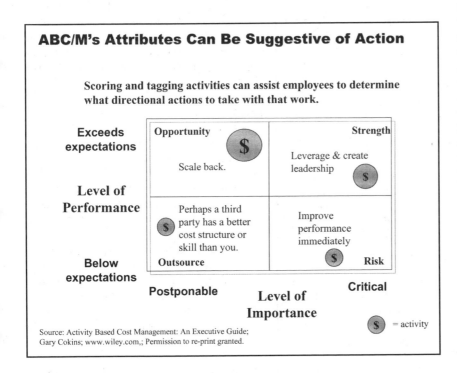

ABC/M's Attributes Can Be Suggestive of Action

Scoring and tagging activities can assist employees to determine what directional actions to take with that work.

Source: Activity Based Cost Management: An Executive Guide; Gary Cokins; www.wiley.com,; Permission to re-print granted.

Figure 8.4—ABC/M's Attributes Can Suggest Action

by managers and employees, when the attributes' targeted activities or cost objects are grouped together, any subjectivity begins to become directionally reliable (assuming there was no bias in the scoring of every single attribute). As a result, the attributed costs introduce emotionally compelling business issues, like the example above. Attributes make ABC/M data come alive to some people. And when the attributed ABC/M data are exported into OLAP software and executive information system (EIS) tools, they can have a very stimulating impact on users.

LOCAL VERSUS ENTERPRISE-WIDE ABC/M

A common misconception is that the scope of an ABC/M system must be enterprise-wide. That is, the expenses included in the system must account for all the employees in the organization and 100 percent of a time period's expenditures. (Or alternatively, the expenses must include all the people in a substantial portion of the organization, such as a factory or service-delivery arm.) People with this misconception have usually been exposed only to ABC/M models or systems that are used for calculating the total costs of a product or service line used to determine their total profitability.

In practice, the vast majority of ABC/M is applied to subsets of the organization for process improvement rather than revenue enhancement and profit margin increases. An example of a subset is an order-processing center or equipment maintenance function. These ABC/M models and systems are designed to reveal the cost structure to the participants in the main department and related areas. In ABC/M's cost assignment view, the cost structure is seen from the orientation of how the diversity and variation of the function's outputs cause various work to happen, and how much. The costs of the work activities that belong to the processes are also revealed in the ABC/M model as they relate in time and sequence. However, it is ABC/M's powerful revealing of the costs of various types of outputs that serves as a great stimulant to spark discussion and discovery. For example, if an order-processing center learns that the cost per each adjusted order is roughly eight times more costly than for each error-free or adjustment-free entered order, that would get people's attention. This result happens even if the order entry process has been meticulously diagrammed, flowcharted, and documented.

Commercial ABC/M software now enables consolidating some, and usually all, of the local, children ABC/M models into the enterprise-wide, parent ABC/M model. The local ABC/M model data are used for tactical purposes, often to improve productivity. In contrast, the consolidated enterprise-wide ABC/M model is often used for strategic purposes because it helps focus on where to look for problems and opportunities. Also, enterprise-wide models are popular for calculating profit margin data at all levels, including channel-related and customer- and service-recipient-related profit contribution layers.

Table 8.1 illustrates how the unit costs of the output of work can be made visible for a government's highway maintenance department. The benchmarking of relative data can be more powerful than process flow charts in stimulating discussion about what to change.

In short, this approach places intra-ABC/M models within an enterprise ABC/M model. A large parent ABC/M model is simply subdivided into its component children ABC/M models. Commercial ABC/M software accommodates consolidations of children into parent ABC/M models. The costs and information are unaffected regardless of which ABC/M models you work with.

APPLICATIONS OF LOCAL ABC/M

The vast majority of ABC/M data are applied locally. Examples, such as that for the purchasing process, are limitless. Whenever you have people and equipment doing work where the outputs have diversity, a local ABC/M model can be constructed. The objective of local ABC/M models is not to calculate the profit margins of products, service lines, and customers; it is to compute the diverse costs of outputs to better understand how they create the organization's cost structure.

An interesting application is when a marketing, recruiting, or promotion department has employees who are trying to generate new or continuing inbound orders. They may be trying multiple avenues, such as newspapers, radio, television, tradeshows, Websites, billboards, and so forth. The costs for advertising placements are different, and so might be the results in terms of success (including any additional differences in the type of sale, recruit, or sale). This is an ideal case for an ABC/M calculation to determine the costs versus benefits of all the channel combinations to rank in order which are the least to best return on spending.

In addition to analyzing the impact of diverse cost objects, there is also the traditional activity analysis and cost driver analysis. Figure 8.5 reveals the link between an activity driver and its work activity. In a simple fashion it describes how each work activity can be judged based on its need by the product or customer, its efficiency, and its value content.

Some managers believe that the only way to truly cut costs is remove the work activity altogether. Their reasoning is that to try to cut back on costs is rarely effective. They believe there is little point in trying to do cheaply what should not be done at all. That is, a job not worth doing is not worth doing well.

Regardless of how one attacks achieving improvements, the main message here is that work is central to ABC/M. What do we do? How much do we do it? Who do we do it for? How important is it? Are we very good at doing it?

Some refer to the application of local models as activity-based management (ABM), an earlier-generation term for ABC/M, because the uses of the ABC/M data are more operational than strategic. I like to view local ABC/M models using the analogy of a musical symphony orchestra conductor in rehearsal first working the violins, then the trumpets, then all the string instruments, then all the brass instruments, and finally the entire orchestra in a live concert. The combined orchestra represents a consolidated parent ABC/M model, with local models rolled up into a parent model, then performing as a repeatable and reliable system.

When ABC/M is applied at all organizational levels—local departments, processes, enterprise-wide, or across the supply

Table 8.1—Example of Unitized Costs

Type of Roadbed Costs						
Roadbed Types						
Number of lanes	Road surface	Location	total cost	number of miles	work activity	unit cost per mile
four	asphalt	interstate	$270,137,078.40	125,342		**$2,155.20**
					cut grass	$120.00
					electronic signs	$334.25
					fill pot-holes	$150.00
					plow roads	$975.60
					paint stripes	$450.50
					replace signs	$124.85
two	bituminous	rural	**$29,783,384.10**	43,578		**$683.45**
					cut grass	$220.00
					electronic signs	$0.00
					fill pot-holes	$65.00
					plow roads	$250.00
					paint stripes	$112.20
					replace signs	$36.25
four	asphalt	county	**$95,567,207.84**	65,672		**$1,455.22**
					cut grass	etc.
					electronic signs	etc.
					fill pot-holes	etc.
					plow roads	etc.
					paint stripes	etc.
					replace signs	etc.

Source: Activity Based Cost Management: An Executive Guide; Gary Cokins; www.wiley.com,; Permission to re-print granted.

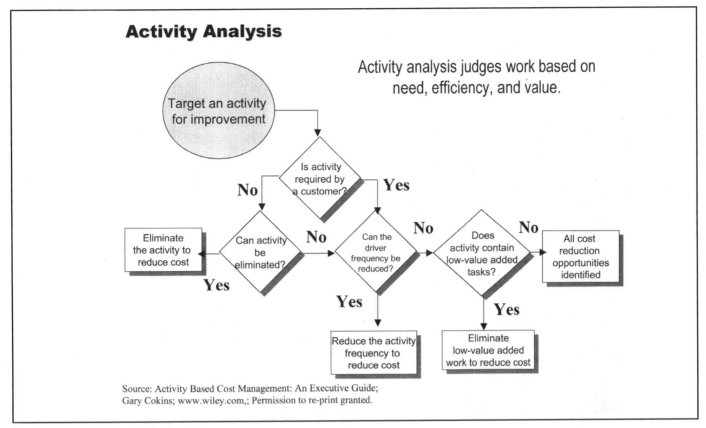

Figure 8.5—Activity Analysis

chain—it provokes intelligent actions and supports better decisions.

IF ABC/M IS THE ANSWER, WHAT IS THE QUESTION?

In addition to the need to address the distortion of true costs that are misreported by traditional systems, the rise in ABC/M has resulted from external factors. The level of competition that most firms face has increased dramatically. In the past, most organizations were reasonably profitable. They could make mistakes, and their adequate profitability would mask the impact of their wrong or poor decisions. But competition has intensified. A company can no longer carry unprofitable products and service lines and unprofitable customers by hoping the profitable ones will more than offset and make up the difference. They can no longer survive with misleading cost allocations and without having visibility of their costs across their end-to-end business processes.

Today the margin for error is slimmer. Businesses cannot make as many mistakes as they could in the past and remain competitive or effective. Price quotations, capital investment decisions, product mix, technology choices, outsourcing, and make-versus-buy decisions today all require a sharper pencil.

More competitors are better understanding the cause-and-effect connections that drive costs, and they are fine-tuning their processes, removing cost of quality (COQ), and adjusting their prices accordingly. The resulting price squeeze from more intense competition is making life for businesses much more difficult. Budget tightening is similarly affecting government and not-for-profit organizations. Knowing what your real costs are for outputs, product costs, and the "costs-to-serve" channels and customers is becoming key to survival. With activity-based costing visibility, organizations can identify where to remove waste, low-value-adding costs, and unused capacity, as well as understanding what drives their costs. They can also see the degree of alignment of their cost structure with their organization's mission and strategy.

Today an organization's road is no longer long and straight; it is windy, with bends and hills that do not give much visibility or certainty to plan for the future. Organizations need to be agile and continuously transform their cost structure and work activities. This is difficult to do when an organization does not understand its own cost structure and economics.

ABC/M IN ADVANCED, MATURE USERS

The advanced and mature users of ABC/M, such as the Coca-Cola Company, are interested in two goals:

1. to institutionalize ABC/M company-wide into a permanent, repeatable, and reliable production reporting system; and
2. to establish the ABC/M output data to serve as an enabler to their ongoing improvement programs, such as TQM, change management, cycle-time compression, core competency, BPR, product rationalization, target costing, and channel/customer profitability.

More recently, new issues for the advanced and mature ABC/M users are emerging; they include the following:

*   integrating the ABC/M output data with their decision-support systems, such as their cost estimating, predictive planning, budgeting, activity-based planning (ABP) systems, customer relationship management (CRM), and balanced scorecard performance measurement systems;
*   learning the skills and rules for resizing, reshaping, re-leveling, and otherwise readjusting their ABC/M system's structure in response to solving new business problems with the ABC/M data;
*   collecting and automatically importing data into the ABC/M system; and
*   automatically exporting the calculated data out of their ABC/M system.

It is evident that among experienced ABC/M users, ABC/M eventually becomes part of their core information technologies.

More specifically, the output data of an ABC/M system is frequently the input to another system, such as a customer order quotation system. ABC/M data also complement other productivity or logistics management tools such as simulation software, process modelers, business process flow charters, executive information systems (EIS), and online analytical programs (OLAP). In the future we will see a convergence of these tools that to many organizations are separate software applications but now can be integrated to become part of the manager's and analyst's tool suite.

Section 2

Cost Estimating

Chapter 9

Estimating[1]

Larry R. Dysert, CCC

INTRODUCTION

Cost estimating is one of the cornerstones of cost engineering and total cost management. The objective of this chapter is to introduce the reader to the various classifications of cost estimates, and the estimating methodologies and procedures used to prepare cost estimates.

Cost estimating is the predictive process used to quantify, cost, and price the resources required by the scope of an investment option, activity, or project. The output of the estimating process, the cost estimate, may be used for many purposes, such as

- determining the economic feasibility of a project,
- evaluating between project alternatives,
- establishing the project budget, and
- providing a basis for project cost and schedule control.

Cost estimating may be used to quantify, cost, and price any investment activity, such as building an office building or process power plant, developing a software program, or producing a stage play. The basic estimating steps are the same:

- understand the scope of the activity to quantify the resources required,
- apply costs to the resources,
- apply pricing adjustments, and
- organize the output in a structured way that supports decision-making.

For the purposes of this chapter, the primary focus will on estimating as applied to support the creation of capital assets (a building, industrial facility, bridge, highway, etc.); however, the estimating processes described can be applied to any investment activity.

---

[1] For more information on definitive estimating, see Appendix C.

LEARNING OBJECTIVES

After completing this chapter, the reader should be able to

- understand the classification of cost estimates,
- understand some of the common methodologies used in preparing cost estimates,
- relate estimate accuracy to the level of scope information and methodologies used in preparing cost estimates,
- understand how to apply risk analysis to determine contingency in an estimate,
- understand how to present and review estimates, and
- apply the knowledge gained to specific project estimating situations.

ESTIMATE ACCURACY

As potential projects are considered, there are many decision points at which to decide whether a specific project should be continued to be developed. Each subsequent decision-making point during the project life cycle typically requires cost estimates of increasing accuracy. Estimating is thus an iterative process that is applied in each phase of the project life cycle as the project scope is defined, modified, and refined.

The cost estimate is obviously of paramount importance to the success of a project. The capital cost of a proposed project is one of the key determinants in evaluating the financial viability and business case of the project. From an owner's perspective, if the cost estimate is not accurate, the financial return from the capital investment may not be realized; and compounding this problem is the fact that other deserving projects may not have been funded. It is obvious that estimating is critical for the economic and optimal use of an owner's limited capital budget.

From a contractor's perspective, accurate estimating is just as important. In a lump-sum bidding situation, the profit margin of the contractor is dependent on the accuracy of his estimate. If the project is exceptionally large, the loss from an inaccurate estimate on a lump-sum bid can potentially put a contractor out of business. For cost-plus projects, the contractor will face less direct economic risk from an inaccurate estimate, but the damage to the contractor's reputation can be severe.

The cost estimate, however, serves other purposes besides establishing the budget for a project. It also serves as a tool or resource used for both scheduling and cost control of projects. The estimate not only establishes a project budget, but plays an equally important role in monitoring the budget during project execution. It is the relationship between estimating, scheduling, and cost control, which is typically identified by the term "cost engineering" that serves as a driver for successful and cost-effective projects. Thus, an effective estimate must not only establish a realistic budget, but must also provide accurate information to allow for scheduling, cost monitoring, and progress measurement of a project during execution.

ESTIMATE CLASSIFICATIONS

Estimate classifications are commonly used to indicate the overall maturity and quality for the various types of estimates that may be prepared; and most organizations will use some form of classification system to identify and categorize the various types of project estimates that they may prepare during the life cycle of a project. Unfortunately, there is often a lack of consistency and understanding of the terminology used to classify estimates, both across industries as well as within single companies or organizations.

AACE International (AACE) developed the "Recommended Practice for Cost Estimate Classification" (AACE 17R-97, see appendix E) to provide generic guidelines for the general principles of estimate classification that may be applied across a wide variety of industries. This document has been developed to

- provide a common understanding of the concepts involved in classifying project cost estimates;
- fully define and correlate the major characteristics used in classifying cost estimates so that different organizations may clearly determine how their particular practices compare to the AACE guidelines;

- use degree of project definition as the primary characteristic in categorizing estimate classes; and
- reflect generally accepted practices in the cost engineering profession.

AACE 17R-97 maps the phases and stages of project estimating with a maturity and quality matrix; providing a common reference point to describe and differentiate various types of cost estimates. The matrix defines the specific input information (i.e., design and project deliverables) that is required to produce the desired estimating quality at each phase of the estimating process. The matrix defines the requirements for scope definition and indicates estimating methodologies appropriate for each class of estimate. Table 9.1 shows the generic AACE cost estimate classification matrix.

AACE identifies five classes of estimates. A Class 5 Estimate is associated with the lowest level of project definition (or project maturity), and a Class 1 Estimate is associated with the highest level of project definition. Five characteristics are used to distinguish each class of estimate from another. The five characteristics used in the AACE recommended practice are

- degree of project definition;
- end usage of the estimate;
- estimating methodology;
- estimating accuracy; and
- effort required to produce the estimate.

Degree of project definition is the primary (or driving) char-

Table 9.1—Generic Cost Estimate Classification Matrix

ESTIMATE CLASS	Primary Characteristic	Secondary Characteristic			
	LEVEL OF PROJECT DEFINITION Expressed as % of complete definition	END USAGE Typical purpose of estimate	METHODOLOGY Typical estimating method	EXPECTED ACCURACY RANGE Typical +/- range relative to best index of 1 [a]	PREPARATION EFFORT Typical degree of effort relative to least cost index of 1 [b]
Class 5	0% to 2%	Screening or Feasibility	Stochastic or Judgment	4 to 20	1
Class 4	1% to 15%	Concept Study or Feasibility	Primarily Stochastic	3 to 12	2 to 4
Class 3	10% to 40%	Budget, Authorization, or Control	Mixed, but Primarily Stochastic	2 to 6	3 to 10
Class 2	30% to 70%	Control or Bid/ Tender	Primarily Deterministic	1 to 3	5 to 20
Class 1	50% to 100%	Check Estimate or Bid/Tender	Deterministic	1	10 to 100

Notes:
[a] If the range index value of "1" represents +10/-5%, then an index value of 10 represents +100/-50%.
[b] If the cost index value of "1" represents 0.005% of project costs, then an index value of 100 represents 0.5%.

acteristic used to identify an estimate class. The other characteristics are "secondary," with their value typically determined by the level of project definition.

In addition to the generic estimate classification system, a more specific version has been created for the process industries (Table 9.2). The term "process industries" is intended to include firms involved with the manufacturing and production of chemicals, petrochemicals, pulp/paper and hydrocarbon processing. The commonality among this industry (for the purpose of estimate classification) is their reliance on process flow diagrams (PFDs) and piping and instrument diagrams (P&IDs) as primary scope defining documents. These documents are key deliverables in determining the level of project definition, and thus the extent and maturity of estimate input information, and subsequently the estimate class for an estimate for a process industry project.

This estimate classification system for the process industries is meant to supplement the generic standard. Over time, additional matrices will be developed which are specific to other industries (such as general construction, highway construction, software development, etc.).

GLOSSARY TERMS IN THIS CHAPTER

allowance ◆ battery limits ◆ basis ◆ basis of estimate
budget ◆ budgeting ◆ code of accounts (COA)
contingency ◆ cost ◆ cost estimate
cost estimating relationship (CER) ◆ direct cost
price variation ◆ profitability ◆ sunk cost
taxation ◆ taxes ◆ time value of money

Included with the supplemental guideline for the process industries is a chart that maps the maturity of estimate input information (project definition deliverables) against the classes of estimates (Table 9.3 on page 9.4).

This is a checklist of basic deliverables found to be in common practice in the process industries. The maturity level is an

Table 9.2—Cost Estimate Classification Matrix for the Process Industries

| ESTIMATE CLASS | Primary Characteristic | Secondary Characteristic | | | |
	LEVEL OF PROJECT DEFINITION Expressed as % of complete definition	END USAGE Typical purpose of estimate	METHODOLOGY Typical estimating method	EXPECTED ACCURACY RANGE Typical variation in low and high ranges [a]	PREPARATION EFFORT Typical degree of effort relative to least cost index of 1 [b]
Class 5	0% to 2%	Concept Screening	Capacity Factored, Parametric Models, Judgment, or Analogy	L: -20% to -50% H: +30% to +100%	1
Class 4	1% to 15%	Study or Feasibility	Equipment Factored or Parametric Models	L: -15% to -30% H: +20% to +50%	2 to 4
Class 3	10% to 40%	Budget, Authorization, or Control	Semi-Detailed Unit Costs with Assembly Level Line Items	L: -10% to -20% H: +10% to +30%	3 to 10
Class 2	30% to 70%	Control or Bid/Tender	Detailed Unit Cost with Forced Detailed Take-Off	L: -5% to -15% H: +5% to +20%	4 to 20
Class 1	50% to 100%	Check Estimate or Bid/Tender	Detailed Unit Cost with Detailed Take-Off	L: -3% to -10% H: +3% to +15%	5 to 100

Notes:
[a] The state of process technology and availability of applicable reference cost data affect the range markedly. The +/- value represents typical percentage variation of actual costs from the cost estimate after application of contingency (typically at a 50% level of confidence) for given scope.
[b] If the range index value of "1" represents 0.005% of project costs, then an index value of 100 represents 0.5%. Estimate preparation effort is highly dependent upon the size of the project and the quality of estimating data and tools.

Table 9.3—Estimate Input Checklist and Maturity Matrix for the Process Industries

General Project Data:	ESTIMATE CLASSIFICATION				
	CLASS 5	CLASS 4	CLASS 3	CLASS 2	CLASS 1
Project Scope Description	General	Preliminary	Defined	Defined	Defined
Plant Production/Facility Capacity	Assumed	Preliminary	Defined	Defined	Defined
Plant Location	General	Approximate	Specific	Specific	Specific
Soils & Hydrology	None	Preliminary	Defined	Defined	Defined
Integrated Project Plan	None	Preliminary	Defined	Defined	Defined
Project Master Schedule	None	Preliminary	Defined	Defined	Defined
Escalation Strategy	None	Preliminary	Defined	Defined	Defined
Work Breakdown Structure	None	Preliminary	Defined	Defined	Defined
Project Code of Accounts	None	Preliminary	Defined	Defined	Defined
Contracting Strategy	Assumed	Assumed	Preliminary	Defined	Defined
Engineering Deliverables:					
Block Flow Diagrams	S/P	P/C	C	C	C
Plot Plans		S	P/C	C	C
Process Flow Diagrams (PFDs)		S/P	P/C	C	C
Utility Flow Diagrams (UFDs)		S/P	P/C	C	C
Piping & Instrument Diagrams (P&IDs)		S	P/C	C	C
Heat & Material Balances		S	P/C	C	C
Process Equipment List		S/P	P/C	C	C
Utility Equipment List		S/P	P/C	C	C
Electrical One-Line Drawings		S/P	P/C	C	C
Specifications & Datasheets		S	P/C	C	C
General Equipment Arrangement Drawings		S	P/C	C	C
Spare Parts Listings			S/P	P	C
Mechanical Discipline Drawings			S	P	P/C
Electrical Discipline Drawings			S	P	P/C
Instrumentation/Control System Discipline Drawings			S	P	P/C
Civil/Structural/Site Discipline Drawings			S	P	P/C

approximation of the degree of completion of the deliverable. The degree of deliverable is indicated by the following letters:

- **None (blank)**—Development of the deliverable has not yet begun.
- **Started (S)**—Work on the deliverable has begun. Development is typically limited to sketches, rough outlines, or similar levels of early completion.
- **Preliminary (P)**—Work on the deliverable is advanced. Interim cross-functional reviews have usually been conducted. Development may be near completion except for final reviews and approvals.
- **Complete (C)**—The deliverable has been reviewed and approved as appropriate.

ESTIMATING METHODOLOGIES

In general, estimating methodologies commonly fall into two broad categories: conceptual and deterministic. As can be seen from the cost estimate classification matrices (Tables 9.1 and 9.2), as the level of project definition increases, the estimating methodology tends to progress from conceptual (stochastic or factored) methods to deterministic methods.

With conceptual estimating methods, the independent variables used in the estimating algorithm are generally something other than a direct measure of the units of the item being measured. They usually involve simple or complex modeling (or factoring) based on inferred or statistical relationships between costs and other, typically design-related, parameters. Often, the cost estimating relationships used in conceptual estimating methods are at least somewhat subject to conjecture.

For deterministic estimating methods, the independent variables used in the estimating algorithm are more or less a direct measure of the item being estimated, such as straightforward counts or measures of items multiplied by known unit costs. Deterministic estimating methods require a high degree of precision in the determination of quantities, pricing, and the completeness of scope definition. Of course, any particular estimate may involve a combination of conceptual and deterministic methods.

There is another key difference between conceptual and deterministic estimating methods. Conceptual estimating methods require significant effort in data-gathering and methods development before estimate preparation ever begins. There is a significant effort in historical cost analysis to develop accurate factors and estimating algorithms to support conceptual estimating. Preparing the conceptual estimate itself takes relatively little time, sometimes less than an hour.

In contrast, a deterministic (or detailed) estimate requires a large effort during the actual preparation of the estimate. The evaluation and quantification of the project scope can take a substantial amount of time, sometimes weeks or even months for extremely large projects. Research and application of accurate detailed pricing information, and application of specific estimating adjustments to the quantified scope, can also take considerable time.

The estimating method used for any particular estimate will depend on many factors: the end use of the estimate, the amount of time and money that is available to prepare the estimate, the estimating tools and data available, and, of course, the level of project definition and design information on hand [1].

Conceptual Estimating Methodologies
Conceptual estimating methods are typically used for Class 5 and Class 4 (and sometimes Class 3) estimates. They are often referred to as "order-of-magnitude" (OOM) estimates in reference to their typically wide range of estimate accuracy (as previously defined in the estimate classification matrices). They provide a relatively quick method of determining the approximate probable cost of a project without the benefit of detailed scope definition. As indicated in the estimate classification matrices, these estimates may be used for the following:

*   establishing an early screening estimate for a proposed project or program,
*   evaluating the general feasibility of a project,
*   screening project alternatives (such as different locations, technologies, capacities, etc.),
*   evaluating the cost impacts of design alternatives, and
*   establishing a preliminary budget for control purposes during the design phase of a project.

Conceptual estimates are generally based on little project definition (i.e., engineering deliverables), thus subjecting them to a wide range of estimate accuracy. Their accuracy can depend on several factors, including the level of project definition, the quality of the past historical cost data used in development of the factors and algorithms, as well as the judgment and experience of the estimator. These limitations should, of course, be recognized in using conceptual estimating methods. Nonetheless, there are many cases where conceptual estimates can be very reliable, especially in estimating repeat projects. Generally, the emphasis with conceptual estimating is not on detailed accuracy, but on obtaining a reasonable cost estimate of sufficient accuracy to insure that the results are meaningful for management to make the decision at hand.

There are a wide variety of conceptual or OOM estimating methodologies. Several of the more commonly used methods are end-product units, physical dimensions, capacity factor, various ratio or factor methods, and parametric modeling. Most conceptual estimating methods rely on relationships of one form or another.

End-Product Units Method
This conceptual estimating method is used when the estimator has enough historical data available from similar projects to relate the end-product units (capacity units) of a project to its construction costs. This allows an estimate to be prepared relatively quickly, knowing only the end-product unit capacity of the proposed project. Examples of the relationship between construction costs and end-product units are

*   the construction cost of an electric generating plant and the plant's capacity in kilowatts,
*   the construction cost of a hotel and the number of guest rooms,
*   the construction cost of a hospital and the number of patient beds, and
*   the construction cost of a parking garage and the number of available parking spaces.

To illustrate, consider a client that is contemplating building a 1,500 luxury hotel in a resort area. The client needs an approximate cost estimate for the proposed hotel as part of the feasibility study. Assume that a similar luxury hotel has been recently completed at a nearby resort and the following information is available:

The hotel just completed included 1,000 guest rooms, as well as a lobby, restaurants, meeting rooms, parking garage, swimming pool, and nightclub. The total construction cost for the 1,000 room hotel was $67,500,000. The resulting cost per room is thus calculated as $67,500,000/1000 = $67,500 per room.

Therefore, we can use this information to determine the cost of the 1,500 room hotel of comparable design and a nearby location as $101,250,000 ($67,500/room x 1,500 rooms).

While this cost estimate may serve to meet the needs of the feasibility study, it has ignored several factors that may impact costs.

For example, it has ignored any economies-of-scale that may be generated from constructing a larger hotel and has assumed that the cost of the common facilities (lobby, restaurants, pool, etc.) vary directly with the increase in the number of rooms. If the data exists to understand the cost impact of these differences, then adjustments may be made to the initial cost estimate. Similarly, if the location or timing of the proposed hotel had differed significantly from the known cost data point, then cost indices can be used to adjust for these differences.

Physical Dimensions Method
Somewhat similar to the end-products units method is the physical dimensions estimating methodology. The method uses the physical dimensions (length, area, volume, etc.) of

the item being estimated as the driving factor. For example, a building estimate may be based on square feet/meters or cubic volume of the building; whereas pipelines, roadways, or railroads may be based on a linear basis.

As with the end-product units method, this method also depends on historical information from comparable facilities. Consider the need to estimate the cost of a 3,600-m² warehouse. A recently completed warehouse of 2,900 m² in a nearby location was recently completed for $623,500, thus costing $215/m². The completed warehouse utilized a 4.25-m wall height, thus containing 12,325 m³ and resulting in a cost of $50.59/m³ on a volume basis ($623,500/12,325 m³).

In determining the cost for the new warehouse, we can estimate the new 3,600 m² warehouse using the m² basis at $774,000 ($215/m² x 3,600m²). However, the new warehouse will differ from the one just completed by having 5.5-m-high walls; so we may decide that estimating on a volume basis may provide a better indication of costs. The volume of the new warehouse will be 19,800 m³ (3,600 m² x 5.5m), and the new estimate will be $1,002,000 (rounded to the nearest $1,000).

Again, we have ignored the cost impact of economies-of-scale in developing the estimate, and any other differences in quality between the two warehouses. If additional information is available, we may make further adjustments to the cost estimate. If location or timing differences had existed, we would also account for those cost impacts by utilizing cost indices or other adjustments.

Capacity Factor Method

A capacity factored estimate is one in which the cost of a new facility is derived from the cost of a similar facility of a known (but usually different) capacity. It relies on the non-linear relationship between capacity and cost. In other words, the ratio of costs between two similar facilities of different capacities equals the ratio of the capacities multiplied by an exponent:

$$\$B/\$A = (Cap_B/Cap_A)^e$$

where

$A and $B are the costs of the two similar facilities, and Cap_A and Cap_B are the capacities of the two facilities. This is shown in Figure 9.1.

If we rewrite this equation to use as an estimating algorithm, it becomes:

$$\$B = (\$A)(Cap_B/Cap_A)^e$$

where

$B is the cost of the facility being estimated, $A is the known cost of a similar facility, Cap_B is the capacity of the facility being estimated,

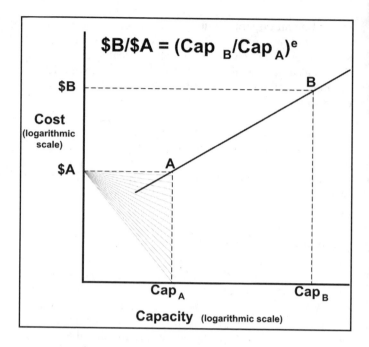

Figure 9.1—Capacity Factor Relationship

Cap_A is the capacity of the similar facility, and

"e" is the exponent or proration factor.

The exponent "e" typically lies between 0.5 and 0.85, depending on the type of facility, and must be analyzed carefully for its applicability to each estimating situation. The exponent "e" used in the capacity factor equation is actually the slope of the curve that has been drawn to reflect the change in the cost of a facility as it is made larger or smaller (Figure 9.1). These curves are typically drawn from the data points of the known costs of completed facilities. The slope will usually appear as a straight line when drawn on log-log paper. With an exponent value less than 1, scales of economy are achieved such that as facility capacity increases by a percentage (say, 20 percent), the costs to build the larger facility increase by less than 20 percent.

The methodology of using capacity factors is sometimes referred to as the "scale of operations" method or the "six tenth's factor" method due to the common reliance on an exponent value of 0.6 if no other information is available. With an exponent of 0.6, doubling the capacity of a facility increases costs by approximately 50 percent, and tripling the capacity of a facility increases costs by approximately 100 percent.

It is also important to realize that, although the data when plotted on a log-log graph will usually appear as a straight line over a small range of capacity values, it is probably not constant over the entire range of possible capacities or facility sizes. In reality, as facility capacities increase, the exponent tends to increase as illustrated in Figure 9.2. As an example, between the capacities A and B (in Figure 9.2), the capacity factor exponent may have a value of 0.6; however between the capacities B and C, the exponent has a value of 0.65. Between the capacities C and D, the value of the exponent may have risen to 0.72. Eventually, as the facility capacity increases to the limits of existing technology, the exponent tends towards a value of 1. At this point, it becomes more economical to build two facilities of a smaller size than one large facility. In other words, cost becomes a linear function of capacity, and scales of economy are no longer obtained.

Capacity factored estimating can be quite accurate. If the capacity factor used in the estimating algorithm is relatively close to the actual value, and if the facility being estimated is relatively close in size to the similar facility of known cost,

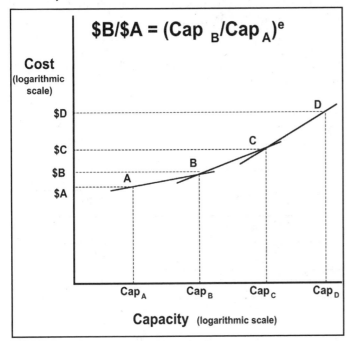

Figure 9.2—Capacity Factor Exponents Are Not Constant Across All Capacity Ranges

then the potential error from capacity factoring is quite small, and is certainly well within the level of accuracy that would be expected from such a conceptual estimating method. For example, if the new facility is triple the size of an existing facility, and the actual capacity factor is 0.80 instead of an assumed 0.70, you will have underestimated the cost of the new facility by only 10 percent, calculated as $(3^{.8} - 3^{.7})/3^{.7}$. Similarly, for the same threefold scale-up in facility size, but the actual capacity factor should be 0.60 instead of an assumed 0.70, you will have overestimated the facility cost by only 12 percent, calculated as $(3^{.7} - 3^{.6})/3^{.6}$.

Thus, if the facility size being estimated is reasonably close to the size of the known facility, and a realistic capacity factor exponent is used, error from the capacity factoring algorithm is small. However, this error can be compounded by other assumptions we must make in an actual estimating situation. Typically, we must also adjust for differences in scope, location and time between the estimated facility and the known facility. Each of these adjustments can also add to the level of error in the overall estimate.

Let's examine a typical situation where we need to estimate the costs of a 100,000 BBL/day hydrogen peroxide unit to be built in Philadelphia and completed in 2004. We have recently completed a 150,000 BBL/day plant in Malaysia with a final cost of $50 million in 2002. Our recent history shows a capacity factor of 0.75 is appropriate. The simple approach is to just use our capacity factor algorithm:

$$\$B = (\$A)(Cap_B/Cap_A)^e$$
$$\$B = \$50M \times (100/150)^{.75} = \$36.9M$$

This would be fine for as far as it goes, but as we have noted in our earlier discussions of estimating methodologies, we have thus far ignored differences in quality (or scope), location, and time.

For this example, let's adjust for the differences in scope, location, and time. The plant in Malaysia included piling, tankage, and owner costs that will not need to be included in the proposed plant for Philadelphia. Construction in Philadelphia is expected to cost 1.25 times the construction costs in Malaysia (location adjustment). Escalation will be included as a 1.06 multiplier from 2002 to 2004 (an obviously simple approach). There are costs for additional pollution requirements in Philadelphia that were not included in the cost of the Malaysian plant. Taking these into account, the estimate now appears like this:

150,000 BBL/day plant in Malaysia	$50M
deduct piling, tankage, owner costs	-$10M
adjusted cost for scope	=$40M
Malaysia to Philadelphia adjustment (x 1.25)	= $50M
escalate to 2004 (x 1.06)	= $53M
factor = $53M x (100/150).75	= $39M
add pollution requirements (+$5M)	= $44M

The key steps in preparing a capacity factor estimate, therefore, are the following:

- Deduct costs from the known base case that are not applicable in the new plant being estimated.

- Apply location and escalation adjustments to normalize costs. (This now determines what the adjusted scope for the base case will cost in the new location and time frame.)
- Apply the capacity factor algorithm to adjust for plant size.
- Add any additional costs which are required for the new plant but which were not included in the known plant.

The capacity factor estimating method provides a relatively quick and sufficiently accurate means to prepare early estimates during the concept screening stage of a project. The method requires historical cost and capacity data for similar plants and processes. Although published data on capacity factors exists, the best data would be from your own organization and requires a level of commitment to maintain. When using this method, the new and existing known plant should be near duplicates, and reasonably close in size. You must account for differences in scope, location, and time. Each of the adjustments that you make adds additional uncertainty and potential error to the estimate. Despite this, capacity factor estimates can be quite accurate and are often used to support decision-making at the pre-design stage of a project.

Ratio or Factor Methods
Ratio or factored estimating methods are used in situations where the total cost of an item or facility can be reliably estimated from the cost of a primary component. For example, this method is commonly used in estimating the cost of process and chemical plants, where the cost of the specialized process equipment makes up a significant portion of the total project cost. This is often referred to as "equipment factor" estimating.

Equipment factored estimates are used to develop costs for process and utility units for which the behavior of the costs of the direct labor and bulk materials used to construct the facilities is correlated with the costs (or the design parameters) of the major equipment. Typically, this estimating methodology relies on the principle that a ratio or factor exists between the cost of an equipment item and costs for the associated nonequipment items (foundations, piping, electrical, etc.) needed to complete the installation.

An equipment factored estimate can typically be generated when project definition (engineering complete) is approximately 1 percent to 15 percent complete (Class 4). An equipment list should be available at this point in the project. This estimate is often a feasibility estimate used to determine whether there is a sufficient business case to pursue the project. If so, then this estimate may be used to justify the funding required to complete the engineering and design required to produce a funding or budget estimate (Class 3).

Depending on the particular factoring techniques and data used, the factors may estimate Total Installed Costs (TIC) or Direct Field Cost (DFC) for the facility. Usually, the factors

generate costs only for the Inside Battery Limits (ISBL) facilities, and require the Outside Battery Limit Facilities (OSBL) costs to be estimated separately; however sometimes appropriate factors are used to estimate the costs of the complete facilities. Therefore, it is extremely important to understand the basis of the particular factors being used in an equipment factored estimate.

In 1947, Hans Lang first published an article [11] in *Chemical Engineering* introducing the concept of using the total cost of equipment to factor the total estimated cost of a plant:

Total plant $ = total equipment $ x equipment factor

Lang proposed three separate factors based on the type of process plant (Table 9.4). Lang's factors were meant to cover all the costs associated with the total installed cost of a plant including the Battery Limits Process Units (ISBL Costs) and all Offsites Units (OSBL Costs).

The following is an example of a Lang Factor estimate for a fluid process plant:

Total estimated equipment cost	= $1.5M
Total plant cost	= $1.5M X 4.74
Total plant cost	= $7.11M

Table 9.4—Lang Factors

Type of Plant	Factor
Solid Process Plant	3.10
Solid-Fluid Process Plant	3.63
Fluid Process Plant	4.74

Lang's approach was rather simple, utilizing a factor that varied only by the type of process. Since that first publication, many different methods of equipment factoring have been proposed, and some methods have become very sophisticated. The term "Lang Factor," however, is often used generically to refer to all the different types of equipment factors.

In 1958, W. E. Hand [10] elaborated on Lang's work by proposing different factors for each type of equipment (columns, vessels, heat exchangers, etc.), rather than process type. Hand's factors estimated DFCs, excluding instrumentation. Hand's published equipment factors ranged from 2.0 to 3.5 (which might correlate to approximately 2.4 to 4.3 including instrumentation). Hand's factors excluded indirect field costs (IFC), home office costs (HOC), and the costs for offsite or outside battery limit (OSBL) facilities. These costs would need to be estimated separately.

An example of an estimate prepared for a fluid processing plant using Hand's equipment factoring techniques appears in Table 9.5. In this example, the total cost of all equipment items for each type of equipment was multiplied by a factor for that specific type of equipment to derive the DFC for that equipment type. For instance, the total cost of all vertical vessels ($540K) was multiplied by an equipment factor of 3.2 to obtain an installed DFC of $1,728K. The DFC costs for all equipment types totals $7,753K. Direct Field Labor (DFL) was estimated at 25 percent of DFC or $1,938K. The IFC were then estimated at 115 percent of the DFL costs, totaling $2,229K. The sum of the DFC and IFC costs make up the total field costs (TFC) of $9,982K. HOC are factored as 30 percent of DFC, which totals $2,326K. For this estimate, the project commissioning costs were factored as 3 percent of DFC, and contingency was factored as 15 percent. The total installed cost (TIC) for this estimate thus totals $14,422K.

Note the various equipment factors displayed in this example. Total equipment cost to DFC is a factor of 2.8 (a typical range would be 2.4 to 3.5). Total equipment cost to TFC is a factor of 3.6 (with a typical range being 3.0 to 4.2). Total equipment cost to total project cost, including contingency, is a factor of 5.1 (a typical range would be 4.2 to 5.5). This correlates closely with Lang's original overall equipment factor of 4.74 for fluid plants.

Arthur Miller proposed another enhancement to the concept of equipment factors in 1965 [13]. Miller recognized the impact of three specific variables that affect the equipment material cost to a greater degree than they affect the cost of the associated bulk materials and installation. These three factors are: the size of the major equipment, the materials of construction (metallurgy) of the equipment, and the operating pressure. Miller noted that as the size of a piece of major equipment gets larger, the amount of corresponding bulk materials (foundation, support steel, piping, instruments,

Table 9.5—Equipment Factored Estimate Example

Acct No	Item Description	Adj Factor	Labor $	Eqmt $	Eqmt Factor	Total	Eqmt Mult	% Total
51	Columns			650,000	2.1	1,365,000		
52	Vertical Vessels			540,000	3.2	1,728,000		
53	Horizontal Vessels			110,000	2.4	264,000		
54	Shell & Tube Heat Exchangers			630,000	2.5	1,575,000		
55	Plate Heat Exchangers			110,000	2.0	220,000		
56	Pumps, Motor Driven			765,000	3.4	2,601,000		
				2,805,000				
	DIRECT FIELD COSTS	25% Of DFC	1,938,000			7,753,000	2.8	53.8%
10	Temporary Construction Facilities							
11	Construction Services/Supplies/Consumables							
12	Field Staff/Subsistence/Expense							
13	Payroll Burdens/Benefits/Insurance							
14	Construction Equipment/Tools							
15	International Expense							
	INDIRECT FIELD COSTS	115% Of DFL				2,229,000		15.5%
	TOTAL FIELD COSTS					9,982,000	3.6	69.2%
20	Project Management							
21	Project Controls/Estimating							
22	Project Procurement							
23	Project Construction Management							
24	Engineering/Design							
25	Home Office Expenses							
	HOME OFFICE COSTS	30% Of DFC				2,326,000		16.1%
	TOTAL FIELD and HOME OFFICE COSTS					12,308,000	4.4	85.3%
30	Owner's Costs							
31	Project Commissioning Costs	3%	Of DFC			233,000		
32	Escalation							
33	Other Non-Assignable Costs							
34	Contingency	15%	Of Above			1,881,000		
35	Fee							
	OTHER PROJECT COSTS					2,114,000		14.7%
	TOTAL PROJECT COSTS					$14,422,000	5.1	100.0%

etc.) required for installation does not increase at the same rate. Thus, as the equipment increases in size, the value of the equipment factor decreases.

A similar tendency exists for metallurgy and operating pressure. If the equipment is made from more expensive materials (stainless steel, titanium, monel, etc.), the equipment factor will become smaller. If the operating pressure increases, the equipment factor gets smaller. Again, as the equipment becomes more costly due to expensive materials of construction or higher operating pressures, the costs for the associated bulk materials required for installation increase at a lower proportion or rate, and the resulting equipment factor becomes smaller.

Miller suggested that these three variables could be summarized into a single attribute known as the "average unit cost" of equipment. The average unit cost of equipment is

Total cost of process equipment/number of equipment items

If the average unit cost of equipment increases, then the equipment factor is scaled smaller. The correlation between increasing average unit cost of equipment and decreasing equipment factors was statistically validated in subsequent studies [16, 18].

Thus far, the equipment factors we have discussed have been used to generate all in DFC or TIC costs. Another method of using equipment factors is to generate separate costs for each of the disciplines associated with the installation of equipment. Using this methodology, each type of equipment is associated with several discipline-specific equipment factors. For example, one discipline equipment factor will generate costs for concrete, another factor will generate costs for support structural steel, another generates the cost for piping, etc. An advantage to this approach is that it provides the estimator with the capability to adjust the costs for the individual disciplines based on specific knowledge of the project conditions, and improves the accuracy of the equipment factoring method. It also allows the costs for each specific discipline to be summed and compared to other similar projects. Miller, and later, Guthrie [9] described this methodology.

An example of using discipline specific equipment factors is shown in Table 9.6 on page 9.11. The example shows discipline equipment factors for a 316SS shell & tube heat exchanger with a size range of 350 to 700 m². In this example, the equipment cost of $10,000 is multiplied by each of the indicated factors to generate the DFC costs for that discipline. For example, the equipment installation labor is factored as $10,000 x 0.05 = $500; piping material and labor is factored as $10,000 x 1.18 = $11,800; etc. The total DFC costs for installation of this heat exchanger is $28,600 (including the equipment purchase cost of $10,000). This equates to an overall DFC equipment factor of 2.86. These costs do not include IFC,

HOC, or OSBL Costs.

Development of the actual equipment factors to be used in preparing process plant estimates is a tedious and time-consuming affair. Although some published data exists on equipment factors (see the articles included in the references) much of this data is old, and some of the assumptions in normalizing the data for time, location, and scope are incomplete or unavailable. A clear explanation of what is or what is not covered by the factors is sometimes missing. Lacking anything better, the published data provides a starting point for your database of equipment factors; however the best information will be data that comes from your own organization's project history and cost databases and that matches your engineering and construction techniques.

Overall equipment factors from total equipment cost to DFC/TIC (true "Lang" factors) are the easiest to generate. Historical data from completed projects should be normalized to a common time and location/labor productivity baseline. The total equipment costs, direct field costs, and total installed costs should be very easy to derive from the historical data. The results can then be analyzed, plotted, and tested to establish overall equipment "Lang" factors.

Developing individual equipment factors that vary based on the type of equipment, or separate factors for each discipline, is much more complicated. Generally, it is difficult to derive the required data from the actual cost histories for completed projects. Project accounting and cost coding typically does not collect actual cost data in the necessary format. Instead, these types of equipment factors are typically developed by generating detailed estimates for a matrix of equipment types, size ranges, metallurgies, operating pressures, etc. The estimates are then carefully analyzed to develop individual equipment and adjustment factors so that equipment size, metallurgy, and operating pressure can be accounted for.

The factors developed in this manner can then be tested and calibrated against actual project histories. The proposed equipment factors (and adjustment factors, if necessary) are applied to the actual equipment costs for completed projects, and the results from the factoring exercise are compared to the actual project costs to determine if a reasonable degree of accuracy has been obtained. If the factoring results vary widely from the actual costs, or are consistently low or consistently high, then an analysis to determine the reasons will need to be performed, and development of the factors will continue until sufficient accuracy can be obtained.

When preparing an equipment factored estimate, the first step, of course, is to estimate the cost for each piece of process equipment. The equipment list needs to be examined carefully for completeness, and compared against the process flow diagrams (PFDs) and/or the piping and instrument diagrams (P&IDs). When an equipment factored estimate is prepared, the equipment list is often still in a preliminary stage.

Table 9.6 - Discipline Equipment Factor Example

Exchanger, Shell & Tube, 316 Stainless Steel, 350 - 700 SM

	Equipment Cost	Eqmt Install Labor	Concrete	Structural Steel	Piping	Electrical	Instruments	Painting	Insulation	Total DFC Costs
Factor		0.05	0.11	0.11	1.18	0.05	0.24	0.01	0.11	2.86
Cost	$10,000	$500	$1,100	$1,100	$11,800	$500	$2,400	$100	$1,100	$28,600

Although the major equipment is identified, it may be necessary to assume a percentage for auxiliary equipment that has not yet been defined.

Equipment sizing should also be verified. At this preliminary stage of engineering, a common problem is that equipment is often sized at 100 percent of normal, operating duty. However, typically, by the time the purchase orders have been issued, some percentage of oversizing has been added to the design specifications. The percentage of oversizing that occurs varies by the type of equipment, and an individual organization's procedures and guidelines. It is prudent to check with the process engineers and determine if an allowance for oversizing the equipment as listed on the preliminary equipment list should be added before pricing the equipment.

The purchase cost of the equipment may be obtained by several methods: purchase orders or cost information from recent equipment purchases, published equipment cost data, preliminary vendor quotations, or firm vendor quotations. Since the material cost of equipment can represent 20 percent to 40 percent of the total project costs for process plants, it is extremely important to always estimate the equipment costs as accurately as possible. When using equipment factoring methods to develop the project estimate, this becomes even more important. If historical purchase information is used, you must ensure that the costs are escalated appropriately, and adjusted for location and/or market conditions as required.

Once the equipment cost is established, the appropriate equipment factors need to be established and applied. Ensure that adjustments for equipment size, metallurgy, and operating conditions are included if necessary. Also, any specific project or process conditions need to be evaluated to determine if additional scope-based adjustments to the factored costs are required. For example, the particular plot layout of the project being estimated may require much closer equipment placement than is typical. Therefore, you may want to make some adjustment to account for the shorter piping, conduit, and wiring runs than the factors would normally account for. Locating a project in an active seismic zone may require adjustments to foundations, support steel, etc.

Once the equipment factored costs have been developed, you must account for the remainder of the project costs that are not covered by the equipment factors. Depending on the particular type of equipment factors used, this may require developing the costs for indirect field costs, home office (project administration and engineering/design) costs, outside battery limit costs, etc.

Equipment factored estimates are typically prepared during the feasibility stage of a project. They can be quite precise if the equipment factors are appropriate, the correct adjustments have been applied, and the list of process equipment is complete and accurate. They have an advantage over capacity factored estimates in that they are based upon the specific process design for the project. It is extremely important to understand the basis behind the equipment factors being used, and to account for all costs that are not covered by the factors themselves.

Ratio or factored methods may often be used in other situations, such as estimating the cost for outside battery limit facilities (OSBL) from the cost of inside battery limit facilities (ISBL); or estimating the costs of indirect construction cost from the direct construction costs. Derivation of the appropriate multiplying factors from accurate historical cost information is critical to the resulting accuracy from this estimating methodology.

Parametric Method
A parametric cost model is an extremely useful tool for preparing early conceptual estimates when there is little technical data or engineering deliverables to provide a basis for using more detailed estimating methods. A parametric model is a mathematical representation of cost relationships that provide a logical and predictable correlation between the physical or functional characteristics of a plant (or process system) and its resultant cost [NASA]. A parametric estimate comprises cost estimating relationships and other parametric estimating functions that provide logical and repeatable relationships between independent variables, such as design parameters or physical characteristics and the dependent variable, cost.

Capacity factor and equipment factor estimates are simple examples of parametric estimates; however sophisticated parametric models typically involve several independent variables or cost drivers. Yet similar to those estimating methods, parametric estimating is reliant on the collection and analysis of previous project cost data in order to develop the cost estimating relationships (CER's).

The development of a parametric estimating model can appear to be a daunting task; however, the use of modern computer technology (including popular spreadsheet programs) can make the process tolerable, and much easier than it would have been years ago. The process of developing a parametric model should generally involve the following steps [3, 7]:

1. cost model scope determination,
2. data collection,
3. data normalization,
4. data analysis,
5. data application,
6. testing, and
7. documentation.

The first step in developing a parametric model is to establish its scope. This includes defining the end use of the model, the physical characteristics of the model, the cost basis of the model, and the critical components and cost drivers. The end use of the model is typically to prepare conceptual estimates for a process plant or system. The type of process to be covered by the model, the type of costs to be estimated by the model (TIC, TFC, etc.), the intended accuracy range of the model, etc. should all be determined as part of the end-use definition. The model should be based on actual costs from complete projects, and reflect your organization's engineering practices and technology. The model should generate current year costs or have the ability to escalate to current year costs. The model should be based on key design parameters that can be defined with reasonable accuracy early in the project scope development, and provide the capability for the estimator to easily adjust the derived costs for specific complexity or other factors affecting a particular project.

Data collection and development for a parametric estimating model requires a significant effort. The quality of the resulting model can be no better than the quality of the data it is based upon. Both cost and scope information must be identified and collected. The level at which the cost data is collected will affect the level at which the model can generate costs, and may affect the derivation of the CERs. It is best to collect cost data at a fairly low level of detail [19]. The cost data can always be summarized later if an aggregate level of cost information provides a better model. It is obviously important to include the year for the cost data in order to normalize costs later. The scope information should include all proposed design parameters or key cost drivers for the model, as

well as any other information that may affect costs.

The type of data to be collected is usually decided upon in cooperation with the engineering and project control communities. It is usually best to create a formal data collection form that can be consistently used, and revised if necessary.

After the data has been collected, the next step in the process of developing a parametric model is to normalize the data before the data analysis stage. Normalizing the data refers to making adjustments to the data to account for the differences between the actual basis of the data for each project, and a desired standard basis of data to be used for the parametric model. Typically, data normalization implies making adjustments for escalation, location, site conditions, system specifications, and cost scope.

Data analysis is the next step in the development of a parametric model. There are many diverse methods and techniques that can be employed in data analysis, and are too complex to delve into in this chapter. Typically, data analysis consists or performing regression analysis of costs versus selected design parameters to determine the key drivers for the model. Most spreadsheet applications now provide regression analysis and simulation functions that are reasonably simple to use. The more advanced statistical and regression programs have goal-seeking capabilities, which can also make the process easier.

Generally, a series of regression analysis cases (linear and nonlinear) will be run against the data to determine the best algorithms that will eventually compose the parametric model. The algorithms will usually take one of the following forms:

Linear Relationship

$$\$ = a + bV_1 + cV_2 + \ldots$$

Nonlinear Relationship

$$\$ = a + bV_1^x + cV_2^y + \ldots$$

where

V$_1$ and V$_2$ are input variables;

a, b, and c are constants derived from regression; and

x and y are exponents derived from regression.

The various relationships (cost versus design parameters) are first examined for "best-fit" by looking for the highest "R-Squared" value. R^2 has the technical sounding name of "coefficient of determination," and is commonly used as a measure of the goodness of fit for a regression equation. In simple terms, it is one measure of how well the equation explains the variability of the data. The resulting algorithms from the regression analysis are then applied to the input data sets to determine on a project-by-project basis how well the regression algorithm predicts the actual cost.

Regression analysis can be a time-consuming process (especially with the simple regression tools of a spreadsheet program), as iterative experiments are made to discover the best-fit algorithms. As an algorithm is discovered that appears to provide good results, it must be tested to ensure that it properly explains the data. Advanced statistical tools can quicken the process but can be more difficult to use. Sometimes, you will find that erratic or outlying data points will need to be removed from the input data in order to avoid distortions in the results. It's also very important to realize that many costs relationships are nonlinear, and, therefore, one or more of the input variables will be raised to a power (as in the equation above). You will need to experiment both with the variables you are testing against, and the exponential powers used for the variables. Regression analysis tends to be a continuing trial-and-error process until the proper results are obtained that appears to explain the data. Several individual algorithms may be generated and then later combined into a complete parametric model.

The data application stage of the development process involves establishing the user interface and presentation form for the parametric cost model. Using the mathematical and statistical algorithms developed in the data analysis stage, the various inputs to the cost model are identified; and an interface is developed to provide the estimator with an easy and straightforward way in which to enter this information. Electronic spreadsheets provide an excellent mechanism to accept estimator input, calculate costs based upon algorithms, and display the resulting output.

One of the most important steps in developing a cost model is to test its accuracy and validity. As mentioned previously, one of the key indicators of how well a regression equation explains the data is the R^2 value, providing a measure of how well the algorithm predicts the calculated costs. However, a high R^2 value by itself does not imply that the relationships between the data inputs and the resulting cost are statistically significant.

Once you have performed the regression analysis, and obtained an algorithm with a reasonably high R^2 value, you still need to examine the algorithm to ensure that it makes common sense. In other words, perform a cursory examination of the model to look for the obvious relationships that you expect to see. If the relationships from the model appear to be reasonable, then you can run additional tests for statistical significance (t-test and f-test), and to verify that the model is providing results within an acceptable range of error.

One of the quick checks to run is to test the regression results directly against the input data to see the percent error for each of the inputs. This lets you quickly determine the range of error, and interpreting the results can help you to deter-

mine problems and refine the algorithms. After all of the individual algorithms have been developed and assembled into a complete parametric cost model, it is important to test the model as a whole against new data (data not used in the development of the model). You should consult statistical texts for more information about testing regression results and cost models.

Lastly, the resulting cost model and parametric estimating application must be documented thoroughly. A user manual should be prepared showing the steps involved in preparing an estimate using the cost model, and describing clearly the required inputs to the cost model. The data used to create the model should be documented, including a discussion on how the data was adjusted or normalized for use in the data analysis stage. It is usually desirable to make available the actual regression data sets and the resulting regression equations and test results. All assumptions and allowances designed into the cost model should be documented, as should any exclusions. The range of applicable input values, and the limitations of the model's algorithms should also be explained.

As an example of developing a parametric estimating model, we will examine the costs and design parameters of induced-draft cooling towers. These units are typically used in industrial facilities to provide a recycle cooling water loop. The units are generally prefabricated and installed on a subcontract or turnkey basis by the vendor. Key design parameters that appear to affect the costs of cooling towers are the cooling range, approach, and flow rate. The cooling range is the difference in temperature between the hot water entering the cooling tower and the cold water leaving the tower. The approach is the difference in the cold water leaving the tower and the design wet bulb temperature of the ambient air; and the flow rate measures the desired cooling capacity of the tower.

Table 9.7 on page 9.14 provides the actual costs and design parameters of six recently completed cooling towers. The costs have been normalized (adjusted for location and time) to a Northeast U.S., Year 2000 timeframe.

This data provides the input to the data analysis steps of running a series of regression analyses to determine a sufficiently accurate algorithm for estimating costs. After much trial and error, the following cost estimating algorithm was developed:

$$\text{Cost} = \$86,600 + \$84500(\text{Cooling Range in Deg F})^{.65} -$$
$$\$68600(\text{Approach in Deg F}) +$$
$$\$76700 \text{ (Flow Rate in 1000GPM)}^{.7}$$

From this equation, we can see that the cooling range and

Table 9.7—Cost and Design Information for Recent Cooling Tower Projects

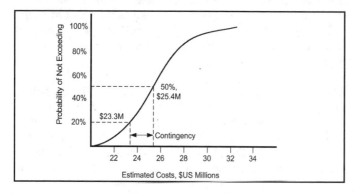

develop a simple spreadsheet model that will accept the design parameters as input variables, and calculate the costs based on the parametric estimating algorithm.

Parametric cost models can be a valuable resource in preparing early conceptual estimates. They are often used during both the concept screening and feasibility stages of a project. Parametric models can be surprisingly accurate for predicting the costs of even complex process systems. Parametric

Table 9.9—Data for Cost Graph Based on Parametric Estimating Example

flow rates affect costs in a nonlinear fashion (i.e., they are raised to an exponential power), while the approach affects costs in a linear manner. In addition, the approach is negatively correlated with costs. Increasing the approach will result in a less costly cooling tower (as it increases the efficiency of the heat transfer taking place). These appear to be reasonable assumptions. In addition, the regression analysis resulted in an R^2 value of 0.96, which indicates the equation is a "good-fit" for explaining the variability in the data, and the F-Test shows statistical significance between the input data and the resulting costs.

In Table 9.8, the design parameters are displayed as used in the model (raised to a power where needed) and shown against the actual costs and the predicted costs from the estimating algorithm. In addition, the amount of the error (the difference between the actual and predicted costs), and the error as a percent of actual costs are shown. The percentage of error varies from -4.4 to 7.1 percent for the data used to develop the model.

Using the estimating algorithm developed from regression analysis, we can develop tables of costs versus design parameters (Table 9.9), and plot this information on graphs (Figure 9.3).

This information can then be rapidly used to prepare estimates for future cooling towers. It would also be very easy to

Induced Draft Cooling Tower Costs Based On Parametric Model			
Cooling Range (Deg F)	**Approach (Deg F)**	**Flow Rate (1000 GPM)**	**Predicted Cost**
30	15	25	$559,000
30	15	30	$658,000
30	15	35	$752,000
30	15	40	$843,000
30	15	45	$930,000
30	15	50	$1,014,000
30	15	55	$1,096,000
30	15	60	$1,176,000
30	15	65	$1,254,000
30	15	70	$1,329,000
30	15	75	$1,404,000
40	15	25	$717,000
40	15	30	$816,000
40	15	35	$911,000
40	15	40	$1,001,000
40	15	45	$1,089,000
40	15	50	$1,173,000
40	15	55	$1,255,000
40	15	60	$1,334,000
40	15	65	$1,412,000
40	15	70	$1,488,000
40	15	75	$1,562,000

Table 9.8—Predicted Costs for Cooling Tower Parametric Estimating Example

Induced Draft Cooling Tower Predicted Costs from Parametric Estimating Algorithm						
Cooling Range (Deg F)$^{.65}$	**Approach (Deg F)**	**Flow Rate (1000 GPM)$^{.7}$**	**Actual Cost**	**Predicted Cost**	**Error**	**% Error**
9.12	15	15.46	$1,040,200	$1,014,000	-$26,200	-2.5%
9.12	15	13.23	$787,100	$843,000	$55,900	7.1%
11.00	15	15.46	$1,129,550	$1,173,000	$43,450	3.8%
11.00	20	15.46	$868,200	$830,000	-$38,200	-4.4%
8.10	10	10.81	$926,400	$914,000	-$12,400	-1.3%
10.08	8	12.05	$1,332,400	$1,314,000	-$18,400	-1.4%

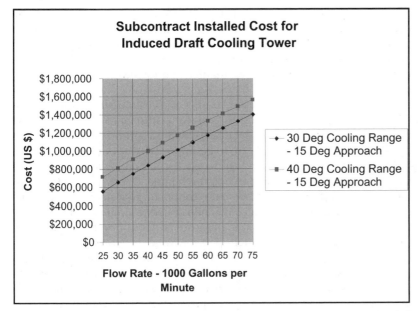

Figure 9.3–Graph of Cooling Tower Costs Based on Parametric Model

recent purchase orders, current labor rates, subcontract quotations, project schedule information (to determine escalation requirements), and the construction plan (to determine labor productivity and other adjustments).

In a completely detailed estimate, all costs are detailed including the DFC, IFC, HOC costs, and all other miscellaneous costs for both the ISBL and OSBL facilities. One variation of the detailed estimate is a semi-detailed estimate in which the costs for the ISBL process facilities are factored, and the costs for the OSBL facilities are detailed. Another variation is the forced-detailed estimate in which detailed estimating methods are used with incomplete design information. Typically in a forced-detailed estimate, detailed takeoff quantities are generated from preliminary drawings and design information.

estimating models can be developed using basic skills in estimating, mathematics, statistics, and spreadsheet software. It is important to understand that the quality of results can be no better than the quality of the input data, and great care should be taken during the data collection stage to gather appropriate and accurate project scope and cost data.

Deterministic (Detailed) Estimating Methodologies[1]

A detailed estimate is one in which each component of a project scope definition is quantitatively surveyed and priced using the most realistic unit prices available. Detailed estimates are typically prepared to support final budget authorization, contractor bid tenders, cost control during project execution, and change orders (Class 3 through Class 1 estimates). Detailed estimates use a deterministic estimating methodology and require a substantial amount of time and cost to prepare. It is not unusual for detailed estimates on very large projects to take several weeks, if not months, to prepare and can require thousands of engineering hours to prepare the required technical deliverables.

The following is a description for detailed estimating activities associated with a process or industrial project, but could easily be adopted for other types of construction-related projects, such as commercial construction. At a minimum, the required engineering and design data required to prepare a detailed estimate include process and utility flow drawings, piping and instrument diagrams, equipment data sheets, motor lists, electrical one-line diagrams, piping isometrics (for alloy and large diameter piping), equipment and piping layout drawings, plot plans, and engineering specifications. Pricing data should include vendor quotations, current pricing information from

The following steps comprise the activities undertaken during preparation of a detailed estimate:

1. prepare project estimate basis and schedule,
2. prepare direct field cost (DFC) estimate,
3. prepare indirect field cost (IFC) estimate,
4. prepare home office cost (HOC) estimate,
5. prepare sales tax/duty estimates,
6. prepare escalation estimates,
7. prepare project fee estimate (for contractors),
8. prepare cost risk analysis/contingency determination, and
9. review/validate estimate.

The first step in preparing a detailed estimate is to begin establishing the project estimate basis and schedule. This is essentially the preplanning phase for the estimate. As mentioned, a detailed estimate for a large industrial facility may take weeks to prepare, and involve several estimators and extensive support from engineering. The estimate basis documents the activities and course of action that will be used to prepare the estimate. The first activity is to review the organization's estimating guidelines and procedures with the estimating team. The project work breakdown structure (WBS) should be reviewed with the project controls team, and agreement should be reached on the estimate format, structure, and deliverables. The detailed estimate is typically used to support cost control during execution of the project and should be structured to accomplish that purpose. The listing of engineering and technical deliverables to be used to prepare the estimate should be reviewed, and the procedures for receiving and tracking the drawings and other design information established. The estimating team should identify the estimating resources, techniques, and data that will be used during estimate preparation. Any estimate exclusions that are known at this time should be reviewed and documented.

[1]See Appendix C for additional refernce material.

The estimate schedule should be prepared, documenting when the various engineering deliverables are to be supplied, when each of the major sections of the estimate should be completed, and when estimate reviews will be scheduled. The estimate basis and schedule should be reviewed with the project team at an estimate kickoff meeting prior to estimate preparation. The estimate kickoff meeting provides an opportunity for the entire project team to understand the roles and responsibilities of the various participants, and to review the plans for the estimate preparation activities and estimate schedule. On very large projects, it is often beneficial to establish a few key contacts that will act as the liaisons between estimating and engineering. Any questions developed by the estimators during estimate preparation are funneled through a liaison that will then work with the responsible engineering representative to develop the answers.

Preparing the DFC estimate is the most intensive activity of preparing the detailed estimate. The project scope should be reviewed and understood, and all technical deliverables assembled. On large projects, the engineering drawings and technical information may be submitted to estimating over time. As each drawing or other information is received from engineering, it should be logged and kept track of. Performing the estimate takeoff (described in more detail below) should take place according to the estimating department (and any special project) guidelines. This involves quantifying all the various material and labor components of the estimate. Care should be taken to ensure that all quantities are accounted for, but not double-counted. Material pricing is applied to the material quantities using the best pricing information available. The labor hours are assigned to the labor activities, adjusted for labor productivity, and wage rates applied. Any estimate allowances are established. Any owner supplied materials or other owner costs are accounted for. The DFC estimate is then summarized and formatted. Finally, the DFC estimate should be reviewed for completeness and accuracy.

After the DFC estimate has been prepared, the IFC estimate is started. The DFC estimate should be reviewed, and the total labor workhours identified. The labor workhours are typically a basis for factoring many of the of IFC costs. The indirect estimate factors should be determined and applied. Indirect labor wage rates and staff labor rates are established and applied, and any indirect estimate allowances are accounted for. The IFC estimate is then summarized, formatted, and reviewed for completeness and accuracy. The construction manager should be specifically involved in the initial review of the IFC estimate.

The HOC estimate is then prepared. For a detailed estimate, the various project administration and engineering disciplines should provide detailed workhour estimates for their project activities. The appropriate wage rates are then applied to the workhour estimates. Home office overhead factors are determined and applied to develop the home office overhead costs and expenses. The HOC estimate is then summarized, formatted, and reviewed.

Other miscellaneous activities and costs are then estimated. If sales tax is applicable to all (or portions) of the facility, they will need to be estimated using the appropriate local sales tax rates. If materials are to be imported, duties may be charged and will need to be estimated. Escalation costs should be estimated based on the project schedule. Depending on the project delivery method and contracting strategy, appropriate project fee estimates will need to be calculated and included. Finally, a cost risk analysis study should be performed and appropriate contingency is included in the estimate.

As with an equipment factored estimate, particular attention should be paid to pricing the process equipment for a detailed estimate as it contributes such a large share of the costs (20 to 40 percent of the total installed cost of the facility). Estimating the costs for process machinery and equipment requires many sources of input. The minimum information requirements for pricing equipment include the process flow drawings, the equipment lists, and the equipment process data sheets (usually prepared by the process engineering group). Often, the equipment process data sheets are provided to the mechanical/vessels engineering group to prepare narrative specifications and request for quotation (RFQ) packages.

Whenever possible, these engineering groups (perhaps in association with the procurement group) should be responsible for providing the equipment material purchase costs to the estimator for inclusion in the project estimate. Although estimating is typically responsible for pricing the material costs for bulk materials, the process and mechanical engineers are best able to accurately determine equipment material pricing, and are generally in close contact with potential equipment vendors. Slight differences in equipment specifications can sometimes result in large differences in pricing which an estimator may be unaware of. Formal vendor quotes for equipment pricing are preferred; however sometimes time constraints in preparing the estimate do not permit solicitation of formal vendor quotes. In this case, equipment pricing may depend on informal quotes from vendors (i.e., phone discussions), in-house pricing data, recent purchase orders, capacity factored estimates from similar equipment, or from parametric pricing models.

The estimator should be responsible for checking the equipment list against the flow diagrams (or P&IDs) to ensure that all equipment items are identified and priced. The estimator must also be responsible for verifying that the costs for all equipment internals and accessories (trays, baffles, ladders, etc.) are included with the cost of the appropriate equipment.

As opposed to most bulk commodity accounts (where the materials are generally available locally), freight costs for equipment can be significant and should usually be identified explicitly. Also, any vendor assistance and support costs should be identified and included with the material costs of the equipment. Major spare parts for process equipment will also need to be accounted for and included in the estimate.

Equipment installation costs are usually prepared by the estimator, with assistance from construction where required. Construction assistance is usually needed for heavy lifts, or where special installation methods may be used. The placement of large process equipment in an existing facility may also require special consideration. Workhours for equipment installation are usually based on weight and equipment dimensions, which are obtained from the equipment process data sheets). Using the equipment weights (or dimensions), the installation workhours are typically determined from curves based on historical data. Other forms of in-house or published data may also be used. When referencing the labor workhour data for equipment, the estimator must be careful to include all labor associated with the pieces of equipment (vessel internals, etc.). Depending on the information available, the labor hours to set and erect a heavy vessel may not include the hours to erect, takedown, and dismantle a guy derrick, gin poles, or other special lifting equipment. Special consideration may also be required to ensure costs for calibration, soil settlement procedures, special internal coatings, hydrotesting and other testing costs are included in the estimate. Some equipment may be erected by subcontractors or the vendor, and included in the material purchase costs. Care must be taken to identify these situations.

As with the rest of the estimate, the responsibility of the estimator is to make sure that all costs are accounted for. For equipment in particular, this requires attention to detail, working closely with engineering and construction, and asking the right questions. With chemical process plants being so "equipment-centric," the costs for purchasing and installing equipment make up a significant portion of the total installed cost of the facility.

Detailed estimates are the most accurate of the estimating methods, but also require the most time and effort to prepare. Although detailed estimates are desirable for final budget authorization, the level of engineering progress needed and the time required for estimate preparation will sometimes preclude them from being used for this purpose. In today's economy, budgeting and investment decisions are often needed sooner than a detailed estimate would allow. Semi-detailed and forced-detailed estimates will often be employed for final budget authorizations, and a complete detailed estimate may be prepared later to support project control.

TAKE-OFF

As mentioned previously, estimating take-off is the process of quantifying the material and labor quantities associated with the project. The term *take-off* is also used to refer to the quantities themselves (often known as a bill of quantities). Take-off involves a detailed examination of the engineering drawings and deliverables to count the number of each item appearing on the drawings. The quantities of like items are then summarized according to the control structure (WBS/RBS) of the project. Once the take-off is complete, and total quantities for each like item summarized, the items can be costed (or priced), and the results added together resulting in the estimated direct field costs for the project.

Generally, the process of "take-off" for the estimate is much more efficient when standard estimating guidelines are established and followed. This provides advantage enough when a single estimator is preparing a specific estimate, but is even more important when multiple estimators are working on the same project. Guidelines for preparing an efficient take-off include the following:

- Use preprinted forms for the orderly sequence of item descriptions, dimensions, quantities, pricing information, etc.
- Abbreviate (consistently) whenever possible.
- Be consistent when listing dimensions (i.e., length x width x height).
- Use printed dimensions from drawings when available.
- When possible, add up the printed dimensions for a given item.
- Measure all dimensions carefully.
- Use each set of dimensions to calculate multiple quantities where possible.
- Take advantage of design symmetry or repetition.
- List all gross dimensions that can be used again to rough check other quantities for approximate verifications.
- Convert imperial dimensions (feet/inch) to decimal equivalents.
- Do not round until the final summary of quantities.
- Multiply the large numbers first to reduce rounding errors.
- Do not convert the units until the final quantities are obtained.
- Items should be measured/converted to the same units consistently throughout the take-off.
- Mark the drawings as quantities are taken off. Use different colors to identify various types of components or items, as well as to identify items on hold, etc.
- Verify the drawings taken-off versus the approved drawing list to be used with the estimate. Check off drawings on the drawing list as take-off is completed.
- Keep similar items together, different items separate.
- Organize the take-off to match the control structure and format of the estimate.
- Identify drawing numbers, section numbers, etc. on the

take-off forms to aid in future checking for completeness, and for incorporating late changes later on.

- Be alert for notes shown on drawings, changes in scale used on different drawings, drawings that are reduced from original size, discrepancies between drawings and specifications, and changes in elevation that may not be obvious, etc.
- Be careful to quantify all labor operations that may not have a material component.

By keeping a uniform and consistent take-off process, the chance of error or omission is greatly reduced, and productivity is increased. Multiple estimators will find it easier to work on the same project; and if a personnel change takes place, it is much easier for a new estimator to pick up.

After the take-off is completed, the quantities can be extended, consolidated, and priced. If a procurement department or other resources will be utilized to investigate certain pricing (major equipment, large bulk material purchases, subcontracts, etc.), a listing should be compiled and sent to the appropriate person.

With today's computerized estimating software, the process of take-off is often performed directly into the estimating software, rather than compiled manually onto forms. The software will often prompt for key dimensions and/or parameters for the specific item being quantified and perform many of the required calculations automatically. In some cases, electronic digitizers can be used which automate the time-consuming task of measuring quantities from drawings and can help to reduce errors. Using a digitizer, an estimator can measure the area of a concrete slab, the length of a piping run, or count a quantity of valves by tracing a boundary, touching end points, or selecting items from a paper drawing. In combination with the estimating software, the digitizer performs the required calculations required to accurately quantify the various items. The estimating software can also summarize quantities, and apply pricing.

COSTING VERSUS PRICING

Costing is the process of applying unit costs to the individual quantities of items associated with the estimate. For a detailed estimate, this is usually in the form of labor hours, wage rates, material costs, and perhaps subcontract costs. These costs may come from a variety of sources such as an estimating database (either in-house or commercial), vendor quotes, the procurement department, estimating experience, etc.

Pricing, on the other hand, is adjusting the costs that have been applied for specific project conditions, and commercial terms. Pricing includes adjustments to cost to allow for overhead and profit, to improve cash flow, or otherwise serve the business interests of the party preparing the estimate. Thus, the level and type of pricing adjustments depends on the particular party preparing the estimate.

For example, to a concrete contractor preparing a bid for a defined scope of foundation work, his costs will include the direct material and labor costs associated with pricing and installing the foundations. However, the price reflected by his bid will include not only his costs, but also an allowance for his overhead and profit; so the price reflected in his bid is higher than his cost.

Pricing also includes adjustments to costs for specific project conditions. Depending on the specific cost information used in preparing the estimate, material costs may need to be adjusted for location, materials of construction, or to account for differences between the item being installed and the item you may have an available cost for. Labor hours may require productivity adjustments for a variety of conditions such as weather, amount of overtime, interferences from production, material logistics, congestion, the experience of the labor crews, the level of contamination control, etc. Labor rates may also need to be adjusted for location, crew mix, open shop versus union issues, and specific benefit and burden requirements.

ESTIMATE ALLOWANCES

Allowances are often included in an estimate to account for the predictable but undefinable costs associated with project scope. Allowances are most often used when preparing deterministic or detailed estimates. Even for this class of estimate, the level of project definition may not enable certain costs to be estimated definitively. There are also times when it is simply not cost-effective to quantify and cost every small item included with the project. To account for these situations, an allowance for the costs associated with these items may be included in the estimate.

Allowances are often included in the estimate as a percentage of some detailed cost component. Some typical examples of allowances that may be included in a detailed construction estimate are

- design allowance for engineered equipment,
- material take-off allowance,
- overbuy allowance,
- unrecoverable shipping damage allowance, and
- allowance for undefined major items.

A design allowance for engineered equipment is often required to account for continuing design development that occurs even after placement of a purchase order for the equipment. At the time of a detailed estimate, vendor quotes are usually available to account of the purchase cost of the equipment. However, for specialty engineered equipment, it is often likely that the quoted cost is not the final cost incurred by the project. We don't necessarily understand when or how the costs will increase, but we can often predict that they will based on past project experiences. After initial placement of the order for specialty equipment, continuing design activities may tighten tolerances, increase the quality of finish required, change metallurgies, etc. The predicted additional cost will frequently be included in the estimate as an design allowance for engineered equipment (or design development allowance) and be applied as a percentage of the total cost of engineered equipment, or the total cost of specific engineered equipment types when the percentage allowance will vary by equipment type. Typical percentages are from 2 to 5 percent of engineered equipment cost.

Material take-off allowances are usually intended to cover the cost of undefinable materials at the time of estimate preparation. The completeness of bulk material take-off can vary widely, depending on the status of engineering deliverables at the time estimate preparation begins. For example, all of the small-bore piping may not be included on the design drawings, or perhaps not all of the embeds and related small accessories are identified in the concrete design. A material take-off allowance may be included to cover for the lack of complete project definition. It may also account for those small items it is simply not economical to take-off or detail in the estimate. Generally, material take-off allowances are included as both a material and labor cost. They are intended to cover materials that are an actual part of the project and will thus need to be installed. Material take-off allowances are typically applied as a percentage of direct commodity costs by discipline (or trade). The percentages will vary by discipline, and from project to project depending on the estimating methods used and the level of engineering deliverables to support the estimate. Percentages may run from 2 to 15 percent of discipline costs.

Overbuy allowances provide for inventory losses due to such things as damage at the jobsite, cutting loss or waste, misuse of materials, theft, etc. Every project experiences these types of losses, depending on jobsite location and other project conditions. Some organizations may split these into several separate allowances (breakage, theft, etc.). Overbuy allowances usually apply to material costs only, may vary from 2 to 10 percent of discipline material costs.

Damage to equipment and materials during shipment can be expected on virtually every project. Usually, the cost of damage is covered by insurance if detected upon arrival at the jobsite and dealt with expeditiously. An allowance for unrecoverable shipping allowance is intended to cover such losses that are not covered by insurance. This allowance will vary based on project conditions, project material delivery and handling procedures, and the types of material and equipment being shipped.

Occasionally, an order-of-magnitude cost for a major segment of scope must be stated before definition of that work has begun. A particular area of scope may simply not have progressed in design as far as the rest of the project, but a cost for that scope must be included in the estimate. In this case, the cost is included as an allowance and may simply be a best "guestimate" to be included in the estimate until a later time when better definition can be obtained. This is sometimes referred to as an allowance for an undefined major item.

Other miscellaneous allowances may sometimes be included in an estimate for situation where a statistical correlation is more reliable that a detailed quantification, or where it is not economical to perform a detailed take-off. Percentage allowances are often included for such items. Material and/or labor costs routinely covered by such items include:

- percentage of hand excavation/backfill (vs. machine excavation/backfill),
- formwork accessories,
- structural steel connection materials,
- bolts, gaskets, etc.,
- piping hangers, guides, etc.,
- miscellaneous welding operations, and
- hydrotesting, other testing operations.

Specific application of estimating allowances will depend on many things. For conceptual estimates, such as a capacity factored estimate, allowances may not be required as the estimating methodology itself covers all scope and costs included in the project. Allowances are usually more applicable to semi-detailed and detailed estimates, with the cost value of allowances (or percentage costs) becoming less as project definition increases. The specific allowances and values will usually depend on specific organization estimating procedures and experience.

ESTIMATE ACCURACY

An estimate is a prediction of the expected final cost of a proposed project (for a given scope of work). By its nature, an estimate is associated with uncertainty, and, therefore, is also associated with a probability of overrunning or underrunning the predicted cost. Given the probabilistic nature of an estimate, it should not be regarded as a single point number or cost. Instead, an estimate actually reflects a range of potential cost outcomes, with each value within this range associated with a probability of occurrence.

Typically, however, the preparation of an estimate results in a single value. If we prepare a conceptual estimate using capacity factored techniques, we calculate a single point value as the estimated cost. When preparing detailed estimates, as the sum of many individual estimating algorithms, we also calculate the estimate total as a single point value. What we need to understand is the uncertainty associated with that single point value, and the true probabilistic nature of an estimate.

Most of the end-uses of an estimate require a single point value within the range of probable values to be selected. For example, when used to develop a project funding amount or budget, we must select a single value to represent the estimate. When taking into account the uncertainty associated with an estimate, we will often add an amount (contingency) to the initially developed point value to represent the final estimate cost. When doing so, we must take into account such things as the accuracy range of the estimate, confidence levels, risk issues, and other factors in selecting the best single point value to represent the final value of the estimate.

Estimate accuracy is an indication of the degree to which the final cost outcome of a project may vary from the single point value used as the estimated cost. It should generally be regarded as a probabilistic assessment of how far a project's final cost may vary from the single point value that is selected to represent the estimate. Accuracy is traditionally represented as a +/- percentage range around the point estimate; with a stated confidence level that the actual cost outcome will fall within this range. This common +/- percent measure associated with an estimate is merely a useful simplification given the reality that each individual estimate will be associated with a different probability distribution explaining its unique level of uncertainty.

Estimate accuracy tends to improve (i.e., the range of probable values narrows) as the level of project definition used to prepare the estimate improves. Generally, the level of project definition is closely correlated with engineering progress; thus, as the level of engineering progresses, estimate accuracy improves. This is shown in Figure 9.4.

This chart is intended only as an illustration of the general relationship between estimate accuracy and the level of engineering complete. As shown in Figure 9.4, and described in the Recommended Practices on Estimate Classification, there is no absolute standard range on any estimate or class of estimate. For the process industries, typical estimate ranges are illustrated as follows:

*   Typical Class 5 Estimate:
        High range from +30 to +100%
        Low range from -20 to -50%
*   Typical Class 4 Estimate:
        High range of from +20 to +50%
        Low range of from -15 to -30%
*   Typical Class 3 Estimate:
        High range of from +10 to +30%
        Low range of from -10% to -20%

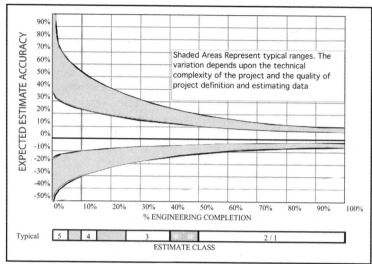

Figure 9.4—Relationship Between Estimate Accuracy and Engineering Progress

Although the percent of engineering complete (or level of project definition) is an important determinant of estimate accuracy, there are many other factors that also affect it. Some of these other factors include the state of new technology in the project, the quality of reference cost information used in preparing the estimate, the experience and skill of the estimator, the estimating techniques employed, the level of effort budgeted to prepare the estimate, and the desired end use of the estimate. Other important factors affecting estimate reliability are the project team's capability to control the project, and the capability to adjust the estimate for changes in scope as the project progresses.

Consideration of all of these factors is the reason that the high and low ranges of typical estimate accuracy are themselves variable. It is simply not possible to define a precise range of estimate accuracy based solely on the percentage of engineering complete or class of estimate. Any specific estimate may not exhibit the patterns shown above. It is possible to have a Class 5 estimate with a very narrow estimate range, particularly for repeat projects with good historical costs upon which to base the estimate. Conversely, it is possible to have a Class 3 or Class 2 estimate with a very wide accuracy range, particularly for first-of-a-kind projects or those employing new technologies.

The +/- percent accuracy range of the estimate should be determined from an assessment of the design deliverables and estimating information used in preparation of the estimate. Cost risk analysis studies will often be used for individual projects to determine their accuracy range based on this type of information. The resulting output of the cost risk analysis model should then establish a final estimate cost based on the level of confidence (or risk) acceptable to management in order not to overrun the project budget.

When discussing estimate accuracy, it is also important to realize that for early conceptual estimates, variations in the design basis will have the greatest impact on costs. Estimating tools and methods, while important, are not usually the main problem during the early stages of a project when estimate accuracy is poorest. In the early phases of a project, effort should be directed towards establishing a better design basis than concentrating on utilizing more detailed estimating methods.

CONTINGENCY AND RISK ANALYSIS

Contingency is, in many respects, the most misunderstood element contained in an estimate. This is due in large part to how the different members of a project team view contingency from their own frame of reference. A project manager may want the project budget to include as much funding as possible in order not to overrun the budget and may want as a large contingency value included in the estimate as he can get away with. An engineering manager may want contingency funds to cover any overruns in engineering, while the construction manager hopes that engineering doesn't use any of the contingency funding so that he has the entire amount to use in funding construction overruns. Corporate management may think of all requests for contingency as "padding" the estimate, and may consider any use of contingency funds as only being required because a project is poorly managed.

To the estimator, contingency is an amount used in the estimate to deal with the uncertainties inherent in the estimating process. The estimator regards contingency as the funds added to the originally derived point estimate to achieve a given probability of not overrunning the estimate (given relative stability of the project scope and the assumptions upon which the estimate is based). Contingency is required because estimating is not an exact science. One definition of an estimate is that it is the expected value of a complex equation of probabilistic elements, each subject to random variation within defined ranges. Since the value assigned to each individual component of an estimate is subject to variability, the estimate total itself is also subject to variation.

Figure 9.5 illustrates the potential variability of a single component of an estimate. In this example, the variability is shown as a normal probability distribution around the estimated value of $100. Since this is a normal probability distribution, the probability of underrun (shown as the area under the curve to the left of the vertical dotted line) equals 50%, the same as the probability of overrun (the area under the curve to the right of the dotted line). The estimate line item has an estimated cost of $100; however the accuracy range of the cost varies from $50 to $150, or an accuracy range of +/- 50%. Unfortunately, most items of cost in an estimate do not exhibit a normal probability distribution in respect to its potential variability. Most of the time, variability is more closely associated with a skewed distribution. Figure 9.6 shows the vari-

ability of an estimate line item for which the accuracy range of the cost is skewed to the high side.

In this example, the item has been estimated at $100; however the accuracy range of the cost varies from $80 to $140, or -20 to +40 percent. With an estimated value of $100, this example shows that there is only a 40 percent probability of underrun, while there is a 60 percent probability of overrun. In order to equalize the probability of underrun and overrun, an amount would need to be added to the original point value of $100. This amount would be considered contingency. Contingency would not change the overall accuracy range of $80 to $140; however it would increase the probability of underrun while decreasing the probability (risk) of overrun.

Most items of cost in an estimate will demonstrate some measure of skewness, usually to the high side where the probability of overrun is higher than the probability of underrun. However, there are usually items where the skewness will be to the low side as well. The variability of the total estimate is then a function of the variability associated with each individual line item. Since the probability distribution of most line

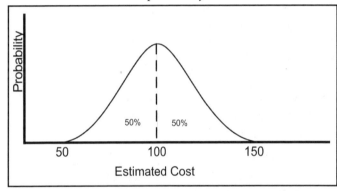

Figure 9.5—Variation of an Estimate Line Item with Normal Probability Distribution

items is skewed to the high side, the overall probability distribution for the estimate as a whole is also typically skewed to the high side. Contingency is thus usually a positive

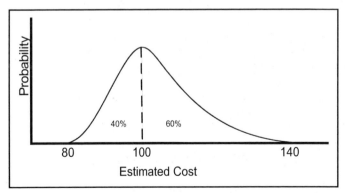

Figure 9.6—Variation of an Estimate Line Item with a Skewed Probability Distribution

amount of funds added to cover the variability surrounding the point value of the estimate, and to reduce the chances of overrunning the point estimate to an acceptable level.

Items typically covered by contingency include the following:

- errors and omissions in the estimating process;
- variability associated with the quantification effort;
- design that may not be complete enough to determine final quantities at the time of estimate preparation;
- some items that may defy precise quantification but are required to be estimated;
- some items to be quantified that are generally computed by factored or other conceptual methods;
- labor productivity variability;
- labor availability, skills, and productivity that may vary from that originally assumed;
- the fact that there is no such thing as an "average" tradesman that installs every incremental quantity of an item at the "average" rate typically used in preparing the estimate;
- weather, which may vary from that assumed affecting labor productivity;
- wage rate variability;
- wages that may vary from that assumed in the estimate due to inflationary reasons, changes in assumed crew mix, labor availability, and market conditions;
- material and equipment costs;
- material and equipment costs that may vary from those in the estimate due to inflationary reasons and market conditions;
- certain materials of construction that may be substituted from that assumed in the estimate; and
- changes in actual quantities that may change discount schedules from that assumed in the estimate.

Contingency specifically excludes the following:
- significant changes in scope,
- major unexpected work stoppages (strikes, etc.),
- disasters (hurricanes, tornadoes, etc.),
- excessive, unexpected inflation, and
- excessive, unexpected currency fluctuations.

Risk analysis is a process that can be used to provide an understanding of the probability of overrunning (or underrunning) a specified estimate value. It provides a realistic view of completing a project for the specified estimate value by taking a scientific approach to understanding the uncertainties and probabilities associated with an estimate and to aid in determining the amount of contingency funding to be added to an estimate. Its purpose is to improve the accuracy of project evaluations (not to improve the accuracy of an estimate).

Risk analysis generally uses a modeling concept to determine a composite probability distribution around the range of possible project cost totals. It provides a way in which to associate a level of risk with a selected project funding value. If the original point value of an estimate is assumed to be approximately the midpoint of the possible actual cost outcomes of project cost, that means that there is a 50 percent probability that the final outcome will exceed the estimated cost (without contingency). In reality, there is usually a greater probability that costs will increase rather than decrease. This means that the distribution of project cost outcomes is skewed, and there is a higher than 50 percent probability that final actual costs will exceed the point estimate (and this is historically the case).

Two types of risk analysis are commonly used:

- strategic risk analysis models that evaluate the level of project definition and project technical complexity in determining the overall risk to project cost, and
- detailed risk analysis models that evaluate the accuracy range for individual or groups of estimate components in determining the overall risk to project cost.

Both forms of risk analysis models usually generate overall probability distributions for the expected final cost outcomes for the project, and tables equating confidence levels with specific final cost values. The resulting probability distributions of final cost outcomes can be used to determine an amount to be included in the estimate as contingency. Basically, management typically makes this determination based on the level of risk they are willing to accept. The difference between the selected funding value and the original point estimate is the amount of contingency.

Table 9.10 shows an example of a cumulative probability distribution table produced by a typical risk analysis model. In this example, the original point estimate (before contingency) is $23.3 million. As can be seen from this table, the point estimate of $23.3M results in only a 20 percent probability of not exceeding (or underrunning) this value.

If we wanted to achieve a 50 percent probability of underrun (and thus a 50 percent probability of overrun), we would need to fund the project at $25.4M. This would mean adding a contingency amount of $2.1M in the estimate, equivalent to 9 percent of the original point value of the estimate. If we wanted to provide a 70 percent probability of not exceeding our project funding, we would need to fund $26.6M, which would add a contingency amount of $3.3M to the estimate (equivalent to 14.2 percent of the point estimate).

This can also be shown in a typical graphical output from a risk analysis model for the same estimate as shown in Figure 9.7.

As can be seen from this graph, increasing the amount of contingency increases the probability of not exceeding the project funding amount (the point estimate plus contingency).

Note: Contingency does not increase the overall accuracy of the estimate—it doesn't change the overall accuracy range of approximately of $18.5M to $32.5M.

Contingency does, however, reduce the level of risk associated with the estimate and improve project evaluations when

Table 9.10—Sample Cumulative Probability Distribution Table

Cumulative Probability of Underrun	Project Estimate		
	Indicated Funding Amount (Million $)	Estimated Contingency (Million $)	(%)
10%	$22.3		
20%	$23.3		
30%	$24.2		
40%	$24.8		
50%	$25.4	$2.1	9.0%
60%	$26.0		
70%	$26.6	$3.3	14.2%
80%	$27.4		
90%	$28.6		

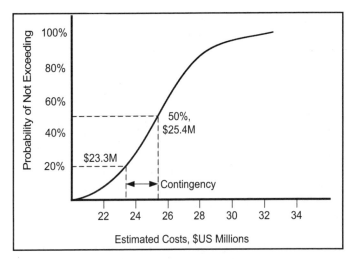

Figure 9.7—Graphical Cumulative Probability Distribution

properly used.

Appropriately applied, risk analysis provides an effective means of determining an amount for estimate contingency, and of providing management with information about the variability of project estimates. In addition, the process of preparing a risk analysis model typically identifies specific project areas associated with both risk and opportunity. Those areas identified with high risk can then become focus areas in order to reduce and mitigate any risk issues, and the areas of low risk can become focus areas in order to capitalize on the opportunities they may provide.

STRUCTURING THE ESTIMATE

The control structure for a project is the breakdown of the total work into manageable units or packages for the purposes of estimating and control of cost and schedule. The structure will vary with the size and complexity of the project, as well as the reporting requirements. The proper structuring of a project for control purposes contributes greatly to the effective implementation of project control procedures and the success of the project itself.

To maintain some kind of order in the estimate (and later in project execution), it is necessary to segregate costs into various categories:

- material vs. labor vs. subcontracts,
- direct costs vs. indirect costs vs. home office costs, and
- concrete vs. structural steel vs. piping vs. other construction disciplines.

The control structure should be established as early as possible in the project life cycle, because it will set the pattern for accumulation of project costs, and it should be used to form the basis for the structuring the estimate. The process of producing the project's control structure, often known as work breakdown planning, is often an ongoing process requiring updates as the scope of the project is refined during the project life cycle. The segregation of costs can be referred to as establishing the project "coding" structure, and more specifically as the "code of accounts." Codes are the umbilical cords between cost accounting and cost engineering (estimating and cost control).

Large projects will often use work breakdown structures (WBS) and resource breakdown structures (RBS) as components of the overall coding structure. Smaller projects will often use a simpler code of accounts based simply on the disciplines or construction trades used on the project.

The WBS and RBS are basic project management tools that define the project along activity levels that can be clearly identified, managed, and controlled. The WBS is the division of a project, for the purposes of management and control, into sub-projects according to its functional components. The WBS typically reflects the manner in which the work will be performed, and should reflect the way in which cost data will be summarized and reported.

A WBS should be customized to be specific to a particular project, and is usually organized around the geographical and functional divisions of a project. It forms the high-level structure for an estimate. Figure 9.8 illustrates how a typical WBS might be organized.

The RBS is a breakdown of all labor and material resources required in the execution of the project. The RBS identifies functional lines of authority, and extends to the level at which work is actually assigned and controlled. The RBS typically remains consistent from project to project (at least for the same project types). Figure 9.9 illustrates a sample project RBS.

The matrix of the WBS and RBS forms the full project control structure or project breakdown system (PBS). The intersection points of the WBS and RBS structures is called a "cost center," and corresponds to a defined unit of work and the resources involved in executing that work. Each cost center equates to a specific "cost code." Figure 9.10 displays a sample project breakdown structure.

Corresponding with the PBS is a numbering system used to identify each cost center. The collection of codes used to designate the intersection of WBS and RBS identifiers forms the project's "code of accounts." Table 9.11 shows a sample coding structure.

For a specific unit of work, the labor to pour concrete in the hydrocracker unit, the cost code would be 01-02-C-2-003-1 (Onsite-Hydrocracker-Construction-Concrete-Pour-Labor). The code of accounts formally refers to the full coding structure (including project identifier, WBS, and RBS elements), but the term is often used in regards to the RBS elements only. The coding structure must reflect the manner in which the project will be executed and the way in which costs can reasonably be expected to be collected. The coding structure should also reflect the way in which your particular organization executes projects. Of importance is that the estimate, which predicts project execution, should be organized and structured to match the project code of accounts.

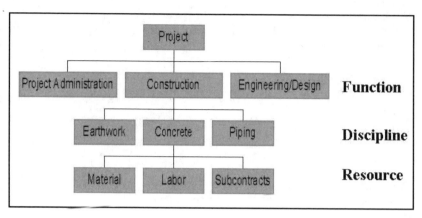

Figure 9.9—Sample RBS

The coding structure adopted by an organization should be documented in detail. Typically a code book is published and made available to all project personnel. The code book should contain a code by code listing that documents a description of not only what should be included under a specific code, but also what is excluded (for those items that could be easily misunderstood).

ESTIMATE/COST/SCHEDULE INTEGRATION

The integration of the project cost estimate with the project schedule and cost control system is crucial for effective project management and control. Accomplishing this goal can be difficult at best; yet the estimate, schedule, and cost system must share information with each other for each to be as accurate as possible. The schedule will provide dates that are essential to calculating escalation, cash flow, and commitment forecasts. The estimate provides labor hours and craft breakdowns essential to determining schedule activity durations and resource loading. The estimate also provides cost and quantities to the cost control system. The cost reporting system's record of labor and material expenditures needs to be correlated with schedule progress and remaining durations for schedule activities correlated to the forecasts-to-complete in the cost system.

The relationship between the cost estimate and schedule is not always straightforward. The natural breakdowns (or hierarchy) of cost and schedule structures are different. The cost system is organized to estimate, monitor and control dollars. The schedule system is organized to plan, monitor and control time. The control and monitoring of both variables are not necessarily compatible, and most often, the same people do not perform both tasks. The goal, then, is to align estimate cost data and schedule data at a level to support integration.

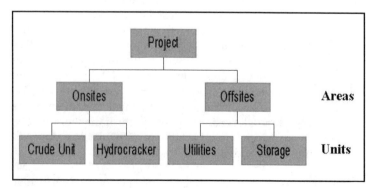

Figure 9.8—Sample WBS

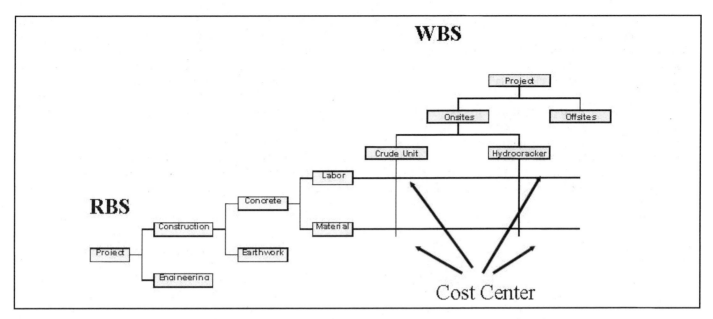

Figure 9.10—Sample Project Breakdown Structure

Table 9.11—Sample Project Coding Structure

AREA	UNIT	FUNCTION	DISCIPLINE	DETAIL	RESOURCE
01 - Onsites	01 - Crude Unit	A - Project Administration	1 - Earthwork	001 - Formwork	1 - Labor
	02 - Hydrocracker	B - Enginering/Design	2 - Concrete	002 - Rebar	2 - Material
	03 - Vacuum Unit	C - Construction	3 - Structural Steel	003 - Pour	3 - Subcontract
		...	4 - Piping	004 - Embeds	
02 - Offsites	01 - Utilities		5 - Equipment	005 - Finish	
	02 - Storage		...		
	03 - Pipeway				

One approach is to breakdown the estimate to the level of schedule activities. This can result in a tremendous amount of detail in the cost estimate and compromise efficient cost and schedule control. Some of the problems resulting from the one-to-one approach are the following:

- Collecting costs by detailed schedule activities is generally not feasible.
- Schedule activities are subject to much more change within the project than traditional cost codes.
- Tracking bulk material costs by activity is cumbersome and requires high administrative costs.
- Costs are often not incurred at the same time as construction activities.

The goal must be to determine an appropriate level of detail to correlate cost and schedule. It is important not to let either the estimate or the schedule drive the other down to an inappropriate level of detail. It is also important not to integrate at too high of a summary level.

Integrating at a sufficient level of detail involves keeping the estimate and schedule structures identical to a certain level of WBS. Below this level, additional cost accounts and schedule activities are defined separately as required by each. The desire is to interface at a level where meaningful relationships exist.

Figure 9.11 illustrates a typical cost or estimate structure for a process plant, while Figure 9.12 illustrates a sample schedule structure for the same project. At some point, the cost and schedule WBS structures will diverge to meet each structure's particular control needs.

The basic methodology for integrating the cost estimate and schedule, therefore, is to let the estimator and scheduler communicate on the high-level WBS, and determine the levels at which cost items and schedule activities can be correlated. Then each further defines the lower level of detail required for particular needs. Meaningful information can then be transmitted at the appropriate level of detail between the two.

It should be acknowledged that one-to-one relationships between estimate cost items and schedule activities are not possible. Early and continuous communication between the estimator and scheduler can determine the best level at which to maintain compatibility and exchange information. The estimator can promote integration by assigning as many

identification fields to the estimate line items as possible (i.e., building location, room number, system number, piping line number, foundation number, etc.). This will greatly assist in transferring estimate cost data and resource needs to the schedule. Computerized estimating and scheduling systems are making great strides in providing two-way communication between systems.

The cost estimate can be very sensitive to, and is usually prepared in correlation with, a specific schedule. If the schedule is undefined or subject to change, the estimate is compromised and should reflect the appropriate cost risk. Changes

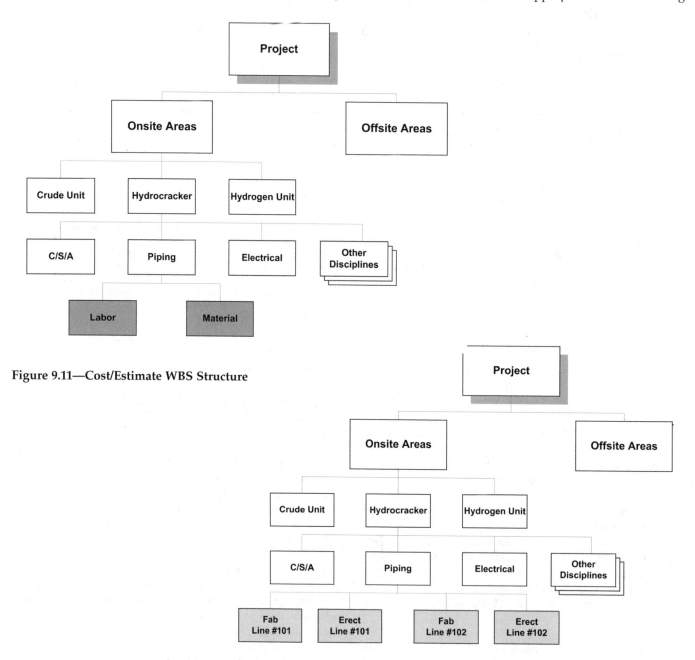

Figure 9.11—Cost/Estimate WBS Structure

Figure 9.12—Schedule WBS Structure

to the project plan that affect either schedule duration or completion dates may significantly affect project cost. The basis estimating algorithm is as follows:

$$\text{Total \$} = (\text{Qty} \times \text{unit material \$}) +$$
$$(\text{Qty} \times \text{unit labor hours} \times \text{wage rate})$$

The unit material $, unit labor hours, and wage rate can all be dependent on the assumed schedule and plan. Unit material costs are schedule dependent for impacts of inflation and seasonal variations. Unit labor hours are schedule dependent for seasonal labor availability, climate, and schedule impacts due to execution plan changes (affecting productivity). Wage rates are also sensitive for impacts of inflation, seasonal variation, and execution plan changes (affecting overtime and/or shift premiums).

Many costs in a project are very dependent on the duration. project management and related costs are often estimated (and incurred) on a "level of effort" basis. If the project duration is extended, cost for these activities is directly affected. Construction indirect costs, such as construction management, field office, construction equipment rental, security office, and site maintenance, etc., are also affected in a similar way.

Some costs are dependent on when they occur in the calendar year. Labor productivity can be adversely affected by weather (both snow and rain in the winter, or hot weather in summer). Construction indirects, such as weather protection or other construction support costs, can also be similarly affected.

Project costs can also be affected by schedule impact of execution plan changes. Changes to the execution plan to shorten the project duration may cause out-of-sequence construction, overtime, shift premiums, congestion, and inefficient labor usage, etc., adversely impacting costs. A delay in equipment delivery may extend the project schedule increasing duration dependent costs. On the other hand, this may also result in increased efficiencies if labor resources can be allocated more efficiently, perhaps resulting in less overtime and shift premiums.

It is thus important to evaluate the effects of schedule and duration when preparing the estimate. Besides the obvious of accounting for the escalation costs to incorporate into the estimate, schedule impacts may directly affect labor productivity as well as labor and material pricing. It is also essential to plan early for estimate/schedule integration so that estimate results can be shared with the schedule as required to assist in resource loading, and to aid in earned value analysis and progress reporting.

ESTIMATE REVIEW

Because an estimate is of critical importance to a project's success, it makes sense that the estimate should undergo a rigorous review process. The estimate should be evaluated not only for its quality or accuracy, but also to ensure that it contains all the required information and is presented in a way that is understandable to all project team members and client personnel. A structured (if not formal) estimate review process should be a standard practice for all estimating departments.

The following sequence of steps will discuss a formal review process for an internally prepared appropriation grade estimate (an estimate submitted for capital budget authorization). The level of detail and diligence used during the estimate review cycle will vary both with the strategic importance, total value, and purpose of the particular estimate. These steps can be easily adapted on a fit-for-use basis. In this discussion, we are focused on reviewing and validating an estimate—we are not discussing bidding strategies which can involve many other factors and decisions.

Estimate Review Cycles
The principle purpose of an estimate review process is to present information about both the estimate and the project in a way that allows the reviewer to evaluate that the estimate is of sufficient quality to meet its intended purpose. The estimate review process usually comprises a series of estimate reviews, beginning with internal estimating department reviews, engineering reviews, project team reviews, and continuing with reviews by various levels of management, depending on the importance of the project.

Estimating Team/Estimating Department Review
The first review of the estimate should, of course, be held by the estimating team that prepared the project estimate. This is essentially a screening review to ensure that the math is correct (extensions of pricing are correct, summaries add up properly, etc.), that the estimate is documented correctly (comprehensive basis of estimate document is prepared), and that it adheres to estimating department guidelines. Typically, this review is held by the lead estimator with the members of his estimating team. On very large projects or those of significant importance, this review may be held by the estimating department manager or supervisor.

Check the Math
The first item to review is to ensure that all of the math used in the estimate is correct. With today's computerized estimating systems, this is much less of a concern than twenty years ago when estimates were primarily prepared by hand using simple calculators; however math errors can still occur. This can be a major concern when using an electronic spreadsheets, such as Excel, for preparing the estimate (as opposed to a commercial computerized estimating system).

Surprisingly, it is very easy to make a formula error in a spreadsheet, such as inserting a row or column which does not get included in a subtotal. All spreadsheet formulas, subtotals and totals should be examined carefully for correctness. From a client's point of view, nothing will help to lose credibility in the entire estimate faster than a finding a math error that went undetected.

Basis of Estimate

The comprehensive basis of estimate (BOE) document should be reviewed carefully to ensure that it is both correct and complete. The BOE is an extremely important document. The dollar amount indicated on an estimate is meaningless without knowing the parameters, or what is included and not included in the estimate. The BOE serves to clearly define the design basis, planning basis, cost basis, and risk basis of the estimate.

- **Design Basis**: The overall scope of the project should be summarized, with additional detail provided for each area/unit/work package of the project. Specific inclusions and, even more importantly, specific exclusions of items or facilities should be documented. All assumptions regarding project scope should be documented. If available, equipment lists should be attached or referenced, and a listing of all drawings, sketches, and specifications used in the preparation of the estimate should be documented, including drawing revision date and number.
- **Planning Basis**: This portion of the BOE should document information from the integrated project plan that affects the estimate. It should include specific information about any contracting strategies for engineering, design, procurement, fabrication, and construction. It should include information about resourcing and project execution plans such as the length of the workweek, use of overtime, and number of shifts, etc. It should include information about the project schedule and key milestone dates affecting the estimate.
- **Cost Basis**: The source of all pricing used in the estimate should be documented in this section of the BOE. This would include the source of all bulk material pricing, the pricing of major equipment (referencing quotes or purchase orders if used), and all labor rates including office, engineering, fabrication, and construction. The source of all labor workhours should be documented, along with any assumptions regarding labor productivities. All allowances included in the estimate should also be clearly identified. It is also important to document the time basis of the estimate (i.e., what point in time is assumed), and the basis for cost escalation included in the estimate.
- **Risk Basis**: Since, by definition, every estimate is a prediction of probable costs, it is clear that every estimate involves uncertainty and risk. Contingency is typically included in an estimate to cover the costs associated with this uncertainty. This section of the BOE should document how the contingency was determined, and identify key areas of risk and opportunity in the cost estimate.

It is important to ensure that the BOE is clear and easily understood, and to verify that all information and factors documented in the BOE have been consistently applied throughout the estimate (i.e., wage rates, labor productivities, material pricing, subcontract pricing, etc.). Again, the estimate can lose credibility if different pricing or labor rates have been used for the same item within the estimate detail.

Estimating Department Guidelines

A careful review should be done to verify that the cost estimate follows standard estimating guidelines for the department. This would include a review to verify that standard estimating procedures were followed regarding estimate format, cost coding, presentation and documentation. This would include items such as the following:

- Verify that the proper estimating methods, techniques, and procedures were used that match the stage of project completeness. In other words, different estimating techniques will be utilized depending on the type and completeness of the engineering documents and deliverables available to create the estimate.
- Confirm that the estimate summary and details are organized and presented in the proper format (i.e., following the project WBS and code of accounts); and that the format is consistent with the intended purpose of the estimate (i.e., an estimate serving as a basis for cost control contains sufficient detail).
- Ensure that all estimate backup information is organized properly. Can all values on the summary page of the estimate be traced to the estimate detail pages, and can all information on the estimate detail pages be traced to the estimate backup or source documents?
- Verify that all allowances and factors are appropriate for the type of estimate being prepared and are consistent with comparable projects and estimates.

This level of estimate review helps to ensure that all estimates prepared by the department are utilizing established guidelines and are presented in a consistent manner from project to project.

ENGINEERING/DESIGN REVIEW

The next level of estimate review should be held with the engineering team and should evaluate the estimate in terms of accurately representing the project scope. The core members of the engineering team are key participants in this review, along with the lead estimator and estimating team.

Completeness of Engineering Deliverables

One of the first items to review is the listing of all drawings, sketches, specifications, and other engineering deliverables used in preparing the estimate to ensure that it is complete (see design basis above). The lead engineers need to cross-reference this listing against their own engineering drawing and deliverables lists to make sure that all relevant information was passed on to the estimating team. The revision numbers of drawings should be checked to ensure that they match the intended revision for the estimate. If late changes to the engineering drawings have occurred, and are intended to be incorporated into the estimate, this needs to be checked to ensure that all late changes have been included.

Equipment List

For those projects involving major equipment, the equipment list and equipment pricing should be double-checked by the engineering team for completeness and accuracy. Equipment is often one of the key drivers of cost and scope, and needs to be checked carefully for completeness and accuracy.

Design Basis of Estimate

The engineers should review the BOE and summary of project scope carefully to verify and correlate their understanding of the project scope with that expressed in the estimate. All exclusions expressed in the BOE should be agreed to, and all allowances and assumptions verified. If an estimator has had any questions about interpretation of the drawings or engineering deliverables, now is the time to discuss the estimator's interpretation with the engineers and to make sure that the project scope is accurately reflected in the estimate. All drawings used for the estimate should be available during this review. Sometimes it can help to have the estimator explain how each drawing was used in the preparation of the estimate (i.e., was a hard takeoff performed from isometric drawings; was a quantity developed from a P&ID and plot plan, etc.).

Engineering/Design Costs

The engineering team should also review the assumptions and costs associated with the engineering and design portion of the estimate. The engineering team needs to feel comfortable that the amount of money included in the estimate for engineering, design, and support is adequate for the level of effort expected to be expended on the project.

Risk Basis of Estimate

Lastly, the engineering team should review the risk basis of the estimate, and be in position to agree with the analysis of cost risk associated with the estimate. The level of risk associated with scope definition, and with engineering/design costs should be of particular interest to the engineering team, and concurrence sought.

As mentioned, the goal of this portion of the estimate review is to make sure that the scope of the project as understood by engineering is reflected in the estimate. At the end of the engineering review, the estimate should have the full support of the engineering team during subsequent reviews.

PROJECT MANAGER/PROJECT TEAM REVIEW

Once the estimate has been reviewed closely by the estimating and engineering teams, it is ready for review by the Project Manager and the rest of the project team. The objective now is to gain the entire project team's support of the estimate, and especially that of the project manager. This is also the first point where the estimate should be able to pass overall validation tests, in addition to a quality review.

Estimate Documentation

The first part of this review should be the examination of the estimate documentation by the project team and project manager. This includes the BOE, as well as the estimate summary and estimate detail pages. The purpose is to ensure that the estimate is presented in an understandable manner. If standard estimating guidelines have been followed (as discussed above), all estimates should be presented in a consistent, and understandable style. It is very important that the project manager fully understand how the estimate is prepared because he/she often becomes the person responsible for presenting (and defending) the estimate to upper management, and later to the eventual customer. The entire project team should also understand the entire estimate package, format and contents.

Cost Review

Engineering should have already reviewed the engineering, design, and associated support costs. Now is the time for the other key members of the project team (project manager, project controls, procurement, construction manager, commissioning manager, etc.) to examine their respective costs, which are included in the estimate, and to obtain agreement that they are correct. Although primarily the responsibility of the estimating team, the scope related costs should also be reviewed by the rest of the project team to gain consensus. In particular, the following areas should be discussed:

- Verify that the latest project schedule agrees with the estimate (particularly as it relates to escalation).
- Examine the project administration and other home office-related costs for reasonableness (engineering/design costs should have already been reviewed).
- Conduct a final constructability review to ensure that the methods of installation and construction assumed in the estimate are reasonable and cost-effective.
- Review the construction indirect costs (i.e., field staff, temporary facilities, temporary services, construction equipment and services, construction tools and consumables, etc.) to make sure they are reasonable.
- Ensure that all required start-up and commissioning materials are included (if necessary). This is often an area of costs which is overlooked.

For international projects, there may be many more items of cost that should be carefully reviewed. These may include such items as international labor adjustments for productivities and wage rates, adjustments for workweek variations, material cost adjustments for both local and globally sourced materials, international freight costs, international duties and taxes, labor camp costs, premiums for expatriate costs, etc.

Estimate Validation

In most organizations, the project manager is ultimately held responsible for the execution of the project. Therefore, the project manager has a vested interest in performing "sanity checks" or otherwise validating the estimate as reasonable. Most experienced project managers will have various rules-of-thumb that they will want to use to verify against the estimate. Regardless, the estimate should include an estimate review "metrics" report which summarizes and compares several key benchmark ratios and factors versus historical (and sometimes estimated) values from similar projects.

The goal is to ensure that key metrics from the estimate are in line with the same metrics from similar projects. If there is a large discrepancy, it must be explainable by the particular circumstances of the estimated project versus the similar completed projects. Such comparison metrics may includes values such as percent of administration (home office) costs, percent of engineering/design costs, equipment to total field cost ratios, equipment to totals project cost ratios, cost per piece of equipment, workhours per piece of equipment, cost to plant capacity ratios ($/BBL, $/SM), etc. Sometimes the metrics will be generated down to the discipline level where you may look at ratios, such as cost per diameter inch of piping, cost per cubic meter of concrete, cost per ton of steel, etc. In addition to examining key benchmark metrics and ratios, another form of estimate validation may involve preparing a quick check estimate using order-of-magnitude estimating methods. Again, any large discrepancies between the estimates should be explainable by the peculiarities of the project.

Estimate validation is a very important activity during the project review cycle, and the proper tools need to be in place to allow this to occur. Benchmarking key estimate ratios and metrics depends upon having a project history database in place to collect, analyze, and present the required information. Similarly, the capability to provide quick-check estimates depends on having the correct strategic and conceptual estimating information and tools ready for use.

Risk Basis of Estimate

The project manager and project team should again review the risk basis of the estimate and agree with the analysis of cost risk associated with the project. The project manager, in particular, should agree with the risk assessment and contingency amounts, and be able to defend it in subsequent review to upper or corporate management.

Reconciliation to Past Estimates

Lastly, the project manager will usually be interested in reconciliation of the current estimate to the preceding estimate (or estimates). This is an important, but often overlooked, aspect to the overall estimate review process. The current estimate can gain credibility by comparing it with earlier estimates and clearly explaining the differences and reasons for the differences. The reconciliation can usually be presented at a high level without excessive detail, but the backup should be available in case it is required during the review.

Management Reviews

The last series of reviews is usually held by various levels of corporate management. The number of upper management reviews and the level of management they are presented to typically varies with the strategic importance and/or total estimated cost of the particular project. These reviews are typically held at a very high level of analysis and usually do not involve the details of the estimate. Upper management reviews often focus on substantiating the overall adequacy of the estimate in regards to its intended use. In other words, can management be assured that the level of detail available for the estimate, the estimating methods employed, and the skills of the estimating and project teams support their decision-making process on whether to proceed?

As with the project manager review, estimate validation is a key element of the upper management reviews. It is important to be able to explain and demonstrate that metrics for the current estimate are in line with data from other similar projects—i.e., that the estimate is reasonable. It is also important to show where the metrics may be substantially different from other projects, and provide explanations for the differences.

Management will also be interested in the cost-risk assessment. It is important to clearly and concisely explain how the contingency amount was developed and what the levels of risk are. It is then up to management to accept the level of risk indicated or change the amount of contingency and accept more or less risk for the project. When reviewing the risk analysis, it is always important to discuss the areas of high risk, and what is being done to mitigate those risks.

Up until the management reviews, the estimate review will have typically concentrated on the project as defined by the project scope documents. If the project was built according to the defined project scope alternative, what will it cost? Usually, the recommended alternative for project scope has long since been determined and agreed to by the project team, and the engineering deliverables created for preparing the estimate have been focused on a single design alternative. However, many times management will start asking questions concerning other alternative scopes or designs. One of the certainties is that management will always think the project cost is too high and will now be probing to determine if there are lesser cost options. Therefore, it is important to have available for the management reviews any earlier design/cost alternatives, and the decision tree leading to the selected design.

The effectiveness of an estimate review relies on the information presented and the manner in which it is presented. The above discussion has concentrated on how to structure a sequence of estimate reviews for internally prepared estimates to ensure that estimates are well-documented, consistent, reliable, and appropriate for their intended use. After this review cycle, the level of estimate accuracy should be apparent, reflective of the scope information available for preparing the estimate, and capable of supporting the required decision-making process for the project. Next, we will discuss techniques for reviewing estimates prepared by others.

REVIEWING ESTIMATES PREPARED BY OTHERS

The foregoing discussion has focused on structuring an estimate review process for the estimates that we internally prepare to ensure that the estimate is of a high quality and supports the decision making process of our management. Often, we may also find ourselves in a position to review (and/or approve) estimates prepared by others and that may or may not have gone through a rigorous internal review cycle as described above. When reviewing estimates by others, we always want to keep in mind the basic fundamentals previously described. Complicating the matter, however, is the problem that many times the amount of time allowed for a complete estimate review is very short. Thus the review of an estimate prepared by others is usually accomplished by a critical assessment of the estimate and its documentation, and a series of questions to assist in evaluating the level of diligence used in preparing the estimate. The following discussion centers on guidelines that we can use to efficiently review estimates prepared by others.

Basis of Estimate
The first thing to assess is the BOE. Is it well-organized and complete? Does it provide the required information regarding the design basis, planning basis, cost basis, and risk basis of the estimate? Does the design basis clearly document the scope of the project, and have all engineering deliverables used in developing the estimate been identified? Have all scope assumptions been acknowledged? Is the planning basis (schedule, resource plan, construction plan, etc.) reasonable? Is the basis of cost (material prices, labor rates, labor productivities) reasonable, in line with expectations, and consistently applied throughout the estimate? Has the risk basis been clearly defined, and is it reasonable for the level of information available to prepare the estimate?

Estimating Personnel Used
Next, you will want to know who prepared the estimate, and what their level of estimating experience is. Do they have established estimating procedures and guidelines? Was the estimate checked and reviewed before publication?

Estimating Methodology and Procedures
What estimating methods, techniques and procedures were used in preparing the estimate? Are they appropriate for the level of information available and project type? Were different estimating methods used for different parts of the estimate? Is the level of detail in the estimate sufficient for the purpose of the estimate? Were parts of the project difficult to estimate, and why? Was sufficient time available to prepare the estimate? What adjustments were made to the estimate for location, complexity, etc., and are they reasonable? Was the estimate prepared utilizing a code of account structure?

Estimate Documentation
Is the estimate documented clearly? Are the estimate summary and detail pages well-organized and presented at an appropriate level of detail? Is every cost appearing on the estimate summary traceable to the estimate detail and other estimate backup?

Estimate Validation
Hopefully, the estimate for review will include a metrics report showing key estimating metrics and benchmark ratios for the estimate and similar past projects. You should review this report and question any significant differences. You should also have your own set of metrics and statistics from your own project history to compare against.

At this point, you may also develop your own quick-check estimate (using conceptual estimating techniques) for comparison purposes. This is always a good technique to see if the estimate being reviewed is reasonable. If there is a significant difference, then question the estimator and listen to their explanations and opinions for the deltas. Significant differences between the check estimate and the estimate being reviewed may indicate the need for taking a more thorough examination of the estimate detail.

Estimate Detail
If the preceding inquiry (or should we say interrogation) has gone well, and you are confident that the estimate appears to have been prepared in a professional manner, you are ready to delve into some of the estimate details to verify estimate quality. The goal is to check that selected areas of the estimate can withstand further scrutiny. The key here is to not get too deep into the details and lose sight of the forest for the trees. An important point to remember here is the "80/20 rule." This principle generalizes that 80 percent of the cost will come from 20 percent of the estimate line items. For any

particular estimate, the significant cost drivers may vary. Sometimes, the main cost driver may be a particular process unit of the project; other times it may be the type of process equipment or machinery throughout the project; and still other times it may be the overall bulk material quantities or labor hours. You should examine the estimate summary and detail pages closely to ascertain which aspects of the estimate you may want to examine in closer detail. Basically, you should examine in detail those items of the estimate that will have the most significant cost impact if estimated incorrectly.

One review technique that is often employed is to thoroughly examine and review the estimating steps that were used for a particular part of the estimate. Select an area of the estimate, and ask how the quantities were derived. Don't just take their word for it, however. Ask the estimators to show you the drawings from which the quantities were generated. Perform a quick takeoff to see if the quantities can be verified. Ask what the basis was for the unit material price and labor workhours. Have these been consistent throughout the estimate? What adjustments were made and why? If the answers to your questions are evasive, it may call into question the credibility of the entire estimate, and a more thorough review of the complete estimate may be necessary. If your questions are answered confidently, and the answers can be verified against the engineering deliverables and scope information, then you may decide to check the rest of the estimate details in a more cursory fashion.

Typically in this situation, once you have shown the wherewithal to compel the estimator to back up any claims or explanations, then he discovers he can't just "pull the wool over your eyes." From that point forward, you will usually find that you are getting honest answers to your questions.

The goal of an estimate is to predict the probable cost of a project. The goal of an estimate review is to determine that a high quality and sufficiently accurate estimate has been prepared. The review should ensure that the proper estimating methods, procedures, techniques, data, and guidelines have been employed in the preparation of the estimate. The use of a structured estimate review cycle and estimating review techniques will help to ensure that quality estimates are consistently prepared which effectively support the decision-making process by management.

PRESENTING THE ESTIMATE

The method in which you present an estimate to your customer (internal company management or external client) is extremely important. An estimate should never be presented as just a list of numbers, or estimating calculations. A number (or even a range of numbers) is meaningless without the supporting information that describes what the number represents, and, sometimes even more importantly, what it doesn't represent. In general, a complete estimate report will include the following:

- basis of estimate (BOE),
- estimate summaries,
- estimate detail,
- estimate benchmarking report,
- estimate reconciliation report, and
- estimate backup.

We have previously talked about the BOE in the prior discussion on estimate reviews. This is a critically important document in describing the scope that is represented by the estimated cost and in conveying all the assumptions that have been embedded into the estimate. A well-written BOE document can go a long ways towards providing confidence in the estimate itself.

Typically, various estimate summaries may be prepared according to the project WBS. For example, one estimate summary may be prepared by project area, and then broken down by process system, while another summary may be prepared by process system and then broken into project areas within each process system. The various parties interested in the estimate will all have different ways in which they want to see the estimate summarized, depending on the classification and end-use of the estimate being prepared. It is very important that every value appearing on an estimate summary be easily tracked back to the estimate detail.

The Estimate Detail typically shows all of the individual cost estimating relationships (CERs) used in preparing the estimate. For a conceptual estimate, it may be a page or less of calculations; however, for a large detailed estimate it may include hundreds of pages of individual line items. This report is also prepared according to the project WBS, and may be provided in a variety of different sort options.

An estimate benchmarking report will often be included. It should show benchmark information and metrics with other similar projects. For example, for a building estimate, this report may show the cost per square meter of building area ($/m^2) compared to recent similar projects. The key benchmark metrics and ratios presented may include the following items:

- project administration costs as percent of total project cost,
- engineering costs as percent of total project cost,
- ratio of equipment cost to total project cost,
- construction labor as percent of total field cost,
- total field costs as percent of total project cost,
- project cost per unit of capacity, and
- average composite crew rate by trade.

An estimate reconciliation report should also be prepared that reconciles the current estimate with any previous estimates prepared for the same project. This report should identify the cost differences dues to changes in scope, changes in pricing, changes in risk, etc.

Lastly, all estimate backup should be compiled and available. This information may not need to be presented to the estimate customer, but should be available if questions arise. This will include all notes, documentation, drawings, engineering deliverables, and vendor quotes, etc., that were used in preparation of the estimate.

ESTIMATING RESOURCES

Reliable estimate preparation depends on information. Besides the engineering and design information needed to quantify the scope of the project, other information is also required, such as

- conceptual estimating factors;
- material cost and pricing information;
- labor workhour charts and information;
- labor productivity information;
- labor wage rates, composite crew mixes, etc.; and
- other estimating factors and information.

Successful estimators will rely on a myriad of resources to obtain this information. Estimating guideline and procedure manuals will be used to promote standard estimating methods and procedures. In-house cost history manuals will provide historical cost data for completed projects. Special cost studies may have been developed to serve as resources for particular estimating applications, such as special scaffolding studies, concrete placement studies, labor productivity studies, etc. Engineering and design manuals and specifications will be used to identify the specific materials of construction, and all related labor operations required to complete the scope of work.

Every completed project should be documented by a final job report covering everything about a project from design considerations to construction execution strategy to cost summaries. Selected data from the final job reports should be collected and stored in a computerized database and made available to all estimators. Estimators continually rely on past project information and cost data in the preparation of new estimates.

Collections of labor charts will typically provide standard labor workhour units by task. These are generally normalized for location and time and serve as a base for estimate preparation, and then are adjusted for specific project requirements. They will often be supplemented by commercial estimating database publications. In-house and commercial material cost databases and publications will also be needed. Current wage rate information should be maintained, including union agreements, for all locations the estimator may be involved with. A library of vendor catalogs

should also be maintained. Many of these are now available on the Internet. These may provide technical information, pricing information, and other data required by an estimator. There are hundreds of sources published every year that contain useful information for an estimator. This includes AACE publications: (*Recommended Standards and Practices*, *Professional Practice Guides*, *Cost Engineering Magazine*, etc.), as well as publications from other professional organizations and commercial sources.

Estimating software is another important resource. Estimating software can enhance the accuracy and consistency of estimates, while reducing the time required to prepare estimates. The software may be commercial estimating software or be developed in-house. When using the cost databases supplied with commercial estimating software, it is always important to calibrate the data to your specific needs and estimating situations. Estimating software should also be regarded as simply a tool to facilitate the preparation of estimates by estimators. Estimating software can't convert a non-estimator into an estimator.

All of the resources described above serve to help the most important resource to successful estimating—well trained and experienced estimators. Estimating is a profession requiring an ongoing commitment to training and development.

CONCLUSION

As potential projects are considered as investment opportunities, management will require various estimates to support key decision points. At each of these points, the level of engineering and technical information available to prepare the estimate will change. Accordingly, the techniques and methods to prepare the estimates will also vary. The basic estimating techniques are well established, and this chapter has been intended to review the estimating process and relevant estimating methodologies for the various types of estimates.

The determination of using a conceptual approach versus a detailed approach will depend on many factors: the end use of the estimate, the amount of time and money available to prepare the estimate, the estimating tools available, and the previous historical information available. A conceptual estimating approach (capacity factored, equipment factored, parametric) requires a significant effort in data-gathering and methods development before estimate preparation ever begins. In contrast, a detailed estimating approach requires a large effort during the actual preparation of the estimate.

With either approach, the challenge for the estimator is to evaluate the unique combination of required material and labor resources in order to prepare a cost estimate for a project to be completed in the future. The use of structured estimating techniques and tools, high-quality engineering deliverables, and good historical data and pricing information, combined with estimating skill and experience, will assure that the best possible estimate is prepared. The desired end result is to prepare estimates that are well-documented, consistent, reliable, appropriate, accurate, and that support the decision-making process for the project.

Estimating is obviously a vital component to project success. Estimates are used not only to establish project budgets, but also to provide accurate information to support scheduling, cost monitoring, and progress measurement of a project during execution. Estimating is, thus, but one component to total cost management—the integration of cost engineering and cost management principles used in managing the total life cycle cost investment in strategic assets.

REFERENCES

1. AACE International. *Recommended Practice for Cost Estimate Classification*. 17-R-97. Morgantown, West Virginia.

2. AACE International. *Recommended Practice for Cost Estimate Classification—As Applied in Engineering, Procurement, and Construction for the Process Industries* 18-R-97. Morgantown, West Virginia.

3. Black, Dr. J. H. 1984. "Application of Parametric Estimating to Cost Engineering." *AACE Transactions.* Morgantown, West Virginia: AACE International.

4. Chilton, C. H. 1950. "Six-Tenths Factor Applies to Complete Plant Costs," *Chemical Engineering*. April.

5. Dysert, L. R. 1999. "Developing a Parametric Model for Estimating Process Control Costs." *AACE Transactions,* Morgantown, West Virginia: AACE International.

6. Dysert, L. R. and Elliott, B. G. 2000. "The Estimate Review and Validation Process." AACE Transactions, AACE International, 2000

7. Dysert, L. R. and Elliott, B. G. 1999. "The Organization of an Estimating Department." *AACE Transactions.* Morgantown, West Virginia: AACE International.

8. Guthrie, K. M. 1969. "Data and Techniques for Preliminary Capital Cost Estimating."*Chemical Engineering*. March.

9. Guthrie, K. M. 1970. "Capital and Operating Costs for 54 Chemical Processes." *Chemical Engineering*. June.

10. Hand, W. E. 1964. "Estimating Capital Costs from Process Flow Sheets." *Cost Engineer's Notebook.* Morgantown, West Virginia: AACE International. January.

11. Lang, H. J. 1947. "Cost Relationships in Preliminary Cost Estimation." *Chemical Engineering*. October.

12. Lang, H. J. 1948. "Simplified Approach to Preliminary Cost Estimates." *Chemical Engineering*. June.

13. Miller, C. A. 1965. "New Cost Factors Give Quick Accurate Estimates." *Chemical Engineering*. September.

14. Miller, C. A. 1978. "Capital Cost Estimating – A Science Rather than an Art." *Cost Engineer's Notebook.* Morgantown, West Virginia: AACE International.

15. NASA. *Parametric Cost Estimating Handbook.*

16. Nishimura, M. 1995. Composite-Factored Engineering. *AACE Transactions.* Morgantown, West Virginia: AACE International.

17. Querns, Wesley R. 1989. "What is Contingency, Anyways?" *AACE Transactions.* Morgantown, West Virginia: AACE International.

18. Rodl, R. H., P. Prinzing, and D. Aichert. 1985. Cost Estimating for Chemical Plants. *AACE Transactions.* Morgantown, West Virginia: AACE International.

19. Rose, A. 1982. "An Organized Approach to Parametric Estimating." *Transactions of the Seventh International Cost Engineering Congress.*

20. Williams, R., Jr. 1947. "Six-Tenths Factor Aids in Approximating Costs." *Chemical Engineering*. December.

21. Woodward, Charles P., and Mark T. Chen. 2002. "Cost Estimating Basics." *Skills and Knowledge of a Cost Engineer.* 4th Edition. Morgantown, West Virginia: AACE International.

22. Woodward, Charles P., and Mark T. Chen. 2002. "Order-of-Magnitude Estimating." *Skills and Knowledge of Cost Engineering.* 4th Edition. Morgantown, West Virginia: AACE International.

23. Woodward, Charles P., and Mark T. Chen. 2002. "Definitive Estimating." *Skills and Knowledge of Cost Engineering.* 4th Edition. Morgantown, West Virginia: AACE International.

Chapter 10

Process Product Manufacturing[1]

Dr. Kenneth K. Humphreys, PE CCE

INTRODUCTION

To perform an operating or manufacturing cost estimate properly, and to determine the potential profitability of a process, all costs must be considered in certain specific categories. The distinction between the various categories is quite important, as they are treated differently for purposes of calculating taxes and profitability.

LEARNING OBJECTIVES

After completing this chapter, the reader should be able to

- understand how to determine the operating and manufacturing costs of a continuous process on a conceptual basis,
- distinguish between direct and indirect costs in manufacturing as compared to construction,
- relate operating costs at full production to reduced costs at less than full plant capacity, and
- understand depreciation rules and their relationship to operating and manufacturing costs.

TYPES OF OPERATING COST ESTIMATES AND ESTIMATING FORMS

As is true for a capital cost estimate, the purpose of an operating cost estimate is the controlling factor in determining the type of estimate to be performed. Preliminary or order-of-magnitude estimates are often used to screen projects and to eliminate uneconomical alternatives. More detailed estimates are then applied when the screening process has reduced the choice to a relatively few alternatives.

In performing the operating cost estimate, particularly on a

preliminary basis, good judgment is necessary to avoid excessive attention to minor items, which, even if severely over- or underestimated, will not have a significant effect on the overall estimate.

In performing the operating cost estimate, it is also necessary to calculate costs at reduced production rates as well as at design capacity. Operating costs are decidedly nonlinear with respect to production rate.

This fact and the fact that virtually no plant or process operates all of the time at full design production rate make it imperative that reduced production rates be considered. This subject is discussed in considerable detail later in this chapter.

Finally, when estimating the effect of changes or additions to an existing process, the cost analysis should be performed on an incremental basis to evaluate the effect of the change as well as on an overall basis to determine if the entire project is worthy of being continued even without the change. Frequently a process change will not be economical, but the total project will be attractive. In other cases, the incremental costs of a change will appear to be quite profitable, but this profit will not be enough to offset losses entailed in the existing portion of the plant. Thus both types of analyses must be made.

Operating cost estimates can be performed on a daily, unit-of-production, or annual basis. Of these, the annual basis is preferred for the following reasons:

- It "damps out" seasonal variations.
- It considers equipment operating time.
- It is readily adapted to less-than-full capacity operation.
- It readily includes the effect of periodic large costs (scheduled maintenance, vacation shutdowns, catalyst changes, etc).
- It is directly usable in profitability analysis.
- It is readily convertible to the other bases, daily cost and unit-of-production, yielding mean annual figures rather than a potentially high or low figure for an arbitrarily

[1] Excerpted by permission from Humphreys, K. K., and P. Wellman. 1996. *Basic Cost Engineering*. 3rd ed. New York: Marcel Dekker, Inc.

Date ____
By ____

Location:_____

Product(s): _____
Process: _____

Capital Investment:

Total _____
Less working capital _____

Nelson Index _____ CE Index_____
M&S Index _____ Annual

Operating

Less salvage value _____
Depreciable investment _____

ENR Index _____ Days _____
Annual production: _____

	Raw Materials	Annual quantity	Unit cost	$/year	$/ ____
(1)	_____	_____	_____	_____	_____
(2)	_____	_____	_____	_____	_____
(3)	_____	_____	_____	_____	_____
(4)	_____	_____	_____	_____	_____
(5)		Gross raw material cost (sum of lines 1 to 4):		_____	_____

Misc. credits and debits

(6)	_____	_____	_____	_____	_____
(7)	_____	_____	_____	_____	_____
(8)	_____	_____	_____	_____	_____
(9)		Total debit (credit) (sum of lines 6 to 8):		_____	_____
(10)		Net raw material cost (lines 5 + line 9):		_____	_____

	Direct expense	Unit	Quantity	Unit cost	$/year	$/
(11)	Steam	M lb	_____	_____	_____	_____
(12)	Water ( )	M gal	_____	_____	_____	_____
(13)	Water ( )	M gal	_____	_____	_____	_____
(14)	Electricity	kW-hr	_____	_____	_____	_____
(15)	Fuel ( )	___	_____	_____	_____	_____
(16)	Fuel ( )	___	_____	_____	_____	_____
(17)	Labor				_____	_____
(18)	Supervision				_____	_____
(19)	Maintenance				_____	_____
(20)	Factory supplies				_____	_____
(21)	Indirect overhead				_____	_____
(22)	Payroll overhead				_____	_____
(23)	Laboratory				_____	_____
(24)	Contingencies				_____	_____
(25)	Total direct conversion cost (sum of lines 11 to 24):				_____	_____

	Indirect expense					
(26)	Depreciation				_____	_____
(27)	Real estate taxes & insurance				_____	_____
(28)	Depletion allowances				_____	_____
(29)	Amortization				_____	_____
(30)	Total indirect conversion cost (sum of lines 26 to 29):				_____	_____
(31)	Total conversion cost (line 25 + line 30):				_____	_____
(32)	Total operating cost (line 31 + line 10:				_____	_____
(33)	Packing and shipping expense				_____	_____
(34)	TOTAL COST FOR PLANT (line 32 + line 33):				_____	_____

Figure 10.1—Typical Production Cost Estimating Form

selected time of year.

A basic flowsheet of the process is vital to preparation of an estimate. This flowsheet should detail to the maximum extent possible the quantity, composition, temperature, and pressure of the input and output streams to each process unit.

In addition, to properly prepare an operating or manufacturing cost estimate, a prepared estimating form should be used to assure that the estimate is performed in a consistent manner and to avoid omitting major items. Figure 10.1 is an example of a suitable form for this purpose.

The estimating form acts as a checklist and as a device for cost recording and control. It must include the date of the estimate; the capital investment information, which was previously determined; an appropriate cost index value reflecting the date of the capital cost estimate; the plant location; the plant design capacity; the annual anticipated plant operating days and/or annual production rate; and the plant or product identification. In any event, if a form is not used, the cost engineer should be equipped with a checklist and should be familiar with the technical aspects of the process. An estimate should never be made without specific technical knowledge of the process.

Last, wherever possible, cost data used in the estimate should be obtained from company records of similar or identical projects (with adjustment for inflation, plant site differences, and geography). For preliminary estimates, company records are probably the most accurate available source of cost data.

If not available from company records, cost data also may be obtained from literature sources. Bear in mind, however, that such data are not always reliable. Published information must always be used with care. It is often inadequately explained and frequently is improperly dated. Date of publication is meaningless, because the data may be months or years old and may require adjustment to current cost levels. Too often it seems that in the rush to complete an estimate, people will grasp any number they can find without fully understanding how it was derived, or what it represents.

COST OF OPERATIONS AT LESS THAN FULL CAPACITY

The preceding discussion emphasized the necessity of performing operating and manufacturing cost estimates both at full plant capacity and at conditions other than full capacity. Frequently, the inexperienced estimator will perform an estimate assuming operations only at full design capacity. This approach is totally erroneous as it does not consider unscheduled downtime, market fluctuations in product demand, time required to develop markets for a new product, and so forth.

> **GLOSSARY TERMS IN THIS CHAPTER**
>
> direct cost ◆ fixed cost ◆ contingency
> distribution cost ◆ general and administrative expenses
> general works expense ◆ indirect cost ◆ manufacturing cost
> operating cost ◆ semivariable cost ◆ variable cost

Figure 10.2 on page 10.4 is an illustration of cost effects of operation at less than full capacity. This figure takes into account the fixed, variable, and semivariable costs discussed earlier.

Semivariable costs, those which are partially proportional to production level, may include, among others, the following:

- direct labor,
- supervision,
- general expense, and
- plant overhead.

Other costs that may be semivariable, depending upon individual circumstances, are royalties and packaging. Packaging may be either variable or semivariable depending upon the particular situation.

Royalties may be variable, semivariable, fixed, or even a capital expense. Thus they must be carefully examined to be certain that they are included in the proper cost category. A royalty fee that is paid in a lump sum should be capitalized. Royalties that are paid in equal annual increments are treated as fixed costs. Those paid as a fee per unit of production or sales are variable costs, and those that are paid in a sliding scale (ie, at a rate per unit of production that declines as production increases) are semivariable. In certain cases, royalty agreements may contain elements of more than one cost category—for example, an annual fee (fixed) plus a charge per unit of production (variable).

Fixed-cost items, in addition to royalties if applicable, include the following:

- depreciation,
- property taxes, and
- insurance.

Variable costs generally include the following:

- raw materials,
- utilities,
- royalties (if applicable),
- packaging (if applicable),

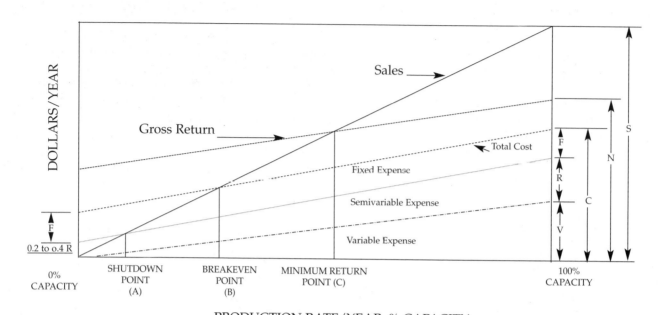

Figure 10.2—Cost Effects of Operations at Less Than Full Plant Capacity

- marketing, and
- catalysts and chemicals.

Figure 10.2 graphically demonstrates the implications of operating at less than full capacity. In this figure, at 100 percent of capacity, the following apply:

- F is the fixed expense;
- V is the variable expense;
- R is the semivariable expense;
- C is total operating cost;
- S is sales income; and
- N is the income required to achieve the minimum acceptable return on investment before taxes (P) for the capital investment (I).

As can be seen from the figure, the variable expense declines to zero at 0 percent of capacity, fixed expense is constant, and semivariable expense declines at 0 percent of capacity to from 20 to 40 percent of its value at full capacity.

This simple plot is used to determine the following:

- the minimum production rate at which the desired return on investment will be achieved (C);
- the breakeven point, or that point at which income will exactly equal total operating cost (B); and
- the shutdown point, or that point at which it is advisable to shut down the plant rather than operating at lower

production rates (A).

The plot readily identifies the range of production rates at which the following apply:

- the return on investment will equal or exceed the desired minimum (all production rates C);
- the return on investment will be less than the desired value but will be greater than zero (production rates < C but > B);
- the process will result in a loss, but losses will be minimized by continuing to operate the plant rather than shutting it down (production rates ≤ B but > A); and
- losses will become so large that it is less expensive to close the plant and pay fixed expenses out of pocket rather than to continue operations (production rates ≤ A).

The breakeven and shutdown points can also be determined mathematically as follows:

$$B \text{ (breakeven point)} = \frac{(F + nR)}{S - V - (1 - n)R} \quad \text{(equation 10.1)}$$

$$A \text{ (shutdown point)} = \frac{nR}{S - V - (1 - n)R} \quad \text{(equation 10.2)}$$

where

n = decimal fraction of semivariable costs incurred at 0

production (usually about 0.3)

Similarly, the total cost line can be expressed as

$$C_p = [V + (1 - n)R]p + F + nR \qquad \text{(equation 10.3)}$$

where
C_p = total cost at production rate p
p = actual annual production rate as a fraction of plant capacity

Since total annual sales are proportional to production (assuming no stock-piling of production), and, therefore, have no value at zero output, the equation for the sales line is

$$S_p = (S \times p) \qquad \text{(equation 10.4)}$$

where
S_p = sales income at production rate p.

The point at which the sales and total cost lines cross is the breakeven point for the plant and is equal to the level of output at which sales is equal to total cost.

RAW MATERIALS COSTS

Depending upon the particular process, raw materials costs can constitute a major portion of operating costs. For this reason, a complete list of all raw materials must be developed using the process flowsheet as a guide. In developing the raw materials list, the following information must be obtained for each raw material:

- units of purchase (tons, pounds, etc),
- unit cost,
- available sources of the material,
- quantity required per unit of time and/or unit of production, and
- quality of raw materials (concentration, acceptable impurity levels, etc.).

In estimating the quantity of each raw material, appropriate allowance must be made for losses in handling and storage, process waste, and process yield.

Price data for purchased raw materials are generally available to a high level of accuracy from many sources. Purchased price information can generally be obtained from the suppliers. Alternatively, supplier catalogs and price lists can be used, as can published data. The *Wall Street Journal, European Chemical News*, and similar trade and business publications are all good sources of spot data.

In estimating the cost of any raw material it must be remembered that, in general, raw material costs vary with quality (concentration, surface finish of metals, impurities, etc) and generally decrease in unit cost as quantity increases. There is little sense, for example, in relying on a cost figure for reagent-grade hydrochloric acid in 5-lb bottles when the process can utilize much lower cost commercial-grade hydrochloric acid (muriatic) in tank car or tank truck lots.

Another major factor to be considered is availability of the raw material. Does sufficient productive capacity exist such that the market can supply the demands of the proposed process? A sudden large new demand for a raw material can, and often does, cause substantial price increases, particularly if the material is available only in small quantities or as a by-product of another process.

In pricing raw materials, it must also be remembered that the prices are generally negotiated and that the discounts obtained can result in prices substantially less than quoted or published data. Where available, company experience in negotiating supply orders for the same or similar materials should be used to estimate the amount of any such probable discounts.

A common pitfall in operating and manufacturing cost estimates is to neglect the cost of raw materials manufactured or obtained in-house or from another company division because they are not purchased. Such raw materials, however, do represent a cost to the company and do have value. In the estimate, therefore, they should be included as a cost at their market value or company book value. The market value to be used is the going market price corrected for any direct sales costs which are not incurred due to internal use. In addition, internal company freight, handling, and transfer costs must be added.

If the captive raw material is an intermediate product that has no established market price, the cost should be based upon the value of the nearest downstream product or material for which an established market price exists. The cost is equal to the value of the downstream product less direct sales costs not incurred plus internal company transfer costs less manufacturing costs for operations avoided by using the intermediate product instead of processing it further.

Other raw materials cost items that are easily overlooked are fuels that are used as raw materials (eg, natural gas in methane conversion processes) and periodic makeup of losses to catalysts and other processing materials. In the case of catalysts and similar materials, the initial fill of such items is usually treated as a capital expense if its useful life exceeds one year. Otherwise it is considered as a start-up expense.

Fuels that are used as a raw material should be treated in the same manner as any other raw material. Those which are used for utility purposes should be treated as a utility cost. Finally, in estimating raw materials costs, it must be recognized that prices are usually quoted FOB the supplier's plant or basing point, not at the point of use. Thus freight to the point of use and local handling costs must be added to the quoted prices.

Current freight tariffs for each commodity should be checked when preparing the estimate since they are complex and often illogical and cannot be generalized.

BY-PRODUCT CREDITS AND DEBITS

All process by-products, including wastes and pollutants, must be considered in the operating cost estimate. Thus, every output stream shown on the process flowsheet must have a cost assigned to it. Obviously, these costs may be credits (in the case of salable or usable by-products) or debits (in the case of wastes or unsalable by-products).

Items that are not immediately obvious as by-products are nuisance expenses. No longer can a plant discharge pollution at will into the air or water nor can high noise levels, thermal discharges, odors, etc remain unabated. These are all by-products, albeit undesirable ones, and the cost of treating them must be included in the estimate—either in the overall process costs or as a by-product debit. Similarly, the capital cost estimate must include the costs of associated pollution and nuisane abatement equipment.

Nuisance costs also are not confined to things that leave or are discharged from the plant. In many cases, nuisances that are entirely confined to the plant premises (eg, high noise levels) must be eliminated due to safety and employer liability considerations.

Salable by-products have values, which can be established in the same manner as determining the cost of raw materials. The by-product credit then may be estimated from the market prices or anticipated selling prices of the by-products less any costs of processing, packaging, selling and transporting them to market. In many cases it is necessary to do a complete capital and operating cost estimate on the by-product processing facilities in order to determine the latter costs.
If the by-product is not sold but instead is converted to another salable product, it is valued at the market value of the subsequent product less the associated conversion and transfer costs. Wastes similarly carry the negative value associated with their treatment and disposal. Again, it may be necessary to perform another complete capital and operating cost estimate to determine these costs.

Credits should be taken for by-products with great care. Many processes have been economic failures because assumed by-product credits were not realized. In many cases, the production of a by-product can glut its market, particularly if the current market is a small one. Similarly, introduction of the by-product into competition with other materials can depress prices due to competitive pressures.

A notable example of this type of situation is the sulfur market. In the mid-1960s sulfur was in short supply and carried an inflated price. At that time, many estimates were being made on pollution control devices and systems that would produce sulfur as a by-product and were justified on the basis of the high by-product credits for sulfur. However, due to improved methods of sulfur production and the additional sulfur being produced as a by-product, in a very short period of time, the market for sulfur and sulfur products such as sulfuric acid changed to a state of oversupply and depressed prices. As a result, many supposedly profitable processes actually became uneconomical.

UTILITY COSTS

The estimation of utility costs, particularly in light of rapidly increasing energy costs, is another critical area of operating cost estimation.

In estimating utility costs, it is necessary first to determine the requirements for each utility including a reasonable allowance for nonproduction items, such as plant lighting, sanitary water, etc. An allowance should also be made for miscellaneous usage and contingencies. Table 10.1 is a typical utility summary of the nature that is required.

In addition to the utility summary, consumption patterns should be examined to determine if consumption will be at a uniform rate during each day and from day to day. If consumption rates fluctuate, utility pricing may be based not only on total consumption, but also in the peak demand rate and, in some cases, the time of day in which the peak occurs. A further consideration is whether or not the utility must be available on a noninterruptable basis. If the process has an alternate utility source or can tolerate periodic cutbacks in utility supplies, rates may be available that are somewhat lower in cost than noninterruptable rates. The estimate also should consider the fact that in certain areas, noninterruptable rates are not available and electric power, natural gas, etc., can be curtailed by the utility companies at any time if residential demands exceed available supplies. In these situations both the capital and operating cost estimates must consider standby alternative utility sources, such as emergency power generators or combustion units that can operate on alternate fuels, etc.

In general, utility costs decrease as demand increases (although there is a growing tendency toward national and state policies to increase unit cost with quantity artificially in order to encourage reductions in consumption).
Electric power charges are usually based upon a demand factor—the maximum power draw during a 15- to 30-min period in any given month. A load factor is computed as the ratio of average usage to the demand factor and rates are estab-

Table 10.1—Typical Utility Summary

	Power (kWh/hr)	Water required (gpm)	Water recovery and makeup (gpm)
Mine	1,830	1,000	
Crushing plant	1,920		
Concentrating plant	18,550	38,650	36,720
Pelletizing plant	4,050	1,330	
Subtotal:	26,350	40,980	36,720
Utilities:			5,580
Makeup water	400		
Plant lighting	300		
Sanitary water	150	500	
General facilities	150	300	
Miscellaneous and contingencies	150	520	
Total:	27,500	42,300	42,300

lished to give preference to high load factors (i.e., steady consumption). The rate schedules also generally include an escalation factor, which is tied to increases in fuel costs.

Electric rates in the past were remarkably stable for many, many years, and it was common estimating practice to arbitrarily assume a cost of the order of a cent or two per kW-hr for preliminary estimating purposes. This is no longer true, and no generalization can be made about electric rates. The estimator must obtain current rates from the utility companies serving the proposed plant and can no longer safely assume any "rule-of-thumb" figure for power costs. If the power is not purchased and instead is obtained from a captive company-owned generating system, utility costs must be based upon a study of the system itself.

Natural gas prices depend on quantity required. Steam costs are dependent upon many factors, including pressure, cost of fuel, temperature, credit for heating value of condensate, etc. If company data are not available on steam cost, it must be estimated taking into account fuel cost, boiler water treatment, operating labor, depreciation on investment, maintenance, and other related costs of steam production. Black [1] has suggested that steam costs can be approximated as 2 to 3 times the cost of fuel.

Water costs are highly variable depending upon the water quality needed and the quantity required. Purification costs, if contamination occurs before disposal, must also be included, as must cooling costs if the process results in heating of process water. In most jurisdictions, water may not be discharged into streams or the natural water table unless it is equal or better in quality and temperature as when it was withdrawn from the stream.

Fuel costs vary with the type of fuel used, the Btu value of the fuel, and the source of supply. Careful consideration should be given in the estimate not only to fuel cost but to the type of firing equipment required and to required fuel storage facilities. Often these factors can rule out what would otherwise be the least expensive available fuel.

Another factor to be considered is that, as mentioned earlier in this chapter, certain fuels, although lower in cost than alternative fuels, may not be available in sufficient quantities, if at all. In some cases, a fuel may be abundant in warm weather but in short supply during the heating season, necessitating use of alternate fuel supplies or planned production cutbacks or stoppages during periods of severe winter weather.

In estimating utility requirements, equipment, efficiency losses, and contingencies must be considered. Utility consumption generally is not proportional to production due to economies of scale and reduced energy losses per unit of volume or production on larger process units. Black [1] has suggested that utility consumption varies to the 0.9 power of capacity, rather than in direct proportion to capacity.

Last, while not normally thought of as a utility, cost of motor fuels and greases for all mobile equipment must be estimated. Fuel costs are based upon annual operating hours for each piece of equipment times fuel consumption per hour, times the prevailing cost for the fuel to be used. Greases and lubricant costs are directly related to fuel costs, and amount to approximately 16 percent of the fuel cost for most types of equipment.

LABOR COSTS

Labor costs, particularly in a labor-intensive process, may be the dominant cost factor in an operating or manufacturing cost estimate. To properly estimate these costs, a staffing table must be established in as detailed a manner as possible. This table should indicate the following:

1. the particular skill or craft required in each operation,
2. labor rates for the various types of operations,
3. supervision required for each process step, and
4. overhead personnel required.

It is not always possible to determine the extent of supervision and overhead personnel required. In such cases, alternate methods of estimating these costs may be used as discussed later in this book. However, if sufficient data are available, these factors should be included in the staffing table for maximum estimate accuracy.

Table 10.2 is a typical staffing table for a complete estimate. This table illustrates the detail required in a complete staffing table. Note that the table includes general and administrative personnel, production workers, maintenance workers, and direct supervision.

Once the staffing table is developed (at a minimum including all direct production labor), labor costs can readily be estimated from company records of wages and salaries by position, union wage scales, salary surveys of various crafts and professions, or other published sources. Because labor rates are prone to rapid inflation, often at rates sharply different from general inflation rates, care must be taken to obtain current figures and to properly project future wage rates.

Generally, data on wage rates includes shift differentials and overtime premiums. If not, these factors must be added to the extent applicable.

Further, when estimating around-the-clock, 168-hr/wk operations, allowance must be made for the fact that a week includes 4.2 standard 40-hr weeks. Even with four work crews on "swing shift," one crew must work 8 hr/week of overtime to keep the plant in steady operation. Depending upon local custom, laws, and union contracts, this overtime is generally payable at 1.5 to 3 times the normal hourly rate.

An alternate method of calculating labor requirements, if sufficient data are not available to establish a staffing table, is to consider a correlation of labor in workhours per ton of product per processing step. This relationship, which was developed by Wessell [6], relates labor requirements to plant capacity by the following equation:

$$\frac{\text{Operating workhours}}{\text{tons of product}} = t \left[\frac{\text{number of processing steps}}{(\text{capacity, tons/day})^{0.76}} \right] \quad \text{(equation 10.5)}$$

where

$t = 23$ for batch operations with a maximum of labor,
$t = 17$ for operations with average labor requirements, and
$t = 10$ for well-instrumented continuous process operations.

As pointed out previously, the relationship between labor requirements and production rate is not usually a direct one. The Wessell equation recognizes that labor productivity generally improves as plant throughput increases. It can also be used to extrapolate known workhour requirements from one plant to another of different capacity.

Another shortcut method of estimating labor requirements, when requirements at one capacity are known, is to project labor requirements for other capacities to the 0.2 to 0.25 power of the capacity ratio.

A significant factor to be considered in estimating labor costs is overtime. As mentioned earlier, around-the-clock, 24-hr/day, 7-day/week operations have an inherent overtime penalty of 8 hr/week. With this exception, and occasional overtime to cover for absent workers, overtime is usually not a major consideration in manufacturing and production operations.

However, in estimates involving construction projects, or those which anticipate regular scheduled overtime, these costs can be substantial and must be carefully evaluated.

Scheduled overtime over an extended period can result in substantial decreases in worker productivity resulting in a major cost penalty for productivity losses in addition to the higher direct costs of premium pay at 1.5, 2, or even 3 times normal hourly rates.

Scheduled overtime involves a planned, continuing schedule for extended working hours for individual workers or even entire crews. It is not occasional overtime caused on an irregular basis by absenteeism, equipment malfunctions, etc.

Unfortunately, scheduled overtime rarely saves money or accelerates production. Two articles which appeared in the *AACE Bulletin* in 1973 [2, 5] amply illustrated this point. These articles, prepared by representatives of the Construction Users Anti-Inflation Roundtable (now the Business Roundtable), clearly demonstrated that scheduled overtime rarely, if ever, is beneficial, and that overtime should be avoided in favor of additional employees working normal shifts or partial shifts.

Table 10.2—Typical Complete Staffing Table

	Shifts per day	Days per year	Number of labor personnel	Wages for labor, $			Number of salaried personnel	Salaries ($)		Total wages or salaries ($)
				Hour	Day	Year		per person	Total	
GENERAL										
Administrative and services										
General superint.	1						1	80,000	80,000	80,000
Chief engineer	1						1	60,000	60,000	60,000
Personnel officer	1						1	36,000	36,000	36,000
Personnel clerk	2						2	24,000	48,000	48,000
Payroll clerk	4						4	30,000	120,000	120,000
Accountant	3						3	36,000	108,000	108,000
Guard	6	365	8.4	11.04	529.92	193,600				193,600
Stock clerk	6	365	8.4	11.04	529.92	193,600				193,600
Safety engineer	1						1	48,000	48,000	48,000
Chief chemist	1						1	52,000	52,000	52,000
Drafter	3						4.2	28,000	117,600	117,600
Sample collector/tester	12						16.8	36,000	604,800	604,800
Stenographer	3						3	24,000	72,000	72,000
Subtotal						387,200			1,346,400	1,733,600
MINE										
Administrative and services										
Mine superintendent	1						1	72,000	72,000	72,000
Mining engineer	2						2	56,000	112,000	112,000
Geologist	1						1	48,000	48,000	48,000
General foreman	1						1	52,000	52,000	52,000
Rod carrier	2	260	2	12.04	192.64	50,000				50,000
Clerk	2						2	28,000	56,000	56,000
Warehouser	3	260	3	13.04	312.96	81,200				81,200
Janitor	2	260	2	11.04	176.64	46,000				46,000
Party chief	1						1	48,000	48,000	48,000
Subtotal						177,200			388,000	565,200
Production										
Shovel operator	9	260	9	18.36	1,321.92	343,600				343,600
Shovel oiler	6	260	6	12.04	577.92	150,400				150,400
Truck driver, haulage	24	260	24	14.04	2,695.68	700,800				700,800
Powderer	1	260	1	13.72	109.76	28,400				28,400
Powderer helper	2	260	2	12.04	192.64	50,000				50,000
Truck driver, service truck, and fuel truck	6	260	6	13.04	625.92	162,800				162,800
Operator, crane	3	260	3	13.04	312.96	81,200				81,200
Operator, drill	9	260	9	17.07	1,226.88	318,800				318,800
Operator helper, drill	9	260	9	12.04	866.88	225,200				225,200
Operator, tractor	9	260	9	13.40	964.80	250,800				250,800
Laborer	18	260	18	11.72	1,687.68	438,800				438,800
Shift foreman/woman	3						3	52,000	156,000	156,000
Dumper	3	260	3	11.40	273.60	71,200				71,200
Front end loader oper.	1	260	1	13.72	109.76	28,400				28,400
Primary crusher oper.	3	260	3	13.56	325.44	84,400				84,400
Primary crusher/general laborer	4	260	4	11.04	353.28	91,600			0	0
										91,600
Subtotal						3,026,400			156,000	3,182,400

Table 10.2—Typical Complete Staffing Table (continued)

	Shifts per day	Days per year	Number of labor personnel	Wages for labor, $ Hour	Wages for labor, $ Day	Wages for labor, $ Year	Number of salaried personnel	Salaries ($) per person	Salaries ($) Total	Total wages or salaries ($)
GENERAL										
Administrative and services										
General superint.	1						1	80,000	80,000	80,000
Chief engineer	1						1	60,000	60,000	60,000
Personnel officer	1						1	36,000	36,000	36,000
Personnel clerk	2						2	24,000	48,000	48,000
Payroll clerk	4						4	30,000	120,000	120,000
Accountant	3						3	36,000	108,000	108,000
Guard	6	365	8.4	11.04	529.92	193,600				193,600
Stock clerk	6	365	8.4	11.04	529.92	193,600				193,600
Safety engineer	1						1	48,000	48,000	48,000
Chief chemist	1						1	52,000	52,000	52,000
Drafter	3						4.2	28,000	117,600	117,600
Sample collector/tester	12						16.8	36,000	604,800	604,800
Stenographer	3						3	24,000	72,000	72,000
Subtotal						387,200			1,346,400	1,733,600
MINE										
Administrative and services										
Mine superintendent	1						1	72,000	72,000	72,000
Mining engineer	2						2	56,000	112,000	112,000
Geologist	1						1	48,000	48,000	48,000
General foreman	1						1	52,000	52,000	52,000
Rod carrier	2	260	2	12.04	192.64	50,000				50,000
Clerk	2						2	28,000	56,000	56,000
Warehouser	3	260	3	13.04	312.96	81,200				81,200
Janitor	2	260	2	11.04	176.64	46,000				46,000
Party chief	1						1	48,000	48,000	48,000
Subtotal						177,200			388,000	565,200
Production										
Shovel operator	9	260	9	18.36	1,321.92	343,600				343,600
Shovel oiler	6	260	6	12.04	577.92	150,400				150,400
Truck driver, haulage	24	260	24	14.04	2,695.68	700,800				700,800
Powderer	1	260	1	13.72	109.76	28,400				28,400
Powderer helper	2	260	2	12.04	192.64	50,000				50,000
Truck driver, service truck, and fuel truck	6	260	6	13.04	625.92	162,800				162,800
Operator, crane	3	260	3	13.04	312.96	81,200				81,200
Operator, drill	9	260	9	17.07	1,226.88	318,800				318,800
Operator helper, drill	9	260	9	12.04	866.88	225,200				225,200
Operator, tractor	9	260	9	13.40	964.80	250,800				250,800
Laborer	18	260	18	11.72	1,687.68	438,800				438,800
Shift foreman/woman	3						3	52,000	156,000	156,000
Dumper	3	260	3	11.40	273.60	71,200				71,200
Front end loader oper.	1	260	1	13.72	109.76	28,400				28,400
Primary crusher oper.	3	260	3	13.56	325.44	84,400				84,400
Primary crusher/general									0	0
laborer	4	260	4	11.04	353.28	91,600				91,600
Subtotal						3,026,400			156,000	3,182,400

Table 10.2—Typical Complete Staffing Table (continued)

	Shifts per day	Days per year	Number of labor personnel	Wages for labor, $			Number of salaried personnel	Salaries ($)		Total wages or salaries ($)
				Hour	Day	Year		per person	Total	
Grate kiln operator, roving	3	365	4.2	17.04	408.96	149,200				149,200
Balling drum operator, roving	3	365	4.2	13.40	321.60	117,200				117,200
Pellet load-out operator	3	365	4.2	13.40	321.60	117,200				117,200
Pellet load-out loader	3	365	4.2	12.04	288.96	105,600				105,600
Pelletizing-general laborer	10	365	14	11.04	883.20	322,400				322,400
Front-end load operator	1	260	1	13.04	104.32	27,200				27,200
Grader operator	1	260	1	13.40	107.20	28,000				28,000
Tractor operator	1	260	1	13.40	107.20	28,000				28,000
Boom truck operator	1	260	1	13.04	104.32	27,200				27,200
Subtotal						2,712,800			767,200	3,480,000
Maintenance										
General foreman/forewoman	1						1	60,000	60,000	60,000
Foreman/forewoman, concentrator	2						2	52,000	104,000	104,000
Foreman/forewoman, crusher	1						1	52,000	52,000	52,000
Foreman/forewoman, pelletizer	2						2	52,000	104,000	104,000
Millwright, crusher	6	365	8.4	17.40	835.20	304,800				304,800
Millwright, concentrator	10	365	14	17.40	1,392.00	508,000				508,000
Millwright, pelletizer	10	365	14	17.40	1,392.00	508,000				508,000
Oilers, concentrator	2	365	2.8	12.04	192.64	70,400				70,400
Oilers, crusher	1	260	1	12.04	96.32	25,200				25,200
Oilers, pelletizer	1	365	1.4	12.04	96.32	35,200				35,200
Welders	4	260	4	17.40	556.80	144,800				144,800
Machinists	2	260	2	18.04	288.64	75,200				75,200
Blacksmiths	2	260	2	17.72	283.52	73,600				73,600
Tool room attendant	2	260	2	11.72	187.52	48,800				48,800
Foreman/forewoman, electrical	2						2.8	52,000	145,600	145,600
Electrician	12	365	16.8	18.04	1,731.84	632,000				632,000
Subtotal						2,426,000			465,600	2,891,600
TOTAL:						**10,427,600**			**4,011,200**	**14,438,800**

Quoting from one article [5]:

> Studies indicate that when a job is placed on overtime there is a sharp drop in productivity during the first week with a substantial recovery which holds for about two weeks and is followed by a fairly steady decline. At the end of seven to nine weeks the productivity on an overtime basis is no greater than the productivity would be on a 40-hour week. In this period there is an increase in work accomplished of about 12 percent. After seven to nine weeks of operation, productivity continues to decline and the work accomplished is less than would have been accomplished on a 40 hour per week schedule. After 18 to 20 weeks there is no gain in total work accomplished . . . .

SUPERVISION AND MAINTENANCE COSTS

As discussed above, supervision costs should be established, if at all possible, through a staffing table and tabulation of associated costs.

Unfortunately, for most preliminary estimates, particularly those for proposed new processes, this is not possible.

In such cases, costs of supervision can be roughly estimated by taking a fixed percentage of direct labor costs based upon company experience. In the absence of prior data on similar operations, a factor of 15 to 20 percent is generally satisfactory. The validity of the latter factor can readily be seen when considering the fact that one front-line supervisor can effectively manage no more than 8 to 10 workers, i.e., supervision workhours of 0.100 to 0.125 per direct labor workhour. With front-line supervision (i.e., foremen or forewomen) at labor rates approximately 50 to 60 percent above general labor rates, 15 to 20 percent supervision factor is evident.

Maintenance labor costs, like supervision costs, should be delineated in the labor staffing table if at all possible. However, other than company records of existing similar plants, reliable data on maintenance costs are generally not available, and the staffing table approach is usually not feasible. For this reason, maintenance costs are often estimated as a fixed percentage of depreciable capital investment per year. For complex plants and severe corrosive conditions, this factor can be 10 to 12 percent or higher. For simple plants with relatively mild, noncorrosive conditions, 3 to 5 percent should be adequate.

Maintenance costs are a semivariable category, which is generally distributed about 50 percent to labor and 50 percent of materials. For a preliminary estimate, the various factors making up plant maintenance can be back calculated from the total maintenance number using the following approximate percentages:

- direct maintenance labor, 35 to 40 percent;
- direct maintenance labor, supervision, 7 to 8 percent;
- maintenance materials, 35 to 40 percent; and
- contract maintenance, 18 to 20 percent.

Then as the project evolves toward a final staffing plan, the factors can be improved and are finally replaced with numbers generated from the staffing table. The back calculation allows one to estimate the number of people required early in the project. When operating at less than 100 percent of capacity, maintenance costs generally increase per unit of production. Such operations can be estimated as follows:

Percent of capacity	Maintenance cost as percentage of cost at 100 percent capacity
100	100
75	85
50	75
0	30

Maintenance generally increases with age of equipment, although most estimates use an average figure to simplify the estimate. This apparent error is offset in the overall estimate by use of average or "straight-line" depreciation, whereas accelerated depreciation is in fact generally used for tax purposes. Figure 10.3 illustrates the validity of using an average maintenance figure over the life of a project.

Finally, for major projects, it may be necessary to include costs for additional maintenance supervisors. However, for small plant additions, additional supervision is generally not required.

OPERATING SUPPLIES AND OVERHEAD COSTS

Generally, operating (or factory) supplies are a relatively minor cost of operations. Nevertheless, these must be included in the operating or manufacturing cost estimate. Such costs include miscellaneous items, such as lubricating oil, instrument charts, wiping cloths, etc. Lacking more detailed information, they may be estimated as a percentage of payroll. This percentage can range from a few percent to 20 percent or more, depending upon plant complexity and whether or not routine maintenance items and supplies are included or accounted for separately. For example, 6 percent of payroll is probably an adequate allowance for operating supplies in a coal preparation plant, while 20 percent is probably more reasonable for an oil refinery, a more complex operation requiring a cleaner environment. The best source of such costs, however, is always company records of similar past projects.

Overhead or burden costs are operating and manufacturing costs, which, while not directly proportional or related to production, are associated with payroll or general and administrative expense. Such costs, depending upon what they represent, are either semivariable or indirect costs.

The major semivariable overhead costs are so-called payroll overheads. These are costs associated with employee "fringe benefits." They include workers' compensation, pensions, group insurance, paid vacations and holidays, Social Security, unemployment taxes and benefits, profit-sharing programs, and a host of others. The extent of these costs varies markedly from industry to industry, and company records are the best measure of their magnitude. However, in the absence of company data, payroll overheads may be roughly estimated at 25 to 40 percent of direct labor plus supervision, plus maintenance labor costs for the U.S. For other countries this factor must be adjusted to suit local conditions. In heavily socialized nations, payroll overheads can exceed 100 percent of the basic labor costs.

In addition, payroll overhead must be applied to indirect overhead (clerical, administrative, etc., personnel) if not previously included in cost estimates for this item.

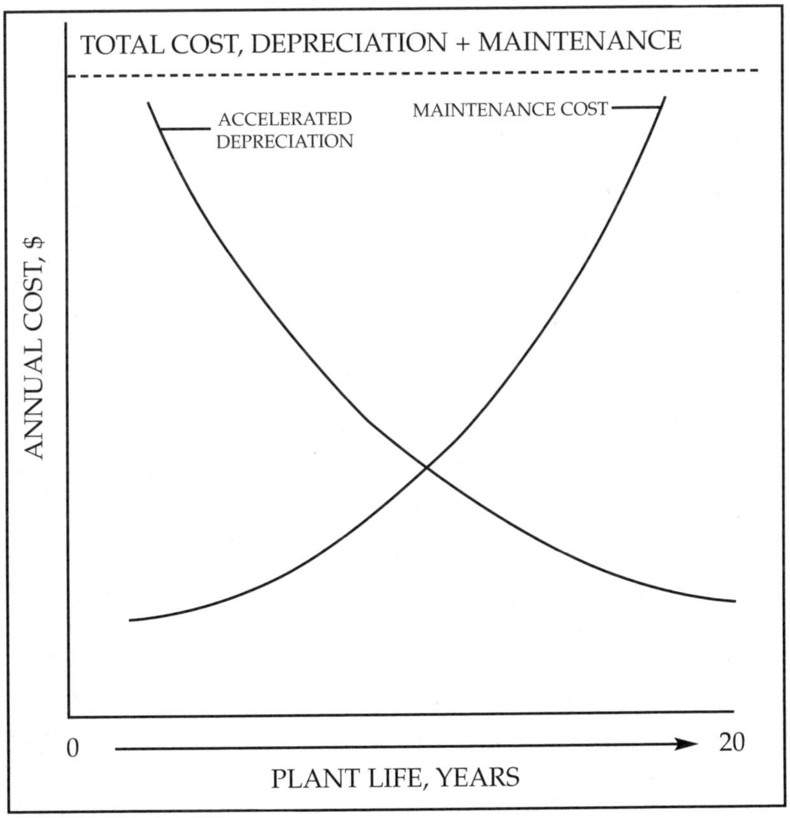

It must be noted that, if company data are used, care must be exerted to avoid including items in payroll overhead, which are, by accounting definition of the company, included in general expense.

Further, it should be recognized that in some industries, notably the U.S. and Canadian coal mining industry, a major portion of fringe benefits is based upon royalties levied by the unions on production rather than being a function of labor costs. Such royalties are variable production costs and must be treated as such.

The expense of operating company testing and research laboratories is another overhead expense which must be included in the estimate. Generally, such costs are indirect costs, although in the case of product laboratories they may be direct semivariable costs.

Laboratory overhead is best estimated based upon company experience. Lacking suitable data, these costs can be estimated as follows:

- from workhours required plus associated overhead,
- from literature sources, and
- as a percentage of direct labor costs.

If the last is used, laboratory overhead costs may range from 3 to 20 percent or more for complex processes. A suitable figure for average situations might be 5 to 10 percent.

ROYALTIES AND RENTALS

As was discussed earlier in this chapter, royalties may be variable, semivariable, fixed, or capital costs (or a combination of these), depending upon the conditions of the royalty agreement. The same is true of rental costs.

Single-sum royalty, rental, or license payments are properly considered as capital investment items, whereas payments in proportion to production or fixed payments per annum are treated as direct operating costs.

Royalty expenses, in the absence of data to the contrary, are treated as a direct expense and may be estimated at 1 to 5 percent of the product sales price.

Due to the complexity of agreements for royalty payments and to variations in tax laws and accounting methods, extreme care should be exercised to be sure that such costs are properly included in the appropriate expense category.

Figure 10.3—Comparison of Maintenance and Depreciation Costs Over the Life of a Plant

CONTINGENCIES

As is true with a capital cost estimate, any operating or manufacturing cost estimate should include a contingency allowance to account for those costs that cannot readily be determined or defined or that are too small to estimate individually but may be significant in the aggregate. The contingency allowance applies both to direct and indirect costs and ranges from 1 to 5 percent (and more in some cases), depending upon the uncertainty in the data used to prepare the estimate and the risk associated with the venture.

Hackney [3] has suggested the following guidelines for contingency allowances in operating and manufacturing cost estimates:

1. installations similar to those currently used by the company, for which standard costs are available—1 percent;
2. installations common to the industry, for which reliable data are available—2 percent;
3. novel installations that have been completely developed and tested—3 percent; and
4. novel installations that are in the development stage—5 percent.

GENERAL WORKS EXPENSE

General works expense or factory overhead represents the indirect cost of operating a plant or factory and is dependent upon both investment and labor. Black [1] suggested that factory overhead be estimated by the sum of investment times an investment factor and labor times a labor factor. In this case, labor is defined as total annual cost of labor, including direct operating labor, repair and maintenance, and supervision; and labor for loading, packaging, and shipping.

Black's suggested labor and investment factors for various industries are as follows:

Industry	Investment factor (% per year)	Labor factor (% per year)
Heavy chemical plants (large-capacity)	1.5	45
Power plants	1.8	75
Electrochemical plants	2.5	45
Cement plants	3.0	50
Heavy chemical plants (small capacity)	4.0	45

Alternately, for preliminary estimates, indirect overhead may be approximated at 40 to 60 percent of labor costs or 15 to 30 percent of direct costs. Humphreys [4] has suggested 55 percent of operating labor, supervision, and maintenance labor for the mineral industries. Again, these factors may be somewhat higher outside the U.S. depending upon local customs and laws.

It is important to note that indirect or factory overhead (general works expense) does not include so-called general expense (i.e., marketing or sales cost) and administrative expense.

DEPRECIATION

Depreciation, while not a true operating cost, is considered to be an operating cost for tax purposes. It is customarily listed as a fixed, indirect cost.

The purpose of depreciation is to allow a credit against operating costs, and hence taxes, for the nonrecoverable capital expense of an investment.

The basis for computation of depreciation is the total initial capital expense for tangible assets, including interest during construction and start-up expense. The depreciable portion of capital expense is equal to the total initial investment less working capital and salvage value.

In theory, working capital can be totally recovered at any time after the plant or process is shut down. Similarly, salvage value, the scrap or sales value of the process equipment at the end of its useful life, can, in theory, be recovered at any time after plant shutdown. Thus, the sunk and permanently lost capital is the total initial investment less working capital and salvage value (including land value). Through depreciation, this sunk investment may be recovered as an operating expense over the useful life of the project.

Unfortunately, the true useful life of a project generally does not correlate with the permissible depreciation period dictated by tax laws. The U.S. Internal Revenue Service (IRS) establishes criteria for useful life of various investments that must be observed in cost and tax calculations whether or not these criteria actually reflect the true projected life of the plant or process. Table 10.3 lists typical permissible depreciation periods (the class life) for various plants and investments as approved by the IRS. In countries other than the U.S., local taxing authorities should be consulted to determine the permissible life that can be used in depreciation calculations for any particular type of investment.

Taxing authorities usually permit the use of any generally accepted method of depreciation calculation provided that it is applied in a consistent manner to all investments applicable to the plant or process being considered. Different depreciation techniques may not be applied to various portions of the total investment. Further, effective in 1981 in the U.S., a specialized system known as the accelerated cost recovery system (ACRS) was mandated by law. Subsequently, in 1986, the U.S. tax laws were revised again, and the ACRS system was replaced by a system called the modified accelerated cost recovery system (MACRS). Both systems are described later in this chapter.

Most industrial firms utilize accelerated depreciation in their actual operating cost and tax calculations. Such techniques permit a major portion of the investment to be deducted from costs in the early years of the life of the plant, thus deferring taxes to the latest possible date.

However, for the purpose of making preliminary operating and manufacturing cost estimates, straight-line depreciation is normally used even though the company may in fact use accelerated depreciation in its books.

The reason for this apparent anomaly is, as explained in the previous discussion, that maintenance costs, which are known to increase with time, are generally assumed to be constant with time. As shown in Figure 10.3, accelerated depreciation increases with time. Assuming both to be constant (i.e., assuming straight-line depreciation), this generally results in offsetting errors, as the actual sum of the two factors, for most plants, tends to be constant, or essentially constant, over the life of any given plant.

To calculate straight-line depreciation, annual depreciation is simply made equal to the depreciable portion of the initial capital investment divided by the depreciable life of the project.

In the case of projects with components having different depreciable lives, each component may be depreciated separately, or the weighted average life may be used on the total depreciable investment.

Mathematically, annual straight-line depreciation is equal to

where

D_{Sl}	=	annual straight-line depreciation,
C	=	depreciable portion of capital investment, and
Y	=	IRS-approved life, in years.

There are many other acceptable depreciation techniques, of which the double-declining balance and sum-of-years-digits methods, both forms of accelerated depreciation, are the most commonly used.

In the double-declining balance method, an annual depreciation deduction is permitted on the undepreciated portion of the investment at a rate equal to twice the straight-line rate.

For example, if an investment has an approved life of 5 years for depreciation purposes, the straight-line deduction is 20 percent of the original depreciable investment per year. Thus, the double-declining balance deduction is twice this rate, or 40 percent.

For example, with an investment of $1 million, a salvage value of zero, and a 5-yr life, annual double-declining balance depreciation allowances are as follows:

Year	Investment	Depreciation at 40%	Undepreciated Balance
0	$1,000,000	-	$1,000,000
1	1,000,000	$ 400,000	600,000
2	600,000	240,000	360,000
3	360,000	144,000	216,000
4	216,000	86,400	129,600
5	129,600	129,600[a]	0
Total		$1,000,000	

[a]In the final year of the life, the total remaining undepreciated balance may be deducted.

Mathematically, the double-declining balance method is

$$D = \frac{2(F - CD)}{n} \qquad \text{(equation 10.7)}$$

where

     D = depreciation in any given year

$$D_{Sl} = \frac{C}{Y} \qquad \text{(equation 10.6)}$$

F	=	initial asset value
CD	=	cumulative depreciation charged in prior years
n	=	asset life, in years

Note that in the double-declining balance method, the basis for depreciation ordinarily is the total depreciable investment without deducting for salvage values other than land value. In this method, the investment is depreciated down to the salvage value, and the final undepreciated balance may not be less than salvage value.

Another common method of computing accelerated depreciation is the "sum-of-years-digits" method. This technique is based upon the depreciable portion of the investment, i.e., excluding land and salvage value.

To use this technique, the approved years in the life of the plant are summed. Deductions are based on the remaining years of plant life divided by the sum of years. For example, with a 5-year life, the sum of years digits equals $5 + 4 + 3 + 2 + 1 = 15$. In the first year 5/15 of the depreciable investment is deducted; 4/15 in the second year, 3/15 in the third year; and so forth.

Table 10.3—Depreciation Class Lives and Recovery Periods

	Recovery periods (in years)		
	Class life	GDS (MACRS)	ADS
SPECIFIC DEPRECIABLE ASSETS USED IN ALL BUSINESS ACTIVITIES, EXCEPT AS NOTED:			
Office furniture, fixtures, and equipment	10	7	10
Information system	6	5	5
Data handling equipment, except computers	6	5	6
Airplanes (airframes and engines), except those used in commercial or contract carrying of passengers or freight, and all helicopters (airframes and engines)	6	5	6
Automobiles, taxis	3	5	5
Buses	9	5	9
Light general purpose trucks	4	5	5
Heavy general purpose trucks	6	5	6
Railroad cars and locomotives, except those owned by railroad transportation companies	15	7	15
Tractor units for use over-the-road	4	3	4
Trailers and trailer-mounted containers	6	5	6
Vessels, barges, tugs, and similar water transportation equipment, except those used in marine construction	18	10	18
Land improvements	20	15	22
Industrial steam and electric generation and/or distribution systems	22	15	22
DEPRECIABLE ASSETS USED IN THE FOLLOWING ACTIVITIES:			
Agriculture	10	7	10
Cotton ginning assets	12	7	12
Cattle, breeding, or dairy	7	5	7
Any breeding or work horse that is 12 years old or less at the time it is placed in service	10	7	10
Any breeding or work horse that is more than 12 years old at the time it is placed in service	10	3	10
Any race horse that is more than 2 years old at the time it is placed in service	None	3	12
Any horse that is more than 12 years old at the time it is placed in service and that is not a race horse, breeding horse, nor a work horse	None	3	12
Any horse not described above	None	7	12
Hogs, breeding	3	3	3
Sheep and goats, breeding	5	5	5
Farm buildings except single-purpose agricultural or horticultural structures	25	20	25
Single-purpose agricultural or horticultural structures (GDS = 7 years before 1989)	15	10	15
Mining	10	7	10
Offshore drilling	7.5	5	7.5
Drilling of oil and gas wells	6	5	6
Exploration for and production of petroleum and natural gas deposits	14	7	14
Petroleum refining	16	10	16
Construction	6	5	6
Manufacture of grain and grain mill products	17	10	17
Manufacture of sugar and sugar products	18	10	18
Manufacture of vegetable oils and vegetable oil products	18	10	18
Manufacture of other food and kindred products	12	7	12
Manufacture of food and beverages—special handling devices	4	3	4
Manufacture of tobacco and tobacco products	15	7	15
Manufacture of knitted goods	7.5	5	7.5
Manufacture of yarn, thread, and woven fabric	11	7	11
Manufacture of carpets and dyeing, finishing, and packaging of textile products and manufacture of medical and dental supplies	9	5	9
Manufacture of textured yarns	8	5	8

Table 10.3—Depreciation Class Lives and Recovery Periods (continued)

	Recovery periods (in years)		
	Class life	GDS (MACRS)	ADS
Manufacture of nonwoven fabrics	10	7	10
Manufacture of apparel and other finished products	9	5	9
Cutting of timber	6	5	6
Sawing of dimensional stock from logs, permanent or well established	10	7	10
Sawing of dimensional stock from logs, temporary	6	5	6
Manufacture of wood products and furniture	10	7	10
Manufacture of pulp and paper	13	7	13
Manufacture of converted paper, paperboard, and pulp products	10	7	10
Printing, publishing, and allied industries	11	7	11
Manufacture of chemicals and allied products	9.5	5	9.5
Manufacture of rubber products	14	7	14
Manufacture of rubber products—special tools and devices	4	3	4
Manufacture of finished plastic products	11	7	11
Manufacture of finished plastic products—special tools	3.5	5	3.5
Manufacture of leather and leather products	11	7	11
Manufacture of glass products	14	7	14
Manufacture of glass products—special tools	2.5	3	2.5
Manufacture of cement	20	15	20
Manufacture of other stone and clay products	15	7	15
Manufacture of primary nonferrous metals	14	7	14
Manufacture of primary nonferrous metals—special tools	6.5	5	6.5
Manufacture of foundry products	14	7	14
Manufacture of primary steel mill products	15	7	15
Manufacture of fabricated metal products	12	7	12
Manufacture of fabricated metal products—special tools	3	3	3
Manufacture of electrical and non-electrical machinery and other mechanical products	10	7	10
Manufacture of electronic components, products, and systems	6	5	6
Any semiconductor manufacturing equipment	5	5	5
Manufacture of motor vehicles	12	7	12
Manufacture of motor vehicles—special tools	3	3	3
Manufacture of aerospace products	10	7	10
Ship and boat building machinery and equipment	12	7	12
Ship and boat building dry docks and land improvements	16	10	16
Ship and boat building—special tools	6.5	5	6.5
Manufacture of locomotives	11.5	7	11.5
Manufacture of railroad cars	12	7	12
Manufacture of athletic, jewelry, and other goods	12	7	12
RAILROAD TRANSPORTATION:			
Railroad machinery and equipment	14	7	14
Railroad structures and similar improvements	30	20	30
Railroad wharves and docks	20	15	20
Railroad track	10	7	10
Railroad hydraulic electric generating equipment	50	20	50
Railroad nuclear electric generating equipment	20	15	20
Railroad steam electric generating equipment	28	20	28
Railroad steam, compressed air, and other power plant equipment	28	20	28
Motor transport--passengers	8	5	8
Motor transport--freight	8	5	8
Water transportation	20	15	20
Air transport	12	7	12
Air transport (restricted)	6	5	6
Pipeline transportation	22	15	22

Table 10.3—Depreciation Class Lives and Recovery Periods (continued)

	Class life	Recovery periods (in years) GDS (MACRS)	ADS
TELEPHONE COMMUNICATIONS:			
Telephone central office buildings	45	50	45
Telephone central office equipment	18	10	18
Computer-based telephone central office switching equipment	9.5	5	9.5
Telephone station equipment	10	7	10
Telephone distribution plant	24	15	24
Radio and television broadcasts	6	5	6
TELEGRAPH, OCEAN CABLE, AND SATELLITE COMMUNICATIONS (TOCSC):			
TOCSC--Electric power generating and distribution systems	19	10	19
TOCSC--High frequency radio and microwave systems	13	7	13
TOCSC--Cable and long-line systems	26.5	20	26.5
TOCSC--Central office control equipment	16.5	10	16.5
TOCSC--Computerized switching, channeling, and associated control equipment	10.5	7	10.5
TOCSC--Satellite ground segment property	10	7	10
TOCSC--Satellite space segment property	8	5	8
TOCSC--Equipment installed on customer's premises	10	7	10
TOCSC--Support and service equipment	13.5	7	13.5
CABLE TELEVISION (CATV):			
CATV--Headend	11	7	11
CATV--Subscriber connection and distribution systems	10	7	10
CATV--Program origination	9	5	9
CATV--Service and test	8.5	5	8.5
CATV--Microwave systems	9.5	5	9.5
ELECTRIC, GAS, WATER, AND STEAM, UTILITY SERVICES:			
Electric utility hydraulic production plant	50	20	50
Electric utility nuclear production plant	20	15	20
Electric utility nuclear fuel assemblies	5	5	5
Electric utility steam production plant	28	20	28
Electric utility transmission and distribution plant	30	20	30
Electric utility combustion turbine production plant	20	15	20
Gas utility distribution facilities	35	20	35
Gas utility manufactured gas production plants	30	20	30
Gas utility substitute natural gas (SNG) production plant (naphtha or lighter hydrocarbon feedstocks)	14	7	14
Substitute natural gas-coal gasification	18	10	18
Natural gas production plant	14	7	14
Gas utility trunk pipelines and related storage facilities	22	15	22
Liquefied natural gas plant	22	15	22
Water utilities	50	20 (1)	50
Central steam utility production and distribution	28	20	28
Waste reduction and resource recovery plants	10	7	10
Municipal wastewater treatment plant	24	14	24
Municipal sewer	50	20 (2)	50
Distributive trades and services	9	5	9
Distributive trades and services--billboard, service station buildings and petroleum marketing land improvements	20	15	20
Recreation	10	7	10
Theme and amusement parks	12.5	7	12.5

Notes: (1) 25-year straight line may apply if placed in service after June 12, 1996. See IRS Publication 946.
(2) In those cases where guidelines are not listed for any given industry or type of equipment, or where the listed guidlines are clearly inappropriate, the depreciable life of such property shall be determined according to the particular facts and circumstances.
Source: *Depreciation*, U.S. Department of the Treasury, Internal Revenue Service, Publication No. 534, 1994.

Using the same example as given above for the double-declining balance method, sum-of-years-digit depreciation deductions would be as follows:

Year	Investment	Depreciation($)	Undepreciated balance
0	$1,000,000	-	$1,000,000
1	1,000,000	5/15 = 333,333	666,667
2	1,000,000	4/15 = 266,667	400,000
3	1,000,000	3/15 = 200,000	200,000
4	1,000,000	2/15 = 133,333	66,667
5	1,000,000	1/15 = 66,667	0
Total		$1,000,000	

The sum-of-years-digits method is expressed mathematically as

$$D_y = C \left[\frac{2(n - Y + 1)}{n(n+1)} \right] \qquad \text{(equation 10.8)}$$

where

D_y = depreciation in year Y

C = depreciable portion of investment

n = asset life, in years

There are numerous other acceptable depreciation methods including some that are combinations of the above methods. However, the three methods described above are the most commonly used techniques.

Also as mentioned earlier, if constant maintenance costs are assumed, no matter which depreciation technique is actually used by the company, the straight-line technique should be generally used for are all preliminary estimates.

ACCELERATED COST RECOVERY SYSTEM

In 1981 a major revision of tax laws in the U.S. replaced the pre-existing depreciation systems described above with a system known as the accelerated cost recovery system (ACRS). ACRS is mandatory for all capital assets acquired after 1980 and before 1987 when another system of depreciation, the modified accelerated cost recovery system (MACRS), became mandatory. However, the tax laws specify that any acquisition must continue to be depreciated on its original basis. Thus, since many capital assets have depreciable lives of up to 60 years, the old depreciation systems, MACRS, and ACRS will coexist and be used by cost professionals for many years into the future.

Under ACRS, capital assets are not subject to depreciation in the customary sense. It is not necessary to estimate salvage values or useful lives for equipment. Instead, the law establishes various property classes and provides for deductions calculated as specific percentages of the cost of the asset. Property classes are listed below:

- **Three-year property**, which is defined as "property that has a mid-point class life of four years or less, or is used for research and experimentation, or is a race horse more than two years old when placed in service, or any other horse that is more than 12 years old when placed in service." This obscure and somewhat confusing-sounding definition includes automobiles, light trucks, and short-lived personal property.
- **Five-year property**, which is defined as property not otherwise defined and which is not real property. This class includes most types of equipment and machinery.
- **Ten-year property**, which is public utility property having a midpoint class life of more than 18 but not more than 25 years. Also included are manufactured homes, railroad tank cars, certain coal utilization property, theme and amusement park property, and other property as defined in the act.
- **Fifteen-year property**, which is long-lived public utility property.
- **Ten-year and fifteen-year real property classes**. The 15-year class consists of real property with a midpoint class life in excess of 12.5 years. All other real property falls into the 10-year class.

Detailed descriptions of each property class may be obtained upon request from the IRS.

Under the 1981 law, ACRS deductions were phased in on a gradual basis over a period of years. Allowable deductions for personal property are listed in Table 10.4. Fifteen-year class real property deductions vary from Table 10.4 and are based in part on the month in which the property was placed in service. IRS regulations should be consulted to determine applicable deduction rates.

It should also be noted that the ACRS requirements place certain limitations on deductions for disposition of property prior to the end of its class life, and also provide for optional use of alternate percentages based on the straight-line method of depreciation.

The logic of the standard ACRS percentages as outlined in Table 10.4 becomes apparent when it is realized that the 1981 to 1984 rates are approximately equal to those for 150 percent declining-balance depreciation with a switch to straight-line depreciation in later years. The 1985 rates similarly approximate 175 percent declining-balance depreciation, and the rates for 1986 are essentially those for the double-declining-balance method, both with a switch to the sum-of-years-dig

Table 10.4—ACRS Deductions (%) for Personal Property and 10-Year Real Property

	Year property was put in service		
	1981-1984	**1985**	**1986**
3-year property			
1st year	25	29	33
2nd year	38	47	45
3rd year	37	24	22
5-year property			
1st year	15	18	20
2nd year	22	33	32
3rd year	21	25	24
4th year	21	16	16
5th year	21	8	8
10-year property			
1st year	8	9	10
2nd year	14	19	18
3rd year	12	16	16
4th year	10	14	14
5th year	10	12	12
6th year	10	10	10
7th year	9	8	8
8th year	9	6	6
9th year	9	4	4
10th year	9	2	2
15-year personal property			
1st year	5	6	7
2nd year	10	12	12
3rd year	9	12	12
4th year	8	11	11
5th year	7	10	10
6th year	7	9	9
7th year	6	8	8
8th year	6	7	7
9th year	6	6	6
10th year	6	5	5
11th year	6	4	4
12th year	6	4	3
13th year	6	3	3
14th year	6	2	2
15th year	6	1	1

its method at the optimum point in time. Thus ACRS is merely a combination of previously used and widely accepted methods of computing accelerated depreciation.

MODIFIED ACCELERATED COST RECOVERY SYSTEM

When the ACRS depreciation system was adopted in the United States, it was phased in over a period of five years ending in 1986 and was originally anticipated to remain in effect after that time. The 1986 tax reform act, however, further revised the depreciation regulations and, effective in 1987, implemented a new system called the modified accelerated cost recovery system (MACRS).

MACRS expanded the ACRS property classes from 5 to 8, revised the depreciation periods for most items (see Table 10.3), and redefined the classes. The definitions including minor tax law changes since 1987 are as follows:

- **Three-year property**, which was redefined as including "tractor units for use over the road, any race horse over 2 years old when placed in service, and any other horse over 12 years old when placed in service." Also included in this class is qualified rent-to-own property. Three-year property generally includes those items with an IRS-approved class life of 4 years or less. The major change in this class was the elimination of automobiles, light trucks, and other short-lived personal property, which were moved to the 5-year class.
- **Five-year property**, which was totally redefined as including "trucks, computers and peripheral equipment, office machinery, and any automobile." Most items with an IRS-approved class life of 4-plus years and less than 10 years are included under this category. This class includes taxis, buses, property used in research and experimentation, breeding cattle, dairy cattle, and furnishings (furniture, rugs, etc) used in residential rental real estate.
- **Seven-year property**, which is defined in part as including "office furniture and fixtures, any property that does not have a class life, and that has not been designated by law as being in any other class and, if placed in service before 1989, any single purpose agricultural or horticultural structure." This category covers any items with an IRS-approved class life of 10 years or more and less than 16 years. It effectively includes almost all industrial machinery and equipment. It also includes agricultural machinery and equipment.
- **Ten-year property**, which includes "vessels, barges, tugs and similar water transportation equipment, and, if placed in service after 1988, any single-purpose agricultural or horticultural structure, and any tree or vine bearing fruit or nuts. This category includes those items with an IRS-approved class life of 16 years or more and less than 20 years.
- **Fifteen-year property**, which includes items with an IRS-approved class life of 20 years or more and less than 25 years plus wastewater treatment plants and equipment used for two-way exchange of voice and data com-

munications. This class includes improvements made directly to land or added to it, such as shrubbery, fences, roads, and bridges. It also includes any retail motor fuels outlet, such as a convenience store.

- **Twenty-year property**, which includes items with an IRS-approved class life of 25 years or more, excluding real property and including sewer systems. Farm buildings (other than single-purpose agricultural or horticultural structures) fall into this category.
- **Twenty-seven and one-half-year property**, which includes residential rental property.
- **Nonresidential real property**, which includes real property other than residential rental property. For this category, the recovery period for depreciation is 31.5 years for property placed in service before May 13, 1993, and 39 years for property placed in service after May 12, 1993.

The depreciation allowances under the MACRS system, like the ACRS, do not consider salvage value. For the 3-, 5-, 7-, and 10-year categories, the MACRS depreciation schedule (Table 10.5 on page 10.22) is equivalent to 200 percent declining-balance switching to straight-line at the optimum point to maximize the deduction. In the first year, a half-year convention applies. The assumption is made that the item being depreciated was placed in service for only 6 months no matter what the actual date of service was. However, if more than 40 percent of the cost basis was placed in service during the last 3 months of the year, a mid-quarter convention applies, ie, it is assumed that the equipment was in service for only 1.5 months of the first year.

For the 15- and 20-year categories, the depreciation schedule, as shown in Table 10.4, is 150 percent declining balance with a switch to straight line at the optimum point. The half-year and half-quarter conventions also apply to these categories.

For the real property categories, straight-line depreciation must be used with a mid-month convention in the first year.

If all of the foregoing seems confusing and convoluted, it is. The logic of tax laws and their complexity is rarely clear, and the MACRS system is a significant example of how the political process can complicate what should otherwise be an easily understood subject.

To further complicate the calculation of depreciation, the MACRS system allows for an alternate method. As shown in Table 10.3, the alternate depreciation system (ADS) permits straight-line depreciation over specified periods which are equal to, or longer than, the regular MACRS recovery periods (GDS, the general depreciation system). Generally, the taxpayer must specifically choose to use the alternate method; otherwise the regular MACRS system applies. In a very few cases, the alternate system must be used. The exceptions are small in number and generally are not of concern to the cost engineer.

Table 10.5—MACRS Deduction Rates

If the recovery year is:	3-year	5-year	7-year	10-year	15-year	20-year
	33.33	20.00	14.29	10.00	5.00	3.750
1	44.45	32.00	24.49	18.00	9.50	7.219
2	14.81	19.20	17.49	14.40	8.55	6.677
3	7.41	11.52	12.49	11.52	7.70	6.177
4		11.52	8.93	9.22	6.93	5.713
5						
	5.76	8.92	7.37	6.23	5.285	
6			8.93	6.55	5.90	4.888
7			4.46	6.55	5.90	4.522
8				6.56	5.91	4.462
9				6.55	5.90	4.461
10						
				3.28	5.91	4.462
11					5.90	4.461
12					5.91	4.462
13					5.90	4.461
14					5.91	4.462
15						
					2.95	4.461
16						4.462
17						4.461
18						4.462
19						4.461
20						
						2.231
21						

The alternate system, however, is always a bad choice economically. The regular system permits far more rapid deductions and resultant tax savings. The alternate system is easier to understand and is simple to calculate but is a poor choice—it costs money. Nevertheless, the government permits poor economic decisions. The wise cost engineer should avoid them.

AMORTIZATION, DEPLETION, INSURANCE, AND REAL ESTATE TAXES

Amortization is a term which is applied to writing off or recovering any portion of the initial capital expense which is intangible in nature and as such has no definable useful life. A lump-sum royalty payment is an example of such an investment. Such intangible assets are written off as an operating cost over the life of the plant or process using exactly the same calculation techniques as are used for depreciation of tangible assets. Alternately, intangible assets may be written off as a function of production over the life of a project. In some cases amortization is, for simplicity, included in the depreciation charge (albeit erroneously). However, for practical purposes the distinction between depreciation and amortization is usually of no consequence.

Depletion allowances, while not considered to be an operating cost, must be included in estimates involving extraction of a natural resource, e.g., in coal mining. These allowances are deductions from gross income prior to calculation of taxes on income. Thus they are, in effect, tax credits granted by law to compensate for eventual exhaustion of an irreplaceable natural resource such as coal or oil. They are computed as a fixed percentage of the market value of the resource in its first usable and salable form, even though the resource may be further processed and eventually sold in another form at a different cost. Depletion rates are established by law and are periodically changed. Thus it is necessary when performing an estimate first to determine the currently applicable rate.

Insurance and real estate (or property) taxes must also be included in the estimate if not previously considered in determining general works expense. In most areas, these costs total about 1.5 to 3 percent of investment per year. Two percent is about average for locations in the U.S.

DISTRIBUTION COSTS

The costs of packing and shipping products to market (i.e., distribution costs) are highly variable and dependent upon product characteristics. In many cases, especially with consumer products, these costs often exceed the cost of producing the product itself.

Distribution costs may include the following:

- cost of containers, including their repair, testing, cleaning, etc. (if reusable), and their depreciation or rental (if nonexpendable);
- transportation costs; and
- applicable labor and overheads for packing and shipping.

If the product is sold FOB the plant, the cost of transportation is borne by the customer and need not be considered in the estimate. If, however, it is sold on a delivered basis, transportation costs must be included.

The mode of transportation and the shipping distance drastically affect transportation costs. In general, pipelines, barges, and tankers are the least expensive forms of transportation. Rail shipment is somewhat higher in cost, and truck shipment is the most expensive. Freight tariffs are regulated by the states (intrastate shipments) and the federal government

(interstate shipments) and vary from product to product. In general, for any given product, freight costs per ton-mile are lowest for long hauls (250 to 300 miles or more) and high volumes. Short-distance haulage and small shipments incur considerably higher freight rates.

PRACTICE PROBLEMS AND QUESTIONS

1. (a)Define fixed cost, variable cost, and semivariable cost. What items are included in each?
    (b) At zero production, what percentage of semivariable cost is normally incurred (as a percentage of total semivariable cost at full production)?
    (c) What are the definitions of the breakeven and shutdown points?

---

2. In a manufacturing operation, at 100 percent of capacity, annual costs are as follows:

    Fixed expense $ 4,730,400
    Variable expense   6,446,400
    Semivariable expense   5,652,500
    Sales   23,986,800

Question: Assuming that semivariable costs at zero production equal 30% of such costs at 100 percent of capacity, determine the shutdown and breakeven points.

Answer: Shutdown at 12.5 percent of capacity and breakeven at 47.3 percent of capacity

---

3. You work for a chemical company that plans to install $60,000,000 worth of new equipment this year. You estimate that this equipment will have a salvage value of $5,000,000 at the end of its useful life.

Question: What are the IRS-approved depreciation allowances for the first five years?

Answer: Year 1, $8.574 MM; Year 2, $14.694 MM; Year 3, $10.494 MM; Year 4, $7.494 MM; and Year 5, $5.358 MM.

4. (a) In the above problem, what is the straight-line depreciation for each of the first five years?
    (b) This technique is recommended for preliminary estimates. Why? *get net estimate on*
    Answer: (a) $5.5 MM per year   *cost.*

5. Assume that for accounting purposes rather than tax purposes, your company uses double declining balance depreciation. Calculate the double declining balance depreciation allowances for each of the first five years of equipment life for problem 3.

Answer: Year 1, $12 MM; Year 2, $9.6 MM; Year 3, $7.68 MM; Year 4, $6.144 MM; Year 5, $4.9152 MM

6. What is a depletion allowance? How is it calculated?

7. What are general and administrative expenses?

8. What is general works expense?

9. Why should operating cost estimates be made on an annual basis rather than a daily or unit-of-production basis?

10. How can the cost of grease and lubricants be estimated for motor vehicles and mobile equipment?

11. How can fuel cost be estimated for motor vehicles and mobile equipment?

12. In order to estimate process labor requirements, what must first be established?

13. How many standard 40-hour/week shifts are required to staff a plant around the clock, 7 days a week?

14. What is a good rule of thumb for estimating electric power costs?

15. What rule of thumb can be used to estimate the cost of steam?

16. In scaling up utililty requirements for larger pieces of equipment, what rule of thumb can be used to estimate the utility requirements?

17. Is it advisable to use scheduled overtime work in industrial plants?

18. If a plant operates at 50% of capacity, what will its approximate maintenance cost be as a percentage of maintenance costs at full capacity.

19. For preliminary estimates, annual maintenance costs are generally assumed to be constant even though they are known to increase with time. Straight-line depreciation is also assumed despite the fact that accelerated depreciation will be used in actual operations. Why are these two clearly erroneous assumptions made?

20. Are royalties and rental co fixed, or capital costs?

REFERE

1. J. H. Black. 1991. Operating Cost Estimation. ʲᵉⁱᵉⁿ and Optimization Engineering. (K. K. Humphreys, ed.) New York: McGraw-Hil.
2. R. M. Blough. 1973. Effect of Scheduled Overtime on Construction Projects. AACE Bulletin 15 (5). 155–158, 160 (October).
3. J. W. Hackney. 1971. Estimate Production Costs Quickly. Chemical Engineering. 183 (April 17).
4. K. K. Humphreys. Coal Preparation Costs. Coal Preparation. 5th ed. (J. W. Leonard, ed.) Society of Metallurgy and Exploration. Littleton, Colorado. chap. 3.
5. W. McGlaun. 1973. Overtime in Construction. AACE Bulletin. 15 (5). 141–143 (October).
6. H. E. Wessell. 1952. New Graph Correlates Operating Labor Data for Chemical Processes. Chemical Engineering. 209 (July).

Problem #2

$$B = \frac{(F + nR)}{S - V - (1-n)R}$$

$F = 4,730,400$

$V = 6,446,400$

$R = 5,652,500$

$S = 23,986,800$

$n = 30\%$

$$A = \frac{nR}{S - V - (1-n)R}$$

Problem #3

use table 10.5 MACRS

Deduction Rate Pg. 10.22

choose column "7 yr" because it is 10 yrs or more but less than 16 yrs

$Yr 1 = .1429\% \times 60,000 = 8.574m$

$Yr 2 = .2449\% \times 60,000 = 14.094m$

Chapter 11

Discrete Product Manufacturing

Dr. Robert C. Creese, PE CCE

INTRODUCTION

Discrete part or product manufacturing refers to the production of separate, individual products, whereas continuous manufacturing is concerned with large units to be further processed, such as a roll of sheet steel, or units in fluid form with no distinct shape. Discrete parts typically are solid products that have the dimensions and sizes for final use, whereas solid continuous products will be further processed into specific shapes. Discrete production often yields low quantities; the average lot size is less than 75 units. Discrete manufacturing employs specialized tools for the various products, so set-up and tooling changes are much more frequent in discrete manufacturing than in continuous manufacturing.

Another variable in discrete manufacturing is whether the manufacturing is that of an individual component part of a product or with the assembly or joining of parts to form a completed product. Assembly is often the final operation in the production of a manufactured product before it goes to the customer. For example, assembly lines are the final phase in the manufacture of automobiles, and this involves the assembly of many components. However, one of those components, the engine, is a subassembly of various components, one of which is the engine block. The engine block is considered as a discrete manufactured part, whereas the automobile is considered as a discrete manufacturing assembly. The focus of this section is on the discrete manufactured part, although the approach is similar for discrete manufactured assemblies.

LEARNING OBJECTIVES

After completing this chapter, the reader should be able to:

- understand the operations, terms, and philosophies used in discrete product manufacturing;
- understand basic cost relationships, cost bases, and classification of costs; and
- understand time-based and quantity-based break-even analysis and when it is best to use each approach.

OPERATIONS IN DISCRETE PART MANUFACTURING

There are a wide variety of products produced in discrete manufacturing, and, thus, an extreme variety of operations performed to obtain the desired shape and properties required of the product. The operations performed vary considerably depending on the material being used for the specific component. Six major groups of component operations and a few of the manufacturing operations of each group are presented in Table 11.1.

Note that some manufacturing operations are repeated in different major component groups, and the machining operations, which is listed in the metal component manufacturing group, would also be heavily utilized in the plastic component manufacturing and in several other groups.

DISCRETE PART MANUFACTURING PHILOSOPHIES

There are several manufacturing philosophies/techniques that have been introduced during the last 50 years to assist in the reduction of manufacturing costs. Some of these philosophies/techniques are: computer-aided process planning (CAPP), cconcurrent engineering, group technology, just-in-time, lean manufacturing, materials requirement planning, supply-chain management, and total quality management. Each of these techniques will be briefly presented to indicate the goals of that philosophy/technique.

- **computer-aided process planning (CAPP)**—The goal of CAPP is to be able to automatically generate the process plan to produce the component from the component drawing and specifications. This would include the sequence of the operations as well as the particular operation parameters and would optimize the processing time, operation costs, and product quality. The two

Table 11.1—Component Operation Classification for Discrete Manufacturing [6, 7, 10]

Major Component Group	Illustrative Manufacturing Operations of Major Component Group
1. Metal Component Manufacturing	
Casting	sand casting, investment casting, die casting, permanent mold casting, squeeze casting, full mold casting, slush casting, etc.
Forming and Shaping	rolling, open-die forging, impression die forging, impact extrusion, drawing, shearing, bending, powder processing, etc.
Machining	turning, drilling, milling, sawing, planning, shaping, grinding, water-jet machining, electrical discharge machining, etc.
2. Plastic Component Manufacturing	injection molding, extrusion, blow molding, pultrusion, thermoforming, compression molding, filament winding, etc. and many of the machining operations
3. Ceramic and Glass Component Manufacturing	
Ceramic	slip casting, extrusion, pressing, injection molding, hot pressing, drying, firing, drawing, etc.
Glass	rolling, float forming, pressing, blowing, etc.
4. Component Surface Modification	case hardening, hot dipping, porcelain enameling, electroplating, thermal spraying, vapor deposition, anodizing, painting, cleaning, peening, etc.
5. Assembly and Joining	arc welding, resistance welding, laser welding, brazing, soldering, adhesive bonding, mechanical fasteners, etc.
6. Micro-Electronic Component Manufacturing	crystal growth, wafer slicing and polishing, photolithography, doping, sputtering, chemical vapor deposition, etching, adhesive bonding, wave soldering, etc.

approaches to CAPP are (1) the variant approach, which searches a database for similar parts and modifies the closest similar component plan for the new component; and (2) the generative approach, which designs the process plan starting from "scratch," that is, generating a completely original approach.

- **Concurrent Engineering**—Concurrent engineering as defined by the Institute for Defense Analysis [9] is a systematic approach to the integrated, concurrent design of products and their related processes, including manufacturing and support. This approach is intended to cause the developer (designers), from the outset, to consider all elements of the product life cycle from conception through disposal, including quality, cost, schedule, and user requirements.

- **Group Technology**—Group technology is a manufacturing philosophy that identifies and exploits the underlying sameness of component parts and manufacturing process [2]. There are two primary approaches, which are (1) classifying parts into families that have similar design features and (2) classifying parts into families that have similar processing operations. This permits the standardization of parts in the design process and, in the second case, pro-

duction of parts as families by permitting cell formation and reducing the set-up times via fewer set-up changes.

- **Just-in-Time**—Just-in-time is the manufacturing philosophy that requires that the supplies (raw materials) are delivered when required, and, thus, inventory costs are theoretically driven to zero as there is no inventory. This is not only for external suppliers but also for internal use as parts go from one operation to the next, so the work-in-process inventory is a minimum. This is closely related to the "Kanban" system or "pull" system in which parts are not produced until ordered.

- **Lean Manufacturing**—Lean manufacturing is a manufacturing philosophy to shorten lead times, reduce costs, and reduce waste. This philosophy is implemented by (1) reducing waste through scrap reduction, improving yields, and developing new products from waste stream materials; (2) improving employee performance, skills, and satisfaction via training, recognition, and employee involvement and empowerment; and (3) investing capital to improve processes, process rates, and capabilities. Lean manufacturing is not "mean" manufacturing, and it is not a short-term process. Rather, it is a continuous improvement process.

- **Material Requirements Planning (MRP)***—MRP is a system that uses bills of material, inventory and open order data, and master production schedule information to calculate requirements for materials. It makes recommendations to release replenishment orders for materials. Further, since it is time-phased, it makes recommendations to reschedule open orders when due dates and need dates are not in phase.

- **Supply Chain Management**—The production of complex products require the integration of many different components from a variety of suppliers. Supply chain management involves the assurance that the parts will arrive from the suppliers when required to avoid large inventories or production stoppages from a lack of parts. Supply chain management also requires the involvement of suppliers in the design process to eliminate unnecessary operations and inefficient designs of components or even unnecessary components. Although the focus is on the movement of materials, it also involves the transfer of information on the status of delivery and financial flow of credit, terms and conditions, and payment schedules as the materials move through the various stages of the supply chain. The goals are to reduce inventory, time-to-market, and costs, and improve quality.

- **Total Quality Management**—Total quality management is a leadership philosophy, organizational structure, and working environment that fosters and nourishes a personal accountability and responsibility for the quality and a quest for continuous improvement in products, services, and processes [8].

BASIC COST RELATIONSHIPS

The basic relationships between the various manufacturing cost terms are illustrated in Figures 11.1 and 11.2 on pages 11.4 and 11.5. Figure 11.1 shows the relationships between the various cost terms in a flow chart form [3], and Figure 11.2 illustrates the terms in a stepwise fashion referred to as the "ladder of costs." The sum of direct material, direct labor, direct engineering, and direct expense is the prime cost. However, many companies do not keep adequate records of direct engineering and direct expenses, and, in many instances, the prime cost is the sum of the direct material and direct labor costs. Usually the design engineering and direct expense are included as overhead costs and not allocated to the specific product. This is partly because only 10 percent of new products make it into the production stage, and most of the design work cannot be assigned to the specific products. The relationships between the cost terms can also be illustrated by equations such as the following:

*prime cost = direct material cost + direct labor cost + direct engineering cost + direct expense

(equation 11.1)

GLOSSARY TERMS IN THIS CHAPTER

administrative expense ◆ break-even analysis
contingency ◆ cost ◆ cost estimating
costing/cost accounting ◆ discrete manufacturing
direct cost ◆ direct labor
indirect cost ◆ indirect labor ◆

**manufacturing cost = prime cost + factory expense

(equation 11.2)

production cost = manufacturing cost + administrative expense

(equation 11.3)

total cost = production cost + marketing, selling, and distribution expense

(equation 11.4)

selling price = total cost + mark-up (profit and taxes)

(equation 11.5)

*prime cost is also called direct cost
**manufacturing cost is also called factory cost

The profit should be related to the value to the customer. Some items will generate more profit than others; parts that one is skilled at producing should yield more profit than new items or those that one does not have the ideal equipment to produce. Equal profits indicate your prices will be too high for items that you have difficulty making and too low for items that are your specialty area.

Profit is usually meant to imply net profit; that is, the profit after all expenses have been incurred and after taxes have been paid. The other profit terms, that is gross profit and operating profit, do not include all the expenses and thus are larger than the net profit term.

COST ESTIMATING FOR DISCRETE PART MANUFACTURING

Direct and Indirect Costs

Direct costs are those costs that can be directly related to a specific part and these most commonly are direct materials and direct labor. There can be other direct costs, such as direct engineering or direct burden expenses, but these are often not separated (even though they should be) and are thus included in the overhead components. The direct materials include all the direct material consumed in the product unless they are small and cost more to track. The direct labor and direct material costs are also referred to as the "out-of-

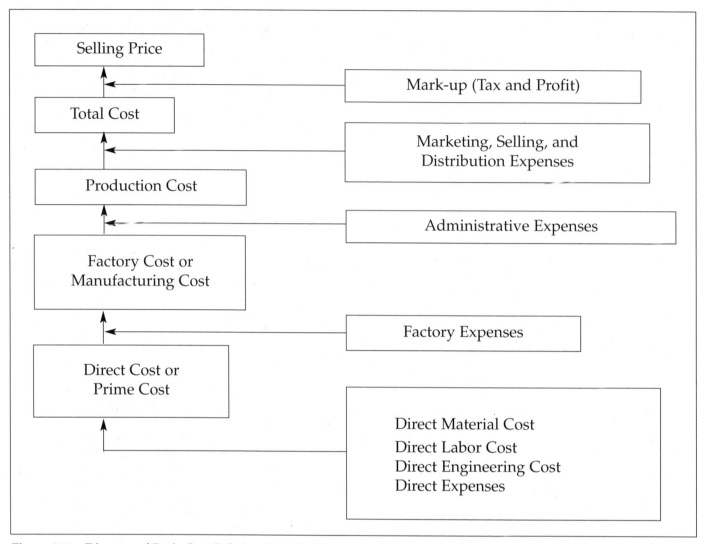

Figure 11.1—Diagram of Basic Cost Relationships for Discrete Part Manufacturing

pocket" costs; they are costs which are being directly paid to others and do not cover any of the direct or indirect overhead costs. The direct labor represents the fully burdened labor costs; that is the benefits as well as the wages.

For example, in the copying of a report on a copy machine, the costs would be the paper cost, the toner cost, the machine rate costs, the operator cost, and the staple cost. The paper and toner would be direct material costs, the operator cost would be a direct labor cost, but the cost of an individual staple is so small compared to the other costs, it typically would be included as part of the indirect burden costs. The machine rate cost includes the operating cost plus capital costs, so it would be a indirect cost but it is applied directly to the product. If one did not make the copy, the direct costs of the operator and the paper would be saved and these would be the "out-of-pocket" costs.

There are different degrees of the indirect costs. In the copying machine example, there is a certain amount of energy consumed to operate the machine each time a copy is made. However, when the machine is on idle, it also consumes some energy, and this cost is built into the burden based upon its expected usage. The capital costs of purchasing and installing the machine are another level of burden based upon the expected life of the machine and the expected copies produced per year. Although these are direct costs, they are considered as indirect costs as the machine is used for a wide variety of reports and not only one report.

Other indirect costs are those which cannot be directly tied to the product such as supervision, administrative salaries, maintenance, janitorial, material handling, and legal, etc. These costs have different degrees of indirectness. For example, the immediate supervisor may have five people working for him, whereas the plant superintendent may have 500.

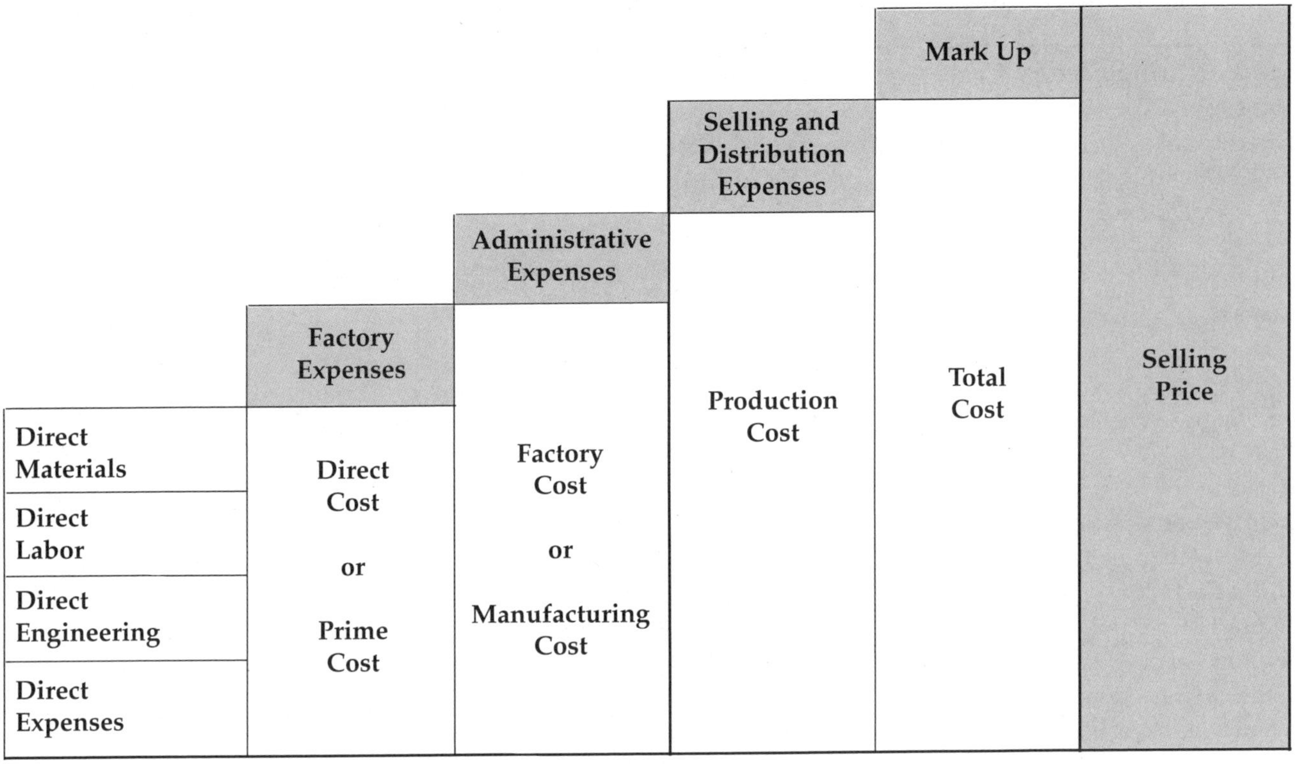

Figure 11.2—Ladder of Costs for Discrete Part Manufacturing

More of the immediate supervisors cost must be allocated in the overhead burden than the plant superintendents overhead for particular component part, but the plant superintendents overhead will be applied over many more component parts. In large companies, indirect costs also include items such as basic and applied research and development, which must be done to develop future products. However, the costs of such activities must be recovered on the current products being produced and these research and development costs for future products are indirect burden costs for the current products.

Cost Estimating Guide Form

There are so many different types of operations and items that can be included on a cost estimating form, that only a general guide can be given. A form particular to the particular products produced must be designed to obtain good cost estimates. The general form is illustrated in Table 11.2 on page 11.6. The mark-up amount is calculated as follows:

mark-up (amount) = total cost x [% MU /[1 - % MU]]
(equation 11.6)

where

total cost = total costs
% MU = decimal percent of mark-up for profits and taxes

For example, if the total costs are $10,000, and the mark up is

20 percent, the mark-up amount would be:

mark-up (amount) = 10,000 x [0.20 /[1.00 − 0.20]] = $2,500

The selling price would be $10,000 plus $2,500 mark-up or $12,500.

To illustrate the use of the form, an illustrative example is presented in Table 11.3 on page 11. 7. The values presented are for illustrative purposes and not specific values or rates to be used. These values must be evaluated for each individual company.

An order has been received for 100 units of a component, which will require 240 lbs of material 1 at $0.75 per pound and 5 lbs of material 2, which is $ 4.00 per pound for each unit. The product requires two operations, operation 1, which takes 0.20hrs/unit at $ 20/hr, and operation 2, which takes 0.40hrs/unit at $25/hr. The special tooling for the job is $ 3,600. The mark-up for profits and taxes is 20 percent of the selling price. The example costs and selling price are presented in Table 11.3, with the unit selling price of $596.38 and a unit cost of $477.10. With a tax rate of 40 percent, one must charge $1.67 for every $1.00 of after-tax profit desired, and this is one reason why businesses dislike the taxes so much.

Table 11.2—General Discrete Costs Estimating Form With Illustrative Example Rates

1. Manufacturing/Factory Cost

a. Prime Cost

Direct Labor	Amount(hours/unit)	Rate($/hr)	Quantity	Total Cost	
Operation 1	–				___
Operation 2	–				___
					___

Direct Materials	Amount(weight/unit)	Rate($/weight)	Quantity	Total Cost	
Material 1					___
Material 2					___
					___

Direct Engineering/Expense	Amount(units)	Rate($/unit)		Total Cost	
Item 1					___
Item 2					___
Item 3 (subcontracted)					___ ___
Total Prime Cost					___

b. Indirect Costs

Indirect Materials	Rate(% of direct materials)	___
Indirect Labor	Rate(% of direct labor)	___
Indirect Engineering/Expense	Rate(% of prime cost)	___
Contingency Costs		
Process Contingency	Rate(% of prime cost)	___
Product Contingency	Rate(% of prime cost plus contingency cost)	___
Direct Supervision	Rate(% of direct labor)	___
Total Indirect Costs		___
Manufacturing/Factory Cost		___

2. Production Plant Cost

Plant Administrative		
Administration, Property Taxes, and Insurance	Rate(% of manufacturing cost)	___
		___
Total Plant Administrative Cost		___

3. Selling Expenses

Marketing Costs	Rate(% of manufacturing costs)	___
Selling Commissions & Salaries	Rate(% of production costs)	___
Shipping Expenses	Rate(% of Prime Cost)	___
Warehousing	Rate(% of prime cost)	___
Total Marketing, Selling & Distribution Costs		___
Total Costs		___

4. Mark-Up

Profit and Taxes	Rate(% of Total Cost)	___
		___
Selling Price		___

Table 11.3—General Discrete Costs Estimating Form With Illustrative Example Rates

1. Manufacturing/Factory Cost						% of Total Cost	
						Component	Cumulative
a. Prime Costs							
Direct Labor	Amount(hours/unit)	Rate($/hr)	Quantity	Total Cost			
Operation 1	0.20 hr/unit	$ 20/hr	100	$400			
Operation 2	0.40 hr/unit	$ 25/hr	100	$1,000			
					$ 1,400	3.0	
Direct Materials	Amount(weight/unit)	Rate($/wt)	Quantity	Total Cost			
Material 1	240 lbs/unit	$ 0.75/lb	100	$18,000			
Material 2	5 lbs/unit	$ 4.00/lb	100	$ 2,000			
					$20,000	41.9	
Direct Eng./Expense	Amount(units)	Rate($/unit)		Total Cost			
Item 1	1 tooling set	$ 3,600		$ 3,600			
Item 2							
Item 3 (subcontracted)					$3,600	7.5	
Total Prime Cost					$25,000		52.4
b. Indirect Costs							
Indirect Materials	20% of direct materials				$4,000		
Indirect Labor	100% of direct labor				$1,400		
Indirect Engineering/Expense	10% of prime cost				$2,500		
Contingency Costs							
Process Contingency	5% of prime cost				$1,250		
Product Contingency	10 % of prime cost plus contingency cost				$ 3,750		
Direct Supervision	20% of direct labor				$ 280		
Total Indirect Costs					$13,180	27.6	
Manufacturing/Factory Cost					$38,180		80.0

2. Production Plant Cost			
Plant Administrative			
Administration, Property Taxes,			
Insurance	5% of manufacturing cost	$1,909	
Total Plant Administrative Cost		$1,909	4.0
Production Costs		$40,089	84.0

3. Selling Expenses			
Marketing Costs	3 % of manufacturing costs	$1,145	
Selling Commissions & Salaries	10% of production costs	$4,009	
Shipping Expenses	4% of prime cost	$1,000	
Warehousing	6% of prime cost	$1,500	
Total Marketing, Selling & Distribution Costs		$7,654	16.0
Total Costs		$ 47,743	100.0

4. Mark-Up			
Profit and Taxes	20% of selling price	$ 11,936	
		$ 11,936	
Selling Price		**$ 59,679**	

Unit Selling Price = $ 59,679/100 = $ 596.79 or $ 600.00/unit

The contingency costs are primarily for new products and processes, and would be low for standard products. The contingency costs are for expected tooling changes and process changes that would be required from expected design errors or incorrect process parameters.

The form is illustrative to indicate the various items that must be tracked to determine the total and unit costs. A form must be designed to the particular operations and materials of the particular company, and, as illustrated in Table 11.1, there are a wide variety of possible operations. It is not practical to design a form to include all types of operations and materials. The costs in the form follow the ladder of costs, and the percentages of the total cost can be included in the form as illustrated in Table 11.3

BREAK-EVEN ANALYSIS

4.1 Introduction

There are two critical issues in break-even analysis [9, 10] that must be considered and they are (a) the cost base and (b) the various break-even points. The two different cost bases are the time base and the quantity base. The quantity-based break-even analysis determines the production quantity at the specific break-even point, and this has worked for marketing, sales, and top management for forecasting yearly sales and other long-range planning activities. However, it provides little assistance at the plant management level where the production quantity is not a variable, but is a quantity specified by the customer.

Time-based break-even analysis focuses on the time to produce the order, which is something under the control of the plant supervision. Time-based break-even analysis determines the production time for the specific break-even point, and this is what can be controlled at the plant level. The same break-even points can be used in either system, but the costs must be considered carefully as the different bases—time and quantity—result in different conclusions with respect to the variability of the costs.

Costs are generally classified as fixed costs, variable costs, and semivariable costs, but whether a cost is fixed, variable or semivariable depends upon the cost base used. One of the difficulties in promoting the time-based system is that what has been treated as a variable cost in the quantity-based system is often fixed in the time-based system and vice-versa. The second issue with break-even points is that increased quantities are desired in the quantity-based system, whereas decreased times are desired in the time-based system.

Cost Bases

Costs are generally classified into three major groups: (1) fixed, (2) variable, and (3) semivariable. How the costs are assigned to a group depends upon the cost base; that is, whether the cost base is the quantity base or the time base. Since production quantity has been the standard base, this base will be considered first. Costs that do not vary with respect to production quantity are considered as fixed costs, and some of the commonly designated fixed costs are property taxes, administrative salaries, research and development expenses, and insurance. Variable costs are those that vary linearly with production quantity, and the most common variable cost items in the production quantity base are direct material costs and direct labor costs. The costs that do not fit into either of the fixed or variable costs are classified as semivariable costs, and an example of semivariable cost is maintenance cost.

When a time-based system is used, many of the cost components in the fixed and variable categories change when compared to the quantity-based system. Costs that do not vary with respect to time are considered as fixed costs, and these would be items such as the direct material costs. For as the production quantity is fixed, the material costs would be fixed. On the other hand, costs such as property taxes, administrative salaries, research and development expenses, and insurance would be considered as variable as they must be recovered over time. Direct labor may be a fixed or variable quantity depending upon the policies used. If the direct labor does not vary per unit of production, then with a fixed quantity, the direct labor cost would be a fixed cost on the time basis. If the labor force were fixed, such as when management does not layoff employees, then it would be similar to a fixed salary and the cost would be variable with respect to the time to do the work.

Break-Even Points

The four break-even points that are considered in the profitability evaluation of products or operations are the shutdown point, the cost point, the required return point, and the required return after taxes point. These points can be evaluated on either the time based or quantity based system. The points can be defined as follows:

- **Shutdown Point (SD)**—The shutdown point is the quantity or time where the manufacturing costs equals the revenues. In the production quantity system, it is the production quantity at which the revenues equal the manufacturing costs. In the production time system, it is the production time at which the revenues equals the manufacturing costs. The manufacturing costs include the material costs, tooling costs, labor costs, and plant/shop overhead costs.

- **Cost Point (C)**—The cost point is the quantity or time where the total costs equals the revenues. In the production quantity system, it is the production quantity at which the revenues equal the total costs and in the production time system, it is the production time at which the revenues equal the total costs. The total costs include the manufacturing costs plus all other costs such as the administrative costs, selling and marketing, research and development expenses, and etc.

- **Required Return Point (RR)**—The required return point is the quantity or time where the revenues equals the total costs plus the required return. In the production quantity system, it is the production quantity at which the revenues equal the total costs plus the required return.

- **Required Return after Taxes Point (RRAT)**—The required return after taxes point is the quantity or time where the revenues equals the total costs plus the required return and the taxes on the required return. In the production quantity system, it is the production quantity at which the revenues equal the total costs plus the required return plus the taxes on the required return. In the production time system the required return after taxes point is the time at which the revenues equals the total costs plus the required return plus the taxes on the required return.

The breakeven points increase in quantity as one proceeds from the shutdown point to the required return after taxes point in the production quantity-based system, which implies higher production quantities are desired. However, the breakeven points decrease in time as one proceeds from the shutdown point to the required return after taxes point in the time-based system. The decrease in time indicates the importance of decreasing production time to increase profitability and is similar to the "just-in-time" concept that focuses on time.

Breakeven Example Problem

A metalcasting example will be used to illustrate both the production quantity-based approach and the time-based approach to determining the four breakeven points. The same data will be used to illustrate that both methods can be utilized, but the time-based system gives results that are more meaningful.

A new job is being considered in the foundry. The order is for 40,000 castings, and the tentative price is $ 3.00/casting. The pattern will be designed for 4 castings per mold, and the pattern cost has been quoted at $ 10,000. The molding line is the rate controlling step in the production process in this particular foundry, and the production rate is 125 molds/hr. The estimated time for the production of the 40,000 castings would be determined by:

(40,000 castings)/(4 castings/mold x 125 molds/hr) = 80 hr

The costs and overheads are included in Table 11.4, and the corporate tax rate is estimated at 40 percent.

Production Quantity-Based Calculations—The calculations for the four break-even points will be made using "X" as the variable representing the number of units of production.

Shutdown Point

Revenues = Production Costs

$3X$ = Material Costs + Labor Costs + Tooling Costs + Plant Overhead Costs

$3X = 1.50X + 0.33X + 10,000 + 8,800$

$3X = 1.83X + 18,800$

$1.17 X = 18,800$

$X = 16,068$ units

Cost Point

Revenues = Total Costs

Revenues = Production Costs + Overhead Costs

$3X = 1.83X + 18,800 + 12,000$

$3X = 1.83X + 30,800$

$1.17X = 30,800$

$X = 26,324$ units

Required Return Point

Revenues = Total Costs   + Required Return

$3X$ $= 1.83X + 30,800$ $+ 9,600$

$3X$ $= 1.83X + 40,400$

$1.17X$ $= 40,400$

X $= 34,530$ units

Required Return After Taxes

Revenues = Total Costs + Required Return + Taxes for Required Return

$3X = 1.83X + 30,800 + 9,600$ $+ 9,600 \times (TR/(1-TR))$

$3X = 1.83X + 40,400 + 6,400$

$1.17X = 46,800$

$X = 40,000$ units

The results from the production quantity model can be summarized as follows:

a. If the production quantity is less than 16,068 units do not accept the order as the manufacturing costs will not be recovered.

b. If the production quantity is between 16,068 and 26,324 units, the manufacturing costs will be recovered, but not all of the overhead costs.

c. If production quantity is between 26,324 and 34,530 units, all costs will be recovered, but not all of the required return will be recovered.

d. If the production quantity is between 34,530 and 40,000 units, all of the costs and the required return will be recovered, but not all of the taxes for the required return will be recovered. (Thus, the required return will not be recovered after taxes as the government will take its share for taxes).

e. If the production quantity is more than 40,000 units, the required return will exceed the desired required return on an after tax basis.

Table 11.4. Cost Data for Time-Based and Quantity-Based Break-Even Example Problem

Cost Item or Revenue	$/unit	$/hr	$	Decimal
Revenue		3.00*	(120,000)	
Manufacturing Costs				
Direct Costs				
Material Costs				
Hot Metal Cost 1.00				
Core Costs 0.35				
Filter Cost 0.10				
<u>Sand Preparation Cost</u>	0.05			
	1.50	1.50*	(60,000)	
Pattern Cost			10,000**	
Labor Costs				
Melting	0.10			
Molding & Coremaking	0.08			
<u>Finishing</u>	0.15			
	0.33	0.33*	(165)	
Indirect Costs				
Plant Overhead Rate		(110)	8,800*	
Overhead Costs				
General Administrative, Sales, and				
Marketing Overhead Rate		(150)	12,000*	
Required Return and Taxes				
Required Return		(120)	9,600*	
Tax Rate (40%)				0.40**
Taxes for Required Return		(80)	6,400*	

---

*values used for quantity based model
**values used for both models
( ) values used for time based model
Conversion Factors for Data:
  Production Rate: 500 units/hr or 0.002 hours/units and thus 0.33$/unit x 500 units/hr = 165 $/hr
  Production Time: 40,000 units/ 500 units/hr = 80 hours and thus 110$/hr x 80 hr = $ 8,800

The results can be graphically illustrated using total costs versus production quantity as illustrated in Figure 11.3. The various breakeven points are shown increasing in quantity from the shutdown point to the required return after taxes.

Figure 11.4 is a plot of unit cost versus production quantity and illustrates the various break-even points. The break-even points on the two graphs are the same values, but the two figures are quite different. The symbols SD, C, RR, and RRAT represent the break-even points at the shutdown, cost, required return, and the required return after taxes.

Time-Based Calculations

The calculations for the four break-even points will be made using "Y" as the variable representing the hours of production.

Shutdown Point
  Revenues = Production Costs
  Revenues = Material Costs + Labor Costs + Tooling Costs + Plant Overhead Costs
  $120,000 = 60,000 + 165Y + 10,000 + 110Y$
  $120,000 = 70,000 + 275Y$
  $275Y = 50,000$
  $Y = 181.8$ hours

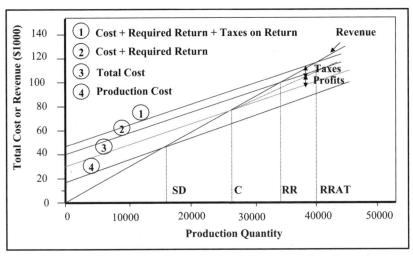

Figure 11.3—Total Cost and Revenues Versus Production Quantity

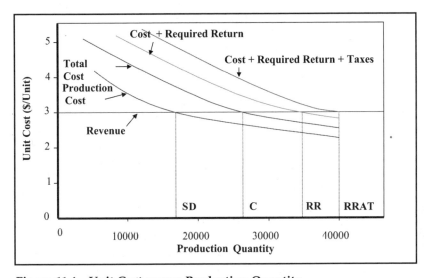

Figure 11.4—Unit Cost versus Production Quantity

Cost Point
Revenues = Total Costs
Revenues = Production Costs + Overhead Costs
$$120,000 = 70,000 + 275Y + 150Y$$
$$120,000 = 70,000 + 425Y$$
$$425Y = 50,000$$
$$Y = 117.6 \text{ hours}$$

Required Return Point
Revenues = Total Costs + Required Return
$$120,000 = 70,000 + 425Y + 120Y$$
$$120,000 = 70,000 + 545Y$$
$$545Y = 50,000$$
$$Y = 91.7 \text{ hours}$$

Required Return After Taxes
Revenues = Total Costs + Required Return + Taxes for Required Return
$$120,000 = 70,000 + 425Y + 120Y + 120Y \times (TR/(1-TR))$$
$$120,000 = 70,000 + 425Y + 120Y + 120Y \times (0.4/(1-0.4))$$
$$120,000 = 70,000 + 425Y + 120Y + 80Y$$
$$625Y = 50,000$$
$$Y = 80.0 \text{ hours}$$

The results are from the production time-based model can be summarized as:

a. If the production time is more than 181.8 hours, do not accept the order as the manufacturing costs will not be recovered.
b. If the production time is between 117.6 and 181.8 hours, the manufacturing costs will be recovered, but not all of the overhead costs.
c. If production time is between 91.7 and 117.6 hours, all of the costs will be recovered, but not all of the required return will be recovered.
d. If the production time is between 91.7 and 80.0 hours, the costs and the required return will be recovered, but not all of the taxes for the required return will be recovered. (Thus, the required return will not be recovered after taxes as the government will take its share for taxes).
e. If the production time is less than 80.0 hours, the required return will exceed the desired required return level on an after tax basis.

The results can be graphically illustrated using total costs versus production time as illustrated in Figure 11.5. The various breakeven points are shown decreasing in time from the shutdown point to the required return after taxes. Figure 11.6 is the profitability plot, which shows the profitability as a function of the production time and the various break-even points. The profitability plot illustrates the importance of reducing production time for increasing profitability. The plot can illustrate either constant amount or constant rates of required return on the break-even points.

The advantage of the time-based break-even analysis is that it can answer questions such as what is the effect of a 4 hour delay due to a machine breakdown. The effect is not obvious from the quantity breakeven analysis, but the time based break-even analysis indicates that 84 hours is between the required return and required return after taxes break-even times; that is all costs are recovered and the required return will be exceeded before taxes but not after taxes. This can be evaluated by determining the profit from the following:

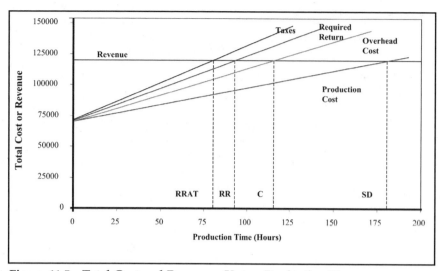

Figure 11.5—Total Cost and Revenues Versus Production Time

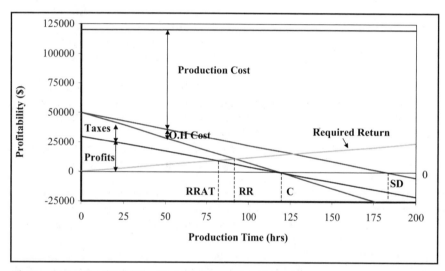

Figure 11.6—Profitability Plot for Time-Based System

Profit = Revenues - Costs
Profit = $120,000 - ($70,000 + 425$/hr x time (hr))
Profit = $50,000 - 425$/hr x 84hr
    Profit = $14,300
    Profit after taxes = (1-TR) x 14,300 = 0.6 x 14,300 = 8,580

Since the required return after taxes was 9,600 and the required return before taxes was $16,000, the $ 14,300 amount is between the two expected values. The loss on the time-base system could also be evaluated at $ 425 (165 + 110 + 150 = 425) per hour, and for 4 hours down the loss would be $1,700.

The loss in the quantity-based system can be obtained by using some of the conversion factors; the loss of 4 hours is equivalent to the production loss of 2,000 units. This loss

would be the labor lost plus the plant overhead and the overhead costs for four hours; thus the loss would be

2,000 units x 0.33$/unit + 4hr x (110 + 150)
=$660 + $1,040 = $1,700

The time-based approach is much easier to determine and more straightforward.

Time-based break-even analysis would also be useful in evaluating the cost of bottleneck delays and provide data for the economic justification of new equipment to improve productivity. The high cost of delays indicate that one of the factors to consider is the evaluation management's performance, and this can be done using a time-based system. The evaluation of bottlenecks and delays is critical in the "theory of constraints" and supply-chain management, and the focus is upon time in these situations.

CONCLUSIONS

Discrete part manufacturing involves the production of separate, individual products, usually in small batches of 75 units or less. A wide variety of operations are used for the manufacturing of discrete parts as well as a wide variety of materials. Various manufacturing philosophies and terms for estimating in discrete manufacturing have been presented. The ladder of costs (Figure 11.2) illustrates the interrelationships between the various cost terms, and a cost estimating form (Tables 11.2 and 11.3) has been presented for discrete manufacturing.

Time-based break-even analysis has been presented along with the traditional quantity-based breakeven analysis to illustrate the differences and similarities in the two approaches in analyzing the same set of data. The classification of costs as to whether they are fixed, variable, or semivariable depends upon which cost base is used, and that is the time base or the quantity base. The four basic break-even points of shutdown, cost, required return, and required return after taxes are illustrated in both the time-based and production quantity-based systems.

The quantity-based approach is appropriate for marketing and sales forecasting as they need to estimate the revenues obtained and predict the sales quantities. However, at the plant level, where scheduling of the daily operations are concerned, the focus is upon time and time-based break-even analysis is more appropriate. Time-based breakeven analysis is also more appropriate to the newer approaches to production management, such as the "theory of constraints," "just-in-time," supply chain management, and "lot-size-of-one," in that the focus is upon time rather than quantity. The profitability plots indicated the importance of production time reductions upon improving profits, which complements the just-in-time philosophy for manufacturing.

PRACTICE PROBLEMS AND QUESTIONS

Problem 1—The data for the following product was obtained for an order of 3,000 parts:

Direct material costs $40,000
Factory Expenses $ 3,000
Direct labor costs $8,000
Administrative Expenses $ 7,000
Direct engineering cost $6,000
Selling and Distribution Expenses $10,000
Direct burden $16,000
Mark-up rate 20 percent
Units produced 3,000

Questions:
a. What is the prime cost?
b. What is the factory cost?
c. What is the production cost?
d. What is the selling price?
e. What is the manufacturing cost?
f. What is the selling price per unit?

Answers:
a. $70,000
b. $73,000
c. $80,000
d. $108,000
e. $73,000
f. $36.00

Problem 2

Item	$/unit	$	Decimal
Sales Revenue	20		
Manufacturing Costs			
Direct	3		
Indirect	2		
Plant Overhead		500	
Overhead		3,500	
Required Return		1,000	
Tax Rate			0.40

Questions: Calculate the break-even points using the production quantity approach on the above data. Illustrate the break-even points on either the total cost-revenue versus the production quantity plot or on a unit cost versus production quantity plot. (Shut-down—33.3 units, cost—266.7 units, required return—333.3 units, after taxes—377.8 units)

Problem 3

Item	$/hr	$	Decimal
Sales Revenue		15,000	
Manufacturing Costs			
Direct	18	4,000	
Indirect	2	1,000	
Overhead	20		
Required Return	10		
Tax Rate			0.40

Questions: Calculate the break-even points on a production time basis for the above data. Illustrate the break-even points on a total cost-revenue versus production time plot. Also construct a profitability plot illustrating the break-even points. (Shut-down—500 hours, cost—250 hours, required return—200 hours, after taxes—176.47 hours)

REFERENCES

1. AACE International. 1990. Standard Cost Engineering Terminology. *AACE Recommended Practice No. 16R 90.* Morgantown, West Virginia: AACE International.
2. Creese, R. C., and I. Ham. 1979. Group Technology for Higher Productivity and Cost Reduction in the Foundry. *AFS Transactions.* Vol. 87. pp. 227–230.
3. Creese, R. C.. M. Adithan, and B. S. Pabla. 1992. *Estimating and Costing for the Metal Manufacturing Industries.* New York: Marcel Dekker.
4. Creese, R. C. 1998. Time-Based Break-Even Analysis and Costing. *1998 AACE International Transactions.* Morgantown, West Virginia: AACE International. pp. ABC.02.1–ABC.02.6.
5. Creese, R.C. 1998. Time-Based Breakeven Analysis. *1998 Joint Cost Management Societies Proceedings.* pp. AACE.02.01–AACE.02.07.
6. Creese, R.C. 1998. *Introduction to Manufacturing Processes and Materials.* New York: Marcel Dekker.
7. Kalpakjian, Serope, and Steven R. Schmid. 2001. *Manufacturing Engineering and Technology.* 4th ed. Upper Saddle River, New Jersey: Prentice Hall.
8. Postula, Frank D. 1989. Total Quality Management and the Estimating Process-A Vision. Paper for BAUD 653. *System Acquisition and Project Management.* July 13.
9. Winner, R. I., et.al. 1988. *The Role of Concurrent Engineering in Weapons Systems Acquisition.* IDA Report

R-338. 1988, December, Institute for Defense Analysis, Alexandria, Virginia.

10. Wright, Paul Kenneth. 2001. *21st Century Manufacturing.* Upper Saddle River, New Jersey: Prentice-Hall.

Section 3

Planning & Scheduling

Chapter 12

Planning

Jennifer Bates, CCE

INTRODUCTION

What Is Planning?

> "A stitch in time saves nine."
> "Prior planning prevents poor performance."
> "When all else fails, follow the instructions."

Each of these expressions has been heard many times, and each in its own way repeats a well-known fact: an undertaking that has the benefit of up-front planning and that is executed according to plan stands the best chance of success. Yet we often find ourselves feeling rushed, ignoring the need to plan, and stumbling ahead, planning as we go. When this happens, we usually end up muttering another oft-heard expression:

> "There's never time to do it right the first time, but there's always time to do it over."

And after doing it over, we often find we've lost time, money, and credibility.

Planning can be defined as influencing the future by making decisions based on missions, needs, and objectives. It is the process of stating goals and determining the most effective way of reaching them. This future-oriented decision process defines the actions and activities, the time and cost targets, and the performance milestones that will result in successfully achieving objectives. The process involves several steps:

- setting objectives,
- gathering information,
- determining feasible alternative plans,
- choosing the best alternative,
- communicating the plan,
- implementing the plan,
- adjusting the plan to meet new conditions as they arise, and
- reviewing the effectiveness of the plan against attainment of objectives.

LEARNING OBJECTIVES

After completing this chapter, the reader should be able to:

- understand the importance of planning and of establishing a "planning culture" in an organization,
- identify the planning tools available to the cost engineer, and
- understand the major elements of planning.

THE IMPORTANCE OF PLANNING

Planning is of the greatest importance, because in its planning, an organization makes implicit assumptions about its future so it can take action today. It would be convenient if cost/benefit studies were available to prove the value of planning. Theoretically, we could measure planning payoff by relating the value of what we have achieved through planning to the cost of the planning. Unfortunately, it is a rare situation that offers the opportunity to quantify both the outcomes attained through planning and the outcome attained without planning. Accordingly, we must rely on other indicators. The Stanford Research Institute did this in a formal study some years ago, finding that companies that supported planning programs experienced superior growth rates when compared to companies that did not. The reason for this becomes obvious when examined in light of the cycle that leads to growth.

Given any project or opportunity, a company develops a plan to maximize that opportunity. In doing so, it uses the best information available. When the plan is implemented, activities are carefully monitored and controlled, using the plan as a reference baseline. Complete records are maintained through the execution phase. Finally, the experience gained is fed back to the company to increase its knowledge base for the next planning action. This cycle represents the learning curve in action—each repetition makes planning for and achieving the next opportunity much easier. Without a firm commitment to the planning cycle, a company is continually "reinventing the wheel," wasting time and money, and jeopardizing its place in the competitive marketplace.

Establishing a Planning Culture

Planning is not done by upper management alone; it exists in a hierarchical structure made up of policies, strategic plans, and operational plans. Different organizational levels produce plans that are quite different in type and scope. Nevertheless, everyone involved in an undertaking must plan, whether their charge is to develop a long-range plan for company growth or to develop a personnel procurement plan for a specific project. There are numerous reasons why a company that encourages a proactive, structured approach to planning will reap significant benefits over a company whose planning approach is reactive or random:

- preparing a clear scope definition minimizes the potential for overlooking an aspect critical to success;
- if undertaken as a team effort, it permits various viewpoints and ideas to be expressed;
- the resultant plan, if well documented, provides a means of communication between the participants;
- the plan provides a baseline for control during the execution phase; and
- post-completion reviews greatly reduce the potential for planning errors on subsequent activities.

Effective planning becomes routine when planning is an integral part of the company's culture. This begins with commitment by top management, continues with communication of that commitment to mid-level managers, and becomes rooted when every employee relates unequivocally with the company's goals. As with any operation, if those who are to manage a plan do not participate in its preparation, their level of commitment to success may be less than total. Therefore, using a team approach to planning builds participant confidence in the organization, stimulates communication among the parties, and promotes their feelings of ownership in the outcome. It also demonstrates that top management has a direction, that decision-making is under control, and that the total organization is working to achieve the same objectives.

An additional, but no less important, result of the team approach is the training "in-action" that lower-tier managers receive as they participate with upper management in the planning process. They are thus better able to assume higher levels of responsibility as opportunities develop, bringing with them a planning philosophy that is fully ingrained.

The effectiveness of planning, even at the independent craft level or crew level, was demonstrated by a University of California study that examined differences in productivity between workers performing tasks in a clear area on the ground and workers performing the same tasks in an elevated area. While it was expected that productivity would be less for tasks performed in an elevated area, just the opposite proved true: the ratio of elevated to on-ground productivity was, surprisingly, greater than 2:1. Analysis of these results showed that while workers would always carefully plan elevated work to minimize their exposure, they would plan on-ground work as it was performed. As a result, productivity was greatly decreased. These findings are supported by other studies showing that when planning takes place concurrent with task execution, workers tend to neglect planning, concentrating instead on operating routines. The obvious lesson? Plan! Plan! Plan! At all levels!

PLANNING TOOLS

When planning tools are mentioned, the tendency is to think in terms of hardware, software, and procedures. Yet, the most fundamental and useful planning tool available is the experience planning team participants have gained during previous undertakings. While impossible to quantify, this experience provides a sound basis for using the other, more tangible planning tools. These include the following:

- **Commercial handbooks and software programs, a variety of which are available**—These should be used, of course, with an understanding of their basis and limitations rather than applying them across the board.
- **Standard, companywide policies and operating procedures that have been officially issued**—Planners can then feel free to use them without having to continually seek management guidance and approval.
- **Model plans that can be adapted as necessary to specific undertakings**—Organizations that tend to undertake repetitive work should develop a model project and plan for each type of work.
- **Checklists that will support planning and help prevent overlooking key items that may have cost or schedule implications.**
- **Historical databases cataloging company experience on past projects in a standard format for use in new endeavors.**
- **Codes of accounts structured to catalog work, cost accounts, resources, and other information**—These are essential if planning is to take advantage of available software. Codes of accounts should be standardized to the extent practical to ensure consistency of data cataloging and use. For work breakdown structures and cost breakdown structures, the codes should be hierarchical to permit capturing information at various levels of detail.

MAJOR ELEMENTS OF PLANNING

Summarizing Goals and the Scope of Work

Every undertaking, whether large or small, has a goal: construct a building, produce a certain number of items, or obtain new or additional financing. This goal should be clearly understood and agreed upon by all planning participants (including top management) before any actual planning is begun. The basic approach to planning involves segmenting the total endeavor into manageable parts, planning each part in detail, combining the parts, testing the total against project objectives, and then refining the planning as necessary to eliminate variances from the objectives.

In addition, great attention should be paid to accurately defining the scope of work since scope definition in and of itself provides a means of identifying areas where planning for changes (as discussed later in this chapter) should take place. The most effective tool to use in ensuring that all work scope is planned is the work breakdown structure (WBS). The WBS is a tree structure of successively further breakdowns of work scope into component parts for planning, assigning responsibility, managing, controlling, and reporting project progress. All planning efforts should be organized to the WBS developed for the project.

Planning takes place in numerous categories, but the most important of these are time, cost, resources, and quality.

Time Planning

Time planning entails developing plans, usually in the form of summary schedules, to accomplish all elements of an objective within an established time period. Later in the life cycle, these summary schedules are developed into detail schedules for accomplishing discrete tasks. This process begins with establishing a need date or other milestone at which all actions must be complete, and works backward from that point.

The second step in time planning is dividing the total effort into component parts. After components are identified, they should be arrayed in the order of their accomplishments. This goes beyond merely preparing a list, however, since

---

GLOSSARY TERMS IN THIS CHAPTER

planning ◆ scheduling
work breakdown structure (WBS)

---

some activities must be handled in strict sequence while others may be executed simultaneously. For still others, a number of options may exist. One of the most advantageous formats for arraying activities is the critical path logic diagram. In this format, arrows or nodes representing each component or activity are displayed in logical sequence, showing dependencies among all activities where an actual constraint is present (e.g., one activity cannot start before another is finished). Since several ways of handling the overall project may exist, it may be appropriate to develop two or more logic diagrams and then test each option. Figure 12.1 contains a simple logic diagram for marketing a new project management software program.

After the logical display is complete, a duration is assigned to each activity, based either on data contained in a software program or on experience of the planning participants. Then, using critical path techniques (as discussed in chapter 13), the total time requirement for the endeavor is determined. If the total exceeds the available time, planners must reevaluate their work and take whatever action is needed to meet time objectives: perhaps optional activities can be dropped and others can be shortened by applying more resources or other schedule compression techniques. The results of time planning can be displayed in numerous ways: the critical path logic diagram mentioned above, a bar chart, or a simple time table. Scheduling is discussed in greater detail in chapter 13.

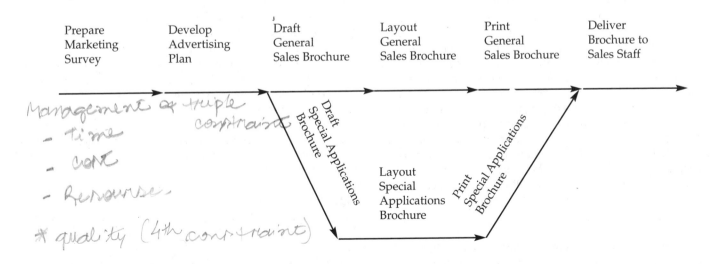

Figure 12.1—Simple Logic Diagram

TOTAL PROJECT COST AND WBS RELATIONSHIP

PHASES	INDIRECTS (1)	DIRECTS			
		Labor		Material	Equipment
Conceptual Engineering	$	WH	$	$	$
Detailed Engineering	$	WH	$	$	$
Procurement	$	WH	$	$	$
Construction	$	WH	$	$	$
Startup	$	WH	$	$	$
Other (2)					

Legend: ☐ The cost breakdown structure (CBS) is composed of all elements in the matrix for which dollars ($) are budgeted. The total dollar value of all of these elements equals the project budget.

⌐ ⌐ The work breakdown structure (WBS) is composed of those direct labor elements in the matrix for which work-hours (WH) are budgeted and lend themselves to work progress measurement.

Footnotes: 1. Supervision above first level, staff, facilities, supplies, and services, etc.
2. Home office overhead, contingency reserve, profit, etc.

Figure 12.2—The Relationship Between WBS and CBS

Cost Planning

Just as total time effort was partitioned, total cost must be partitioned as well. This may be done using a cost break-down structure (similar to the WBS mentioned earlier), which is merely a catalog of all cost elements expected to be incurred, the sum of which equals the budget for the endeavor. Ideally, this segmentation will parallel the time breakdown; in fact, the objective is to have the time breakdown exist within the cost breakdown. This, however, may not be possible since not all costs are directly related to a specific activity; i.e., they may be overhead costs or general and administrative costs, which will appear in the cost breakdown but not in the work breakdown. Where costs and actions do coincide, a control account is created. The basics of determining costs of individual accounts and the subject of budgeting are discussed in other chapters. Figure 12.2 shows the relationship between a WBS and a cost breakdown structure (CBS) for an engineering/procurement/construction project.

Resource Planning

Resources involved in an undertaking generally include personnel, support equipment and tools, permanent materials and installed equipment, and expendable supplies. Some combination of these are involved in each control account that appears on the integration of the WBS/CBS. The decision as to the resources to be applied is primarily based on experience and judgment, although specific undertakings may require other input as well. Every resource requirement must be accounted for in the cost breakdown so that estimates of costs for individual control accounts, as well as total estimated costs, can be generated. Identifying resource requirements is only a first step in the resource planning process, since the resources also must be available in the quantities needed at the proper time. Thus, supporting resource plans will exist behind the total resource plan. In most instances, certain resources will be identified as critical to project success, and their management will be given particular attention.

Quality Planning

The overall objective of planning is to achieve a high-quality result on time and within budget. Quality objectives are met if this is done without undue confusion or disruption. This requires developing a quality plan that consists of the undertaking's requirements (goals), a method for communicating the requirements to those responsible for achieving them, a plan for training the responsible persons, and a way of measuring successful achievement.

Review

Post-action review of the planning that went into an endeavor is an important, yet often neglected area. Still, without good reporting and review even while the undertaking is in process, control does not exist. Therefore, everyone involved must be kept informed as to progress, problems, modifications, and other factors critical to success. This requires making an early assessment of the required reports, meetings, presentations, and project documents, and determining which ones are vital to accurate performance assessment.

Planning for Change

A frequently neglected aspect of planning is contingency planning. Change is inevitable, whether it is internally or externally driven. But even though it is unlikely that the objectives set forth at the beginning of an undertaking will developing a variety of cost budgets plotted against time. change, the possibility of everything going according to plan is quite remote. Recognizing that change is inevitable, plans almost invariably must be based on assumptions subject to some variability. They must not be cast in stone but rather should be flexible enough to allow for changes at any point during the life cycle of the endeavor. A good plan provides sufficient alternatives so it still functions even when extreme changes occur.

PLANNING IN THE CONSTRUCTION INDUSTRY

Research has shown that most owners and construction organizations are very limited in the scope of their construction planning. They tend to emphasize time planning, and to a lesser extent, resource allocation and cash flow, paying minimal attention to work methods, materials management, and similar areas. In fact, many commercial textbooks on project management treat *planning* and *scheduling* as synonymous, and many organizations even use the job classification *Planning and Scheduling Engineer*. Yet the term *planning* is rarely, if ever, part of the job titles of those involved in engineering, field erection, quality, materials, or budget planning. Beyond this, the construction industry has become very dependent on sophisticated scheduling software packages for time planning, while neglecting those available to facilitate other types of planning. Most unusual of all, critical-path-based scheduling programs (that are predicated on strict, logical interrelationships of activities with fixed durations) are being applied in an industry characterized by extreme variability and uncertainty.

How important is construction project planning? Several years ago, a major U.S. contractor studied the factors contributing to the success or failure of its projects. By reviewing the records of several hundred completed projects, some successful in achieving project objectives and some not, factors common to successful projects but lacking in less successful ones were identified. It became evident that the major factor directly influencing success was the quality and depth of early planning by the project management group.

What is the planning record of the construction industry? Many of the construction cost overruns experienced over the past two decades can be attributed to poor planning at some level. A 1981 study covering hundreds of construction projects used an index of 100 to represent the expected cost of a project with reasonable planning. Actual costs were converted to an index relative to that base. Results indicated that actual cost indices ranged from 60 to 500, with an average of 150. In other words, when planning was exceptional, savings reached 40 percent, while poor planning created overruns as high as 400 percent, and even average planning led to projects costing 50 percent more.

Construction industry groups, such as the Business Roundtable and the Construction Industry Institute, have recognized that reasonable planning efforts can yield savings of up to 40 percent if applied to critical areas. This has led them to emphasize the importance of scope definition, value engineering, constructability, materials management, and quality management in successfully attaining project objectives.

Why has the construction industry seemingly lagged in its planning efforts? Several reasons are usually given:

- planning time is often limited,
- staff resources are spread over numerous projects, and
- lessons learned on completed projects cannot be applied directly to new projects.

Valid as these reasons may be, they need not prevent the implementation and use of planning. While planning time may be limited, more time is seldom available. Still, the planning process can be made faster and easier by using standard procedures and models that can be adapted easily to each new project. Checklists also will help to ensure coverage of all areas. The best solution to spreading staff resources over numerous projects is for management to become more selective in choosing projects on which to bid, so the staff can concentrate on the projects that have the most potential. Finally, while previous experience is a valid component of effective planning, the tendency is to place too much emphasis on database information and not enough on investigating the new project. Since no two projects are precisely alike, the information in the database must be adapted to each new project and adjusted accordingly.

Integrating the Elements of Planning

Integrated project or process control is possible only if the planning also has been integrated—in other words, when time, cost, and resource planning have been accomplished against the same basic structure. The WBS and CBS provide the common structure for this planning, since one level of the WBS elements becomes activities for scheduling as well as a center for tracking resources and costs. This enables resource loading the schedules, resource budgeting against time, and

Contingency planning can take at least two forms, both based on "what-if" type questions. The first is developing an alternate plan that can be implemented in the event an adverse situation arises: e.g., what if a concrete pump breaks down in the middle of a large pour? Even though every eventuality cannot be addressed, concentration on critical areas is advised.

The second form of contingency planning addresses budget and schedule and sets out a way to handle unfavorable variances in these areas. In establishing contingency accounts, planners must first attempt to identify risk elements—accidents, vandalism, theft, work quantity variances, productivity, unfavorable weather, adverse labor activity, etc. While certain of these risk elements are insurable, it is seldom at the 100 percent level. Structured techniques are available for evaluating combined exposure to uninsured risk elements in which exposure is usually expressed in terms of a probability of loss not exceeding certain limits. Using this information, amounts are established for both cost and schedule contingency. These accounts are managed with the same care as any other control account.

CONCLUSION

Strong, effective planning is the main ingredient in project or opportunity success, since it focuses the attention of an organization on its future. Planning is the responsibility of all participants: thus companies should strive, through training and practice, to develop a planning culture and to provide the tools necessary to facilitate the planning process. Plans should be documented and made available as appropriate to all individuals involved in the undertaking. Since the future is unknown, and changes will occur despite the best planning efforts, plans must always be flexible. While time and cost planning are important, planning in other areas will reap nearly as many benefits. Finally, management should have rigid standards for bidding on projects, thus allowing staff resources to be applied where they will be most productive.

Planning for success is no small endeavor. When done well, however, it will reap many large rewards.

Portions of this chapter are from previous editions authored by Remo J. Silvestrini, CCE; Dr. James M. Neil, PE CCE; and Jennifer Bates, CCE.

Chapter 13

Scheduling

Anthony J. Werderitsch, PE CCE

INTRODUCTION

Why Scheduling is Important

Scheduling is the process that converts the project work plan into a road map, that if followed, will assure timely project completion. Scheduling is one of the tools used for monitoring and controlling projects to ensure the objectives of cost, quality, and time are met. Schedules provide the baseline against which progress is measured. Schedules are used to assess time impact of changes to the work scope.

Effective project management involves coordinating activities such as planning, organizing, implementing, and controlling time and cost. Time control is usually achieved by preparing and using schedules to make the most efficient use of available time. Scheduling is an important and integral part of the overall planning effort, since the scheduling process forces people to quantify their effort in discrete terms and to place activities in proper relationship to each other. The planning (as discussed in Chapter 12) and scheduling functions are usually performed iteratively in order to accomplish all required tasks within the specified time frames.

Benefits of Scheduling

Scheduling provides a basis for management of the work, improves communications, and facilitates coordination. Using a schedule improves the effective use of resources. The project schedule gives the user a baseline to monitor and control the work.

Scheduling provides a way of contributing input during project execution concerning means, methods, techniques, sequences, or other conditions affecting the plan's outcome. Scheduling provides a means for obtaining feedback since the development and use is a team effort incorporating the ideas and objectives of those responsible for the work. Schedules are good motivational tools providing intended work plans to those having to perform the work and reporting progress against them.

Schedules provide a baseline for measurement and a means for collecting and recording progress. Budgets, costs, and resources can be integrated into project schedule activities providing a basis for measuring cost as well as time performance.

Schedules may be used as a basis for payment applications supporting work completed. Critical path schedules are used and relied upon by courts for amending contract completion dates. When projects are faced with significant cost and time overruns, schedules are used as analytical tools to support assessments of labor efficiencies resulting from compression or extension of time, congested work areas, and disruption to planned work.

The cost engineer must have an understanding of the importance of using schedules effectively. Knowing only the cost and cost estimating functions limits the ability of the cost engineer to perform as a true project controls professional.

LEARNING OBJECTIVES

The purpose of this chapter is to provide a basic understanding of scheduling for seasoned, as well as new, project staff and other department personnel who rely on timely project completion. The objectives are as follows:

- Become familiar with scheduling terms.
- Gain an understanding of scheduling methods and techniques including each one's benefits and risks.
- Become familiar with the most commonly used method and technique that will meet your project objectives.
- Obtain an understanding of work breakdown structures (WBS) and the dependencies between work tasks to enhance team efficiencies.
- Apply overlapping schedule techniques and calculations that reflect real-world management applications.
- Become familiar with managing changes to the schedule.

SCHEDULE DEVELOPMENT

Tools for Developing Schedules

Computer software for developing, progressing, and updating schedules is affordable and readily available. Although computers are the tools, and software provides the means for developing schedules, the individual user must understand what the computer is performing.

While numerous scheduling methodologies exist for developing project schedules, two of the most common are bar charts and critical path. A third method, project evaluation review technique (PERT), is mostly used by government agencies for calculating the most likely duration for networks.

Bar Chart (Gantt Chart) Method

The bar chart, also called a Gantt chart, is primarily meant to control only time elements of a program or project. However, since there are no relationships between the activities, it is not possible to assess the impact of one activity on another nor on the time of completion of the project.

When preparing a bar chart, the work effort must be divided into components, which are then scheduled against time. Preparing a bar chart involves several steps:

1. Analyze the program or project and specify the basic approach to be used in its execution.
2. Segment the program or project into a reasonable number of activities that can be scheduled.
3. Estimate the time required to perform each activity.
4. Place the activities in time order, considering both sequential and parallel performance.
5. Adjust the diagram until the specified completion date, if one exists, is satisfied.

Figure 13.1 below depicts a typical bar chart.

The primary advantage of using a bar chart is that it is simple to read. The plan, schedule, and progress of the program or project can be depicted graphically on a single chart. Figure 13.1 shows the six-activity plan, 15-week schedule, and current status. The current status shows that Activity B has not started and is behind schedule (by 5 weeks), Activity C is slightly ahead of schedule (by 1 week), Activity E is slightly behind schedule (by 2 weeks), and all other activities are on schedule. However, it cannot be determined if Activity B or Activity E will have an impact on another activity or on the project completion. This graphical representation of work versus time is easy to read and provides a simple, understandable way to schedule small undertakings.

Bar charts have not been used successfully for large-scope, one-time-through projects primarily due to the following reasons:

- The inherent simplicity precludes including sufficient detail to enable timely detection of schedule slippages on activities of relatively long duration.
- The dependent relationships between activities cannot adequately be shown; thus, it is difficult to determine how progress delays in individual activities affect project completion.
- Developing bar charts is essentially a manual, graphical procedure, which makes them difficult to establish and maintain for large projects; they also tend to become quickly outdated, thus diminishing their usefulness.

Many large and technically demanding undertakings, such as developing weapons systems or constructing power plants, require schedules showing thousands of activities that take place in widely dispersed locations. Manually developed bar charts cannot adequately display this data, and are thus unsuitable for anything other than a summary display of information.

With today's computer technology, however, if a network

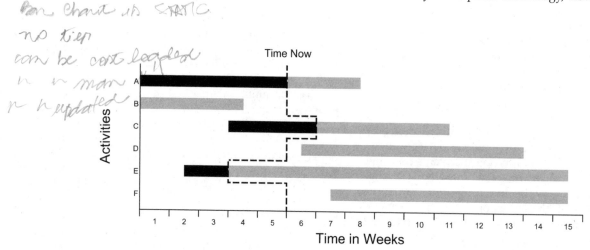

Figure 13.1—Typical Bar Chart.

diagram (as discussed in the following sections) is prepared and the work scheduled, the display of relationships between the activities can be turned off or masked. This masking produces a bar chart, at any level of the project schedule, which can be used as a communication tool for the most complex and largest of projects.

Critical Path Method (CPM)

The disadvantages of manually developed bar charts, coupled with other disadvantages that became evident during the mid-1950s, set the stage for development of network-based project management methodology. One of the methods that emerged to overcome these weaknesses was critical path scheduling. The critical path method (CPM) is a scheduling technique using arrow, precedence, or PERT diagramming methods to determine the length of a project and to identify the activities and constraints on the critical path.

The critical path method enables a scheduler to do the following:

- Determine the shortest time in which a program or project can be completed.
- Identify those activities that are critical and that cannot be slipped or delayed.
- Show the potential slippage or delay (known as float) available for activities that are not critical.

The critical path method (CPM) was designed for, and is useful on, projects where the duration of each activity can be estimated with reasonable certainty; it predicts how long an endeavor will take to complete. It also identifies the activities that control the overall length of the project. CPM is widely used in the process industries, construction, single industrial projects, prototype development, and for controlling plant outages and shutdowns.

CPM computer software, known also as project management software, allows for the assignment of resources to activities. Assigning resources to the activities and allowing the resources to accomplish their assigned work based on their availability provides another variable in the overall project duration. Since the software has this capability, CPM networking is also used by industries with fixed pools of resources such as maintenance and information technology projects.

Project Evaluation Review Technique (PERT)

Project evaluation review technique (PERT) is a probabilistic technique, used mostly by government agencies, for calculating the "most likely" durations for network activities.

During development of the Navy's Polaris Missile Program in the late 1950s, the team had no historical basis to draw upon when estimating the length of time it would take to accomplish certain tasks. For each of the activities, the devel-

---

GLOSSARY TERMS IN THIS CHAPTER

activity ◆ activity description ◆ activity identification arrow diagramming method (ADM) ◆ backward pass bar chart ◆ calendar days ◆ constraints ◆critical path critical path method (CPM) ◆ early finish (EF) early start (ES) ◆ forward pass ◆ free float ◆ gantt chart late finish (LF) ◆ late start (LS) ◆ original duration (OD) overlapping scheduling technique ◆ PERT diagram planning ◆ precedence diagramming method (PDM) network ◆ milestone ◆ relationships; remaining duration schedule calendar ◆ schedule update ◆ scheduling scheduling levels ◆ status ◆ target schedule time scaled network ◆ total float work breakdown structure (WBS) ◆ work days (WD)

---

opers of PERT estimated a best or shortest time, worst or longest time, and the most probable time to accomplish the tasks defined. Concurrent with the PERT network development, the team also developed computer software to run a probability analysis to arrive at a "most likely" duration for each activity and the overall project.

PERT is considered an indeterminate process for activity and project durations, while CPM is considered a deterministic process.

The network of activities developed for PERT are similar to the arrow diagramming method (ADM) and precedence diagramming method (PDM) networks. Because of the similarity and resemblance of a CPM network to PERT, the term PERT has been used as a synonym for CPM.

Discussion of CPM

The most commonly used scheduling method and the technique that will meet your project objectives is CPM incorporating overlapping logic.

CPM is a scheduling technique using arrow or precedence diagrams (networks) to determine the length of a project and to identify the activities and constraints on the critical path. The critical path is defined as the longest chain or chains of activities, in terms of time or duration, through a network.

Two basic methods of critical path scheduling are the following:

- the arrow diagramming method (ADM) (also called activity-on-arrow, or the "i" - "j" method), and
- the precedence diagramming method (PDM) (also called activity-on-node).

Arrow Diagramming Method (ADM)

In arrow diagramming, the nodes in the network are the

beginning and end of each activity. The activity beginning node is commonly referred to as the "i" node and the ending node as the "j" node. Each activity has a unique two number identification. This is referred to as the activity "i - j" number.

The arrow diagramming method (ADM) is a method of constructing a logical network of activities using arrows to represent the activities and connecting them head to tail. This diagramming method shows the sequence, predecessor, and successor relationships of the activities. In ADM networks, project activities are shown on the arrows, with a node or event at each end. The tail of the arrow represents the beginning of the activity, and the head of the arrow represents completion of the activity. The activity number, or identifier, consists of tail and head numbers, which are commonly referred to as the "i" and "j" nodes. This node numbering system is used to number activities.

Each node is uniquely numbered and is represented by a circle. Nodes have no duration. A node represents a particular point in time during the course of a project. It is appropriate to have a convention, which is used to organize or track activity data.

Figure 13.2 shows how a typical arrow diagram network would look.

The sequencing of activities in an ADM network must adhere to the following rules:

- All activities that immediately precede other activities must be complete before the latter activity can be commenced. No activity can start before its predecessors are complete. If this occurs, the activity must be subdivided
- Neither the length of an arrow nor its direction in the

network has any meaning—arrows imply logical relationships only.
- Each activity must have a different activity number.
- Duplicate activity numbers are not permitted.

A unique feature of ADM networks is the use of "dummy" activities. These are activities that have no time duration; they are used only to show relationships between activities that have more than one predecessor and/or to give each activity a unique "i - j" designator. Figure 13.2 also shows an ADM network using a dummy activity.

Precedence Diagramming Method (PDM)
In the precedence diagramming method (PDM), the logic network is constructed using nodes to represent the activities and connecting them by lines that show logic relationships. The nodes (activities) can be circles or boxes. Activities that precede other activities are known as predecessor activities. Activities that follow other activities are known as successor activities. Figure 13.3 shows a typical PDM network diagram. In PDM, the activities are graphically represented by boxes that are assigned the properties of the activity they represent.

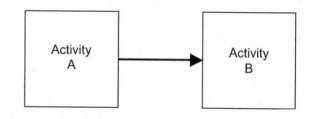

Figure 13.3—PDM Network

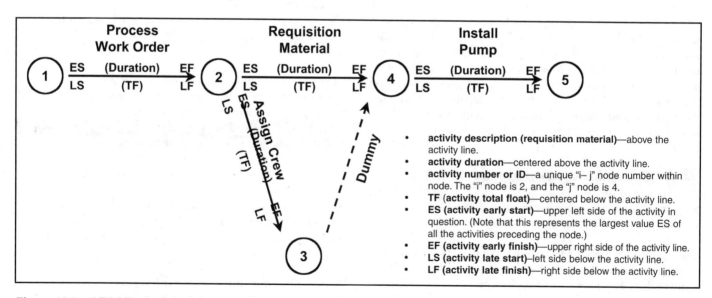

Figure 13.2—ADM Typical Activity Convention and Dummy Activity

The lines in the network represent the interrelationships between activities. These relationships are referred to as links, or constraints. Arrows are not needed; however, arrows are more descriptive than lines.

The nodes are sketched large enough to include certain information about the activity. This practice follows a convention so that others may easily understand the network.

It is common to show the following information for an activity within the PDM node:

- **activity description.**
- **activity ID**—a unique activity number for identification and computer usage.
- **activity duration**—number of work days required to accomplish the activity. Figure 13.4 refers to the OD, original duration.
- **activity schedule dates**—typically both early and late dates are shown.
- **ES (early start)**—earliest point in time that an activity can start based on the network relationships.
- **EF (early finish)**—earliest point in time that an activity can finish based on the network relationships.
- **LS (late start)**—latest point in time that an activity must start in order to avoid delaying the project's completion.
- **LF (late finish)**—latest point in time that an activity must finish in order to avoid delaying the project's completion.
- **activity float values**—typically total float (TF) is shown as in Figure 13.4. Total float is the amount of time that the completion of an activity can be delayed without delaying the project's completion. Total float is equal to the late finish minus the early finish or the late start minus the early start of the activity.

Optional data that may be depicted within the node include resource requirements, codes, and percent complete.

The development of the network involves the identification of the project activities and the relationship between these activities. It is recommended that an activity list be initially developed which identifies the intended relationships. The activity list serves as the tool to be used in the development of the network. Table 13.1 is a typical activity list identifying the project activities and the relationships between these activities. It is common to modify or expand upon this list as the network is developed.

Development of a precedence network diagram represents a graphical depiction of the work plan. The network shown in Figure 13.5 is based on finish to start (FS) relationships.

Table 13.1—Precedence Network Activity List

Activity ID	Description	Predecessor
100	Activity A$_{START}$	-
200	Activity B	100
300	Activity A$_{FINISH}$	100
400	Activity C	300
500	Activity D	200, 400

The successor cannot start until the predecessor is finished. For example, there are five activities, A$_{START}$, A$_{FINISH}$, B, C, and D. Activity A$_{START}$ is the first activity and can start anytime, Activity A$_{START}$ must be finished before Activity A$_{FINISH}$ and Activity B can start. Activity C cannot start until Activity A$_{FINISH}$ is complete. Activity D cannot start until Activity B and Activity C are finished. Figure 13.6 represents the network of this work plan.

The benefit of using the PDM for networking and scheduling is the ease of applying overlapping techniques to the activity relationships.

ACT ID	OD	TF
ACTIVITY DESCRIPTION		
ES	EF	
LS	LF	

Figure 13.4—Typical Precedence Diagram Activity

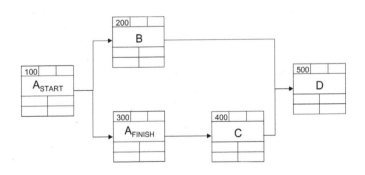

Figure 13.5—Precedence Network Diagram

Overlapping Networks Techniques

The use of overlapping network techniques is common in PDM applications. Overlapping network techniques allow activities to be grouped together, which reduces the number of activities in a network and can reduce the overall time of performance.

The overlapping scheduling technique allows for the development of a schedule, which more closely represents how a planner visualizes actual field conditions. For example, rather than wait for an activity to complete before starting the succeeding activity, it can be said that a successor activity can start a number of days after the start of its predecessor, or that it can finish a number of days after the finish of its predecessor.

Overlapping consists of two parts: a relationship and a lag value or constraint. Four types of overlapping relationships exist:

1. finish-to-start + lag (FS + N) Where "N" is lag,
2. finish-to-finish + lag (FF + N),
3. start-to-start + lag (SS +N), and
4. start-to-finish + lag (SF + N).

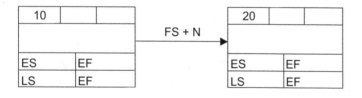

In each case, a number of days (work periods) "N" are indicated that define the overlapped time frame, or the lead-time, between the activities in question. Lags can be either positive or negative, but are assumed to be zero if not specified.

A **finish-to-start + lag (FS + N)** links the finish of the preceding activity with the start of the succeeding activity and indicates that the successor activity cannot begin until the preceding activity is complete. A lag "N" can be placed on the relationship to indicate that the succeeding activity cannot begin until a given time after the preceding activity has finished. A finish-to-start relationship with a lag value of zero is considered the default if no other value is specified. For example, in Figure

10					20		
			FS + N →				
ES	EF				ES	EF	
LS	EF				LS	EF	

Figure 13.6—Finish to Start + Lag Relationship

13.6, Activity 20 cannot start until "N" work periods after Activity 10 is complete.

Typical applications include cure time between the placement of concrete and the stripping of formwork, queuing time between a request for action and when the action takes place, and time for the approval process after a report has been submitted and the action is taken following approval. The alternate approach to this problem would be to include an activity in the network called "concrete cure," "review request," or "review and approval," and assign the added activity a duration of "N" days.

A **start-to-start + lag (SS+N)** relationship links the start of the preceding activity with the start of the following or succeeding activity. It indicates that the successor activity cannot begin until the preceding activity has been started and the specified work periods (lag) or overlap time after the start of the preceding activity has elapsed. For example, in Figure

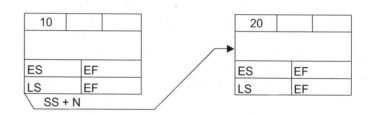

Figure 13.7—Start-to-Start + Lag Relationship.

13.7, Activity 20 cannot start until "N" work periods after the start of activity 10.

Typical applications include the relationship between the pulling wire and cable and wire terminations, or starting the report preparation before all the research information has been completed. These relationships assume that if the work can begin before the preceding activities are complete, an SS + N relationship between them can be utilized. The schedule computations will indicate that the start of the succeeding activities can begin "N" days after the preceding activity has started. The alternate approach to this problem would be to include additional activities in the network to show the start and finish of both the predecessor and successor activities.

A **finish-to-finish + lag (FF + N)** relationship links the finish of the preceding activity with the finish of the following or succeeding activity and indicates that the latter activity cannot be completed until the preceding activity has been completed and the specified work periods (lag) or overlap time has elapsed. For example, in Figure 13.8, Activity 20 cannot finish until "N" work periods after Activity 10 is finished.

Typical finish-to-finish applications include the relationship between the finish of wire terminations and the finish of test equipment, or between finish of research information and finishing the report preparation. These relationships assume that if the successor work can finish "N" work periods after the finish of the preceding activities, an FF + N relationship

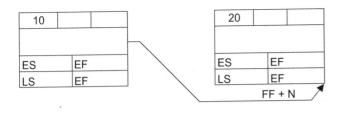

Figure 13.8—Finish-to-Finish + Lag Relationship.

between them can be utilized. The schedule computations will indicate that the finish of the succeeding activities requires "N" days after the finish of the preceding activity. The alternate approach to this problem would be to include additional activities in the network to show the start and finish of both the predecessor and successor activities.

A **start-to-finish + lag (SF + N)** relationship links the start of the preceding activity with the finish of the following or succeeding activity and indicates that the successor activity cannot finish until the preceding activity has started and the specified work periods (lag) or overlap time has elapsed. For example, in Figure 13.9, Activity 20 cannot finish until "N" work periods after Activity 10 is started. This relationship is seldom used because of inherent problems associated with the start of the successor activity and the finish of the predecessor activity. Generally, computer software will not allow this relationship.

The development of an overlapping network involves the

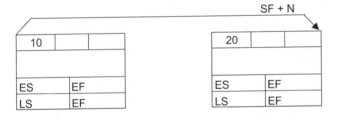

Figure 13.9—Start-to-Finish + Lag Relationship

same efforts as discussed previously for precedence networks. The difference is that during the development of the activity list, overlapping relationships and lead time periods, where applicable, are shown.

The activity list that illustrates overlapping is shown in Table 13.2. It is similar to the network previously used. The differences are that certain activities have been combined and overlapped and overlapping relationships are included. Note that where no overlapping relationship exists, a FS relationship with a lag of zero is assumed.

Figure 13.10 demonstrates that by using overlapping network

Table 13.2—Overlapping Network Activity List

Activity ID	Description	Predecessor
100	Activity A	-
200	Activity B	100 (SS + 10)
300	Activity C	100 (FS)
400	Activity D	200, 300 (FF + 3)

techniques, we can combine the two activities "ASTART" and "AFINISH" into one Activity "A" and show a relationship that Activity "B" can start 10 days after the start of Activity "A". Other changes to the network include that Activity "D" can finish 3 days after the finish of Activity "C".

Figure 13.10—Overlapping Network

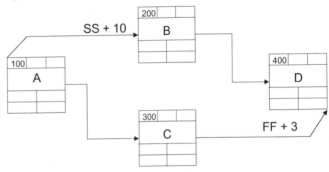

Overlapping network techniques, in turn, reduce the number of schedule computations required.

WORK BREAKDOWN STRUCTURE

The most effective tool to use in ensuring that all work scope is planned is the work breakdown structure (WBS). The WBS is a valuable management tool for planning, organizing, implementing, and controlling projects. The WBS is a tree structure of successively further breakdowns of work scope into component parts for planning, assigning responsibility, managing, controlling, and reporting project progress. The top of the tree represents the whole. Subsequent levels represent divisions of the whole on a level by level basis until the smallest element desired is defined.

Defining Work Breakdown Structure
The best approach to developing a WBS (Figure 13.11 on page 13.8) is to first choose the desired hierarchy (process, organization, or product) and represent the entire project by a specific "project" block. The next step is to branch out beneath the

"project" block into several levels and components, which are

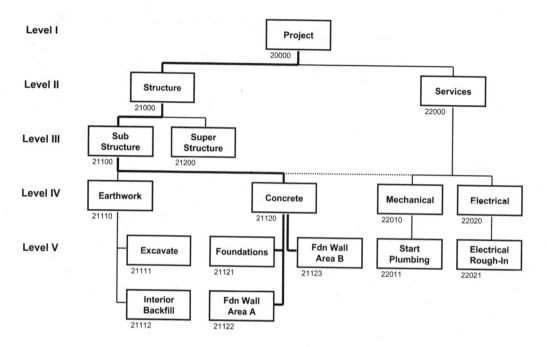

Figure 13.11—Process WBS

equivalent to the "project" block when combined.

For example, structure and services define the second level of the process hierarchy for the project. All project process information can be further defined by these two classifications. For prototype development, other systems classifications may include research and manufacturing.

WBS techniques are valuable tools because they allow project details to be summarized into different groupings for analysis and control purposes.

It is not necessary that all WBS have the same number of levels. For example, the sample breakdown has five levels and a product based WBS may have four levels.

Coding Techniques

Most computer software provides a function for WBS coding that is based on the previously discussed hierarchical structure.

The fundamental element of any WBS is the detailed work activity. What enables the WBS technique to function is proper coding of detailed work activities. Activity definition and coding is best accomplished by numbering from the highest level of each WBS to the lowest level.

The project process-based WBS (Figure 13.11) is used for illustration purposes to demonstrate the method of developing a WBS and its coding structure in detail from top to bottom. As stated previously, the Level II breakdown (structure, and

services) is completely representative of the Level I total project process activity. For illustration purposes, the structure component of the project process is selected for further hierarchy definition, and the line through structure is darkened to show the breakdown process.

Figure 13.11 shows that the Level II structure component is further defined by Level III. The Level III components are substructure and superstructure.

This technique of WBS development is very important. Without utilizing it, the development process usually gets unnecessarily bogged down with efforts to achieve perfection before proceeding to subsequent levels.

The Level III substructure component is further defined by Level IV, consisting of specific processes related to the substructure. One of those, concrete, is selected for further definition of the structure process.

In Level IV, concrete is further defined by three Level V components: Foundations, Foundation Walls Area A, and Foundation Walls Area B.

Once the levels and their components have been defined, it is best to begin numbering them. Count the number of levels and establish a code scheme with an equal number of digits. For example, there are five levels to the process WBS, and, consequently, a five-digit number is used. The number 20000 is the highest level for the process WBS. Working downward and across in the WBS, the Level II components are numbered 21000 and 22000. Summarizing on WBS 2, where the first digit is equal to 2, provides the total project process information.

The lowest level of any WBS of the project constitutes the detailed work activities. Higher levels constitute summaries of the detailed activities.

Activity Coding

Table 13.3 illustrates a listing of detailed schedule activities. Included in Table 13.3 is the process WBS coding. The code for each WBS can be input into one of many activity code fields when using computer-based project management systems. It is necessary that every activity have a unique alphanumeric identifier. It is generally better to use the process-based WBS since it is usually the most detailed WBS.

The WBS for any particular project is usually prepared by project control personnel. However, project control personnel do not perform the actual work. Consequently, it is imperative that project control personnel and the project personnel who actually do the work reach an agreement concerning the WBS.

Table 13.3—Detailed Activity List with WBS Coding

ACTIVITY NUMBER	ACTIVITY DESCRIPTION	PROCESS WBS
10	EXCAVATE	21111
20	FOUNDATIONS	21121
40	FOUNDATION WALLS AREA A	21122
50	FOUNDATION WALLS AREA B	21123
70	BACKFILL INTERIOR OF WALLS	21112
80	START PLUMBING SLAB ROUGH-IN	22011
110	ELECTRICAL ROUGH-IN	22021

In addition to the previous construction example, Figure 13.12 is provided to display a nonconstruction WBS example.

SCHEDULING TECHNIQUES

Making Time Calculations

Once a network has been created and the duration of each activity has been established, both the total time required to reach project completion and the individual start and finish times for each activity can be calculated. The four time values as associated with each activity are Early Start (ES), Early Finish (EF), Late Start (LS), and Late Finish (LF).

The computations required to calculate the above times involve simple addition and subtraction. Manual computation is easy and logical, but it can become tedious and time consuming when done for large networks.

Forward and Backward Pass

The forward pass through the network determines each activity's ES and EF and the project's duration or the earliest date a project can finish. The backward pass through the network determines each activity's LS and LF. The calculations assume that activities begin on the morning of the scheduled start date and end in the evening of the scheduled finish date and that an event or milestone occurs on the evening of the day its last predecessor finished.

Before starting the network calculation, the precedence network list of activities is revisited to include the activity duration as shown in Table 13.4. The activity duration is the

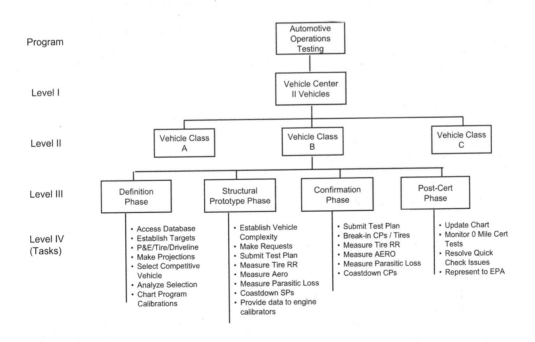

Figure 13.12—Nonconstruction WBS

length of time from start to finish of an activity, estimated or actual, generally quantified in working day or calendar day

Table 13.4—Precedence Network Activity List with Durations

Activity ID	Description	Predecessor	Duration
100	Activity A$_{START}$	-	10
200	Activity B	100	20
300	Activity A$_{FINISH}$	100	10
400	Activity C	300	15
500	Activity D	200, 400	10

time units. Activity duration estimates are developed from historical experience or estimated time to perform the work.

The durations are assigned to the activities as shown in Figure 13.13. In the forward pass, the earliest start and finish times for each activity are calculated, observing the following rules:

- Day 1 is the earliest start date for Activity 100.
- The ES of Activity 100 (A$_{START}$) is equal to 1.
- The EF of the activity is equal to the ES of that activity plus the duration minus 1.
- The ES of any succeeding activity is the EF of the predecessor activity plus 1.
- The ES of an activity is equal to the largest of the EF times of the activities merging to the activity in question plus 1.

The early finish date for Activity A$_{START}$ is day 10 (ESA$_{START}$ + D -1). Day 11 is the early start date for Activities B and A$_{FINISH}$.

The early start for Activity D is day 36 since Activity D's early start is controlled by the largest early finish date of all predecessors (B and C), which is Activity C.

The total project duration is forty-five days.

If the total project duration exceeds the available time, planners must reevaluate their work and take whatever action is needed to meet time objectives: perhaps optional activities can be dropped and others can be shortened by applying more resources or other schedule compression techniques.

In the backward pass, the latest allowable start and finish times for each activity are calculated, observing the following rules:

- The LF of the terminal activity in the network is either assigned as being equal to its EF or assigned the value established by the contract documents.
- The LS of an activity is its LF minus its duration plus 1.
- The LF for all other activities is equal to the numerically smallest LS of succeeding activities minus one day.

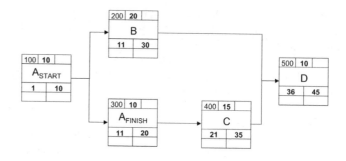

In finish to start relationships, the early start of an activity is equal to the largest of the early finish times of the activities merging to the activity in question plus 1.

$ES_{A\ START} = 1$
$EF_A = FS_A + D_A - 1$
$ES_{SUC} = EF_{PRED} + 1$

Figure 13.13—Forward-Pass Network FS Relationships

Where two or more activities burst from or leave an activity, the numerically smallest LS of the successor activities minus one day is the LF of the activity in question.

Figure 13.14 depicts the results of the backward pass through the network. Note that Activity A$_{START}$'s late start is controlled by Activity A$_{FINISH}$'s late finish.

Work Days and Calendar Days

The calculated dates are shown in consecutive calendar days. This calculation is used for all examples. However, it must be understood that most projects are worked on a five-day workweek with weekends and certain recognized holidays not worked. These nonworking days must be accounted for in the total project duration. Most contracts that stipulate contract time do so in total calendar days including weekend and holidays.

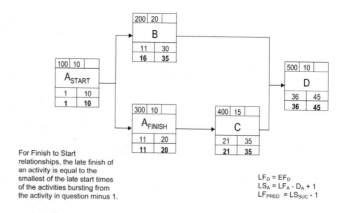

For Finish to Start relationships, the late finish of an activity is equal to the smallest of the late start times of the activities bursting from the activity in question minus 1.

$LF_D = EF_D$
$LS_A = LF_A - D_A + 1$
$LF_{PRED} = LS_{SUC} - 1$

Figure 13.14—Backward Pass Precedence Network FS Relationships

Computerized scheduling applications allow for setting calendars and automatically accounting for weekends and holidays. Also, the dates provided by computerized schedules may, by choice, be in calendar days or dates.

Forward and Backward Passes for Overlapping Relationships

The forward and backward passes for the Overlapping Relationships are shown in Figures 13.15 and 13.16 respectively. The rules discussed earlier are shown with each figure.

In Figure 13.15, the total project duration is forty days, five days shorter than Figure 13.16.

From Figure 13.13, Activity ASTART and AFINISH were combined into Activity A. To account for the overlapped time, the relationship between Activity A and Activity B was changed to SS+10. The FS relationship between Activity A and Activity C remained unchanged. These changes result in the same EF for Activities B and C in Figure 13.15 as in Figure 13.13.

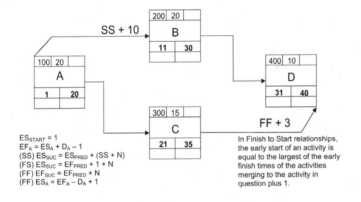

$ES_{START} = 1$
$EF_A = ES_A + D_A - 1$
(SS) $ES_{SUC} = ES_{PRED} + (SS + N)$
(FS) $ES_{SUC} = EF_{PRED} + 1 + N$
(FF) $EF_{SUC} = EF_{PRED} + N$
(FF) $ES_A = EF_A - D_A + 1$

In Finish to Start relationships, the early start of an activity is equal to the largest of the early finish times of the activities merging to the activity in question plus 1.

Figure 13.15—Forward-Pass Overlapping Technique Relationships

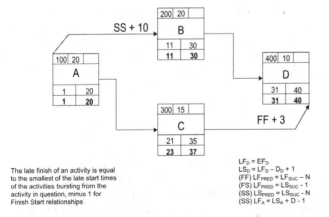

The late finish of an activity is equal to the smallest of the late start times of the activities bursting from the activity in question, minus 1 for Finish Start relationships

$LF_D = EF_D$
$LS_D = LF_D - D_D + 1$
(FF) $LF_{PRED} = LF_{SUC} - N$
(FS) $LF_{PRED} = LS_{SUC} - 1$
(SS) $LS_{PRED} = LS_{SUC} - N$
(SS) $LF_A = LS_A + D - 1$

Figure 13.16—Backward-Pass Overlapping Technique Relationships

Changing the relationship between Activity C and Activity D from FS to FF + 3 allows Activity B to control the finish of Activity D, which results in a savings of 5 days.

Note Activity A's late start and late finish dates are controlled by the late start of Activity B.

Float

Free float is defined as the amount of time that the completion of an activity can be delayed without delaying any other following or succeeding activity.

Free float is equal to the difference between an activity's EF and the ES of the following or succeeding activity minus 1. In the event that two or more activities succeed or follow an activity, the succeeding activity with the smallest ES is used to determine the activity free float amount. The free float of an activity is equal to the smallest value between the activity in question and all succeeding activities minus 1.

Free float belongs solely to the activity. Due to the nature of the computations, free float is reserved for only the last activity in a chain of activities. Custom or preference may dictate whether free float is shown on the network or included in computerized reports.

Total float (TF) is defined as the amount of time that the completion of an activity can be delayed without delaying the completion of the project's terminal activity.

Total float is equal to the difference between the activity's LF and EF, or the difference between the activity's LS and ES.

Total float is shared by the activities in a chain. For this reason, it is a better indicator of the float time an activity possesses. It is cautioned, however, that TF is shared. If a chain of activities possess 15 days of TF and there are four activities in the chain, each activity does not possess 15 days of TF independent of the other activities in the chain. If the first activity in the chain uses all 15 days, the TF along the chain is reduced to zero. Any further delays to any activities in this chain will result in a delay to the project's completion.

Figures 13.17 and 13.18 on page 13.12 depict the networks with the TF values shown.

Critical Path

Total float defines the critical path of the project. The critical path is defined as the longest chain or chains of activities, in terms of time or duration, through a network. It is the chain or chains of activities through a network with the smallest total float value. If the network is continuous, there will be at least one continuous chain through the network. A discontinuous network is one where an imposed activity time constraint has disrupted the chain of activity date calculations.

Figures 13.17 and 13.18 also depict the networks with the crit-

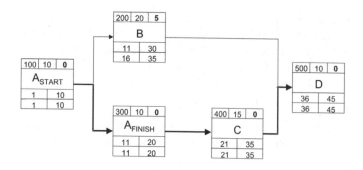

Figure 13.17—Precedence Network FS Relationships Total Float and Critical Path Shown

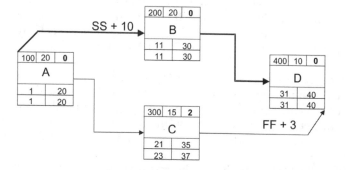

Figure 13.18—Overlapping Technique Relationships Total Float and Critical Path Shown

ical path identified. It is shown as the heavier lined path.

The late finish for Activity A is controlled by the late start of Activity A. The late start of Activity A is critical and controlled by the critical path coming from Activity B. Activity A's late start is LSA = LSB† – SS: (LSA = 11 - 10. LSA = 1.) LFA = LSA + D - 1.

Constraints

The start and finish of certain activities, at times, must be constrained in order to represent what will actually occur. For example, based on network logic, the installation of a pump is scheduled to begin on September 17, but the actual pump delivery from the vendor is not scheduled until October 23. Therefore, the installation of the pump is constrained by the delivery of the pump.

There are six major types of constraints:

1. start-on,
2. start-no-earlier than,
3. start-no-later than,
4. finish-on,
5. finish-no-earlier-than, and

6. finish-no-later-than.

Each of the above constraints affects the schedule differently. "No-earlier-than" (NET) constraints affect only the forward pass calculation in the network. "No-later-than" (NLT) affects only the backward pass calculation. "On" is a combination of NET and NLT and affects both the forward and backward pass.

A constraint may or may not be upheld, depending on network logic. For example, a "Start NET April 7" constraint will control the network calculations if the early start time is before April 7. If, however, the network logic produces an early start time on or after April 7, the network logic will be observed and the constraint will be ignored.

Similarly, if the constraint is "Start NLT April 7" and network logic dictates a late start on or before April 7, the network logic again will control and again the constraint will be ignored. If the network logic produces a late start date after April 7, then the constraint will be observed, and the activity will be scheduled to have a late start date of April 7.

SCHEDULING LEVELS AND REPORTING

Scheduling Levels are schedules used by various management echelons to manage the project. Senior management may require a very summary level referred to as a milestone schedule. Project management and key department interface may only require a summary level of the project activities while hands-on managers require detailed project schedules and short-interval schedules for day-to-day management. Each level is an integral subdivision of the previous level and presents more detailed activities and relationships.

Level 1–Milestone Level Schedule
Level 1 schedules comprise key events or major milestones selected as a result of coordination between the client's and the contractor's management. These events are generally critical accomplishments planned at time intervals throughout the project and used as a basis to monitor overall project performance. The format may be a list, summary network, or bar chart and may contain minimal detail at a highly summarized level. Significant events may include begin program definition, preliminary design complete, purchase major equipment, mobilization, foundations complete, delivery of major equipment components, installation complete. Company management is usually apprised of the project's implementation progress with milestone level schedules.

Level 2—Project Summary Level Schedule
Level 2 schedules are composed of summary project activities depicting critical work and other management selected activities generally indicating the activities' ES and EF dates. Key restraints and relationships between activities are identified and defined. This level of planning is represented by

level 2 schedules and provides an integral plan of the project activities for project management. Milestone schedule dates are compared to those derived from the project summary schedule. Upon review (making adjustments, if necessary) and acceptance, the dates from the project summary are used for the milestone schedule.

When using a network-based schedule, the detailed activities can be rolled up to a summary level and milestone level schedule. As the detailed schedule is developed, it must be summarized to replace the independently developed project summary and milestone schedules.

Typical summary level activities include engineering and design, procurement, major equipment fabrication and delivery, major structures, installation, start-up, and commissioning.

Figure 13.19 shows both a level 1 and 2 schedule.

Level 3—Project Detailed Schedule

Level 3 schedules (Figure 13.20) display the lowest level of detail necessary to control the project through job completion. The intent of this schedule is to finalize remaining requirements for the total project. Detailed scheduling identifies and defines activities that are more detailed than the

project summary level. For example, an activity in the project summary level, such as structural steel engineering and design, would be represented by more meaningful detailed activities of shorter durations such as: define and collect loads, perform analysis, prepare drawings and specifications, and issue documents for procurement. This level of planning also provides better networking capabilities. This level 3 schedule supports the planning effort for determining and assigning resources.

Level 4—Short-Interval Schedule

A Level 4 schedule is a two-to-six week look-ahead schedule that shows resource assigned, detailed, and work activities, and is used for planning and progress reporting purposes, review and assignment of current week work plans, and advance planning for near-term future week work (Figure 13.21). This level is sometimes referred to as short-cycle schedule since the process for its use is a weekly cycle of collecting progress, working the current week, and planning future work assignments.

Short-interval Level 4 schedules are derived from the detailed Level 3 schedule network. These schedules are usually bar charts as they are best used for communicating infor-

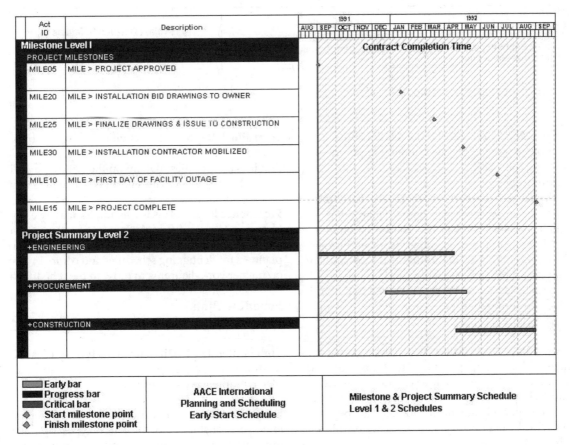

Figure 13.19—Level 1 and Level 2 Schedule

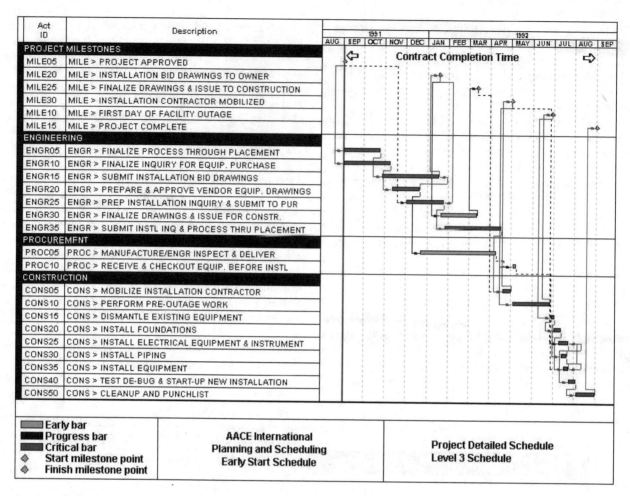

Figure 13.20—Level 3 Schedule

mation and are developed by masking the relationships. It is one of the best tools for conveying the planning requirements to those performing the work.

Schedule Reporting

The following discussion of reports is provided to familiarize planners and schedulers with selected types of computerized report products. These are basic reports. There are numerous other reports of interest to planners, supervisors, and project managers. Schedules comprised of hundreds or thousands of activities can be made manageable and meaningful. Schedules can be selected for each party involved in the project to minimize the number of pages for review that may seem to be overwhelming.

Early Start Dates Report: A listing of activities sorted by early start dates. This listing provides the scheduler and management with the activities that are scheduled to start by ascending dates. Short interval planning uses these lists to prepare for current period and future look-ahead periods. The same report for the overlapping activity schedule identifies the lead time relationships.

Total Float Report: The activities are sorted by total float in ascending value beginning with values of TF = 0. The report first lists all activities that are on the critical path (TF = 0), and then lists all other activities grouped by total float values.

Precedence Report: This is a listing by activity early start dates. However, the significance is the identification of all predecessor and successor activities for each activity. This report is used by planners for debugging schedules and comparing relationships on the network diagrams to those in the schedule reports.

Schedule Plots

Logic Diagrams: These have been used in the sample problems.

Time-scaled Logic Diagram: This type of plot shows activity relationships and displays the activities in their scheduled place in time. (See Figure 13.20)

Early Start Date Schedule: Bar Chart: Bar charts without logic relationships shown. These types of charts are used more frequently by supervision and management to track work. An example of this is the six week look ahead in

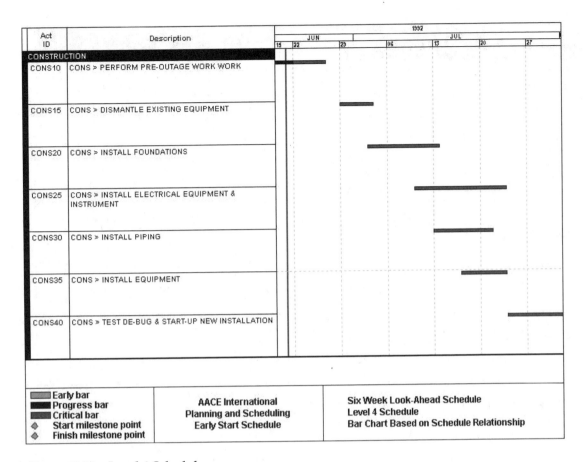

Figure 13.21—Level 4 Schedule

Figure 13.21. Also see Figure 13.22 on page 13.16.

MANAGING CHANGES IN THE SCHEDULE

A schedule is simply a time-phased plan for accomplishing all of the specific activities that have been defined for a project. The schedule is derived and developed from estimated activity durations and the logical relationships or working sequence between activities. Unfortunately, in the real world, the actual work does not always progress in accordance with the original plan and a schedule slippage is usually the outcome.
Actual activity durations may be greater (and sometimes even less) than the original estimated durations. In addition, the working sequence of activities will not always follow the sequence from the schedule. The correction of these changes through schedule updating can forecast any schedule slippage or delay, and, hence, project management personnel can then react to bring the project back on schedule.

The updated schedule, when compared to the original schedule, becomes an indispensable management tool that can be used to assess the overall project impact of any change. For example, the owner or other party following the issuance of the original schedule may impose changes to the original work scope. This may include any engineering design changes, emergent or additional work scope activities, and any change orders that are issued during the performance of the project.

Nearly all projects require special material or equipment to complete. The procurement of these items often accumulates and at times, becomes the critical path. The updating process assesses the impact of the procurement items against the schedule and allows management to expedite the critical items and/or resolve them through activity logic changes.

In addition, owners and government agencies may be slow in issuing permits or approvals. Furthermore, labor strikes, legal disputes, resource availability, accidents and weather conditions are all real dilemmas that many times can only be solved by rescheduling the work. Updating never regains lost work, but it can minimize the overall negative impact.

Consequently, the original schedule should be updated regularly to reflect current information. Updating is a control process, which implies that adjustments in the network may

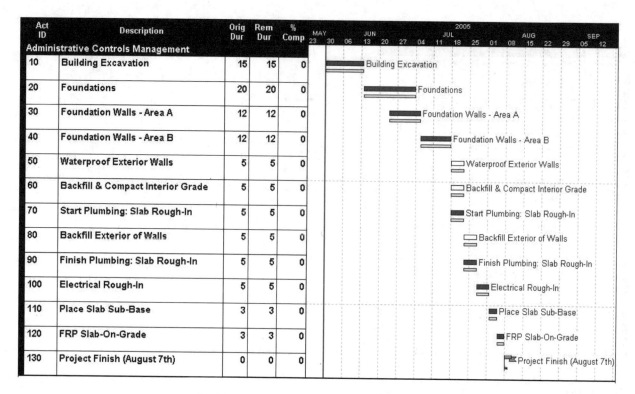

Act ID	Description	Orig Dur	Rem Dur	% Comp	
Administrative Controls Management					
10	Building Excavation	15	15	0	Building Excavation
20	Foundations	20	20	0	Foundations
30	Foundation Walls - Area A	12	12	0	Foundation Walls - Area A
40	Foundation Walls - Area B	12	12	0	Foundation Walls - Area B
50	Waterproof Exterior Walls	5	5	0	Waterproof Exterior Walls
60	Backfill & Compact Interior Grade	5	5	0	Backfill & Compact Interior Grade
70	Start Plumbing: Slab Rough-In	5	5	0	Start Plumbing: Slab Rough-In
80	Backfill Exterior of Walls	5	5	0	Backfill Exterior of Walls
90	Finish Plumbing: Slab Rough-In	5	5	0	Finish Plumbing: Slab Rough-In
100	Electrical Rough-In	5	5	0	Electrical Rough-In
110	Place Slab Sub-Base	3	3	0	Place Slab Sub-Base
120	FRP Slab-On-Grade	3	3	0	FRP Slab-On-Grade
130	Project Finish (August 7th)	0	0	0	Project Finish (August 7th)

Figure 13.22—Slab on Grade Schedule

be necessary and forewarns of potential revisions of major consequences.

Reasons for Updating

There are four major reasons a schedule should be updated regularly:

1. to reflect current project status,
2. to keep the schedule as an effective management tool,
3. to document performance
4. Documentation to plan for changes and support delay analysis

The contractor and owner need to be aware of the current status throughout the project duration. Contractors are concerned with status of their submittals, delivery of equipment and materials, resource availability, coordination and performance of subcontractors, and timely payment for progress completed. Owners are concerned with the status of work including quality and whether the contractor's progress is adequate to meet "turnovers" and completion dates. Both parties need to be aware of changes or delays as they occur and how they affect the project completion date. This will minimize any "surprises" and allow the parties to take necessary actions to get the project back on schedule.

An updated schedule is a tool that provides the project's status at a given time and is used to assess the performance of the owner, designer, and contractor to meet schedule commitments. It provides a record of the accomplishments as to timeliness and completeness. Changes to the work scope or methods of performance need to be included in the schedule updates. This provides management the opportunity to assess impact and plan remedial measures if necessary. In developing a project history, the causes for delays can be identified and measured from the updated schedules to support delay analysis and negotiations.

Updating Intervals for Managing Changes

Generally, project management requires updates to be performed at least monthly and it is not unusual to require weekly status and updates. Most projects facilitate the need to update somewhere between the two extremes. These intervals generally coincide with routine business reporting periods such as monthly progress reports, loan payment schedules, and other fixed reporting requirements. The project status and progress should also be reported periodically with these update reports to provide complete decision making information. Although periodic updates may support business and financial needs, the project manager needs more frequent and routine updating to perform effective management of changes.

Updating Procedures for Managing Changes

Updating and revising a schedule may require several iterations before management and supervision decides on an acceptable plan for implementation.

When status and progress are input to the schedule, an analysis is performed to determine the impact on remaining activities and project completion. Adverse trends may have to be mitigated by adding resources or reviewing logic relationships. Reports, tabular and graphic, should be reviewed with supervision and management and adjustments, if necessary, should be made.

When changes become known, planning sessions must be initiated to determine their impact. For example, how will the change affect current progress? What new activities are needed to define the change? What are their durations and relationships to existing activities? What additional or new resource requirements must be considered?

This process may result in several alternate plans that may require schedules to be prepared. The schedules result in graphical depictions of the alternatives. These schedules assist management in making decisions in selecting optimum solutions.

The following steps are generally performed during the update process:

1. Gather all current information in accordance with routine priorities.
2. Identify and plan for any changes to the work which affect activity duration, logic, work scope, and any other significant information.

2. Input these changes into the project schedule (any additional work or delay should be coded appropriately to reflect "unforeseen" or "delay" work activity).
3. Recalculate the project schedule.
4. Perform analysis and prepare reports for management review.
5. Evaluate and adjust the updated schedule according to management's and supervision's review and direction.
6. Issue updated schedule to all interested parties.

These procedures are generally performed throughout the duration of the project. Standard updating may be performed monthly. Revisions to schedules may be required as they become known, or routinely required on a bi-monthly or quarterly basis. It is important that the updated schedule be issued to all parties in a timely fashion in order to plan and expedite the work effectively and minimize any future delay.

As an example of managing changes and updating a schedule, the preceding schedule (Figure 13.22) has been generated for a slab on grade construction project. The planned start for the project is May 30 and it has a total project duration of 68 days, finishing on August 7.

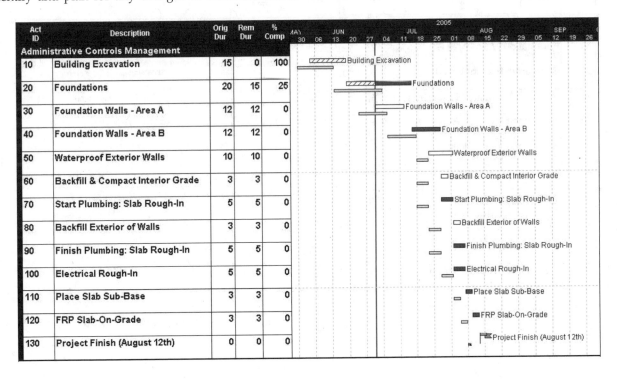

Act ID	Description	Orig Dur	Rem Dur	% Comp
Administrative Controls Management				
10	Building Excavation	15	0	100
20	Foundations	20	15	25
30	Foundation Walls - Area A	12	12	0
40	Foundation Walls - Area B	12	12	0
50	Waterproof Exterior Walls	10	10	0
60	Backfill & Compact Interior Grade	3	3	0
70	Start Plumbing: Slab Rough-In	5	5	0
80	Backfill Exterior of Walls	3	3	0
90	Finish Plumbing: Slab Rough-In	5	5	0
100	Electrical Rough-In	5	5	0
110	Place Slab Sub-Base	3	3	0
120	FRP Slab-On-Grade	3	3	0
130	Project Finish (August 12th)	0	0	0

Figure 13.23—Slab on Grade Schedule Update 1

There are two bars shown for every activity. The scheduling software allows a target bar to be inserted under the schedule bar for each activity.

The target bar does not move or change due to status or progress. Therefore, the target schedule is a static representation of the approved project schedule.

On July 1, a schedule update (Figure 13.23) was conducted to show the current status of the job. The following information was given and entered, and resulted in the following schedule:

- Building Excavation started on June 4 and was completed on June 18 (late start).
- Foundations started on June 19 and are 25 percent complete (in-progress).
- A correction was made to increase the duration of the waterproofing to 10 days (duration change)

The update shows the project now finishing on August 18 with a total duration of 79 Days, eleven days later than the target. After reviewing the update, it was decided to make changes to durations and logic in an effort to regain some time in the schedule. This was done after management consulted the various subcontractors and discussed alternatives. The following changes were made, which resulted in Figure 13.24.

- Waterproof task will be changed to finish 5 days after foundation walls area B (revised relationship).
- Backfill interior wall and backfill exterior walls will be shortened to 3 days each (revised duration).
- Electrical rough-in will be changed to start the same day as finish plumbing: slab rough-in (revised relationship).

The schedule now shows a total project duration of 73 days with a completion date of August 12.

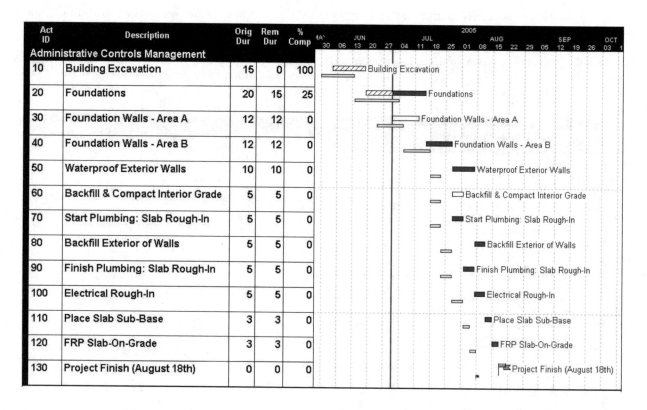

Figure 13.24—Slab On Grade Schedule Update 2

CONCLUSION

The project schedule represents a communication tool that presents the project plan (complete work scope), the order in which it will be worked, and the length of time it will take to complete the activities and the project. The schedule represents the earliest dates the activities and project can occur and the latest dates for activities and project completion that must occur.

PRACTICE PROBLEMS AND QUESTIONS

1. What is meant by early and late start and finish?
2. Define the critical path of a project.
3. What is total float and what does negative total float mean?
4. What is a great tool for communicating the work and why?
5. What are the benefits of progress collection and schedule updates?

Problem 1—Draw a Precedence Diagram Network, and calculate early dates, late dates, and total float for each activity based on the information in the table below.

Activity #	Description	Duration	Relationship
1	Define Plan / Design Project	30 days	No other activity can start until after Activity 1 has begun
2	Procure, Manufacture, and Deliver Major Equipment	60 days	Can begin 15 days after Activity 1 starts
3	Bids / Select Installation Contractor	20 days	Cannot start until Activity 1 is completed
4	Procure, Manufacture and Deliver Controls	40 days	Starts 20 days after plan definition and project design has begun
5	Construct Equipment Foundations and Structure	30 days	Must follow contractor selection
6	Set Major Equipment	15 days	The first piece of major equipment must be received 40 days after procurement has begun, but cannot finish until 10 days after the last piece of major equipment is received. Setting equipment can start 20 days after the foundations and structures have begun
7	Install Controls	20 days	Contractor cannot begin until 15 days after foundations and structures have begun, contractor cannot finish until 5 days after the last of the controls are delivered
8	Start Up & Test Major Equipment	10 days	Occurs after controls are installed and equipment is set
9	Commission Equipment	10 days	Can begin 2 days after start-up and test has begun, but cannot finish until 5 days after start up and test is completed

Problem 2—Draw a precedence diagram network, and calculate early dates, late dates, and total float for each activity based on the information in the following table:

Activity #	Description	Duration	Relationship
1	Define Plan / Design Project	30 days	No other activity can start until activity 1 is finished
2	Procure, Manufacture, and Deliver Major Equipment	60 days	Succeeds the finish of Activity 1
3	Bids / Select Installation Contractor	20 days	Cannot start until Activity 1 is completed
4	Procure, Manufacture and Deliver Controls	40 days	Starts after project design is complete
5	Construct Equipment Foundations and Structure	30 days	Must follow contractor selection
6	Set Major Equipment	10 days	Before the contractor can set major equipment, the equipment must be received and foundation and structure must be completed
7	Install Controls	20 days	Must occur after equipment foundations and structures are completed and controls have been delivered
8	Start Up & Test Major Equipment	10 days	Occurs after controls are installed and equipment is set
9	Commission Equipment	10 days	Starts after start up and test major equipment is complete

REFERENCES

1. Callahan, Michael T., Daniel G. Quackenbush, and James E. Rowings. 1992. *Construction Project Scheduling.* New York: McGraw-Hill, 1992.
2. Werderitsch, Anthony, PE, CCE. 1992. *Planning … Scheduling.* Ann Arbor, Michigan: Administrative Controls Management, Inc.
3. Lewis, James. 2000. *Project Manager's Desk Reference, 2nd Edition.* New York: McGraw Hill.

Portions of this chapter are from previous editions authored by Dr. Brisbane H. Brown, Jr.; Dr. James M. Neil, PE, CCE; and Jennifer Bates, CCE.

Section 4

Progress & Cost Control

Chapter 14

Progress Measurement and Earned Value

Dr. Joseph J. Orczyk, PE CCE

INTRODUCTION

The work tasks needed to complete a construction project range from designing the foundations to clearing and grading a site, to startup and turnover of the completed facility. During the course of the project, the individuals executing it must periodically report their progress on each task. Since the nature of each task varies, no single reporting method is suitable, and several methods of measuring progress are required. The six most common methods are presented in this chapter. Other topics discussed include earned value, how to evaluate worker productivity, and the use of fixed budget systems.

LEARNING OBJECTIVES

After completing this chapter, readers should be able to

- identify the six methods used for measuring work progress,
- understand the concept of earned value and how to use it in fixed budgets to analyze cost and schedule performance, and
- understand how to evaluate worker productivity.

MEASURING WORK PROGRESS

Method 1—Units Completed—This method is applicable to tasks that involve repeated production of easily measured pieces of work, when each piece requires approximately the same level of effort. In most cases, subtasks are not mixed, but if so, they are accomplished simultaneously, and one of the subtasks can be used as the reference task.

Wire pulling is a task where accomplishment is easily measured in terms of linear meters of wire pulled. If the work for pulling a certain type of wire is contained in a single control account, the units completed method can be applied. For

example, if 10,000 linear meters (LM) of wire is to be pulled, and 4000 LM have been pulled, the percent complete is found by dividing 4000 LM by 10000 LM to show 40 percent complete.

Placing and finishing a reinforced concrete slab is a type of work with multiple tasks handled simultaneously (placing and finishing), but progress would normally be reported on the basis of cubic meters (or yards) of concrete placed and finished, or on the number of square meters (or feet) of finished surface.

Method 2—Incremental Milestone—This method is applicable to any control account that includes subtasks that must be handled in sequence. For example, installing a major vessel in an industrial facility includes the sequential tasks or operations listed in Table 14.1. Segmenting a task into subtasks and assigning each an increment of progress for the entire task is called developing "rules of credit [1]." Completing any subtask or operation is considered to be the achievement of a milestone, and each incremental milestone completed represents a certain percentage of the total installation. The percentage chosen to represent each milestone is normally based on the number of workhours estimated to be required to that point in relation to the total.

Method 3—Start/Finish—This method is applicable to tasks

Table 14.1—Rules of Credit for Drums and Tanks

TASK	INCREMENTAL PROGRESS	CUMULATIVE PROGRESS
Received/inspected	15%	15%
Setting complete	20%	35%
Alignment complete	15%	50%
Internals installed	25%	75%
Testing complete	15%	90%
Accepted by owner	10%	100%

that lack readily definable intermediate milestones or those for which the effort/time required is very difficult to estimate. To illustrate, millwright alignment work usually falls into this category. Aligning a major fan and motor may take a few hours or a few days, depending on the situation. Workers know when this work starts and when it is finished, but they never know the percentage completion in between. Other examples include planning activities, flushing and cleaning, testing, and major rigging operations.

In the start/finish approach, a percent complete is arbitrarily assigned to the start of a task, and 100 percent is recorded when the task is finished. A starting percentage of 50 percent is equivalent to a task completed at a constant rate over time, and is reasonable for short duration, lower-value tasks. For tasks with a longer duration or a higher value, a lesser percentage (20-30 percent) would probably be used. This is because the percentage directly affects progress payments, and an owner will hesitate to recognize too much completion in advance. For very short tasks, the start/finish percentages are usually 0 percent/100 percent.

Method 4—Supervisor Opinion—In this method, the supervisor simply makes a judgment of percent complete. The major problem with this approach is that some supervisors are optimists and some are pessimists; thus, there could be major differences of opinion as to the progress reported for the same or similar tasks. This is a subjective approach and should be used only for relatively minor tasks and only where developing a more discrete status is not feasible. Dewatering, temporary construction, architectural trim, and landscaping are candidates for application of this approach.

Method 5—Cost Ratio—This method is applicable to tasks that involve a long period of time or that are continuous during the life of a project, and which are estimated and budgeted on bulk allocations of dollars and workhours rather than on the basis of production. Project management, quality assurance, contract administration, and project controls are areas where the cost ratio method may be applied. With the cost ratio method, percent complete is found as follows:

$$\text{percent complete} = \frac{\text{actual cost or workhours to date}}{\text{forecast at completion}}$$

$$(\text{equation 1})$$

Method 6—Weighted or Equivalent Units—This method is applicable when the task being controlled involves a long period of time and is composed of two or more overlapping subtasks, each with a different unit of work measurement.

Structural steel erection provides a good example of where

this method may be applied. Structural steel is normally estimated and controlled by using tons as the unit of measure. However, as illustrated in Table 14.2, the subtasks included in steel erection each have a different unit of measure. To handle this, each subtask is weighted according to the estimated level of effort (usually workhours) that will be dedicated to that subtask. These weights are called "rules of credit." As quantities of work are completed for each subtask, the quantities are converted into equivalent tons as illustrated in Table 14.2. The total weight of structural steel in this account is 520 tons. See equation 2.

EARNED VALUE FOR FIXED BUDGETS

Introduction—The discussion above pointed out that numerous ways exist for measuring work progress on a single work item. Having done this, the next challenge is to develop a method for determining overall percent complete for a combination of unlike work tasks or an entire project. The system for accomplishing this is called *earned value*, although the terms *achieved value* and *accomplished value* are occasionally used.

A project's budget is expressed in both workhours and dollars, which are the only common denominators of the many accounts within a project.

Earned value is keyed to the project budget. Many projects are constrained by fixed budgets; others have floating, or variable, budgets. Earned value techniques can be applied in both situations, although there are differences in the detail of application. In the following paragraphs, the basics of earned value will be explained, first by assuming the fixed budget situation and then by advancing to the variable budget situation. A comparison of the two methods will then be made.

The System—When developing a control system for any project, the project must be segmented into its controllable parts. To control the work, a work breakdown structure (WBS) is developed, which includes all work tasks that must be controlled for purposes of determining project progress. Each task will have its own dollar and workhour budget. A project cost breakdown structure is created by adding to the WBS all other project accounts that have either a cost or a cost and workhour budget, but which are not used to measure progress (e.g., management, quality control, administration). In other words, the WBS is incorporated within the CBS.

Under earned value, a direct relationship is established between percent complete of an account and the budget for that account. This relationship is expressed by the following formula:

earned value = (percent completed) *(budget for that account)   (equation 3)

As can be seen from this equation, a portion of the budgeted amount is earned as a task is completed, up to the total amount in that account. One cannot earn more than has been budgeted. For example, assume that $10,000 and 60 work-hours have been budgeted for a given account and that account is now 25 percent complete, as measured by one of the methods previously described. In other words, $2,500 and 15 workhours have been earned to date.

Since progress in all accounts can be reduced to earned work-hours and dollars, this provides a way to summarize multiple accounts and calculating overall progress. The formula for this is:

percent complete = (earned workhours or dollars all accounts) /(budgeted workhours or dollars all accounts)

(equation 4)

COST AND SCHEDULE PERFORMANCE

The concepts discussed thus far provide a system for determining the percent complete of single work tasks or combinations of tasks. The next challenge is to analyze the results and to determine how well things are proceeding according to plan. Fortunately, the earned value system lends itself very well to such an analysis.

The System—Budgeted and earned workhours or dollars have been the earned value factors considered to this point, but to these must be added actual workhours or dollars, since it is a combination of the three measures that are needed for the analysis. The earned value system defines these terms as follows:

Budgeted workhours or $ to date represent what is planned to be done. This is called budgeted cost for work scheduled (BCWS).

Earned workhours or $ to date represent what was done. This is called budgeted cost for work performed (BCWP).

Actual workhours or $ to date represent the cost incurred. This is called actual cost of work performed (ACWP).

$$\text{earned quantity} = (\text{allowed credit}) * (\text{summary quantity}) * \frac{(\text{quantity to date})}{(\text{total quantity})}$$

$$\text{earned tons beams} = (0.11) * (520 \text{ tons}) * \frac{(45 \text{ each})}{(859 \text{ each})} = 3.0 \text{ tons}$$

$$\text{percent complete} = \frac{83.5 \text{ tons}}{520 \text{ tons}} = 16.1\%$$

(equation 2)

A variation of this approach uses equivalent units for each subtask. In the example above, each subtask item would be given a unit of measure that is an equivalent ton. For example, each beam would have an equivalent ton value determined as follows:

$$\text{beam equivalent ton} = \frac{(0.11 \text{ allowed credit}) (520 \text{ tons})}{(859 \text{ beams})} = 0.666 \text{ tons/beam}$$

Table 14.2—Rules of Credit Example for Structural Steel

Allowed Credit	Subtask	Total U/M	Total Quantity	To-Date Quantity	Earned Tons
0.02	run foundation bolts	each	200	200	10.4
0.02	shim	%	100	100	10.4
0.05	shakeout	%	100	100	26.0
0.06	columns	each	87	74	26.5
0.11	beams	each	859	45	3.0
0.10	cross braces	each	837	0	0.0
0.20	girts and sag rods	bay	38	0	0.0
0.09	plumb and align	%	100	5	2.3
0.30	connection	each	2,977	74	3.9
0.05	punch list	%	100	0	0.0
1.00	Steel Totals	ton	520		82.5

Schedule variance (SV) = (earned workhours or $) - (budgeted workhours or $) = BCWP BCWS   (equation 5)

Schedule performance index (SPI)   = (earned workhours or $ to date)/(budgeted workhours or $ to date)   (equation 6)
= BCWP/BCWS

Cost variance (CV)   = (earned workhours or $) - (actual workhours or $)   (equation 7)
= BCWP - ACWP

Cost performance index (CPI)   = (earned workhours or $ to date)/(actual workhours or $ to date)   (equation 8)
= BCWP/ACWP

Schedule performance is a comparison of what was planned to what was done. In other words, workhours were budgeted and earned. If the budgeted workhours are less than the earned workhours, it means more was done than planned, and the project is ahead of schedule. The reverse would place the project behind schedule.

Cost performance is measured by comparing what was done to the cost incurred. To do this, earned workhours are compared to actual workhours. If the cost incurred were greater than what was done, the project has overrun its budget. The above relationships are expressed by the formulas listed as equation 5, equation 6, equation 7, and equation 8.

A positive variance and an index of 1.0 or greater denotes favorable performance. See Figure 14.1 for a plot showing the relationships between BCWS, BCWP, and ACWP.

PRODUCTIVITY

Project managers are always interested in knowing how well actual productivity (workhours/unit) compares with the figures used in planning and budgeting the work. While a comparison of earned to actual workhours may appear to provide an evaluation of productivity, it does so only if actual quantities of work exactly equal those budgeted. Since this is rarely the case, another mechanism is needed to evaluate productivity. **Credit Workhours**—Credit workhours (CWH), like earned Workhours (EWH), are a derived quantity that provides a vehicle for handling work quantity variations between budgeted and actual without distorting crew productivity figures. CWH equals the budgeted productivity workhour unit rate

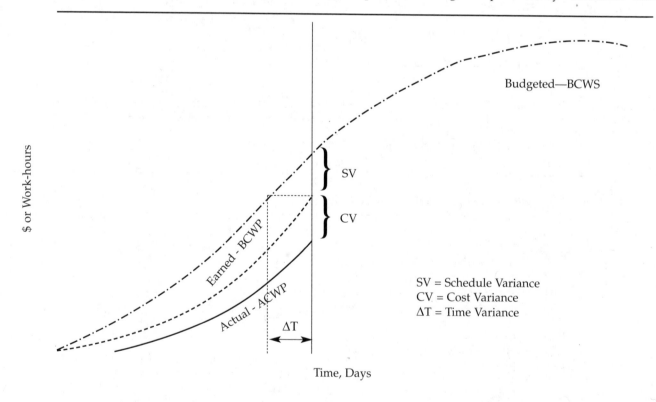

Figure 14.1—Relationships Between BCWS, BCWP, and ACWP

(WH/unit) for a given task multiplied by the number of units completed. Since the actual units of work in a work package may vary from the budgeted (estimated) number of units, CWH may be either greater or less than the EWH. CWH equals EWH only if budgeted and actual quantities of work are equal. If any work task is omitted during the planning/estimating phase (i.e., no workhour budget exists), CWH is not calculated for that package; calculations are confined to work packages for which workhours were allocated. A Productivity Index (PI) may be calculated for a single work package or a combination of work packages (or the total project) using the following formula: (see equation 9 and equation 10).

Table 14.3—Rules of Credit

Allowed Credit	Subtask	U/M	Total Quantity	To-Date Quantity	Earned Quantity
0.40	erect pipe	LF	3030	1800	
0.40	end connections	each	180	75	
0.10	pipe hangers supports	each	290	116	
0.10	pipe trimmed	%	100	30	

Credit Workhours (CWH) = (budget unit rate) * (actual quantity) (equation 9)

Productivity Index (PI) = (sum of credit workhours) / (sum of actual workhours) (equation 10)

SAMPLE PROBLEMS

1. Given the rules of credit and work completed for fabricated pipe spools in Table 14.3, find the equivalent linear feet of pipe in place. This pipe spool account is estimated and controlled by using linear feet of pipe as the summary unit of measure.

2. Given in Table 14.4 are data from a project's status reports at the end of a reporting period. Complete the worksheet, determine the percent complete for slabs at grade, elevated slabs, and the summary account, concrete.

3. You have summarized all control accounts in area A of a project to the end of the reporting period. You note that you had scheduled 28,000 workhours, have earned 26,000 workhours, and have paid for 25,000 workhours. Analyze the cost and schedule status in area A at the end of the reporting period by calculating SV, SPI, CV, and CPI.

4. In planning and budgeting a fixed price project, a given work package was estimated to include 200 units of work. Estimators further utilized a unit rate of 4 work-

Table 14.4 —Data From Project Start Reports

Code	U/M	Quantity Total	Quantity To-Date	Budget WH	Earned WH
03110	SM	500	500	5,000	
03210	CWT	10	9	1,000	
03310	CM	1,000	750	10,000	
Subtotal slabs at grade	XXX	XXX	XXX		
03120	SM	550	55	6,000	
03220	CWT	10	2	1,000	
03320	CM	2,500	0	15,000	
Subtotal elevated slabs	XXX	XXX	XXX		
TOTAL CONCRETE	XXX	XXX	XXX		

hours per unit of work, so they budgeted for 800 work-hours in this account. In the field, it was subsequently determined that there were really 240 units of work to be performed. This was strictly an estimating error, and, with no contingency fund available, the budget remained at 800 workhours. At the end of the latest reporting period, work was 50 percent complete (120 units), and 432 workhours had been paid for. Is this package overrunning or underrunning cost, and is productivity better or worse than planned?

5. A project is composed of two work packages, form and pour. From the weekly report data given in Table 14.5, calculate BCWS, ACWP, BCWP, CWH, SPI, CPI, and PI per period and cumulative. The original budget rates are 2.0 WHS/SM for forming and 1.8 WHS/CM for pouring.

Portions of this chapter are from previous editions authored by Dr. James M. Neil, PE CCE

Table 14.5—Data From Weekly Reports

Week	FORM SCHED. QTY.	FORM ACT. QTY.	FORM ACT. WHS	POUR SCHED. QTY.	POUR ACT. QTY.	POUR ACT. WHS
1	120	80	200	10	-	-
2	220	160	330	30	10	25
3	240	240	430	30	35	70
4	160	240	410	30	40	64
5	60	120	280	20	30	50
6	-	-	-	-	15	35

Chapter 15

Earned Value for Variable Budgets

Dr. Joseph J. Orczyk, PE CCE

INTRODUCTION

The concepts discussed in chapter 14 are based on a fixed budget scenario, which is most often the case in fixed-price work. However, in the case of cost reimbursable contracts and other situations where the budget is subject to considerable variation, the fixed budget system will not be appropriate for making judgments on cost and schedule performance. In those cases, earned value determinations should be based on a variable budget system. This chapter examines variable budget systems and when to use them.

LEARNING OBJECTIVES

After completing this chapter, readers should be able to

- understand variable budget systems, and
- determine when to use a fixed versus a variable budget.

EARNED VALUE—VARIABLE BUDGETS

The System—The variable budget system is particularly suited for a project that is initiated on the basis of an incomplete definition and that has a floating budget. Each identified work package is assigned a budget (workhours and/or dollars) based on the best available work quantity information at that point in time. Then, as each work package is fully defined, its budget is adjusted to reflect final work quantities.

What Is a Quantity Adjusted Budget?—A quantity adjusted budget (QAB) varies directly with the quantity of work and is calculated by multiplying the budgeted workhour rates (and/or dollar rates) by the actual work quantities. For example, assume that the initial budget for constructing a foundation estimated 1,000 cubic yards of concrete at 10 workhours (WH) per cubic yard for a total of 10,000 workhours. However, if the actual design quantity were only 950 cubic yards, the quantity adjusted budget would be equal to 950 cubic yards times the 10 workhours, or 9,500 workhours.

In a sense, this is not really a new budget, but is rather a forecast reflecting the latest designed material quantities to be installed at budgeted productivity. The forecast then becomes the yardstick for measuring project achievement. The real budgets under this system are the unit rates.

The project's final quantity adjusted budget cannot be established until design engineering is complete, which is usually well after the start of construction. The initial quantity adjusted budget must therefore be based on forecasted quantities from sampling and early takeoffs. The quantity adjusted budget is adjusted as better quantity data are supplied from the engineering office, and the adjustments impact project progress measurement. Since frequent quantity adjusted budget adjustments can cause fluctuations in progress measurement, it is advisable to use the initial budget as the quantity adjusted budget until such time as reasonably firm quantity information becomes available. Quantity data is developed in a code by code sequence as engineering progresses and final commodity reviews are completed: earthwork is normally first, followed by concrete, structural steel, and so on. If the quantity adjusted budget is developed code by code in the same sequence as the final commodity reviews, the transition from budget to quantity adjusted budget becomes a smooth and gradual process. See Tables 15.1 and 15.2 for examples of calculating quantity adjusted budget and progress.

Cost and Schedule Performance—The methods previously discussed for calculating percent complete, schedule variance (SV), schedule performance index (SPI), cost variance (CV), and cost performance index (CPI), as described under the fixed budget system, are fully applicable in the variable budget system. Earned workhours may be calculated by multiplying percent complete by the quantity adjusted budget, or, for those activities tracked under the units completed method, by multiplying the units completed by the budgeted unit rate.

Productivity Analysis—Under the variable budget system, the cost performance index is equal to the productivity index because the quantity adjusted budget automatically accounts for quantity variations. A separate calculation of a productiv-

Table 15.1—Calculating QAB (Using WH)*

Work Item	UOM	Original Budget Quan. (000)	WH (000)	Budgeted Unit Rate	Design Quantity	QAB WH (000)
Earthwork	CY	234	193	0.825	257	212
Concrete	CY	94	2,201	23.41	102	2,388
Steel erection	TN	2.5	119	47.6	2.2	105
Mechanical equip.	EA	1.1	152	138.2	1.3	180
Piping	LF	180	470	2.61	210	548
Electrical systems	LF	84	220	2.62	79	207
TOTAL			3,355			3,640

*Note: The same approach would be used for calculating QAB $

Table 15.2—Calculating Percentage Complete Using QAB

Work Item	UOM	QAB Job-to-Date Design Quantity (000)	WH (000)	Quantity (000)	Percentage Complete	Earned WH (000)
Earthwork	CY	257	212	100	38.9	82
Concrete	CY	102	2,388	42	41.2	984
Steel erection	TN	2.2	105	0.85	38.6	40
Mechanical equip.	EA	1.3	180	0.4	30.8	55
Piping	LF	210	548	35	16.7	92
Electrical systems	LF	79	207	22	27.8	58
TOTAL			3,640			1,311

$$\text{total percent complete} = \frac{\text{total earned workhours}}{\text{total QAB}} = \frac{1,311}{3,640} = 36.0\% \qquad \text{(equation 1)}$$

ity index using credit workhours is unnecessary.

Cautionary Notes—Reimbursable projects (those on which construction commences before complete design drawings are available) will tend to experience significant rework as a consequence of design changes. The rework in turn increases the budgets of the affected work packages. When determining percent complete, it is incorrect to include in the calculations either the reworked portion of the budgets or the hours earned when doing the replacement work, even though these may be paid for by the client. To get around this, it is necessary to purge such hours from the accounts as rework occurs. Quantity adjusted budgets and actual hours wasted as a result of rework should be transferred to separate accounts outside the basic control structure so that they may later show the extent and cost of rework.

It must also be kept in mind that, when using the quantity adjusted budget method, the percent complete changes with every change in the forecasted quantities and workhours for individual accounts. A change of this type is completely inde-

pendent of work accomplished, so it confuses people and tends to undermine the credibility of a performance tracking system.

As with the fixed budget system, when setting up databases and algorithms for manipulating data, it is important that earned workhours not be totaled by adding the workhours earned during the current period to those accumulated during prior periods. Instead, to-date calculations should be made for each account, and the totals should be generated by adding the earned workhours of all accounts to-date in which hours or dollars have been earned.

Original budget unit rates must represent realistic, achievable objectives, or the quantity adjusted budget will be invalid for all purposes. Another factor that can invalidate the quantity adjusted budget is a failure to keep change orders up to date. The whole premise of cost control is that it requires the budget to be realistic and current. If this is the case, the quantity adjusted budget provides a firm, fair basis for calculating percent complete.

WHICH BUDGET SYSTEM: FIXED OR VARIABLE?

In some instances, the budget system to be used on a project is dictated by the project itself; in other cases, choices exist. For a project started on the basis of incomplete design, the variable budget system should be used, since it is the only one responsive to the inevitable quantity variations that arise as the project becomes fully defined. On well-defined projects, a choice can be made on the basis of characteristics desired in the control system.

The Fixed Budget System Has These Characteristics:

- It provides a direct evaluation of cost and schedule performance.
- It requires a supplementary system for productivity evaluation.
- Bookkeeping is simplified, and there is less potential for operator-caused errors.
- The fixed budgets provide a constant target for management to see, which is ideal for fixed-price work or other work with target budgets. Fixed budgets provide an incentive for working smarter.
- The cost performance index (CPI) and productivity index (PI) are not necessarily the same. Having the two separate indices provides more tools for analysis.
- Performance data is susceptible to distortions if the project budget is not realistically distributed.

The Variable Budget System Has These Characteristics:

- It provides direct evaluation of productivity and schedule performance (cost performance index and productivity index are the same when using workhours; this is also true when using cost if there are no wage rate variances).
- It requires a supplementary system for evaluating cost performance if operating against a fixed or target budget.
- It provides a moving budget that varies directly with both actual quantities of work and budgeted productivity rates for included tasks. This is ideal for projects with open budgets. If applied to projects with a fixed or target budget, a quantity variance account will be required to balance additions and deletions in the work accounts.
- It requires more operator attention to database management because of continually changing baseline information.

Summary Examples—Following is an example illustrating the application of the fixed and variable budget systems to a simple project. Note that when a variable budget system is applied to projects with a fixed budget, a quantity variance account will be required to balance additions and deletions in the work accounts. This example includes calculations for schedule performance index (SPI), cost performance index (CPI), and productivity index (PI) to further illustrate differences among the approaches.

A project is composed of three work packages. The original estimate is shown in Table 15.3. Work was scheduled during the initial planning as shown in Table 15.4.

After the design was completed, two work package quantities had changed. Work package A had 12 units, and work package B had 22 units. As a result, work was rescheduled (see Table 15.5, since the schedule target completion date remains).

Table 15.3—Original Estimate

Package	Quantity	Unit Rate	Total WH
A	10	15	150
B	15	10	150
C	20	5	100
Total			400

Table 15.4—Initial Schedule

Week	A	B	C
1	2		
2	2		
3	2		
4	2	5	
5	2	5	
6		5	
7			5
8			5
9			5
10			5

Table 15.5—Revised Schedule

Week	A	B	C
1	2		
2	3		
3	3		
4	2	5	
5	2	5	
6		5	
7			5
8			6
9			6
10			5

Case #1—Fixed Budget Approach for Fixed Price Contract
The budgeted workhours were redistributed within the available budget as shown in Table 15.6. Redistribution was based on the needed workhours for the actual quantities, but spread within the 400-workhour budget using a factor of 400/440 = 0.909. To meet the original budget of 400 workhours, the field performance must be substantially better than originally estimated.

The data contained in Table 15.7 was taken from weekly reports. The quantity column reflects the planned units/actual units. The workhour column shows the scheduled workhours (using the required unit rate)/actual workhours (also known as BCWS/ACWP). The weekly performance measures were calculated from the data contained in Table 15.7. These are shown in Table 15.8. The cumulative performance measures are shown in Table 15.9.

Table 15.6—Case #1 Redistributed Budget Workhours

Package	Quantity	Budget Unit Rate	Needed WH	Allocated WH	Required Unit Rate
A	12	15	180	164	13.6
B	15	10	150	136	9.1
C	22	5	110	100	4.5
Total			440	400	

Table 15.7—Case #1 Weekly Data

Week	A QTY	A WH	B QTY	B WH	C QTY	C WH	TOTAL WH
1	2/1	28/16					28/16
2	3/2	41/31					41/31
3	3/3	41/40	0/2	0/22			41/62
4	2/3	27/38	5/4	46/40			73/78
5	2/2	27/24	5/4	45/42			72/66
6	0/1	0/15	5/4	45/36			45/51
7			0/1	0/12	5/3	23/18	23/30
8					6/5	27/30	27/30
9					6/6	27/33	27/33
10					5/5	23/28	23/28
11					0/3	0/14	0/14

Table 15.8—Case #1 Weekly Performance Measures

Week	BCWS Sched. WH	ACWP Actual WH	BCWP Earned WH[1]	CWH Credit WH[2]	SPI[3]	CPI[4]	PI[5]
1	28	16	14	15	0.50	0.88	0.94
2	41	31	27	30	0.66	0.87	0.97
3	41	62	59	65	1.44	0.95	1.05
4	73	78	77	85	1.05	0.99	1.09
5	72	66	64	70	0.89	0.97	1.06
6	45	51	50	55	1.11	0.98	1.08
7	23	30	23	25	1.00	0.77	0.83
8	27	30	23	25	0.85	0.77	0.83
9	27	33	26	30	0.96	0.79	0.91
10	23	28	23	25	1.00	0.82	0.89
11	0	14	14	15	N/A	1.00	1.07

Notes:

1. Earned WH = (percentage complete) (budget in WH)
2. Credit WH = (original budgeted unit rate) (units complete)
3. SPI = (earned WH) divided by (scheduled WH)

4. CPI = (earned WH) divided by (actual WH)
5. PI = (credit WH) divided by (actual WH)

Table 15.9—Case #1 Cumulative Performance Measures

Sched. Week	BCWS Actual WH	ACWP Earned WH	BCWP Credit WH	CWH WH	SPI	CPI	PI
1	28	16	14	15	0.50	0.88	0.94
2	69	47	41	45	0.59	0.87	0.96
3	110	109	100	110	0.91	0.92	1.01
4	183	187	177	195	0.96	0.95	1.04
5	255	253	241	265	0.94	0.95	1.05
6	300	304	291	320	0.97	0.96	1.05
7	323	334	314	345	0.97	0.94	1.03
8	350	364	337	370	0.96	0.93	1.02
9	377	397	363	400	0.96	0.91	1.01
10	400	425	386	425	0.97	0.91	1.00
11	400	439	400	440	N/A	0.91	1.00

Case #2—Variable Budget Approach for Fixed Price Contract

The work package budgets were adjusted to reflect the additional work using the original unit rates. A quantity variance account was established to balance the budget to account for the fact that only 400 WH were really in the project's control budget. These facts are shown in Table 15.10.

The data contained in Table 15.11 was taken from the weekly reports. The quantity column shows the planned units/actual units. The workhour column reflects the scheduled workhours (using the budget unit rate)/actual workhours (also known as BCWS/ACWP).

The weekly performance measures were calculated from the data in Table 15.11. They are shown in Table 15.12.

The cumulative performance measures are shown in Table 12.14.

Table 15.10—Case #2 Adjusted Budget

Package	Quantity	Budget Unit Rate	Needed WH
A	12	15	180
B	15	10	150
C	22	5	110
Control budget			440
Quantity variance account			-40
Real budget			400

Table 15.11—Case #2 Weekly Data

Week	A QTY	A WH	B QTY	B WH	C QTY	C WH	TOTAL WH
1	2/1	30/16					30/16
2	3/2	45/31					45/31
3	3/3	45/40	0/2	0/22			45/62
4	2/3	30/38	5/4	50/40			80/78
5	2/2	30/24	5/4	50/42			80/66
6	0/1	0/15	5/4	50/36			50/51
7			0/1	0/12	5/3	25/18	25/30
8					6/5	30/30	30/30
9					6/6	30/33	30/33
10					5/5	25/28	25/28
11					0/3	0/14	0/14

Table 15.12—Case #2 Weekly Performance Measures

Week	BCWS Sched. WH	ACWP Actual WH	BCWP Earned WH[1]	SPI[2]	CPI[3]	WH Deficit[4]	
1	30	16	15	0.50	0.94		
2	45	31	30	0.67	0.97		
3	45	62	65	1.44	1.05		
4	80	78	85	1.06	1.09		
5	50	66	70	0.88	1.06		
6	50	51	55	1.10	1.08	-14	Pkg A
7	25	30	25	1.00	0.83	-2	Pkg B
8	30	30	25	0.83	0.83		
9	30	33	30	1.00	0.91		
10	25	28	25	1.00	0.89		
11	0	14	15	n/a	1.07	-23	Pkg C

Notes:

1. Earned WH = (Budgeted Unit Rate) (Units Completed)
2. SPI = (Earned WH divided by (Scheduled WH)
3. CPI = (Earned WH) divided by (Actual WH)
4. Deficit calculated at completion of package = (original budget) (actual WH)

Table 15.13—Cumulative Performance Measures

Week	BCWS Sched. WH	ACWP Actual WH	BCWP Earned WH[1]	SPI[2]	CPI[3]	WH Deficit[4]
1	30	16	15	0.50	0.94	
2	75	47	45	0.60	.096	
3	120	109	110	0.92	1.01	
4	200	187	195	0.98	1.04	
5	280	253	265	0.95	1.05	
6	330	304	320	0.97	1.05	-14
7	355	334	345	0.97	1.03	-16
8	385	364	370	0.96	1.02	
9	415	397	400	0.96	1.01	
10	440	425	425	0.97	1.00	
11	440	439	440	N/A	1.00	-39

Note that the budgeted cost for work performed (BCWP) in the variable budget system is the same as the credit workhours (CWH) in the fixed budget system. Therefore, the cost performance index (CPI) in the variable budget system is the same as the productivity index (PI) in the fixed budget system.

Case #3—Variable Approach With Variable Budget
This would be handled the same as for the fixed budget, except that both the real and the control project budet would be 440 workhours to reflect the increased quantities. Budget variance would then be as followss:

budget variance = (budget WH) - (actual WH):
    Package A = (180 WH) - (164 WH) = +16 WH
    Package B = (150 WH) - (152 WH) =   -2 WH
    Package C = (110 WH) - (123 WH) = -13 WH
total project   =   +1 WH

**Portions of this chapter are from previous editions
authored by T. Lynn Hyvonen and
Dr. James M. Neil, PE CCE**

Chapter 16

Tracking Cost and Schedule Performance

Dr. Joseph J. Orczyk, PE CCE

INTRODUCTION

To achieve control of an operation, a plan for conducting that operation must exist, since it is the plan that forms the basis for control. Actually, the plan for the project consists of numerous interrelated planning documents such as schedules, budgets, a materials management plan, a subcontracting plan, and so forth. These documents also comprise the project baselines.

A number of formal control structures included in the overall management of the project are collectively grouped under the term *project control*. These include cost control, schedule control, materials control, and quality control. This chapter is concerned primarily with cost and schedule control, tracking project statusand techniques for analyzing project reports.

LEARNING OBJECTIVES

After completing this chapter, readers should be able to

- understand project control baselines and how to track project costs and schedule performance from reports, and
- understand how to analyze project reports to identify trends and forecast potential problems.

BASELINES

Cost Control Versus Financial Control—Cost control is obviously important on any project, but it is important to distinguish between cost control and financial control. Financial control is concerned with receipts and expenditures, which are important to good bookkeeping and accepted accounting practice. The financial control structure must be in accordance with generally accepted rules of accounting, and must serve the requirements that relate to contract payment provisions, taxation, regulations, or project capitalization. Financial accounting also reflects the pricing of a contract, which may differ significantly from its costing (because of unbalancing and the tracking of indirect accounts such as profit and distributable).

Project managers, on the other hand, are concerned with cost—what specific operations should cost and what they do cost. Budget (cost) control should be approached as an application of Pareto's law, which essentially states that 80 percent of the outcome of a project is determined by only 20 percent of the included elements. Thus, in establishing a cost control system, the idea is to isolate and control in detail those elements with the greatest potential impact on final cost, with only summary-level control on the remaining elements. Most project cost elements (materials, equipment, and overhead) can be predicted or established with reasonable accuracy if the project is properly planned and estimated. The greatest variable in the final cost of a construction project is usually the labor cost. Labor cost is a function of worker hourly cost and worker productivity, but although hourly rates are relatively easy to predict, productivity is the real variable. Thus, a contractor must monitor both worker hours expended and productivity as major elements in the cost control program. Of course, the element of quantity control is also included as a basis for progress reporting, as well as estimate verification.

Budget Baselines—The budget baselines for a project are generated through the estimating process. Whether or not the design documents are complete, planners must develop a cost estimate for the project using the most appropriate methods, as discussed in previous chapters. If the project has yet to be fully defined, this estimate is approximate and subject to some variation, but as the project becomes better defined, the estimate is updated to reflect the new definition.

For a fixed price project, good estimating is critical because the estimate establishes the bid price, which must incorporate all elements of cost while providing a reasonable profit to the contractor. The estimate also generates all quantity, cost, and productivity targets to be used for detailed control. Ideally, the estimate will have been prepared using the same work breakdown structure as that used for the control schedule, since doing so directly enables the quantity, cost, and productivity targets to be developed for each control work package.

Schedule Baselines—A major effort during the planning process is developing the work breakdown structure, which is the basis for the schedule. There are multiple levels of schedules and various forms of schedules. The control schedule is, as its name implies, the schedule used for master control of the project. It can be in bar chart format, but on larger projects is best presented in critical path method (CPM) format, particularly a time-scaled CPM. It is important that the control schedule be at a level of detail that can be intelligently reviewed by the planners—too great a level of detail gets beyond human comprehension and can contain illogical and arbitrary constraints. Detailed schedule control is best handled using bar charts to display the schedule data.

The Control Account Baseline—Figure 16.1 shows a control account baseline and illustrates how a planner moves within

a work package (in this case service water piping) from the control schedule level to the detailed level. The piping system is first segmented into the work tasks required for its completion (large pipe, valves, etc.), and the tasks are then scheduled in bar chart format with restraints, as shown. As is so often the case, the tasks are overlapping, and some flexibility exists in their sequencing (soft logic). Use of the bar chart format with float shown for each bar gives field personnel the flexibility needed to accomplish the work. Other information included on the baseline document provides the basis for earned value control and progress payments.

STATUSING

Having established the basis for control, project controllers are then in a position to exercise that control. They do this by receiving reports of actual progress and costs and comparing them to the plan.

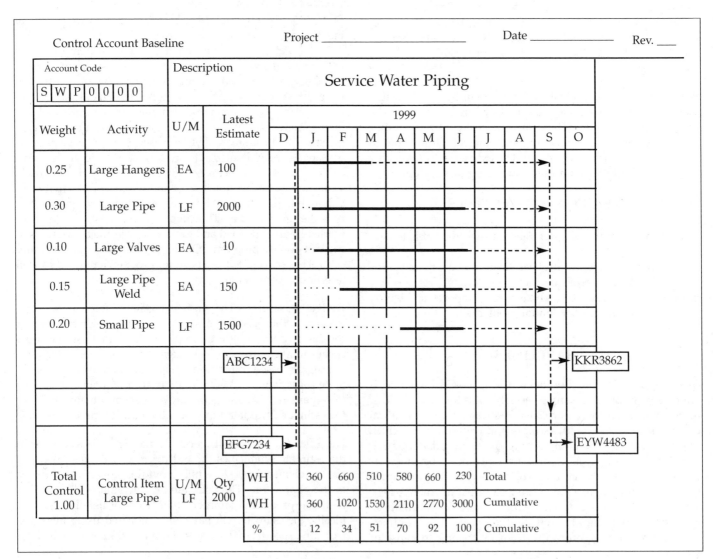

Figure 16.1—Control Account for Service Water Piping

Work Status—In chapter 14, various methods of measuring work progress were explained. On the control account baseline, the methods to be used are established under the unit of measure (U/M) column for each task. These can be rolled up using earned value to show the overall percent complete of the control account. Figure 16.2 represents a reporting format that uses the service water piping of Figure 16.1 as an example. The many control accounts can, in turn, be summarized both at various levels, and for the entire project using earned value.

Cost Status—As noted earlier, the contractor will surely be interested in employing the project's workhour statistics as a major cost-tracking tool, and will use the cost performance index (CPI), productivity index (PI), and cost variance (CV) for workhours as indicators.

Cost in terms of dollars also should be statused. Certain costs, particularly materials furnished and installed by the contractor and labor, are tracked on a control-account-by-control-account basis. Equipment costs and the cost of construction materials and supplies (materials consumed, but not incorporated, in the final product) may be tracked as part of the work control account, but are more likely to be tracked in separate accounts. The CPI and CV for dollars can be calculated for whatever cost items are tracked.

GLOSSARY TERMS IN THIS CHAPTER

cost control ◆ scheduling ◆ status

Tabular reports are appropriate for summarizing cost status in various ways. Typical summaries are as follows:

- A cost summary for each account showing the original control workhours/dollars, current control workhours/dollars, this period workhours/dollars, job-to-date workhours/dollars, remaining to-completed workhours/dollars, estimate-at-completion workhours/dollars, and variance.
- A labor rate report for each craft and control account showing the original control figures for dollars, workhours, and dollars per workhour, and providing for each category the current control, experience this period, job-to-date experience, estimate-at-completion, and variances.
- A quantity and workhour report showing the original control work quantities, workhours, and the workhours per unit of work for each control account, and providing comparable information under the headings of current control, current period, job-to-date, and estimate-at-com-

---

Control Account Baseline   Project _____ Date _____ Rev. _____

Account Code S W P 0 0 0 0	Description	Service Water Piping				This Period / To Date	

Weight	Activity	U/M	Latest Estimate	Week Ending					
				1/3	1/10	1/17	1/24		
0.25	Large Hangers	EA	100	5 / 5	15 / 20	15 / 35	15 / 50		
0.30	Large Pipe	LF	2000				50 / 50		
0.10	Large Valves	EA	10						
0.15	Large Pipe Weld	EA	150						
0.20	Small Pipe	LF	1500						
Total Control 1.00	Control Item Large Pipe	U/ M LF	Control Quantity 2000	25 / 25	75 / 100	75 / 175	90 / 265		
	Field Engineer								

Figure 16.2—Monthly Quantity Report

pletion. This report also can show the earned workhours this period, earned workhours to date, and the labor CPI.

Schedule Status—Schedule status is best displayed using a bar chart. Figure 16.3 contains a sample of an excellent format for summary-level reporting to management. Note that service water piping is summarized as a single line in this figure. The weight column shows the ratio of the total workhours for the activity to the total workhours on the schedule. The number shown in the earned percentage column is the product of the weight column and the actual percent complete of the activity (shown at the end of the actual bar).

ANALYSIS, TRENDING, AND FORECASTING

While it is important to know the exact status of a project at any given point in time, it is equally important to analyze the situation so that appropriate corrective action can be taken if needed. This analysis, as well as trending and forecasting, is discussed in the following paragraphs.

The Cost and Schedule Performance Curves—One of the handiest formats for quickly presenting a project's cost and schedule status is shown in chapter 14 (Figure 14.1). This type of graph shows a plot of the planned budget cumulative

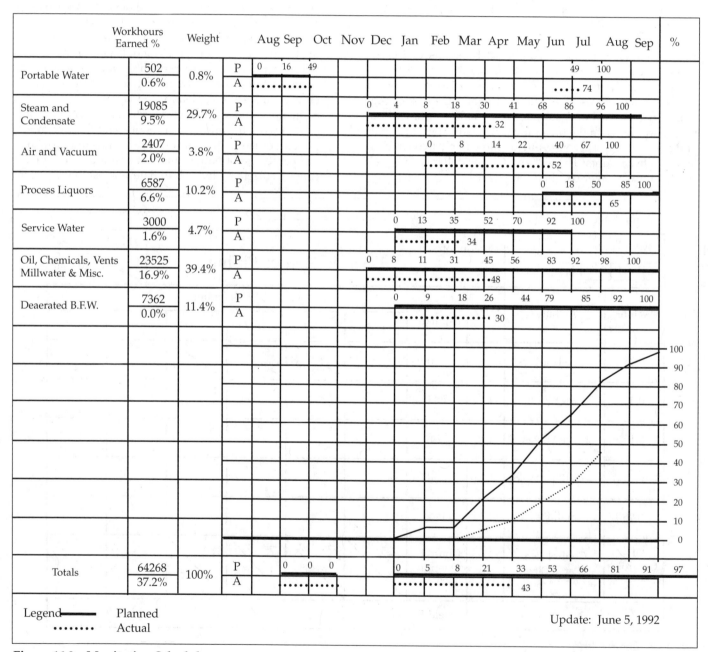

Figure 16.3—Monitoring Schedule

expenditure budgeted cost for work scheduled (BCWS) curves (in terms of either $ or workhours) plus the cumulative actual cost of work performed (ACWP) and the cumulative earned budgeted cost of work performed (BCWP) to the date of the report. The viewer can quickly see the cost and schedule variances and approximately how far the project is ahead of or behind schedule.

Index Tracking—Figure 16.4 contains a graph for tracking the types of indices described in chapter 14 it tracks the productivity index on a cumulative basis, and uses a projected productivity curve, which does not coincide with the 1.0 datum curve. This curve recognizes that productivity is usually expected to be lower during the early stages of a project, reach a peak about midway in the project, and decrease toward closeout. The projected productivity curve allows the actual productivity plot to be more meaningfully evaluated. As shown in the figure, a productivity index of 1.06, which is normally assumed to be favorable, is actually low compared to what it should be for that point in time.

Other Tracking—Figure 16.5 is a variation of figure 16.4. The vertical axis is workhours per percent complete. On this graph, the cumulative plan curve is an upside down image of the projected curve in Figure 16.4 because of the different choice of units on the vertical axis. The graph also includes the plan for period and actual period plots to give it more usability. The point identified as (1) shows actual period performance equal to planned performance. But, when actual cumulative performance is examined, it shows that the project still has a problem because of the poor performance during earlier periods; thus, performance must become bet-

ter than planned if the project is to recover.

Figures 16.6 and 16.7 track a project's building steel erection workhour rates and unit wage rates, respectively. They are self-explanatory.

Figure 16.8 presents a format for tracking bulk quantity items—in this case, wire pulling and terminations. The two curves shown represent the plan. By superimposing actual performance on the graph, the current situation and trends are readily shown. The graph also indicates that terminations were not scheduled to begin until 15 percent of the wire was pulled, which helps ensure that the wire termination crews will have work available to them at all times. This series of curves can be extended to include conduit installation and electrical design as well.

Analysis Techniques—Each report item has significance in itself, but it usually takes a combination of items for the total situation to be shown. For example, poor labor cost performance (cost performance index CPI less than 1.0) is certainly a problem, but the CPI does not point to the cause of that problem, which could be low productivity, a bad quantity estimate, excessive staffing, higher crew rates, or any combination of these. Thus, report data must be available in each of those areas to enable the manager to isolate the problem and take remedial action.

Figure 16.9 shows an analysis tree involving just two report items: schedule performance index (SPI) and total float. Many possible combinations exist. Other analysis trees using other report items can be readily developed.

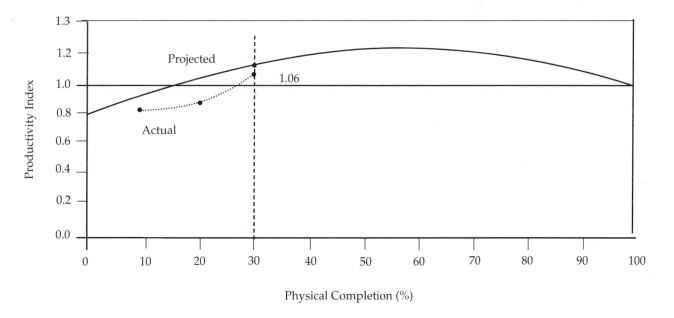

Figure 16.4—Productivity Profile

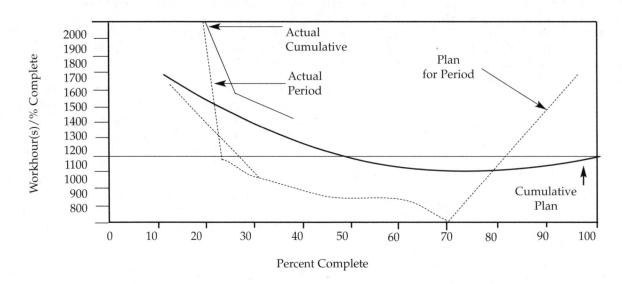

Figure 16.5—Workhour Productivity Trend Chart

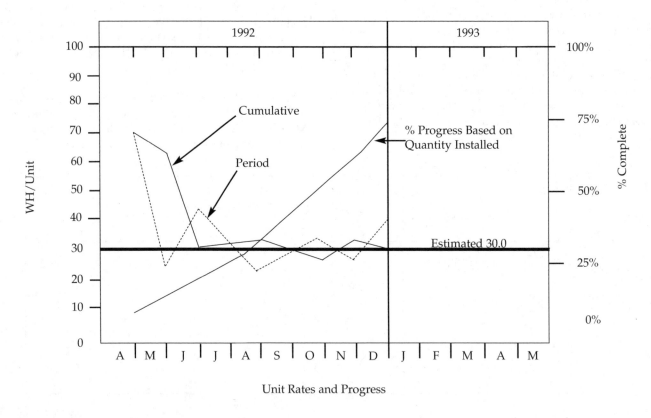

Figure 16.6—Building Structural Steel Erection

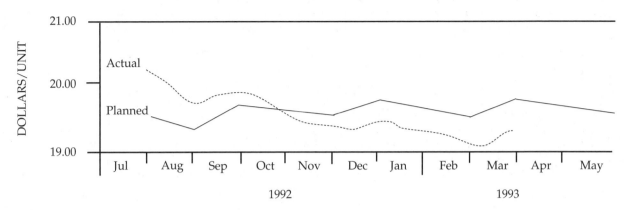

Figure 16.7—Unit Wage Rate

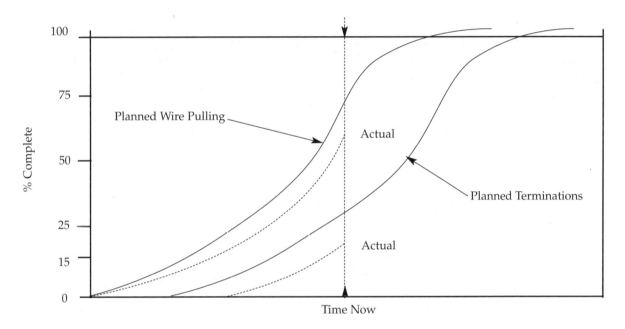

Figure 16.8—Bulk Quantity Curves

Forecasting—There are three basic forecasting approaches.

1. This method is used for forecasting costs and workhours. It assumes that work from a particular point forward will progress at planned rates, whether or not those rates have prevailed to this point.

$$EAC = (ACWP) + (BAC - BCWP)$$

(equation 1)

where:
EAC   = estimate at completion
ACWP = actual cost of work performed to date
BAC   = original budget at completion
BCWP= budgeted cost of work performed to date

2. This method assumes that the rate of progress prevailing to date will continue to prevail.

$$EAC = (BAC) \text{ divided by } (CPI)$$

(equation 2)

where:
CPI   = cost performance index
Other terms as above

3. This method uses curves, and is useful for forecasting any piece of data represented by those curves. The forecaster makes the best extrapolation possible using the typical shapes of the curves and whatever other information may be available to make the projection.

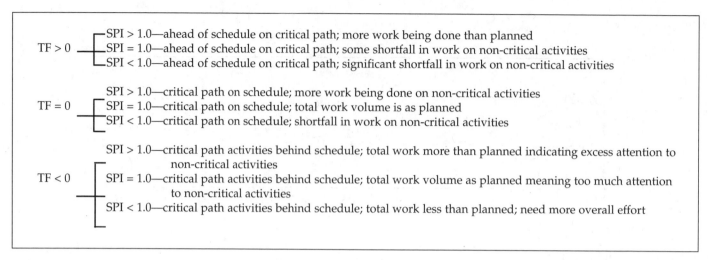

Figure 16.9—Analysis Tree—Total Float and Schedule Performance Index (SPI)

No single forecasting method is recommended. Rather, a forecast by each of the above methods should be performed, since this will provide a range of possibilities.

Portions of this chapter are from previous editions authored by Dr. James M. Neil, PE CCE

AACEI CCE/CCC CERTIFICATION IN-HOUSE TRAINING PROJECT

Date	Hrs	CONTENTS	Instructor(s)	Coach(es)
		Section 1 - Cost		
10/14/08	3	Cost Elements	Jose Lino	Jose Lino / Sam Saad
		Pricing		
		Materials		
		Labor		
		Engineering		
10/28/08	3	Equipment, Parts and Tools	Sam Saad	
		Economic Costs		
		Activity-Based Cost Management		
		Section 2 - Cost Estimating		
11/11/08	2	Estimating	David Cerione	David Cerione
		Process Product Manufacturing		
		Discrete Product Manufacturing		
		Section 3 - Planning & Scheduling		
11/18/08	3	Planning	Bruce Neiswender	Merritt Westbrook
12/09/08	3	Scheduling	Merritt Westbrook	
		Section 4 - Progress & Cost Control		
12/16/08	3	Progress Measurement and Earned Value	Dan Rutkowksi	Dan Rutkowksi
		Earned Value for Variable Budgets		
01/13/09	3	Tracking Cost and Schedule Performance	Julian Ortega	
		Performance and Productivity Management		
		Section 5 - Technical Writing Workshop		
01/20/09	3	Technical Writing / Professional Paper	TBD	TBD
		Section 6 - Project Management		
		Project Management Fundamentals		
		Project Organization Structure		

TECH PAPER OUTLINE

1. title page
2. TOC
3. Abstract
4. list of figures/tables
5. Introduction
6. conclusion
7. References
8. Appendix

deadlines
_____

outline - 1st wk of term 60.
prelion draft - 1 wk march 60.
Final paper - 1 wk ?? 60.
Paper due - 2nd wk April 60.
Exam - 2nd wk of April
         60
June 13 60

Chapter 17

Performance and Productivity Management

Dr. James M. Neil, PE CCE

INTRODUCTION

Companies in the business world are constantly concerned with improving their bottom line—increasing their rate of return on investment, increasing the ratio of profit to revenues, or simply increasing total profit. Using programs with buzzword titles such as productivity improvement, total quality management, re-engineering, time-based competition, horizontal management, down-sizing, and right-sizing, they reorganize, trim staffs, invest in training, automate, computerize, and otherwise do whatever is considered necessary to optimize or maximize the company's performance and beat the competition. But, whatever the name of the program, the goal is the same—spend less to make more money or spend less to provide the same or better service. For production-type activities, this translates into reducing worker and equipment hours per unit of output—i.e., improving productivity. For support and professional activities it means improving efficiency. For all activities, it includes reducing waste of time, materials, and equipment. Altogether it means improving the outcome of the total organization.

LEARNING OBJECTIVES

After completing this chapter, readers should be able to

- analyze worker productivity and performance, and
- identify ways to increase productivity, improve performance, and minimize waste in the workplace.

SUCCESS INDEX

Numerical evaluation of total organizational performance is possible using the success index (SI). It could be called the performance index, but doing so might cause it to be confused with the productivity index (PI) to be described and used later. Equation 1 is the formula for the success index for a profit-oriented business. Equation 2 is for a service organization, such as a government.

$$\text{success index} = \frac{\text{net profit}}{\text{total costs}} \qquad \text{(equation 1)}$$

$$\text{success index} = \frac{\text{value of services rendered}}{\text{costs of providing services}} \qquad \text{(equation 2)}$$

It should be noted that the success index is really an expression of organizational productivity because it relates a form of output (profit or value) to a form of input (cost).

To continue the discussion, the denominators of equations 1 and 2 can be re-expressed as shown in equations 3 and 4:

$$\text{success index} = \frac{\text{net profit}}{\text{essential costs} + \text{cost of waste}} \qquad \text{(equation 3)}$$

$$\text{success index} = \frac{\text{value of services rendered}}{\text{essential costs} + \text{cost of waste}} \qquad \text{(equation 4)}$$

The denominators in both equations now divide total costs into two broad categories—essential costs and cost of waste. Essential costs are those personnel, material, equipment, tax, and other costs that would be incurred if the organization were efficiently organized and running perfectly. As for waste, these are the major categories:

- inefficiencies inherent in the design and operation of the work place;
- individual inefficiencies;
- non-contributing (wasted) time by individuals;
- waste of materials, supplies, and services (misuse, overuse, loss);
- waste of equipment (abuse, misuse, loss); and
- functions that no longer add value to the output of the organization.

In the past, management tended to focus on productivity improvement as the key to reducing costs and/or improving the bottom line, and that subject was and still is given significant attention in technical literature. This is to be expected, since production activity can be readily measured, it can be expressed in hard numbers, its trends are easily noted, and it lends itself to detailed analysis and improvement studies. The problem is that there are many people and much equipment within a company performing functions whose effectiveness and contributions are not properly measured on the basis of output per unit of input. Personnel in this category include most support and professional staff—secretaries, design engineers, managers, etc. Equipment types include word processors, tower cranes, and administrative vehicles.

True, there are outputs associated with many of these individuals and pieces of equipment, but productivity is not the basis for their selection. For example, a receptionist or a security guard must be present to handle whatever comes up; their performances would not be evaluated on the basis of quantity output. Similarly, a tower crane at a building construction site is selected on the basis of lifting capacity at various boom radii—one does not think in terms of tons per hour. There have been efforts to apply productivity measurement concepts to individuals in this category who do have products (e.g., secretaries and design engineers), but with little or no success. In fact, doing so may create stress and cause quality to be compromised as individual goals shift from quality to quantity production of the item designated for measurement (e.g., correspondence processed or drawings produced).

To expand on the above, within an organization's population are people who produce things and people who perform things. Most individuals do both to some degree. Performance may be associated with units of output, but the real performance standard is something other than quantity (e.g., engineering drawing quality, ability to write, or responsiveness in an emergency). Performance is evaluated subjectively (e.g., above average or 7 on a scale of 10).

One would like to assume that every organization seeks to do everything possible to promote performance and productivity. Unfortunately, the real-life situation tends to be as depicted in Figure 17.1. It shows that an individual has a basic capability resulting from many factors. What that individual can produce becomes restricted by organizational constraints.

What should an organization do? To borrow an expression from a US Armed Forces recruiting commercial, the organization should do whatever is necessary to make each individual "the best that he/she can be." That is done by eliminating or minimizing conditions within an organization that limit performance and productivity and by creating conditions that promote them. Remaining sections of this chapter provide guidance for doing this. The first section will focus on the challenge of improving performance of a total organization. That will be followed by a discussion relating specifically to those personnel in the workforce involved in production activity. Finally, the role of incentives in performance and productivity management will be reviewed.

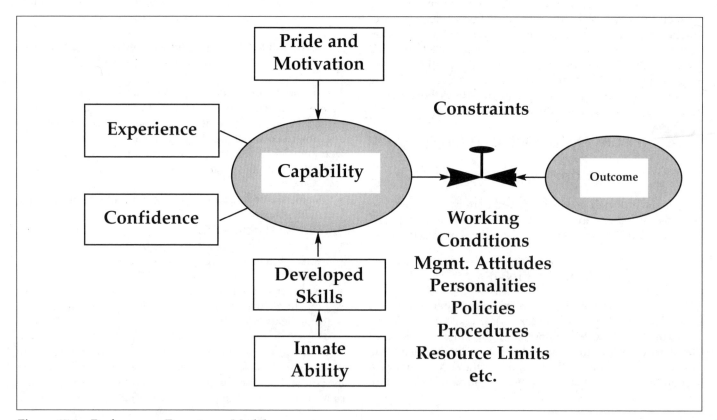

Figure 17.1—Performance Expectancy Model

THE OVERALL PERFORMANCE ISSUE

The Challenge

An organization's success index always will be less than that potentially available had perfection prevailed, because human beings are involved and Murphy's Law (If anything can go wrong, it will!) has yet to be repealed. The problem is illustrated in Figure 17.2, which illustrates how performance potential is lost through inefficiency and waste. The goal must be to eliminate or minimize the factors contributing to that degradation.

Losses Through Inefficiency

Inefficiencies are both organizational and individual. Inconvenient positioning of office reproduction equipment, shortages of equipment or materials, lack of procedures, excessive management layering, and poor lighting are typical organizational inefficiencies. Failure to plan, refusing to use labor-saving equipment (such as a word processor), and sloppy filing are typical individual inefficiencies. All of these translate into time loss and higher costs. The problem with inefficiencies is that the losses tend to be hidden—an observer watching a individual doing what appears to be contributing work may not realize that the work is being done very inefficiently.

GLOSSARY TERMS IN THIS CHAPTER

◆ productivity ◆

Waste Through Interruptions

Everyone acknowledges that interruptions are disruptive, but interruptions are seldom treated as a subject area with significant potential for improving productivity and performance. Take the typical office situation shown in Figure 17.3 where an individual is trying to write a report: a series of interruptions in the form of telephone calls and visitors reduces the individual's average productivity significantly.

If something could be done to reduce these interruptions (e.g., an electronic mailbox, visitor screening, providing better office privacy), the individuals potential output would be improved. The lesson to be learned is simple: review work practices in an organization to determine where avoidable interruptions occur and then take corrective action.

Other Time-Wasters

Interruptions are but one form of time waste; there are many more. First is a list of events or situations that are accepted parts of life in most organizations, but each causes interruptions, and some result in wasted time.

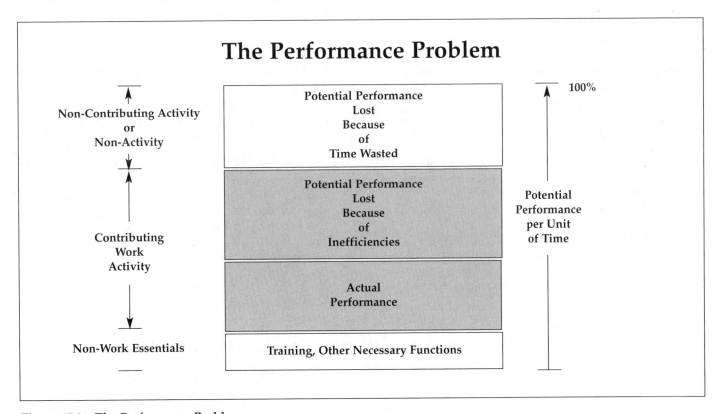

The Performance Problem

Non-Contributing Activity
or
Non-Activity

Contributing
Work
Activity

Non-Work Essentials

Potential Performance
Lost
Because
of
Time Wasted

Potential Performance
Lost
Because
of
Inefficiencies

Actual
Performance

Training, Other Necessary Functions

100%

Potential
Performance
per Unit
of Time

Figure 17.2—The Performance Problem

Office Example—Writing a Report

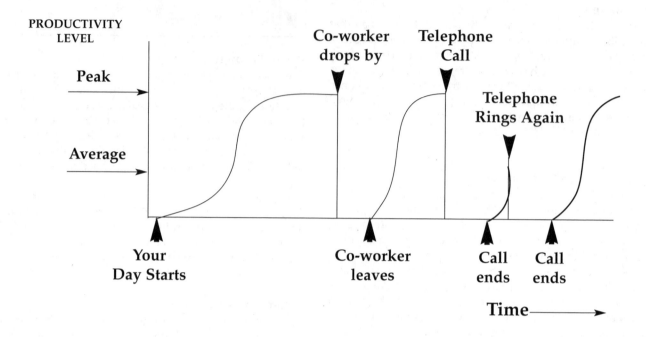

Figure 17.3—Impact of Disturbance on Performance

- official meetings and appointments;
- telephone calls;
- personal breaks and lunch breaks;
- official visitors;
- a need to interrupt current activity to make a copy of something, send a fax, or coordinate with another worker;
- fire drills, hazard alarms, or other emergencies;
- adverse weather;
- power outages;
- equipment breakdowns;
- holds for quality checks or coordination;
- absentees whose work must be absorbed by others;
- turnover of key personnel—new ones must be brought up to speed;
- higher headquarters or outside agency inspections, audits, and reviews;
- secretaries/clerks delivering mail and messages;
- noise and conversations from adjacent work areas;
- unusual activity outside office windows;
- running out of something—paper, staples, etc.;
- misplacing something; and
- forgetting something.

Certain actions or policies may minimize the disruption and time loss effect of some of the above items, but the potential is not significant.

The next list contains more events and situations that create time loss in an office setting. In this case, all of them have sig-

nificant potential for elimination or reduction through better planning and management:

- unnecessary and unstructured meetings;
- people late for meetings;
- social visits or greetings from passing fellow employees;
- sales calls without appointments;
- waiting for engineering and vendor information;
- errors or omissions on engineering drawings;
- lack of communication—somebody didn't "get the word,"
- too many people or organizations involved in getting an answer, approval, or decision;
- excessive time taken to make decisions, or approve/coordinate something;
- too few support personnel available (e.g., clerical) so professional staff must perform own support; and
- inadequate support equipment (e.g., copy machines) causes waiting.

In the case of construction field sites, these are controllable time-wasters:

- ill-defined scope forces constant reworking of schedule;
- contractual disputes;
- labor disputes and adverse union activity;
- arbitrary work rules;
- personality problems among key personnel on owner,

engineer, and contractor staffs;
- late materials or installed equipment deliveries;
- materials and equipment for installation do not meet specifications or have fabrication errors;
- materials and equipment allowed to deteriorate in storage so as to not be usable;
- materials and equipment listed on warehouse inventory cannot be found;
- failure to pick up all needed materials the first time;
- excessive distances between work areas and tool rooms, warehouses, and laydown areas;
- wrong or defective tools issued;
- waiting for support equipment (e.g., crane);
- waiting for an approval to do something;
- lack of information or waiting for instructions;
- issuing instructions after work has started;
- waiting for other crews to get out of way;
- individuals don't understand their roles or responsibilities—must always ask questions;
- limited availability of a critical skill that must be shared among crews (e.g., competent person required by OSHA for certain operations);
- late starts/early quits;
- absentees—work must be reorganized;
- discipline problems;
- permits (such as hot work permits) not available;
- daily renewal of permits;
- conflicts with operating plant personnel on revamp work;
- operating personnel, having not been consulted during development of the project, make changes on the fly;
- changes are issued—both formal and constructive;
- unexpected conditions require work reorganization;
- waiting for access or removal of lockouts;
- over-inspections;
- outdated policies or procedures that must be interpreted to fit current needs;
- work is started before being fully planned and without all resources needed;
- safety incidents; and
- construction mistakes.

Many actions can be taken to eliminate or minimize the time-wasters listed above. For many, the nature of the problem makes the solution obvious. However, to provide several ideas with respect to one major time waster, consider the problem of meetings—too many, too big, too unstructured. Following are some ideas that have worked for others to correct the situation.

- Prepare and implement a written policy/procedure for conduct of meetings.
- Train meeting sponsors on the policy.
- Prepare and work from an agenda for all meetings. Establish a limit of time and start promptly.
- Prepare minutes of meetings to include all decisions made, items remaining open, and actions assigned to individuals (with target dates for completion).
- As an occasional attention-getter, require meeting sponsors to prepare a timesheet for each meeting that lists individuals attending, time spent, and their hourly billing rates (wages + fringes). The sponsor must extend and total the cost figures and submit the summary to his/her supervisor. This makes meeting sponsors think twice about scheduling questionable meetings, encourages them to better plan the meeting, and forces them to think in terms of benefits and costs.
- For any individual late to a meeting, fine them $5 and put it in the coffee or flower fund.
- Arrange the tables and chairs with respect to the entrance so that a latecomer cannot "sneak in." He/she must walk by the chairman and everyone else so that he/she will be totally embarrassed.
- Schedule meetings at beginning of day, just before lunch, just after lunch, or just before quitting time. Scheduling them in the middle of the work day creates a major interruption.

Waste Through Rework

Rework is a special form of waste. One tends to apply the term only to redoing work because the work is flawed or changed. But, one will find countless other forms of rework going on within organizations every day when you use the more general definition of rework: the repeating of an activity (and consequent expenditure of resources) with no value added to the final output. Because activity during rework usually looks the same as when work is done the first time, it is easily overlooked as an area of waste with tremendous potential for reducing costs. Following are common examples of rework in an organization.

- Marketing rework: Constantly looking for new work because the organization cannot attract significant repeat business.
- Management/Supervision Layering—Maintaining excessive levels of supervision—a higher level essentially repeats the work of the lower level.
- Materials Management—Double (or more) handling of materials before use.
- Reorganizations—Reconfiguring an organization with no significant change in missions or workload.
- Physical Relocations—Moving personnel and equipment to accommodate a new organizational structure or otherwise.
- Lack of Electronic Data Links—Receiving data in hard copy and reentering it into another computer system instead of electronically linking computer systems.
- Computer Illiteracy—A manager or other professional staff member who is computer averse still does everything long-hand and turns it over to a clerk for entry into a computer.
- Excessive Administrative Review—Requiring excessive

numbers of approvals on documents such as purchase orders or travel claims.

- Failure to Provide Management Guidance—A manager failing to provide guidance when tasks are assigned and then rejecting the output as not being what he/she was looking for.
- Excessive Quality Control—Maintaining separate contractor and owner quality control operations on a project site.
- Post-Production Engineering Review—Performing a review of engineering deliverables after the deliverables have been fully drafted by the engineering staff. After being marked up, drawings must be redone.
- Reinventing the Wheel—Failing to conduct post-project reviews to develop experience data and lessons learned that can be used in future planning.
- Scope Revision During Detailed Engineering—Failing to completely define scope during conceptual engineering. Detailed designs must be reworked with each scope change. May create construction rework.
- Claims—Expending significant resources in the pursuit of claims, particularly the research and reconstruction of records to find out what really happened.
- Estimating Formats—Developing an estimate against one format and then reconfiguring it for project control.
- Continual Hiring and Training of New Personnel—Experiencing high turnover because the organization is unable to retain trained personnel.
- Misuse of Fax—Using a fax to transmit a copy of something that also is being transmitted in hard copy.
- Not Invented Here—Refusing to acknowledge good ideas that have been demonstrated by others, and, as a matter of hard-headedness, doing it another way.
- Using Second Shift to Continue Work of First Shift—Passing work from one crew to another at a shift change results in lost time as the new shift determines the status of work in place. They also may redo some work.
- Out-of-Date or Incorrect Specifications—Designing against out-of-date or incorrect specifications results in design rework and can create field rework or delays.
- Resolution of Time-Card Discrepancies—Resolving time-card discrepancies because of wrong coding, wrong totaling, etc.
- Untimely Input on Design—Introducing additional design requirements after design development is under way.

The Solution

As one reads through the lists of time and cost wasters above, potential corrective actions are almost obvious. The first step in waste elimination or minimization is to acknowledge that these conditions exist. Through surveys or group discussions, lists of negative conditions can be identified. Usually the list will be too long to attack in total at one time, so the list should be narrowed down to those with the greatest potential for improvement. Specific solutions can be generated through group problem-solving sessions using the various problem-solving tools associated with total quality manage-

ment (TQM)—flow charts, cause and effect diagrams, force-field analysis, and various statistical analyses. As problems from the original list are solved, return to the list and determine if others should be added, and select new targets for improvement. The result of these efforts will be continuous improvement, the ultimate goal of any TQM program. Of course, a proactive approach to waste control is always better than a reactive one. The following specific guidelines are appropriate:

- Plan! Plan! Plan!—this is universal guidance for any operation.
- Establish written policies and procedures—these become the standard references for how things are to be done.
- Involve users (e.g., operators) and constructors in design decisions.
- Control changes —changes degrade performance because they delay and demoralize.
- Give priority emphasis to safety and quality—many claim that performance is directly related to quality and safety.
- Control disturbances and interruptions—examples have already been given. This should be an area of major emphasis.
- Take advantage of modern technology—most productivity gains in the industrial world result from use of better technology.
- Employ partnering and team building—the team approach is always better.
- Communicate—an essential element within a true team.
- Involve employees in planning—this establishes their commitment.
- Use employee group problem-solving techniques.
- Make your work place a good place to work—this promotes employee loyalty and stability, and limits distractions and inefficiency.
- Recognize employee achievements—let them know you appreciate their contributions; this will stimulate continued achievement (see later discussion of incentives).
- Promote first-level quality control—this is the best way to minimize rework.
- Train managers, supervisors, and workers—this promotes professionalism and consistency within the organization while also showing you care. One major industrial firm claims that they get $30 in benefits from every dollar spent on training.
- Be selective in hiring—quality control of personnel cannot be overemphasized.

THE PRODUCTIVITY ISSUE

The Challenge

For any business involved in producing goods or providing services, the productivity of its production personnel and equipment directly influences that business' competitiveness and profitability. It follows that these businesses continually seek ways to improve their productivity. Usually, production is dependent upon some combination of machines and personnel so both must be examined when seeking productivity improvements. In some situations, a company's production potential is totally constrained by the machines being used—they can produce only so may items per unit of time. If so, the solution is to either add more machines or find higher output machines. If human beings are a factor in the rate of production, improving their productivity is more complex.

The construction industry has a somewhat unique challenge when it comes to productivity. It is a fact that a large percentage of construction work is awarded on a fixed-price, target-price or target-workhour basis. In this arena, competing contractors must base their bids or proposals on productivity assumptions for all crafts involved. Then, once the contract is awarded, the contractor has the challenge of meeting or beating the productivity assumptions in order to make a profit or at least not lose money. With labor costs often being 40 percent or more of the total installed cost and with profit margins in construction often being less than 5 percent, it is easy to see how errors in productivity estimation and management can ruin a contractor. Remaining discussion in this section will be examples on recognizing the particular challenges of the construction industry.

A major point to be made and emphasized is that productivity on the same type of work varies significantly from location to location within a country and from country to country. That variation is caused by many factors, which may be grouped as follows.

Variability—Sociological (Area) Factors

Some variation can be attributed to differences in the sociological makeup of the local population, local work ethic, level of mechanization, the education and training levels of workers, the climate, the organized labor situation, and urban vs. rural factors. Recognizing this, most major construction contractors and some owners maintain proprietary data on area productivity differences to be accounted for in their estimating of construction costs. Typically, they will select one area as the base area and give it an index of 1.00. Other areas are given indices that relate their general productivity to the base area, with indices less than 1.00 being less productive and those with indices greater than 1.00 being more productive. For example, these are extracts from an index register used at one time by one owner company:

Houston (base area)	1.00
Baton Rouge	0.85
Corpus Christi	1.10
Chicago	0.80
Denver	0.95

Internationally, the variation is even greater. An article, *International Labor Productivity*, in the January 1993 issue of

AACE International's **Cost Engineering** magazine by J.K. Yates and Swagata Guhathakurta, provides relative productivity data for many countries. Its indices use a format that is the inverse of the above and it provides ranges for each country. Examples:

Washington, D.C. (base area)	1.00
Belgium	1.25-1.52*
Jamaica	1.49-3.05
China	2.60-4.50

*Interpretation—Comparable work in Belgium will require 25-52 percent more workhours than in Washington, D.C.

Variability—Location Factors

As location varies, so do these factors:

- weather patterns;
- altitude;
- access;
- availability of skills;
- availability of logistical support;
- trafficability of site;
- attitude of nearby communities;
- transportation network; and
- local economy.

Variability—Project and Contract Characteristics

No two projects or contracts are exactly alike. These differences definitely influence productivity potential.

- project size; single craft size;
- schedule constraints;
- adequacy of scope definition;
- constructability of design;
- exposure to hazards;
- environmental requirements;
- height or depth of work;
- form of contract;
- budget constraints;
- quality of engineering;
- degree of congestion or confinement;
- relationship to existing facilities; and
- relationship to other construction.

Variability—Human Factors

The ultimate determinants of project performance are the human beings doing the managing and building. Overall performance is a function of these human factors:

- management competence;
- supervisor competence;
- individual worker skills;
- work rules;
- personal pride;
- stability of employment;

- overtime;
- experience/ point on learning curve;
- worker attitudes;
- crew stability/ key personnel turnover;
- owner/contractor relationships;
- value system; and
- personalities.

Variability—Field Organization and Management Factors

Finally, these are those factors which are most completely in the hands of management to control:

- site layout for construction;
- support equipment availability;
- project controls system;
- quality management program;
- technology/methodology used;
- subcontractor performance;
- degree of communication;
- crew balance;
- materials availability and quality;
- tool availability and quality;
- safety program;
- adequacy of support facilities;
- degree of planning;
- vendor performance; and
- control of interruptions.

Variability - Accounting and Estimates

Acknowledging that there are many variables that influence overall productivity on a project, contractors bidding on fixed-price or target-price work must somehow determine how these variables will interact to affect worker productivity on that project. Ideally, a contractor will maintain historical data files containing actual productivity data from past projects. For this data to be useful on future projects, several criteria apply:

- a standard chart of accounts for crew tasks must be used for all projects so that data from one project realistically can be compared to data from another;
- the breakdown of crew tasks for purposes of estimating must be the same as that used for reporting so that estimated and actual performance can be truly compared; and
- in addition to the numerical data collected on each project, the conditions under which work was performed (e.g., weather, congestion, materials shortages) should be described, since those conditions affect the outcome.

When preparing bids for a new project, estimators will research the historical files to find productivity data on similar work performed under similar conditions. Unfortunately, such efforts will be only partially successful, so judgment decisions must be made to adapt data on hand to the new

project. Fortunately, there are some tools available to facilitate this process.

- **Range Estimating**—*Range estimating* is a generic term applied to several commercial and company-developed computer programs that use a Monte Carlo statistical modeling technique to deal with events where the outcome of each event can occur over a range represented by a frequency curve. It is particularly useful for evaluating the combined effect of multiple independent variables on measures of performance such as productivity. The point to be made is that range estimating can be used to quantify the risk associated with productivity variability on a number of different work tasks.

- **Checklists and Worksheets**— Some individuals and companies have developed structured approaches in the form of checklists or worksheets to help them in coming up with productivity estimates. As an example, Figure 17.5 is a description and sample of a *Productivity Index Evaluation Worksheet* developed by the author.

Promoting Productivity

To promote productivity on a project, managers must first be aware of the many factors that can affect it. These have been listed in previous paragraphs. During the pre-mobilization stage and using these lists as checklists, managers can identify those factors with potential to adversely affect productivity. From this list, they can identify those factors that cannot be controlled, those that can be partially controlled, and those that can be completely controlled. It is then a matter of prioritizing the controllable factors and developing positive programs to eliminate or minimize the effects of these factors.

As implied in the previous paragraph, a proactive approach to promoting productivity will yield the greatest return. If, during the course of a project, productivity is not what managers feel it should be, reactive action is required, but it will follow the same steps.

Additionally, since productivity is but a subset of performance, the guidance contained in the solution sub-section of the overall performance issue section, above, is fully applicable to productivity management programs.

PRODUCTIVITY ANALYSIS

Determining Percent Complete

The primary purpose of this section is to explain methods for measuring and analyzing productivity. However, use of these methods requires an understanding of the methods for measuring percent complete of work activities, so these will be described first. There are six methods:

1. **Units completed**—This method is suitable when the

total scope of an activity consists of a number of equal or nearly equal parts, and status is logically determined by counting parts completed and comparing that to the total number of parts in the total activity. Ideally, each unit is of relatively short duration. In engineering, a possible application is in the writing of a number of specifications of a given type where all specifications are considered to have essentially equal weight. In construction it is useful in activities such as earthwork, concrete work, and wire pulling.

2. **Incremental Milestone**—This method is appropriate for activities of significant duration that are composed of easily recognized, sequential subactivities. Percentage completion values are established based on the effort estimated to be required at each milestone point relative to the total for the activity. This method is ideal for control of engineering drawings and can be used in procurement. A typical example for drawing control is:

> Start drafting   0 percent
> Drawn, not checked   20 percent
> Complete for office check   35 percent
> To owner for approval   70 percent
> First issue   90 percent
> Final issue100 percent

Vessel installation and assembly is a classic example in construction. For example:

> Received and inspected   15 percent
>   Setting complete   35 percent
> Alignment complete   50 percent
> Internals installed   75 percent
> Testing complete   90 percent
> Accepted by owner   100 percent

3. **Start/Finish Percentages**—This method is applicable to activities that lack readily definable intermediate milestones and/or the effort/time required is very difficult to estimate. For these tasks, controllers credit 20-50 percent when the activity is started and 100 percent when finished. The reason that a percentage is assigned for starting is to compensate for the period between start and finish when no credit is being given. In engineering, this method is appropriate for work such as planning, designing, manual writing, model building, and studies. It also can be used for specification writing. In construction it is appropriate in any situation where scheduling is detailed with multiple, short-term tasks.

4. **Ratio**—This method is applicable to tasks such as project management, constructability studies, project controls, and comparable activity that involve a long period of time, have no   particular end product, and are estimated and budgeted on a bulk allocation basis rather than

on some measure of production. It also can be used on some tasks for which the start/finish method is appropriate. Percent complete at any point in time is found by dividing hours (or dollars) spent to date by the current estimate of hours (or dollars) at completion. This method is useful on any project where non-production accounts (such as overhead) must be statused individually and summarized with production accounts to determine the overall percent complete.

5. **Supervisor Opinion**—This is a subjective evaluation of percent complete and should be used only where more discrete methods cannot be used. There is a natural tendency to over-estimate the level of completion of an activity in its early stages.

6. **Weighted or Equivalent Units**—This method is applicable where the task is a major effort involving a long period of time and composed of two or more overlapping subtasks, each with a different unit of measurement (e.g., each, yd^3). To set this up all subtasks are listed along with their respective units of measure and quantities. The subtasks are then weighted using relative workhours as weighting standards—the total of all weights equals 1.00 or 100 percent. The progress of each subtask is reported using one of the five measurement techniques described previously. When this percentage is multiplied by that subtask's weighting factor, its contribution to overall task completion is calculated. Those for all subtasks are added to give the overall percent completion of the major activity. A classic example is concrete placement, which is frequently estimated and reported in terms of cubic yards in place; it can be broken up into the subtasks of base preparation, forming, resteel installation, concrete placement, curing, form stripping, and patching. Another example is steel erection, which is traditionally estimated and controlled in terms of tons of steel. The process is illustrated in Table 17.1.

Productivity Measurement of Individual Work Tasks

Owners and contractors are always interested in comparing actual field productivity to that estimated and budgeted. When dealing with a single work activity, the calculation of productivity is very simple:

> productivity = (number of units completed) ÷ (workhours consumed)

What is more difficult is the calculation of productivity at a summary level or for an entire project.

Productivity Analysis at a Summary Level

While a comparison of earned to actual workhours is used by some practitioners to provide an evaluation of productivity at a summary level, that approach is valid only if actual quantities of work are exactly equal to those budgeted. This is not always true, particularly on fixed-price, lump-sum contracts, so another tool is needed to evaluate productivity. That tool is credit work-hours.

Credit workhours (CWH) are derived quantities and are found using this formula for work items completed:

CWH = (budgeted unit rate*) x (units completed to date)
* budgeted unit rate = budgeted hours per unit of work

For individual work packages in progress (not yet complete), this formula is appropriate:
    CWH = (percent complete) x (budgeted unit rate)
The productivity index (PI) for a single work package is found by this formula:

productivity index = (CWH to date) ÷ (actual WH to date)

The productivity index (PI) for a combination of work packages or for a total project uses this formula:

    productivity index = (CWH ÷ actual workhours).

The format of these equations is such that an index of less than 1.0 is unfavorable, while one equal to or greater than 1.0 is favorable.

Use of Productivity Data

It is a waste of time to collect data that is not used for the benefit of the project or the company. Recalling that project estimates include productivity assumptions for the various work tasks, a very important use of the field data is to compare estimated with actual productivities. It is unlikely that estimated and actual productivities associated with a single work task will ever be exactly equal, but significant variations should be cause for concern—the difference may be attributable to a poor estimate and/or it may be attributable to field performance. In any event, significant variations should be investigated and the results shared with the estimators, since their databases may need updating.

Significant variations in the productivity index at the project level may or may not be of concern, depending on the phase of the project. Figure 17.4 shows example plots of a productivity index on both a period and cumulative basis. A productivity index of 1.0 is the datum line. Also shown is the expected cumulative plot. As drawn, that curve reflects the typical course of the cumulative productivity index over the life of an activity or total project—typically it runs below 1.0 during the early reporting periods, increases gradually to a peak of 1.15-1.20 about the 50 percent complete point and then decreases, ideally becoming 1.0 at the 100 percent complete point. On this example, the actual cumulative productivity index has been running consistently below the expected cumulative curve, meaning that, in spite of the fact that at some points the period PI was above 1.0, the cumulative productivity index probably will be less than 1.0 when the project or activity is complete.

INCENTIVES

Why Incentives?

Incentive programs must be included in any discussion of performance and productivity. Such programs have the potential to:

- increase performance and productivity;
- reduce waste;
- reduce absenteeism;
- improve employee morale;

Table 17.1—Steel Erection as Traditionally Estimated and Controlled in Terms of Tons of Steel

Wt.	Subtask	UM	Quantity Total	Equiv. Steel TN*	Quantity To Date	Earned Tons **
0.02	Run fdn bolts	each	200	10.4	200	10.4
0.02	Shim	percent	100	10.4	100	10.4
0.05	Shakeout	percent	.100	26.0	100	26.0
0.06	Columns	each	84	31.2	74	27.5
0.10	Beams	each	859	52.0	0	0.0
0.11	Cross braces	each	837	57.2	0	0.0
0.20	Girts/sag rods	bay	38	104.0	0	0.0
0.09	Plumb and align	percent	100	46.8	5	2.3
0.30	Connections	each	2977	156.0	74	3.9
0.05	Punch list	percent	100	26.0	0	0.0
1.00	STEEL	TON		520.0		80.5

* Equiv. Steel TN = (Wt.) (520 Ton)
** Earned Tons = (% complete) (Equiv. Steel Tons)

    percent complete = (earned tons) ÷ (total tons)
        = (80.5 tons) ÷ (520.0 tons) = 15.5 percent

Notice in this example how tons of steel is the account's unit of measure, and all subtasks are converted to equivalent tons. It also may be noted that percent complete could have been calculated by this formula:

    percent complete = $\sum$ [(weight) x (percent complete each subtask)]

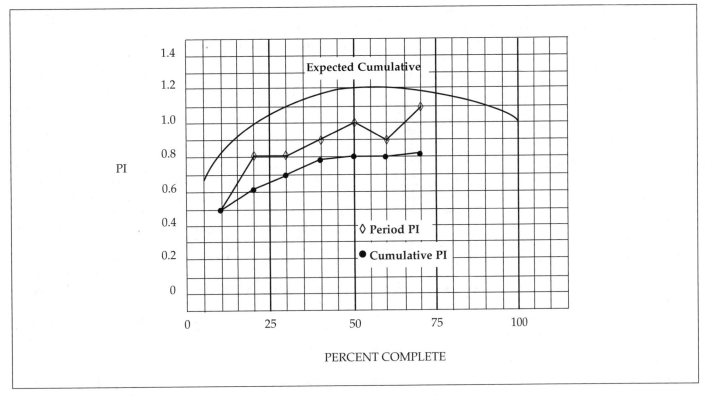

Figure 17.4—Productivity Index

- promote teamwork;
- identify more cost-effective work procedures;
- improve equipment design;
- improve quality; and
- share business risks with employees.

In doing this the profitability of the organization is certainly improved, but, increasing profitability is not the only potential benefit. Users have found incentive programs to be excellent tools for opening lines of communication between managers and employees and for committing employees to the goals of the organization.

The Stimuli

If incentives are intended to stimulate employees to support management goals, it is important that management understand the stimuli that can be mobilized. These may be grouped into two categories from the perspective of the employee.

- Possibility of winning:
  - excitement of winning something;
  - personal satisfaction in achieving a goal;
  - euphoria of being singled out for recognition;
  - financial gain;
  - career enhancement;
  - pride of association with a winning team; and
  - a chance to do something different

- Fear of losing:
  - potential embarrassment; and
  - potential loss of status, job, potential for promotion, etc.

Certainly the best incentive programs are based on the concept of win-win; i.e., both the employer and employee are potential winners. Those that capitalize on the employee's fear of losing are more fragile and can be counterproductive.

Rewards Within the Winning Scenario

Each incentive program in the win category has some reward associated with the achievement of some objective. In designing incentive programs and incentive awards it is important to realize that rewards have two values—intrinsic and extrinsic. The intrinsic value is essentially the exchange or cash value of the reward. The extrinsic value is that value above and beyond the cash value that accrues to the recipient because of what the award means to him or her—some might call this esteem value. It is essential that every reward have some value—it may have either or both intrinsic and extrinsic value, but it is not necessary that it have both. A medal for heroism and the Eagle badge in scouting have little intrinsic value but tremendous extrinsic value to the awardees. If an employer gives a Rolex watch to every employee completing 25 years of service as an incentive to reduce turnover, that watch has considerable intrinsic value but minimal extrinsic value because the quality of an employee's performance during those 25 years is not a factor. Achievement of professional registration has high extrinsic value and also can have significant intrinsic value if it means a raise in pay or chance for promotion.

Rewards whose value is almost totally extrinsic are certainly the most cost effective. The fact that such rewards also can be effective stimuli puts incentive programs within reach of every employer. Specific examples of rewards in both categories will be incorporated within the following discussion of specific programs.

Example Incentive Programs

The following summaries of programs or activities that have been or are being used successfully illustrate the range of incentive program options that may be considered.

- **Open-Book Management**—This incentive program is really a revolutionary way of doing business and might be considered an advanced form of total quality management. As the name suggests, the company's books, strategies, good news and bad news are fully shared with employees, the theory being that employees will make better decisions and perform better if they know exactly how the company operates and what contributes to profits and losses. The incentive involved is a sharing of annual profits among employees, typically 25 percent.

- **The Green Stamp Program**—Under this program, employees earn credits (or green stamps) for achievement of various objectives. Typical objectives are zero defects, no accidents, no late starts/early quits, or no absenteeism during a given period; achievement of a production or productivity goal; approval of a suggestion; etc. The number of credits awarded are commensurate with the achievement. Credits are allowed to accumulate in the employee's account for conversion to gift certificates at his/her convenience. Each credit is usually worth $1. This program has several advantages: (1) the employee can pick the reward; (2) the accumulation feature stimulates continuing achievement; (3) it brings in the influence of an employee's family (they cheer the employee on), since awards can be significant and of the type the whole family chooses; and (4) it is open to all employees.

- **Suggestion Program**—These programs have been around a long time. Employees make suggestions that are reviewed by selected committees for possible adoption. Adopted suggestions usually result in a cash award that is based on anticipated savings. If a suggestion is not adopted, or the benefits are other than cash savings, the reward is usually a letter of appreciation but may include some token merchandise item. Suggestion programs have enjoyed mixed success. A high rate of suggestion rejection or excessively complex and time-consuming submission and processing procedures can quickly dim employee enthusiasm.

- **Sharing Savings**—On fixed-price or target-price contracts, an incentive program can be established whereby field personnel will share in any savings realized. These are usually distributed based on salaries or wages paid during the life of the contract. An interesting form of this has been used by an open shop contractor to keep fixed-price projects within budget. First, all budgeted direct costs within the control of construction crews were allocated to their individual work packages. Then, as crews completed the work, actual costs were accumulated. These costs included labor costs, materials costs, equipment and tool costs, costs of accidents, and any other costs attributable to the crew's assigned work. At well-defined milestone points in the project, a tally was made of budgeted and actual costs in the covered period. Any savings were distributed totally to the workers, the distribution being proportional to worker hours or earnings during the period involved. There were no penalties for overruns—these are assumed to be a result of bad estimates and budgets. This program promotes teamwork and crew balancing, safety, conservation of materials and improved productivity, all while preserving company profit.

- **Target Bonuses**—Often an owner will establish a target completion date or a target cost for a project, knowing those targets can be met only with exceptional effort. To stimulate this effort, they will set aside a sum of money to be divided among the field personnel if the target is met.

- **Honoraria**—These are given to individuals for specific achievements relating to professional development, such as professional registration/certification, writing and publishing a professional paper, or representing the company in a professional forum.

- **Service Awards**—These are usually a combination of a certificate and a merchandise prize to recognize years of service with a company. The value of the merchandise increases with length of service. Often, a special luncheon or dinner is held to distribute these awards.

- **Merit Raises**—Either a portion or all salary increases in a given year are tied to performance evaluations. It is very difficult to create an impartial system for these since evaluations are very dependent upon subjective judgments of individual managers and these can be influenced by politics and prejudices. A selection board approach can minimize this problem.

- **Cross-Training**—An employer who provides cross-training for workers provides a measure of job security for those workers, and this is motivating for the employees.

- **Special Training**—If a limited number of individuals are selected each year for some special training, competition for selection becomes a strong motivator for excellent performance.

Many successful incentive programs capitalize on the extrinsic value of the rewards involved and, in so doing, achieve results at low cost. Examples:

- **The Simple "Atta Boy!"**—A simple pat on the back or word of appreciation, particularly when given in front of everyone in a work unit, can do wonders to motivate many people.

- **Management by Walking Around**—It is good management practice to maintain visibility with employees through frequent visits to work areas during which they chat with employees. By showing sincere interest in the individuals and their work, a manager effectively motivates employees.

- **Letter or Certificates of Appreciation and Achievement**—A document that commends an individual for an accomplishment has high, long-term value since it is written proof of special capability and may be the document needed in some future job search.

- **Certificates of Completion**—These recognize completion of some training program. They have significant value only if the participants in the program had to pass some meaningful test to graduate.

- **Decals**—These are usually used in conjunction with other awards. For example, someone completing a first aid or CPR course would receive both a certificate of completion and a decal to put on their hard hat.

- **Token Awards**—Awards in this category include inexpensive items such as t-shirts, coffee cups, baseball caps, calculators, and pen knives. These are appropriate for individual or crew minor achievements such as short-term safety, quality, or attendance records. Slightly higher-cost items, such as a wind breaker jacket, engraved desk sets, and clocks are suitable for more significant achievements, such as long-term safety or quality records.

- **"Exclusive Clubs" on the Job**—Individuals take pride in being part of a group whose membership criteria is exclusive. A group of earth movers had a "Million Yard Club" on their project. Production, safety, and quality goals can be set to qualify for membership in comparable clubs. Achievement of membership in the club is recognized through certificates, decals on the hard hat, t-shirts, bumper stickers, etc.

- **Employee or Crew of Month**—This program is very common in the service industry. A committee selects the recipients based on recommendations from managers, customer comment forms, or other criteria. The reward is usually a picture of the individual or crew displayed in a prominent location, plus a certificate. It can include a cash award or special luncheon/dinner. This program must be carefully managed so it does not degenerate into a popularity contest or "whose turn is it this month?" form of selection.

- **Problem-Solving Teams**—These are similar to quality circles except they are ad hoc and are given a specific problem to solve by management. Their work can result in cash or credit awards; however, a letter of appreciation or commendation may be adequate. These teams are motivators since they are another form of participative management.

- **Team Builders**—There are a number of relatively inexpensive actions that can be taken to stimulate group morale and team spirit (and thus productivity and quality) on a project or in other workplaces.

- Creating a project logo and using this logo on signage, hard hat decals, bumper stickers, stationery, etc. It is recommended that a project-wide contest be held to design the logo.
- Publish a newsletter. Have a contest to name the newsletter.
- Use the newsletter or bulletin boards for publication of "Hats Off" type notices to recognize accomplishments of individuals.
- Occasionally put out coffee for workers as they check in for work or cool beverages as they leave work on a hot day.
- Have the project photographer take pictures of individuals and crews on the job. Display these pictures on a bulletin board near the check-in area. Perhaps make copies available to pictured individuals.
- An alternate to the above is to provide video coverage of the project with the product being a weekly tape of about 15-30 minutes in length. On this tape review project status, show crews at work, etc. Show the tape during lunch in protected break areas.
- Use a special message board in a prominent location on which the project status is displayed, special accomplishments are announced, and human interest stories told about project participants.
- Sponsor charity work by the workers—food and toy drives, painting or repairing homes for the needy, building playgrounds, etc.
- When a major project milestone is reached, allow an extra hour for lunch and have a catered lunch for the workers. Use this opportunity to give out safety and other awards.
- Sponsor "family day" at the project, plant, or nearby park with a picnic lunch, tours of the project/plant, and games.
- Put first names of workers on their hard hats.
- Sponsor bowling, softball, and other teams in local

leagues.

- Issue press releases on project and employee accomplishments.
- Recognize birthdays or other events with a congratulatory letter.
- Do whatever you can to provide job security for employees—cross-training, information on upcoming jobs, outplacement service, etc.
- If the project receives some cash award for safety or other achievement, divide the award up into $50 packages and give them away in a raffle. All workers who contributed to the achievement are included in the drawing.
- Anything to make the site "a good place to work"—a strong safety program, decent worker facilities, good layout, dust control, etc.

Incentive Program Guidelines

In analyzing the many individual and team incentive programs that have enjoyed success, a number of guidelines evolve.

- Learn from the experiences of others.
- Program must balance both employer and employee goals.
- Get workforce into the planning of program if possible—if union personnel are involved, the union must be involved.
- Keep each program element as simple as possible.
- Criteria for awards must be specific and understandable.
- Performance criteria must be achievable.
- Successful achievement of goals must be within control of target individual or group.
- Programs based on subjective rather than objective criteria are more difficult to manage impartially.
- The program will be most effective if the awards resulting from an accomplishment directly accrue to the individual or team making the accomplishment.
- Mobilize as many of the stimuli as possible in establishing the reward structure.
- Avoid any potential for discrimination in determining award recipients.
- Make certain your program is well publicized.
- Publicize achievements by individuals and teams.
- Ensure that the program is continuously well managed.
- Incorporate potential for many winners.
- Provide opportunities for the entire workforce.
- Don't turn off non-winners—"maybe next time."
- What works in one environment won't necessarily work in another. An example can be cited where a contractor used preferential parking as a reward and the program was very successful. Another contractor tried it and the rewarded workers found their tires slashed.
- Be aware of the tax implications of awards. Merchandise awards of nominal value (example: turkeys, coffee cups, etc.) are not taxable. Cash awards or awards equivalent to cash (example: gift certificates) or costly merchandise

awards (example: TV, pickup truck) are taxable.
- Proceed with caution when launching an incentive program. Start small and work up to more ambitious programs that build on the success of early programs. A failed incentive program can have totally negative effects.

Incentive programs have established a place for themselves in the business world. A variety of programs already have been successful. Companies can learn from these programs and design adaptations of them to fit their particular environments.

The question is inevitably asked, "What is the benefit:cost ratio for incentive programs?" Unfortunately, the author is not aware of any research on the subject and such data would be difficult to compile. However, several individuals with experience with incentive programs have expressed the opinion that the payoff is in the range of 4:1 to 10:1. Whatever the benefit:cost ratio, the results so far have shown that well-managed incentive programs can positively influence teamwork, safety, quality, and overall performance.

CONCLUSION

The ultimate performance index for an organization is the one that relates its net profit or value of services to the costs of achieving that profit or providing those services. An organization seeking to maximize that index must examine the operations of its total workforce, not just those of its production units. It must target waste in all forms—not only materials or equipment waste, but the waste associated with inefficiencies, interruptions, rework, and an assortment of other time-wasters, all of which effectively constrain their employees' ability to produce, perform, and achieve. And, most of all, that organization must provide a workplace with the facilities, procedures, atmosphere, and attitudes that stimulate performance.

PRODUCTIVITY INDEX EVALUATION WORKSHEET

Purpose

This worksheet, Figure 17.5 on page 17.16, is intended to facilitate a comparison of the productivity potential of a proposed project with respect to a completed project. For this purpose, a productivity index of 1.0 is average, a productivity index less than 1.0 is less than average (unfavorable), and a productivity index greater than 1.0 is better than average (favorable).

Evaluating productivity variation among projects is not an exact science. This worksheet serves only to force planners to seriously consider many conditions that can affect productivity and to evaluate their individual effects as well as their cumulative effect. The productivity elements and the weighting factors used are not fixed—users should adjust them to reflect experience over time.

Use of Worksheet

1. For a reference (completed) project, complete an evaluation of each of the 7 categories of productivity elements. This is best done by several individuals familiar with the project so that the results represents group consensus. Note that each category is made up of 2 or more subcategories so that evaluations can be made at the subcategory level to yield the category score. For example, note that the first category, general area economy, has three subelements. Assume that the group makes the following analysis of a completed project:

a. Construction volume in the area at the time of the project was somewhat low compared to previous years when several major plants were built. Now, most construction activity involves homes and small commercial projects. This subcategory is given an index of 110.

b. The unemployment rate in the area was about average for the state, but better than the national average. There were jobs available, but most were of the minimum wage category. This subcategory is given an index of 100.

c. The local business situation was basically healthy, neither robust or depressed. This subcategory is given an index of 100.

d. The resultant score for category 1, general area economy, is:

$$110 \times 4 = 440$$
$$100 \times 4 = 400$$
$$100 \times 2 = \underline{200}$$
$$1,040 \div 10 = 104$$

2. Continue the evaluation of the remaining categories to develop the score for the completed project.

3. Make a similar evaluation for the proposed project. Then compare the scores to determine a multiplying factor to use in estimating productivities on the new project using productivities for similar work on the completed project as a reference.

(productivity multiplying factor for proposed project) = (PI proposed project) ÷ (PI completed project)

4. The above does not consider regional differences in general workforce productivity due to sociological and other differences among worker populations. If planners believe such differences exist, they must further modify the multiplier obtained in paragraph 3 by multiplying it by a factor found by dividing the area productivity index of the proposed project by the area productivity index of the reference project.

5. Use the resultant productivity multiplier in conjunction with relative wage rates to determine relative labor costs for the same volume of work.

6. This worksheet also can be used to normalize data from past projects for entry into the historical database. Since the raw data from each project is distorted because of numerous project-unique conditions, normalizing it has the effect of bringing the data down to a baseline not affected by those conditions.

PRODUCTIVITY INDEX EVALUATION WORKSHEET

Productivity Element	Weight	75-99 Low	100 Average	101-125 High	Score	Product
1. General Area Economy	10	**Prosperous**	**Normal**	**Depressed**	_____	_____
construction volume in area	4	high	average	low		
unemployment situation	4	low	average	high		
local business situation	2	stimulated	normal	dead		
2. Project Character	25	**Complex**	**Average**	**Favorable**	_____	_____
schedule	6	compressed	normal	ample slack		
complexity of work	6	complex	average	simple		
contract form	5	reimbursable	fixed-price	incentive		
project type	5	revamp	new work	repeat work		
size	3	mega	average	small		
3. Craft Workers and Foremen	25	**Poor**	**Average**	**Good**	_____	_____
quality and availability	8	poor	average	excellent		
distance to project	5	more than 60 min	30-60 min	less than 30 min		
substance abuse program	5	none	policy only	full program		
use of overtime and multiple shifts	4	much	some	exception		
rate of force build-up	3	fast	comfortable	(not used)		
4. Project Operating Conditions	20	**Poor**	**Average**	**Good**	_____	_____
congestion and hazards	6	considerable	average	little		
management quality	6	inexperienced	average	highly qualified		
materials and tools availability	3	shortages	average	adequate		
required workmanship	3	exceptional	normal	(not used)		
site access	2	restricted	normal	open		
5. Weather	10	**Poor**	**Average**	**Good**	_____	_____
amount of protected work	2	limited	normal	significant		
precipitation days	2	frequent	normal	occasional		
cold and wind days	2	often	average	rare		
days of extreme heat	2	many	average	rare		
days of extreme humidity	2	many	average	rare		
6. Construction Equipment	5	**Poor**	**Average**	**Good**	_____	_____
condition	3	poor	average	excellent		
maintenance/repair availability	2	remote	nearby	onsite		
7. Delays and Interruptions	35	**Numerous**	**Some**	**Minimum**	_____	_____
rate of changes expected	10	high	normal	low		
materials deliveries	6	uncertain	normal	timely		
operating plant/other interferences	6	frequent	a few	none possible		
site work permits	6	frequent	occasional	not applicable		
labor unrest potential	5	could happen	none expected	(not used)		
public protest potential	2	could happen	none expected	(not used)		
TOTALS	**130**					_____

PRODUCTIVITY INDEX = ($\sum$ PRODUCT) ÷ (13,000) = _____

Figure 17.5—Productivity Index Evaluation Worksheet

Section 5

Project Management

Chapter 18

Project Management Fundamentals

James A. Bent, CCC

INTRODUCTION

In today's difficult and challenging business environment, it is vital that the management of projects results in:

- identifying risks,
- maximizing cost savings,
- minimizing time delays, and
- improving economic return.

These results can only be achieved through:

- effective management of people,
- tough but fair project objectives,
- efficient business techniques, and
- outstanding leadership skills.

The following project management chapters cover these subjects in considerable detail. The roles, functions, and interfaces of company management, project management, engineering management, construction management, and support-service groups are explored. Overall relationships and personnel relationships, essential for successful project execution, are outlined. Throughout, the emphasis is on practical approaches and the relationships of personnel in the project team.

The emphasis is on the need for and substance of early project planning and the related scheduling of time and development of costs. It is essential that all project leaders be effective professional project managers—they need to be organizers, planners, motivators, communicators, and business-persons.

Current studies by the Construction Industry Institute (CII) of state-of-the-art project management methodology have shown that the top category for successful project execution is front-end planning/project organization. The studies have concluded with the following simple but true premise.

If we get it right at the front end, we have a chance of success, though not guaranteed.If we don't get it right, then we have no chance of success.

The following material, mostly flowcharts, illustrates the major factors, functions, and project phases of the project life cycle. Full understanding of all these elements can ensure effective communication channels, tight schedules, low cost, and a clear path for efficient decision-making and economic actions.

But it is in these very elements where many problems develop and become impossible to solve or reduce as the project progresses. The result is more money is spent than necessary, more time is consumed than needed, and there is a constant recycling of options and alternatives that should have been eliminated at an earlier stage. Project ignorance, lack of skill, poor cooperation, and refusal/reluctance to participate properly are commonplace. Biases, prejudices, and personal interests are also part of the equation. All of these elements are compounded by industry-wide lack of up-to-date project training.

LEARNING OBJECTIVES

After completing this chapter, readers should be able to

- understand the roles and responsibilities of project management.

THE CHANGING ROLE OF MANAGING PROJECTS

Over the past 40 years there have been major improvements in project execution, but surprisingly, the most significant developments can be narrowed to less than ten. These developments are the following:

- design quality assurance—value engineering;
- project management performance measurement;
- critical path method (CPM) scheduling;
- fast track scheduling program;
- fast track trapezoidal technique;
- independent construction management;
- partnering; contracting arrangement

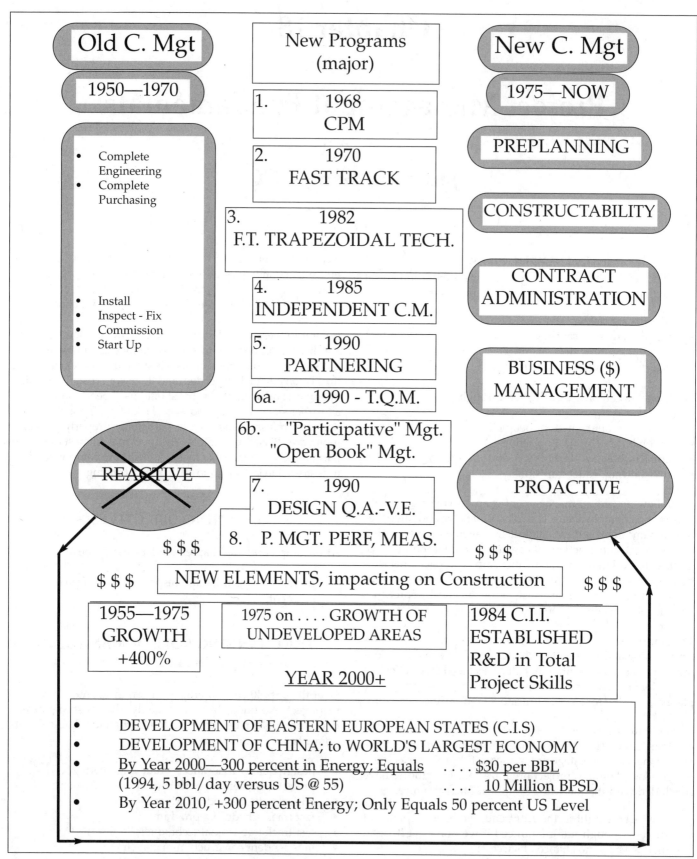

Figure 18.1—The Changing Role of Project Management

- total quality management (TQM); and
- participative and "open book" management.

Project Execution, Old Versus New

Figure 18.1 on page 18.2 is a flowchart that highlights the major changes in project management from the mid-1950s to the present. The old program of sequential completion of the individual phases of engineering, procurement, and construction, where construction management rarely got involved until 4 weeks prior to opening the site, has been replaced by the very challenging, but very efficient, fast track program.

Fast tracking, critical path method (CPM) scheduling, and the trapezoidal technique program are the greatest advances in methodology that have occurred in the past 30 years and followed the explosion of work that took place after World War II. Today's computer systems, while not of the same fundamental importance, greatly assist in the collection and collation of data for these three programs. This data, in turn, is developed into specific cost and schedule project baselines and essential information.

The development of the fast track—trapezoidal technique (F.T.—T.T.) for plant projects, which was first published in 1982, was of particular importance. This technique is used in conjunction with construction complexity and labor density.

Construction complexity and labor density are essential in developing or verifying the quality of a conceptual estimate and planning schedule for process plant projects. When the appropriate factors are properly developed, the resulting cost and schedule numbers can have a probability of 90 to 95 percent.

A Proactive Role

The best of today's construction management now take a proactive role through the newly developed programs of construction preplanning and constructability. This results in a strong construction involvement at the early stage of the project to ensure that engineering design and early planning fully recognize the requirements of an economic construction program. An example of construction preplanning is backwards scheduling, where the overall project schedule is structured around the construction schedule, with design drawing issues and material deliveries being matched to construction needs. If this is done early in the design stage, there is no cost impact on design engineering or purchasing, and the construction cost savings can be considerable, even with the added cost of early construction involvement.

Business management is now considered of greater value than the old standard of aggressively pushing the work, with cost and contractual considerations of lesser consequence

Note: The timing of new major programs and elements, as shown in Figure 18.1, represents the approximate date when

---

GLOSSARY TERMS IN THIS CHAPTER
life cycle ◆ project management

the individual categories were widely used (proven), not when they were first developed.

Project Performance Measurement—Company

The development of a program to measure project performance and personnel skills is essential for any quality program. By the same token, a full benchmarking evaluation is also essential. The real value or added value of a benchmarking program is to provide a state-of-the-art skills base, which is then used to constantly measure the total project performance of the group over time. With a good technical program, the correct balance/mix of skilled personnel, and effective training, there should be a steadily improving project performance that directly results in lower cost/higher quality of a company's capital projects. The measurement program needs to be simple, but effective, utilizing existing information and being directed by the projects quality assurance group. The overall performance goal is to reach a rating of 80 percent, as compared to the current international standard of 55 percent.

DEFINITION OF A PROJECT

A project can be defined loosely as an item of work that requires planning, organizing, dedication of resources, and expenditure of funds in order to produce a concept, a product, or a plant. This chapter focuses on plant projects, all of which require design engineering, the purchase of material, and the installation of that material to the previously completed design engineering.

PROJECT MANAGEMENT FUNCTION

Almost all companies have personnel who are trained, skilled, and dedicated to the execution of the companies' projects. The individuals who lead these efforts are called project engineers and/or project managers. Supporting these project managers are such personnel as design engineers, procurement personnel, contracts officers, estimators, cost engineers, planners, construction managers, and a variety of technical specialists. In many cases, the type, size, and complexity of projects vary greatly, and therefore, the skills and experience of project engineers, project managers, and support personnel can, similarly vary in capability.

The flowchart in Figure 18.2 above shows the major factors that are essential for the successful execution of projects.

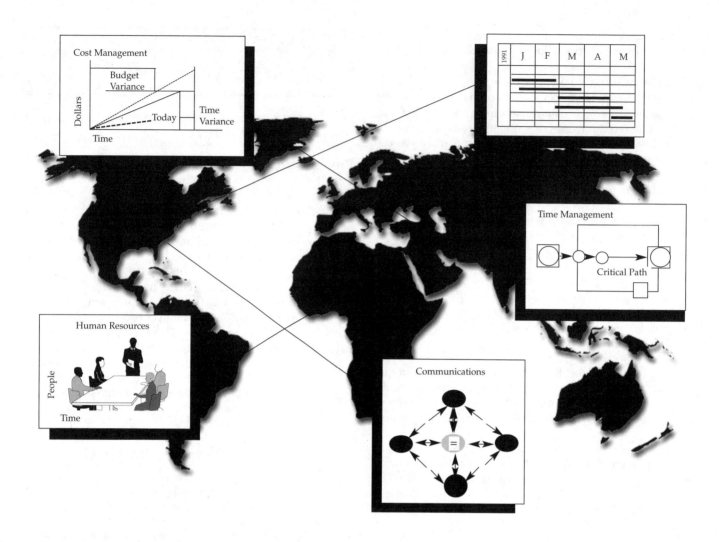

Figure 18.2—Major Factors That Are Essential for the Successful Execution of Projects

Cost Management

Many projects have project cost as the top objective, and this requires the project to be completed at, or less than, the budgeted cost. Significant business skills are essential to meet this objective. There is an industry-wide company policy that the approved project budget can be exceeded by 10 percent, without there being a supplemental funds request.

Time Management

To meet the cost objective, it is necessary to manage time efficiently. This means the predetermined schedule, upon which the cost was based, must be met and met economically. Some projects may have schedule as the top objective. In such cases, acceleration programs are planned and it is probable that there will be corresponding cost increases to the economic-based project.

Human Resources

Of all the resources required for plant projects, the people resources are the most difficult to manage. Interpersonal skills and the effective motivation of people, at all levels, are essential for successful project execution. Lack of human resources, plus a corresponding lack of the correct mix of people skills, are becoming an increasing feature of the project business.

One of the most abused people resource concepts is the "lean and mean" program. The management intent is that a reduced group of people, through advanced skills, can execute as effectively as a larger group, and therefore, save the cost of the people reduction. There is some merit in this concept, but in many cases it is a "device" used by poor management to cut costs. If there is a significant lack of people, there is almost certain to be a corresponding inefficiency in project execution, coupled with an increase in costs.

Communications

A formal and informal structure of effective communications is absolutely essential for successful project execution. In addition to weak people skills, many company organizations and cultures have poor administrative practices that also form barriers to project success. These barriers are common to all companies and are generally referred to as matrix interface conflicts (MICs). The conflicts or barriers are caused by departmental jealousies, rivalries, and failures by management to create a culture where project consciousness and esprit-de-corps are common to all personnel. The total quality management programs sweeping the industry are an attempt to solve these problems.

OVERALL COMPANY PROJECTS LIFE CYCLE

The flowchart in Figure 18.3 shows the general steps common to all plant projects. Experience in this process, recognition of each company program's individualities, and the skills of bridging the matrix interface conflicts, are necessary for project success. Getting the front-end planning right is the key to success.

ENGINEERING REQUEST

The flowchart in Figure 18.4 illustrates the major factors that generate the capital project work. Timely and quality assessments of plant requirements are difficult to achieve but are essential for company profitability. Such assessments result in formal engineering requests for the project work.

PROJECT DEVELOPMENT

The flowchart in Figure 18.5 shows the major components for developing the scope of each project. Each of these components, technical, project conditions, regulatory, cost, and economic, is then further defined and prioritized and it is vital that the priority be clearly established.

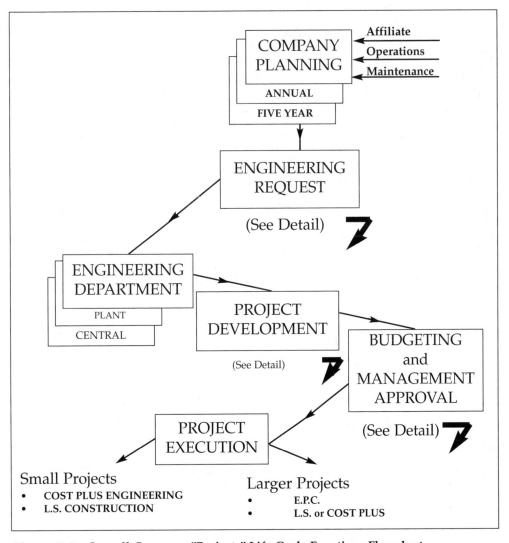

Figure 18.3—Overall Company "Projects" Life Cycle Functions Flowchart

18.5

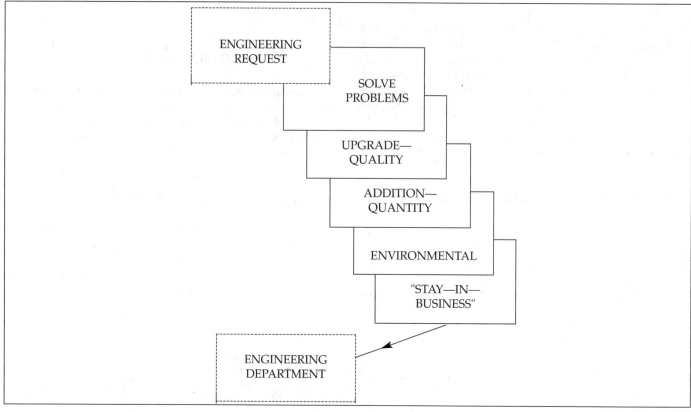

Figure 18.4—Engineering Request—Functions Flowchart

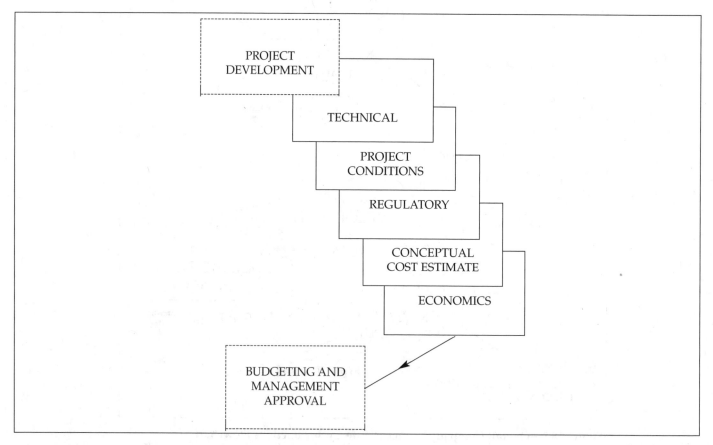

Figure 18.5—Project Development; Functions Flowchart

BUDGETING AND MANAGEMENT

Development of the scope in terms of risk, cost, time, and resources is followed by approval, partial approval, or rejection of each proposed project. Figure 18.6 shows the budgeting and management process, closely followed by the development of the project strategy and project organization. The correct assessment of the people resources, especially the key people, is essential at this early stage.

TYPICAL PROJECT PHASES AND LIFE CYCLE

The time and interface relationship of major project phases is shown in Figure 18.7. Assuming a fast track program, most of these phases will overlap, and the degree of overlapping will depend on the work content of each phase and the efficiency of decision-making present in the project.

PROJECT TEAM CULTURE

Finally, there is the question of company personnel working as a team. Without question, this matter has become the vital issue to profitability, especially as companies downsize and reduce the core. Greater personnel efficiency and increased operational quality are essential requirements in today's difficult business environment. The bean-counter syndrome is a dangerous and unacceptable practice.

The "Bean-Counter" Syndrome

This is a wide spread practice, where effective cost control is absent or greatly diminished. This practice has two major contributing factors. First, the project manager does not want an aggressive, creative, analytical function for the cost engineer and, therefore, relegates the work to a retro-active, record keeping function. Hence the term, bean-counter. Second, the cost engineer can be directly responsible for this practice; as the individual does not possess the essential analytical skills, or does not believe in an aggressive trending approach and/or does not possess the essential people/communication skills. They are, in fact, content with a bean-counting role. There is a much wider acceptance today of the need for dynamic, proactive cost engineering-trending and it is to be hoped that the function will become a pivotal project role, as effective cost trending is essential for project success. After a lifetime of project work this author has learned this fundamental truth:

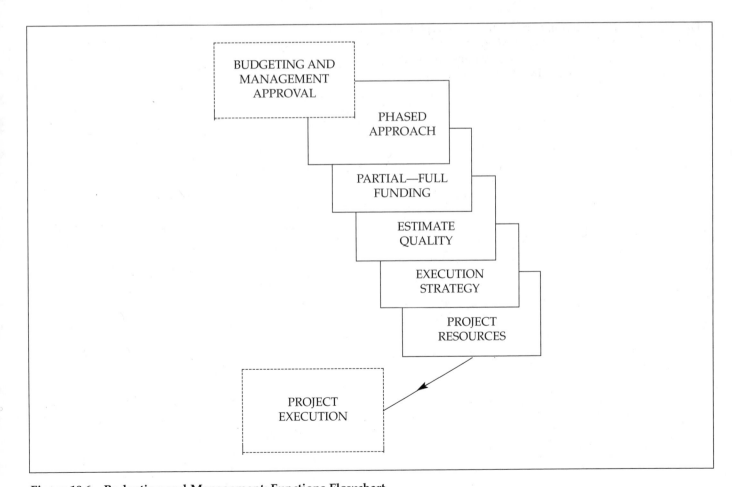

Figure 18.6—Budgeting and Management; Functions Flowchart

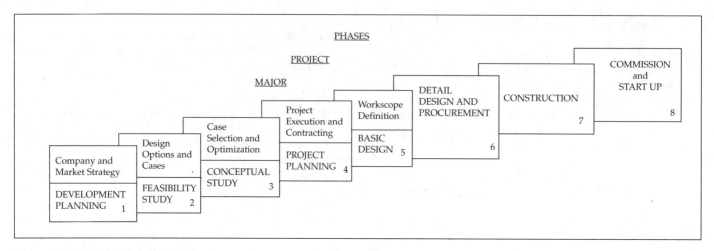

Figure 18.7—Major Phases Flowchart

"Projects are designed and built by people, not companies. People do it singly, or in multiple groups; and if there are skilled people and good relationships, there is a chance of success. If the people and relationships are poor, there is little chance of success."

This chapter is based upon, or portions are excerpted by permission from, *Effective Project Management Through Applied Cost and Schedule Control*, by James A. Bent, CCC, Marcel Dekker, Inc., New York, 1996.

Chapter 19

Project Organization Structure

James A. Bent, CCC

INTRODUCTION

The following are the major constituents of project planning and project organization:

- project organization;
- establishing objectives;
- scope definition control;
- communication and information utilization; and
- constructability planning.

Careful attention to the following details of these constituents will provide a good start to any project.

LEARNING OBJECTIVES

After completing this chapter, readers should

- understand the role of the project manager in project planning, and
- be familiar with project organization and planning.

BACKGROUND TO PAST ORGANIZATIONAL STRUCTURE

The Matrix Structure

Over the past 30 years, the most widely used organization structure has been, and still is, the matrix organization. Most projects are executed with the "matrix," where multiple projects are executed by many departments carrying out the work at the same time, resulting in the project manager having inadequate decision-making authority. Both academics and professional project managers agree that the "matrix organization" is the most complex form of organization structure. Matrix structures were developed to more efficiently use common resources and work many projects at the same time, with the same staff. This provided effective infor-

mation exchange and allowed for efficient management coordination of the total project workload.

Matrixes achieve this by having the working personnel be simultaneously accountable to both the project manager and the departmental manager. In the "matrix," both project managers and departmental managers have authority and responsibility over the work, albeit, there is an agreed division of responsibility. The departmental manager is generally responsible for the technical content and working resources, and the project manager decides on the cost and time baselines. Unfortunately, the person who comes off worst in the "matrix" is the individual who is actually doing the work. He/she reports to two bosses: the project and departmental managers. This leads to divisions of responsibility, problems of loyalty, differences over priorities, poor communications, and lack of single and direct "line authority." The management of personnel and departmental interfaces is a demanding task, and in the "matrix," is often referred to as "conflict management."

The fundamental of "matrix theory" in a project environment, requires the project execution plan to be clearly defined, so that all working groups would then accept, commit to, and work to the agreed execution plan. There would be unanimous support from all and all would be working to the same "plan."

With a strong project management culture and effective company leadership, it was anticipated that the "matrix" would be effective. Initially it was, but as time passed, the "matrix" failed and the research carried out by Peters and Waterman (in their book, *In Search of Excellence* [1]) and many other management experts, has clearly demonstrated this failure. The answer, agreed by all, was a new approach, called quality management. This new approach was spearheaded by Dr. Edward Deming, working in Japan, in the 1960s and1970s.

Demingism and Total Quality Management (TQM)

This made its debut in the US in 1981, at the Ford Motor

Corporation. Yet the transformation of the US industry to Demingism has been slow, even though there is wide acceptance that his quality management approach is essential. TQM, a version of Demingism, has been implemented in the manufacturing industries since the late 1980s and in the engineering/construction industry in the early 1990s. Dr. Deming has developed 14-key sets of criteria for developing a quality management program. This criteria is referred to as "Demingism" and is summarized as follows.

- Client Satisfaction—For the services provided or for the product sold.
- Understanding and Reducing Variation—Every management process, practice, procedure, policy must be evaluated for its effectiveness in allowing the company's individuals to work at maximum effectiveness.
- "Top-Down" Management Leadership and Commitment—Improvement cannot come merely from middle managers and workers "trying harder." There must be full understanding of, and total commitment to, the necessary systematic change and the planned improvements.
- Change and Improvement Must Be Continuous—It must be all-encompassing, involving every "process," individual and outside services and suppliers.
- Ongoing Training and Education is Essential for all employees, and it must be of a high technical quality so that high standards of skills and practices can be implemented by all personnel.
- A Culture of Personnel Pride and Job Satisfaction—At all levels; this requires leadership, program champions, the development of trust and loyalty, personnel empowerment, and the elimination of inadequate performance measurement schemes that can create more losers than winners, resulting in lowering of morale. Such schemes, says Deming, do not account for the "variations" and weaknesses in the company process and can be inaccurate and unfair; and are perceived as such by the employees. Performance measurement is essential, but it should be of the system or process, and individuals should be paid for their experience and responsibilities. Not all personnel will be "star" performers, and the contribution of the company janitor can be equal to that of the chief engineer, when there is a commitment to excellence from both. However, most companies do not agree with Deming on this particular issue and use a "personnel performance" awards program that gives individuals recognition and awards for superior performance. Such a program is Fluor Corporation's "MVP" (most valuable player) program, which was developed through an extensive personnel survey where the staff stated that the company salary program did not properly reward superior performance and that individual awards would be a viable program. Thus the practice of employee empowerment showed a major "need," and Fluor instituted the program in 1994. They currently report that the

program is successful and is a key feature of their continuous improvement program (CIP). Fluor Corporation is an international contractor, with headquarters located in Annaheim, CA.

GENERAL

It is an obvious, but not well-understood fact, that it is people in single, medium, or large size groups who design and build projects, not companies. If there are people available, if they have the required skills, if they have a positive working environment, then success is possible. If none of these conditions pertain or only partially, then success is very questionable. Therefore, there must be a consistent and long-term interest in people needs, their development and their training. When there is little interest, or the interest is not genuine, the long term success of the company is unlikely. The entire total quality management (TQM) program is built around the needs and development of people, and there is unanimous acceptance by industry that total quality management is the key to success. In essence, develop the people, and in turn, the people will develop the profits.

IS THE OWNER COMPANY QUALIFIED TO BE ITS OWN PROJECT MANAGER?

A very fundamental consideration in today's world of company reengineering is the question of the owner functioning as its own project manager. Too often, owners arrive at an affirmative answer through poor analysis. It is a matter of previous experience of the specific project (particularly size), having adequate in-house or consulting resources (skills and numbers), a good project management program and costs.

This is, currently, a major consideration with many operating companies as they downsize their operations. Many companies confuse the issue due to technical/engineering considerations. Having competent engineering personnel, they take on the project management responsibility, but without adequate project experience or project resources. Engineering design competence does not necessarily translate into project capability.

Note: This question was a major issue during the early development of the North Sea Oil and Gas industry (1972-1977). The "answer" at that time, was an emphatic no, from all the large oil companies (as all had limited resources), except for the rare case where contractors declined to bid due to lack of capacity. This problem of limited contractor resources and inadequate technical and engineering expertise was resolved with a project services contract (PSC), and ultimately, partnering and integrated project teams. With a project service contract or reimbursable FOC, owners can "direct" engineering.

DOES THE ORGANIZATION STRUCTURE PROPERLY FIT CONTRACTING ARRANGEMENTS?

Different skills and different numbers of personnel are directly related to contracting arrangements; i.e., lump sum, reimbursable, unit price, project services contract, agent, and independent contractor.

From an owner's perspective, reimbursable contracts can require three times as many owner people as a lump sum contract, and would require personnel with extensive analytical skills. For lump sum, a good design package and strong project discipline (no/little design changes) are essential. Often, there is a mismatch of people resources, in relation to contract arrangements. Having both the wrong contract and the wrong organization/people is a recipe for disaster. Also, a poor management application of the lean and mean principle will result in a serious lack of resources, leading to poor project execution and cost over-runs/schedule slippage.

IS THE PROJECT MANAGER QUALIFIED?

The answer should address technical expertise, project experience, business capability, leadership ability, and people skills. Project, business, and people expertise should have greater consideration, especially for larger projects. On smaller projects and feasibility studies, technical skills would be more important.

DOES THE OWNER PROJECT MANAGER REPORT TO THE CLIENT OR PROJECTS/ENGINEERING?

In contractor groups this is not normally a problem. In owner organizations it is often a problem because the owner project manager normally reports to both groups. My recommendation would be to report to the internal company client so as to "follow" the financial responsibility and to projects/engineering for direction on technical methods.

SHOULD THE PROJECT TASK FORCE (PTF) APPROACH BE UTILIZED?

Significant experience has now shown that the project task force is more efficient for larger projects. The close working relationships allow more efficient communication channels and a more efficient decision-making process. The challenge of welding together many individuals from many parts of the company is a substantial task. The organization structure should follow the current state-of the-art, which has added the new function of a business manager.

> **GLOSSARY TERMS IN THIS CHAPTER**
>
> planning ◆ project management

BUSINESS MANAGEMENT MUST RECEIVE THE CORRECT EMPHASIS

On economically based projects, the emphasis should be on business considerations. There has to be a correct "balance" of technical versus business (estimating, cost control, scheduling, purchasing, contract preparation, contact/construction administration), with emphasis on business considerations.

EFFICIENCY AND EFFECTIVENESS OF THE PROJECT TEAM

There is often the conflict of quality versus quantity. On large projects it is easy to make the mistake of "over-substitution" of numbers of people to satisfy lack of skill. It is a question of degree, as some "substitution" is commonplace. In most cases, lack of good contracting personnel is a major problem. Personnel planning needs to be early, resulting in effective scheduling of all required personnel. Careful consideration should be given to the timing of all key managers and supervisors.

PROJECT ORGANIZATION STRUCTURE— OWNER TEAM (REIMBURSABLE CONTRACT)

On a reimbursable project, the owner should have a "directing position" in order to contain the risk of a contractor taking advantage of "the reimbursable" and manipulating day-to-day execution to enhance profitability. This risk has been well documented by owners and its practice is a key technique of large, international contractors. The balancing force to contain this risk is the quality and skill of the owner's project team, both in the pre-contract activities and the post-contract work execution program. An equal partner relationship (EPR) is an essential requirement and should be built in to the agreement with the appropriate contract clause.

These pre-contract activities should be undertaken by the project team to ensure that the contractor provides competent personnel. It is a contractor practice to train new/inexperienced personnel on their client's reimbursable projects, since the major cost risk is to the client.

Pre-Contract Activities for Contractor Evaluation
- An effective proposal evaluation program should evaluate the quality of the contractor's program, with individ-

ual criteria for technical, project management, commercial/pricing, project control, contractual, and construction.

- If the project is of a substantial size, interviews should be carried out with key personnel (previously nominated).
- Ensure that correct contracting arrangement/conditions are in the contractor's proposal, especially the equal partner relationship clause. Assess the required liability of agent or independent contractor.
- Evaluate contractor proposal program/execution plan and key interfaces of local, corporate, and government.

PROJECT ORGANIZATION CHARTS

These should be dynamic, up-to-date documents, used to identify owner and contractor positions, and during execution of the work, will be the current and future personnel plan, as generally agreed in pre-contract meetings. These charts need to be properly recognized and the organization clearly understood by all project team members. The use of formal job descriptions and duties is recommended.

PROJECT MANAGER AUTHORITY

This individual has full authority to make both design and cost decisions, with appropriate limits of authority and management reporting requirements. On reimbursable projects, the authority of the contractor project manager must be adequate to allow efficient day-to-day operations.

PROJECT CONTROL FUNCTION REPORTS DIRECTLY TO PROJECT OR BUSINESS MANAGER

Many hold the concept that cost control should be an audit function of the project, and therefore report to higher/senior management. I do not support that concept, since it can lead to an adversary relationship and dilute the trust and cooperation that is absolutely essential in the cost effort in the project. There are always independent, periodic cost reviews by senior home office personnel that should be more than adequate for a management audit .

REFERENCES

1. Peters and Waterman. 1984. *In Search of Excellence.* Warner Books, Inc.

This chapter is based upon, or portions are excerpted by permission from, *Effective Project Management Through Applied Cost and Schedule Control*, by James A. Bent, CCC, Marcel Dekker, Inc., New York, 1996.

Chapter 20

Project Planning

James A. Bent, CCC

INTRODUCTION

Note: project organization is covered in chapter 19.

LEARNING OBJECTIVES

After completing this chapter, readers should

- understand the role of the project manager in project planning, and
- understand planning strategies.

ESTABLISHING OBJECTIVES

General

In many cases, the process of developing objectives also can assist in building team commitment and understanding. Objectives always will be a compromise between quality, cost, and schedule and are used as a guide to make decisions. These major objectives then guide development of more detailed goals, procedures, technical criteria, cost targets, and individual milestones. Ideally, a common set of objectives should guide the owner, engineer, and constructor. These objectives provide the work direction to all parties, and as such, would have to be compatible and acceptable. The key to successful acceptance, by all, is a set of well-defined objectives.

Client Satisfaction

Criteria and a measurement program, acceptable to the client, should be developed to produce a periodic and timely report. Client satisfaction should be the single most important objective, and reports, showing poor performance against this objective, should receive top management attention and immediate resolution.

Scope Objective

So that the technical and project scope, as identified in the approved project budget appropriation, will be achieved; a

well-written, but brief scope definition is developed for issue to all (see scope definition control in the following section).

Cost and Schedule Baselines

The required quality and formats of the estimating and scheduling programs should be identified in conjunction with the associated databases and computer systems. All internal and external constraints, interfaces, and influences should be carefully evaluated for both cost and schedule baselines. A critical path method (CPM) computer scheduling system is recommended. Levels of schedule detail, codes of accounts, and work breakdown structures for the cost/estimating program, require careful consideration. Overall and intermediate milestone objectives should be developed. A risk analysis program should identify the ranges of risk for both cost and schedule. The responsibility and management of contingency should be clear and precise. It is the author's judgment that project contingency should be the project manager's responsibility and not treated as a management reserve, as is the practice of some companies.

Quality

Clear and unambiguous criteria should be developed and be fully acceptable to all project parties. The criteria need to be measurable so that a status/progress report can be issued on a regular basis. Quality of project operations, as well as quality of design and construction, need to be covered.

Other

Training, technology transfer, etc., must be fully defined.

Project Objectives Are Prioritized, Documented, and Communicated to Project Team

If this is not done and constantly maintained, then acceptance leading to commitment will be lacking. Establishing clear priorities, with each objective having its relative priority, will allow the multiple groups to work in harmony with each other. Thereafter, a constant effort (part of team building) must be made to keep the project objectives viable.

Effective Project Team Building

Assembling a group of individuals, especially on large projects with large companies, does not make a team. Personnel can come from different locations (worldwide) and different cultures. Time is needed for individuals to recognize and control their individualities, as appropriate, and learn to work together. Individuals usually accept project assignments with little or no knowledge of the individuals with whom they will be working and people accept project assignments hopefully and without full knowledge. It is therefore essential that management and project leaders (all groups) develop a team building program and maintain it throughout the life of the project. Working togetherness, project commitment, cost consciousness, personnel satisfaction, etc., are the deliverables. The cost for this activity should be a recognized budget item.

Effective Community Relations—Local and/or Overseas

There is an ever-increasing opposition from local communities to process projects, due in part to the hazardous nature of many of these projects. An effective and positive public relations effort, in conjunction with direct financial investment in local matters, is necessary and essential.

SCOPE DEFINITION CONTROL

General

This is a matter of project discipline and design control to prevent or identify scope changes that are all too common on fast track projects. A Construction Industry Institute study, "More Construction for the Money," published in January 1983, reports, ". . . Poor scope definition and loss of control of the project scope rank as the most frequent contributing factors to cost overruns."

Effective Interface With Stakeholders, Operations, and Maintenance for Scope Approval

Achieving a proper input for the design from all project parties is a formidable task. This work is usually the direct responsibility of the project engineering manager, and strongly supported by the project manager. If there is no project team, then it would be the responsibility of the project manager. There must be consensus and full understanding, as well as approval, of all parties to the design basis and especially from the design decision-makers. The design basis must be shared openly and with all participating parties. When the design basis is sensitive or proprietary, security procedures must be established. In addition to design, the project execution plan and financial program must be part of the approval process.

Scope Is Well Defined Before Start of Detailed Engineering

This is the purpose of the feasibility study. However, the quality and extent of the early design and project work are a matter of management decision and can vary widely. A poor design package at the start of detailed engineering will result in significant change, rework, and a substantial cost increase. The major deliverable of the feasibility study is the basic design package—statement of requirements (SOR). These should be well-written documents that properly define the technical requirements and have sufficient depth to provide clear direction for all major design issues. They should clearly communicate the intent to the designers and set appropriate boundaries on the project design for detailed decision-making.

The scope document should cover:

- Project description
    project justification, project objectives, economic justification, and if pertinent, facilities description

- Design basis and specs
    process definition
    - description of process
    - process flow diagrams
    - tabular heat and material balance
    - process conditions, special conditions
    - construction of materials
    - startup and shutdown requirements

    mechanical definition
    - p&id drawings—preliminary sizing and piping tie-ins
    - preliminary plot plan
    - preliminary general arrangement
    - preliminary equipment list

    instrument definition
    - define primary control points and purpose
    - define instrument set points, low level alarms, etc.

    safety system
    - hazards analysis (hazops)
    - list of safety devices and their design criteria
    - interlock logic description and diagram

- Project location—elements
    engineering and construction productivity factors (versus database)
    logistics reviews, delivery to and at-site
    infrastructure requirements, at-site
    weather concerns and impacts

- Project conditions
    offshore installations-suppliers
    prefabrication and modules
    operational restraints-conditions
    site and access problems

- Estimate—definition
    work quantities and takeoffs
    engineering, labor, staff hours
    contingency and budget limitations
    risk analysis and identification

- Schedule—definition
    difficulty of proposed completion
    all constraints, restraints and critical relationships
    appropriate levels of detail

Decisions on Scope Are Made in a Timely Manner

This can only be achieved if there is a cohesive, dynamic trending program. Effective communication channels and working togetherness are direct contributors. Management approval process is also a factor.

Dynamic Design Change Control—Formal Program

Project trending and reporting systems, such as the design change order log, are essential. The weekly trend meeting and regular progress meetings provide much of the early identification of change. An effective design control program is centered around an engineering milestone, called the design control point (DCP). If the feasibility study is extensive, the design control point could be operational at the end of the study, and thereafter, all changes would be formally documented. If the feasibility work were minimal, then the design control point would be established at the early part of the project engineering phase. The design control point is reached when the project's original scope is properly defined, agreed to, and approved by all parties. As this approval is reached, the project manager will inform all appropriate parties that the design control point has now been implemented. On very large projects there can be multiple design control points. It is emphasized that the design control point is not a design freeze, as viable design changes should always be an option.

COMMUNICATIONS
INFORMATION UTILIZATION

General

The requirement is to turn data into useful and usable information. Current computers and software systems make the gathering and collation of data a relatively simple task. Thus, correctly establishing the available input data results in obtaining the required output and information. With the establishment of effective communication channels, the information is then directed to the correct recipient.

┌─────────────────────────────────────┐
│ **GLOSSARY TERMS IN THIS CHAPTER** │
│   │
│ planning ◆ project management ◆ scope ◆ schedule │
└─────────────────────────────────────┘

Execution Plan Formal, Written Program

This should be a dynamic document, being revised and updated as conditions/scope change, with proper/timely inputs from all parties. Commitment to "the plan" must then be achieved with all project parties, and especially from management.

These are the three major categories of a good execution plan:

- What is the scope of work?
  (see information in earlier paragraph)
- How is the work to be executed?
- When is the work to be carried out?

- How is the work to be executed?

    - Statement of project objectives
    - Proposed division of work
    - in-house, by company
    - work contracted out
    - development of work packages

    - Contract strategy
    - required scopes and degree of definition
    - forms of contract
    - risk allocation versus. cost of liability

    - Detailed engineering
    - third-party licensers
    - environmental and regulatory; permits

    - Procurement program
    - competitive bidding
    - domestic and international
    - single source; negotiated
    - plant compatibility and spares requirements

    - Construction
    - preplanning program-critical highlights
    - prefabrication, modules
    - pre-commissioning and testing program

    - Commissioning and startup

    - Quality assurance—control and inspection
    - Project organization (see earlier chapter)
    - Project coordination procedure (as follows)

- When is the work to be carried out?
  - Schedule and probability
  - economic versus acceleration
  - critical path and float analysis

  - Resource analysis
  - engineering, construction availability
  - skills and trade union climate

  - Marketing Interface
  - limitations or constraints

  - Cash flow limitations

  - Access problems
  - weather windows, traffic limitations

  - Shutdown—retrofit program

All Scope-Cost Matters Are Routed Through the Project Manager

This is to ensure project consciousness and dynamic trending; this presupposes that the project manager has appropriate authority and decision-making ability for all scope and cost matters.

A Team and Cost Culture Is Developed on the Project

The project manager is directly responsible for creating an environment that will enable project control to be properly exercised. The project manager must be a cost leader, encourage project cost consciousness, seek counsel from all appropriate sources, accept sound advice, and stretch cost/schedule personnel to the extent of their capability. Team building and team stretching are key elements of successful project management.

On smaller projects, where the project manager is also the project control engineer, it is essential that the project manager possess project control skills and/or motivate the supporting/service groups to provide the quality information that is needed for creative analysis and effective decision-making.

Effective project control requires the timely evaluation of potential cost and schedule hazards and the presentation of recommended solutions to project management. Thus the cost/schedule specialist must be a skilled technician and also be able to effectively communicate at the management level. Sometimes, an experienced project control engineer's performance is not adequate because of poor communication skills. Technical expertise will rarely compensate for this lack. As in all staff functions, the ability to "sell" a service can be as important as the ability to perform the service.

On larger projects, project teams are usually brought together from a variety of "melting pots," and the difficulty of establishing effective and appropriate communications at all

levels should not be underestimated. In such cases, the project manager must quickly establish a positive working environment where the separate functions of design, procurement, construction, and project control are welded into a unified, cost-conscious team.

Internal Project Charter Program

This is a newly-developing method to motivate working togetherness by reducing the large coordination procedure to just the key objectives. It is a one or two page document that lists all major parties and their responsibility/accountability and the project objectives. All parties sign the charter, thus demonstrating their commitment to the project plan.

Open Communication Lines at All Times Between All Project Parties

A question of an effective organization, project commitment, working togetherness, and leadership.

Project Coordination Procedure (PCP)—Clearly Defines Communication Channels to All

This would include:

- limits of authority;
- responsibilities of parties;
- correspondence procedures;
- filing and reporting codes;
- document and action schedule
  (for all drawings, documents, reports);
- public relations procedures;
- security and safety procedures; and
- project close-out report.

Trend and Progress Meetings Are Held on Weekly Basis

These meetings are a vital communications tool, and the trend meeting should be a "must" for the project manager. Of the many meetings held during the execution of a project, the weekly trend meeting is probably the most important. This is not a decision-making meeting, but is where information is gathered and shared by key technical/services specialists. The project manager leads the meeting, and the project cost engineer serves as secretary. All current and potential influences, changes, extras, and trends are reviewed and discussed. The key meeting objective is the common sharing, gathering, communicating, and coordinating of all project influences that are developing at the time. Each party to the contract should hold its own weekly trend meeting, followed up by a joint meeting of the main parties, i.e., the owner, engineer, and general contractor.

The Project Management Information System (M.I.S.) Has Effective Levels of Detail

The development of reporting levels of detail must ensure that the information is necessary by management—supervisory function, is accurate, and is timely. Unnecessary detail can be generated easily with today's computer programs, so a vigorous screening effort is therefore, necessary.

CONSTRUCTABILITY PLANNING

General
Constructability and construction pre-planning are often used, interchangeably, to describe the function of each category. They can be considered as functions of "value engineering." Constructability is largely concerned with the technology, methods of installation, and the associated cost. Pre-planning is largely to do with the scheduling of resources, organization, site access, and infrastructure. The purpose of constructability is to reduce costs by considering alternative design and/or installation methods. Typical examples would be steel or precast concrete for a building and for process plants, greater prefabrication and pre-assembly, or even modularization.

Early Economic "Path of Construction" Program
This is an evaluation of the physical sequence of construction work to produce the lowest cost. Many factors are involved, such as:

- physical site conditions, weather;
- restraints of drawings, material delivery, schedule critical path sequences;
- economics of crew sizes and supporting resources; and
- plant operations, safety regulations, etc.

With such early planning, design or material alternatives can be considered at little or no additional cost. The data that is developed is then used in the project scheduling program.

Formal Constructability Programs Are an Integral Part of Project Execution
This is to ensure that the early initiative, as outlined above, is maintained to project completion.

Front-End Planning Actively Incorporates Construction Input
It is essential that capable and experienced construction personnel are assigned to the project at this early stage and that their constructability and preplanning evaluations are a proper part of project development. Sometimes, owners are not prepared to pay for this service and do not appreciate the cost benefit of this early work.

"Construction Driven" Scheduling as Key to CPM Program
This is also known as "backwards" scheduling, meaning that the project CPM schedule is structured around the construction schedule, assuming that the construction schedule has been developed on a "best economic" basis. Engineering and material deliveries then can be matched to the economic construction program, at no cost penalty. Research has clearly shown that the cost benefits of this approach are considerable.

CONCLUSION

It is again emphasized that project planning and project organization structure, as reported by the Construction Industry Institute, make up the number 1 activity on any project, and when this work is properly executed, the financial payout is immediate and substantial.

If we start a project with a good scope definition, have a good organization, and all parties are committed to working togetherness, then project success is a reality.

This chapter is based upon, or portions are excerpted by permission from, *Effective Project Management Through Applied Cost and Schedule Control*, by James A. Bent, CCC, Marcel Dekker, Inc., New York, 1996.

Chapter 21

Project Labor Cost Control

Dr. Joseph J. Orczyk, PE CCE

INTRODUCTION

Construction labor costs are the most variable element of the project construction budget. Therefore, labor cost control is paramount to profitability for all contractors. Owners also need to control labor costs for work performed in-house and for work performed by contractors on a reimbursable basis. In order to control costs, project management must first develop a realistic budget. Just as a yardstick that is not exactly 36 inches long is of little use for measuring distances, an inaccurate budget is useless for measuring labor cost performance. Secondly, in order to maintain an accurate budget, project management must continually compare the actual dollars and workhours to the budget dollars and workhours to identify deviations. Once deviations are identified, project management must take swift corrective action to minimize cost overruns. Creating realistic budgets and maintaining them requires choosing an excellent and efficient cost control system for controlling construction labor costs.

Good construction labor cost control methods utilize the feedback and corrective action elements of the control cycle. The two prevalent construction labor cost control reporting systems are the earned value method and the unit rates method. Each method has the following elements: measuring inputs, measuring outputs, and report processing. The discussions in this chapter are illustrated using data from the concrete accounts of a pre-engineered warehouse project. The labor cost estimate for the concrete accounts is shown in Table 21.1 on page 21.2.

LEARNING OBJECTIVES

After completing this chapter, the reader should be able to:
- calculate installed quantities (progress) for construction activities;
- define how actual labor workhours are collected using time cards;
- analyze labor cost performance using earned value;
- analyze labor cost performance using unit rates;

- define the three components of labor costs—quantities installed, production rates, and wage rates; and
- Analyze labor cost performance using variance analysis.

LABOR COSTS AND PRODUCTIVITY

Every construction project incorporates a large amount of skilled and unskilled craft labor. The greatest variable in the final cost of a construction project is the labor cost. Labor cost is a function of worker hourly wage rate and worker productivity, but although hourly rates are relatively easy to predict, productivity is the real variable (see list below). Thus, a contractor must monitor both worker hours expended and productivity as major elements in the cost control program.

Of course, the element of quantity control is also included as a basis for progress reporting as well as for estimate verification. The craft labor cost may be paid directly by the project owner, the prime contractor, or the subcontractor. If the craft labor is paid by the subcontractor, the prime contractor experiences the craft labor cost as a subcontract cost. Depending upon whether the subcontract is cost plus or lump sum, the prime contractor may or may not be at risk for labor inefficiencies. A similar relationship exists between the prime contractor and the project owner. The labor cost control methods included in this chapter are applicable to those organizations at risk (financial or otherwise) due to labor inefficiencies.

Some factors affecting construction craft productivity include the following:

- crew sizes and craft composition;
- craft density (area per worker);
- interference with other crews;
- scheduling;
- material availability;
- equipment and tool availability;
- information availability,
- rework due to design, fabrication, and field errors;

- site layout;
- weather; and
- constructability.

Implementing the labor cost control methods included in this chapter can be costly. A cardinal rule of cost control is that the cost of the control techniques be less than the money saved by using the cost control techniques. Cost control should be approached as an application of Pareto's Law, which essentially states that 80 percent of the outcome of a project is determined by only 20 percent of the included elements. Thus, in establishing a cost control system, the idea is to isolate and control in detail those elements with the greatest potential impact on final cost, with only summary-level control on the remaining elements.

The methods presented in this chapter utilize two-dimensional tables or spreadsheets to present data. These spreadsheets lend themselves to computerization. In fact, many job cost control and project management software will perform the calculations described in this chapter.

MEASURING INPUTS AND OUTPUTS

Table 21.1—Original Estimate

In the example of a home heating system, only one measurement, temperature, is required to control the system. Controlling construction labor costs requires many measurements. The ultimate goal of labor cost control is to expend the fewest dollars to complete the project. In order to achieve this goal, project management must measure the efficiency or cost-effectiveness of each dollar spent. This requires hundreds of measurements of labor dollars and workhours expended and quantities produced. Labor cost efficiencies are measured as a ratio of inputs (workhours or dollars) and outputs (quantities produced).

A construction project is complex and must be broken into controllable parts. This is accomplished using a work breakdown structure (WBS). The WBS is the classification of each project element along activity levels where the activity outputs can be measured and then compared to the resources expended for that activity. Each classification is assigned a cost code for identification. A construction project has hundreds of cost codes. A study of 30 building contractors in Atlanta showed that for a two-million-dollar project, the median number of line items was 400 [2]. This translates into approximately the same number of cost accounts. The WBS must be carefully constructed and documented so that all members of the project team consistently use the correct cost codes for inputs and outputs.

WAREHOUSE PROJECT					
BUILDING CONCRETE LABOR ESTIMATE					
& ACTUAL QUANTITY @ DAY 30					DAY 30
COST CODE	DESCRIPTION	QTY.	UNIT	UNIT COST	LABOR COST	ACTUAL QTY.
	COLUMN PADS 5'-6" x 5'-6" x 1'-0"	64	EACH			
03120	FORMS 4 USES	1,408	SF	$1.50	$2,112	PROD RPT
03110	ANCHOR BOLTS	160	EA	$2.00	$320	132
03210	REBAR '8- #5 BARS EACH WAY	5,340	LB	$0.15	$801	4,380
03310	CONCRETE 4,000 PSI	72	CY	$5.00	$360	56
03340	FINISH	1,936	SF	$0.15	$290	1,510
	FROST WALL 1305' x 2'-0" x 2'-6"	1,305	LF			
03120	FORMS TOP 4"	870	SF	$1.50	$1,305	PROD RPT
03310	CONCRETE 3,000 PSI	242	CY	$5.00	$1,210	242
03340	FINISH	2,610	SF	$0.15	$392	2,610
	SLAB ON GRADE 360' x 360' x 6"	129,600	SF			
03140	FORMS	2,880	SF	$0.50	$1,440	PROD RPT
03220	6 x 6 #6/6 WELDED WIRE FABRIC	129,600	SF	$0.13	$16,848	18,150
03330	CONCRETE 4,000 PSI	2,400	CY	$5.00	$12,000	240
03360	FINISH	129,600	SF	$0.25	$32,400	12,960
03150	CONTROL JOINTS	8,640	LF	$0.50	$4,320	520
03160	EXPANSION JOINTS & COLUMN DIAMONDS	1,800	LF	$1.00	$1,800	180
	DOCK WALL FOOTINGS 135' x 4'-0" x 1'-0"	135	LF			
03120	FORMS	270	SF	$1.50	$405	PROD RPT
03210	REBAR 3-#5 BARS CONT & #4 BENT @ 18" OC	600	LBS	$0.15	$90	540
03310	CONCRETE 4,000 PSI	20	CY	$5.00	$100	15
03340	FINISH	540	SF	$0.15	$81	405
	DOCK WALLS 135' x 1'-6" x 5'-6"	135	LF			
03130	FORMS	1,485	SF	$2.50	$3,713	PROD RPT
03210	REBAR 4-#4 BARS CONT & #4 @ 18" OC	659	LB	$0.15	$99	264
03320	CONCRETE 4,000 PSI	42	CY	$7.00	$294	0
03350	FINISH TOP	203	SF	$0.25	$51	0
03370	PATCH & RUB WALLS	1,485	SF	$0.15	$223	0
TOTAL ESTIMATED LABOR COST					$80,653	

Labor input is measured by workhours expended or by labor dollars spent. Workhours are measured directly using cost codes and time cards. Dollars are calculated by multiplying each workhour expended by the appropriate wage rate (i.e., dollars per workhour). Unlike construction inputs that have the common unit of measurement (i.e., dollars and workhours), the output cannot be measured with a common unit of measure. Consequently, a large number of measures are used for construction outputs. Examples of these measures include cubic yards of excavation, square feet of concrete formwork, tons of structural steel, lineal feet of pipe, and number of electrical terminations.

Cost control requires matching each unit of output to the input (resources) that was required to produce it. Each category of output requires a separate cost account. The input is separated into the appropriate cost account in order to match each unit of output to the resources (inputs) that produced the output. The breakdown of the inputs into the individual cost accounts is accomplished by observing and recording the number of workhours expended each day by cost account. If workhours are not accurately recorded in the correct cost account, the cost control system will be ineffective. The accuracy of cost coding workhours is improved by the following:

- training all personnel in the use of company cost accounts to correctly code time cards;
- checking time cards for correct cost codes before recording in the cost control system; and
- developing and maintaining a well documented WBS.

A major consideration for measuring construction quantities is to determine if an item (such as cubic yards of concrete placed or lineal feet of wire pulled) is installed in one step or several steps. Quantities installed in one step are the easiest to measure. The item is either installed or it is not installed. The project management team can physically measure the output for the reporting period. It is more difficult to measure progress when quantities are installed in several steps.

One method to measure progress is to assign each sequential step its own cost account. However, this would burden the labor cost control system with too many cost accounts. A better way to handle this situation is to use the equivalent units method to report the partially completed units as equivalent units completed. In the equivalent units method, each step is assigned a weight based upon the percentage of the activity's budget dollars or workhours required to complete that step.

The breakdown of the effort that is required for each step is called the "rules of credit." Following is an example of piping rules of credit [3].

- pipe placed in the permanent location—60 percent of the work;
- pipe end connections are welded or bolted—20 percent of the work;

- pipe trim installed and pipe is ready for hydrotest—20 percent of the work.

An example of a daily production report that measures work progress by cost account using the equivalent units (rules of credit) method can be found in Table 21.2. The detailed description of each field in the daily production report for cost account 03140 appears below.

The description column lists all subtasks for account 03140. The field engineer or superintendent records the quantity completed each day for each of the following subtasks: erect forms, wreck forms, and clean and oil forms. The subtask quantities are totaled through the report cut-off date.

Each subtask is weighted according to the estimated level of effort required for that subtask. These weights are the "rules of credit" and are listed for each subtask.

The actual quantity for the subtask is multiplied by the subtask's weight in order to obtain the subtotal of quantity completed for the account. For this example, 767 linear feet (LF) of edge form was erected by day 30. This amount is mul-

---

Table 21.2–Daily Production Report.

WAREHOUSE PROJECT
BUILDING CONCRETE　FORMWORK DAILY PRODUCTION REPORT

COST CODE	DESCRIPTION	UNIT	DAY 16	DAY 17	DAY 18	DAY 19	DAY 20	DAY 21	DAY 22	DAY 23	DAY 24	DAY 25	DAY 26	DAY 27	DAY 28	DAY 29	DAY 30	TOTAL @day 3	RULES OF CREDIT	SUBTOTAL	TOTAL QUANTITY
03120	COLUMN PADS FORMS																				
	ERECT	SF	154		154		176		154		154		176			154	22	1,144	0.6	686	862
	WRECK	SF				154		154		176								484	0.3	145	
	CLEAN & OIL	SF				154		154										308	0.1	31	
03120	FROST WALL FORMS																				
	ERECT	SF	200			200			270		200							870	0.6	522	870
	WRECK	SF				200			200			270			200			870	0.3	261	
	CLEAN & OIL	SF				200			200			270			200			870	0.1	87	
03120	DOCK WALL FOOTING FORMS																				
	ERECT	SF					108							108			28	244	0.6	146	190
	WRECK	SF											108					108	0.3	32	
	CLEAN & OIL	SF											108					108	0.1	11	
03130	DOCK WALLS FORMS																				
	ERECT	SF										297				297		594	0.6	356	356
	WRECK	SF																0	0.3	0	
	CLEAN & OIL	SF																0	0.1	0	
03140	SLAB ON GRADE EDGE FORMS																				
	ERECT	LF								370							397	767	0.6	460	608
	WRECK	LF											370					370	0.3	111	
	CLEAN & OIL	LF											370					370	0.1	37	

tiplied by 0.6, the weight for erecting edge forms, to obtain the equivalent completed units for the account of 460 LF.

The subtotal for each subtask is totaled to obtain the equivalent actual quantity for the account. The total of 608 lf is the sum of 460 LF (erect form) plus 111 LF (wreck forms) plus 37 lf (clean and oil forms).

Earned Value Method

Once the actual inputs and outputs are measured, the project management team compares the actual inputs and outputs to the project budget inputs and outputs. This comparison occurs at both the cost code and project levels (or at any level in the WBS). The dollars and workhours cost cannot be compared directly to the budget dollars and workhours because the actual is only for completed work, whereas the budget dollars and workhours are for the entire project.

In the earned value labor cost control system, the budget dollars or workhours is multiplied by the percent of work completed to calculate the earned value. The percent complete for the cost account is the actual quantity divided by the forecasted total quantity (see equation 1). The forecasted total quantity is the project management team's current assessment of the total quantity included in the cost account. The earned value is compared directly to the actual cost to evaluate project cost performance. Earned value is measured by either workhours or labor dollars. Earned value is also referred to as the budgeted cost of work performed (BCWP).

(equation 1)

Percent complete (single account) = $\frac{\text{(actual quantity)}}{\text{(forecasted total quantity)}}$

The relationship between the earned value and the budget is expressed in equation 2:

(equation 2)

Earned value (BCWP) = (actual percent complete) x (budget for the account)

As can be seen from this equation, a portion of the budget dollars or workhours is earned as a task is completed up to the total budget in that account. One cannot earn more than has been budgeted. If an account has a budget of $3,200 and 100 workhours and the account is now 25 percent complete, then $800 and 25 workhours have been earned. Cost performance is measured by comparing the earned value to the actual cost. Earned value and actual cost can be measured in either dollars or workhours. Also, earned value and actual cost can be for a period or the total to-date. The actual cost comparison can be a ratio or a variance as illustrated in equations 3 and 4.

(equation 3)

Cost Variance (CV) = (earned value) - (actual cost)

(equation 4)

Cost Performance Index (CPI) = $\frac{\text{(earned value)}}{\text{(actual cost)}}$

Note that a positive variance and an index of 1.0 or greater indicate a favorable performance.

Since progress in all accounts can be reduced to earned workhours and dollars as illustrated, then multiple accounts can be summarized and overall progress calculated as shown in equation 5.

(equation 5)

Percent Complete (multiple accounts) = $\frac{\text{(earned value all accounts)}}{\text{(budget cost all accounts)}}$

The estimated total dollars or workhours at completion (EAC) is determined by predicting the overall cost performance index at the completion of the cost account. There are several sophisticated forecasting techniques that are explained in management science texts, but few constructors are comfortable with them and their reliability appear no better than utilizing a few simple approaches. One fact is certain. No two methods, sophisticated or otherwise, produce the same answer. Three basic approaches are provided here [1].

Method 1: assumes that work from this point forward will progress at the budget (CPI = 1) whether or not this performance has prevailed to this point. (See Equation 6.)

(equation 6)

Estimate at Completion (EAC) = (actual cost to-date) + (budget - earned value)

Method 2: assumes that the performance to-date will continue. (See Equation 7.)

(equation 7)

Estimate at Completion (EAC) = (budget) / (CPI)

Method 3: Utilizes historical curves that show the normal variation in the CPI as the cost account progresses. The forecaster simply makes the best extrapolation possible using the typical shapes of such curves and whatever other information may be available to the forecaster to make the projection.
It is recommended that no single forecasting method be used. Rather, include a forecast by each of the above methods in order to provide a range of possibilities.

Both the quantities installed and the labor unit rate determine labor dollars or workhours. The labor unit rate is expressed in either dollars per unit or in workhours per unit. Multiplying the workhours per unit yields the dollars per unit. Overall cost performance depends on both quantity variances and unit rate variances.

As can be seen from the calculation of earned value, cost overruns occur when actual quantities installed total more than the budget quantities. This occurs when the budget quantities is based upon an inadequate scope, when there are mistakes in the estimate takeoff, when scope creep occurs after the budget is prepared, when the field force installs more quantities than what was required, and when there is rework due to poor workmanship. Cost overruns also occur when the actual unit rate (dollars per unit or workhours per unit) is greater than the budget unit rates.

The credit value is the budget unit rate multiplied by the actual quantities of work installed [1, p. 11-4]. The credit value represents what the cost would have been if the actual quantities were installed at the budget unit rate. The credit value is computed using equation 8a or 8b, and the unit of measure can be dollars or workhours. Comparing the credit value to the actual cost measures the performance of the unit rate alone without the confounding effect of changes in quantities. Use the unit cost (dollars per unit) for the budget unit rate to calculate credit dollars (C$). For an analysis by workhours, use the production rate (workhours per unit) to calculate credit workhours (CWH). The unit cost index is the ratio of the credit dollars (C$) to the actual dollars. (See equation 9.) The productivity index is the ratio of the credit workhours (CWH) to the actual workhours. (See equation 10.)

(equation 8a)

Credit dollars = (actual quantity) x (budget unit cost)

(equation 8b)

Credit workhours = (actual quantity) x (budget production rate)

(equation 9)

Unit Cost Index (UCI) = $\dfrac{\text{(credit dollars)}}{\text{(actual dollars)}}$

(equation 10)

Productivity Index (PI) = $\dfrac{\text{(credit workhours)}}{\text{(actual workhours)}}$

A significant feature of an earned value analysis is that the calculated earned value can be compared to the scheduled value to measure schedule performance. The scheduled value is the value in dollars or workhours of work scheduled. It is also known as the budgeted cost of work scheduled (BCWS). The BCWS is computed using either equation 11 or 12.

(equation 11)

Scheduled value (BCWS) = (scheduled percent complete) x (budget dollars or workhours)

(equation 12)

Scheduled value (BCWS) = (quantity scheduled) x (budget unit cost or production rate)

Schedule performance is measured by comparing the earned value to the scheduled value. This comparison can be a variance, as in equation 13, or a ratio, as in equation 14.

(equation 13)

Schedule Variance (SV) = (earned value) - (scheduled value)

(equation 14)

Schedule Performance Index (SPI) = $\dfrac{\text{(earned value)}}{\text{(scheduled value)}}$

Note that a positive variance and an index of one or greater is a favorable performance.

In Table 3, the scheduled value (BCWS) is calculated at the end of day 30 of the project. Day 30 is the cut-off date for the example used in this chapter.

The detailed description of each field in the schedule report for cost account 03140 appears below.

- The budget labor dollars are listed for each account. This is $1,440 for account 03140.
- The start date is expressed as the beginning of the day. The slab edge forms are scheduled to start at the beginning of day 26.
- The number of workdays scheduled by the cut-off date, day 30, is 5 for account 03140. The five days are days 26 through 30 inclusive (26, 27, 28, 29, and 30).
- The BCWS is calculated by multiplying the budget labor dollars or workhours by the percentage of work that should have been accomplished by the cut-off date. For this example, the assumption is that an equal amount of work is scheduled for each day. Therefore, the scheduled percentage complete is equal to the scheduled days at day 30 divided by the total duration. The scheduled percent complete for account 03140 is 5 days divided by 20 days, or 25 percent. The BCWS is 25 percent multiplied by $1,440, or $360.

Table 21.3—Schedule Report

WAREHOUSE PROJECT
BUILDING CONCRETE   BCWS @ DAY 30

COST CODE	DESCRIPTION	LABOR BUDGET	START DATE	DUR.	SCHED DAYS @ 30	BCWS @ 30
	COLUMN PADS 5'-6" x 5'-6" x 1'-0"					
03120	FORMS 4 USES	$2,112	18	16	13	$1,716
03110	ANCHOR BOLTS	$320	20	11	11	$320
03210	REBAR 8- #5 BARS EACH WAY	$801	20	11	11	$801
03310	CONCRETE 4,000 PSI	$360	22	11	9	$295
03340	FINISH	$290	22	11	9	$238
	FROST WALL 1305' x 2'-0" x 2'-6"					
03120	FORMS TOP 4"	$1,305	16	15	15	$1,305
03310	CONCRETE 3,000 PSI	$1,210	19	10	10	$1,210
03340	FINISH	$392	19	10	10	$392
	SLAB ON GRADE 360' x 360' x 6"					
03140	FORMS	$1,440	26	20	5	$360
03220	6 x 6 #6/6 WELDED WIRE FABRIC	$16,848	28	15	3	$3,370
03330	CONCRETE 4,000 PSI	$12,000	29	15	2	$1,600
03360	FINISH	$32,400	29	15	2	$4,320
03150	CONTROL JOINTS	$4,320	31	15	0	$0
03160	EXPANSION JOINTS & COLUMN DIAMONDS	$1,800	28	15	3	$360
	DOCK WALL FOOTINGS 135' x 4'-0" x 1'-0"					
03120	FORMS	$405	21	13	10	$312
03210	REBAR 3-#5 BARS CONT & #4 BENT @ 18" OC	$90	23	8	8	$90
03310	CONCRETE 4,000 PSI	$100	24	8	7	$88
03340	FINISH	$81	24	8	7	$71
	DOCK WALLS 135' x 1'-6" x 5'-6"					
03130	FORMS	$3,713	26	15	5	$1,238
03210	REBAR 4-#4 BARS CONT & #4 @ 18" OC	$99	28	10	3	$30
03320	CONCRETE 4,000 PSI	$294	30	10	1	$29
03350	FINISH TOP	$51	30	10	1	$5
03370	PATCH & RUB WALLS	$223	32	10	0	$0
TOTALS		$80,653				$18,150

In Table 4, labor cost and schedule performance is analyzed using the earned value method. The detailed description of each field in the labor cost report using earned value for cost account 03140 appears below:

- The actual quantity is transferred to this report from the actual quantities provided in Table 21.1 or from the quantities calculated on the daily production report, Table 21.2. Note that some cost accounts appear in more than one work package. The cost account total on this report is the summary of all work packages. For cost account 03140, the actual quantity is calculated at 608 LF. See the daily production report in Table 21.2.

- The budget quantity is transferred to this report from the labor estimate. For cost account 03140, the budget quantity is 2,880 LF.

- The estimate at completion (EAC) quantity is the budget quantity plus or minus any changes or corrections. There are no changes or corrections for cost account 03140.

- The labor budget in dollars is transferred from the labor estimate. For cost account 03140, the labor budget is $1,440.

- The actual cost of work performed (ACWP) is gathered from the daily time cards. For cost account 03140, the ACWP is $288.

Table 21.4—Labor Cost Report Using Earned Value

WAREHOUSE PROJECT
BUILDING CONCRETE

COST CODE	DESCRIPTION	UNIT	ACTUAL QUANTITY	BUDGET QUANTITY	FORECAST QUANTITY	LABOR BUDGET	ACTUAL COST OF WORK PERFORM.	BUDGETED COST OF WORK PERFORM.	BUDGETED COST OF WORK SCHED.	CREDIT DOLLARS	ESTIMATE AT COMPL.	COST PERFORM. INDEX	SCHEDULE PERFORM. INDEX	UNIT COST INDEX
03110	ANCHOR BOLTS	EA	132	160	160	$320	$285	$264	$320	$264	$346	0.926	0.825	0.926
03120	FORM FOOTINGS	SF	1,922	2,548	2,602	$3,822	$3,200	$2,823	$3,333	$2,883	$4,332	0.882	0.847	0.901
03130	FORMS WALLS	SF	356	1,485	1,782	$3,713	$682	$742	$1,238	$890	$3,416	1.087	0.599	1.304
03140	FORM EDGE OF SLAB	LF	608	2,880	2,880	$1,440	$288	$304	$360	$304	$1,364	1.056	0.844	1.056
03150	CONTROL JOINTS	LF	520	8,640	8,640	$4,320	$267	$260	$0	$260	$4,436	0.974		0.974
03160	EXPANSION JOINTS & COLUMN DIA.	LF	180	1,800	1,800	$1,800	$205	$180	$360	$180	$2,050	0.878	0.500	0.878
03210	REBAR #3 TO #7	LBS	5,184	6,599	6,851	$990	$805	$749	$921	$778	$1,064	0.930	0.813	0.966
03220	WELDED WIRE FABRIC	SF	18,150	129,600	129,600	$16,848	$2,425	$2,360	$3,370	$2,360	$17,316	0.973	0.700	0.973
03310	PLACE FOOTING CONCRETE	CY	313	334	338	$1,670	$1,670	$1,546	$1,593	$1,565	$1,804	0.926	0.971	0.937
03320	PLACE WALL CONCRETE	CY	0	42	50	$294	$0	$0	$29	$0	$350			
03330	PLACE SLAB ON GRADE CONCRETE	CY	240	2,400	2,400	$12,000	$1,375	$1,200	$1,600	$1,200	$13,750	0.873	0.750	0.873
03340	FINISH TOP OF FOOTINGS	SF	4,525	5,086	5,194	$763	$638	$665	$701	$679	$732	1.042	0.948	1.064
03350	FINISH TOP OF WALLS	SF	0	203	244	$51	$0	$0	$5	$0	$61			
03360	FINISH SLAB ON GRADE	SF	12,960	129,600	129,600	$32,400	$3,522	$3,240	$4,320	$3,240	$35,220	0.920	0.750	0.920
03370	PATCH & RUB WALLS	SF	0	1,485	1,782	$223	$0	$0	$0	$0	$267			
						$80,653	$15,363	$14,332	$18,150	$14,602	$86,507	0.933	0.790	0.950

- The budgeted cost of work performed (BCWP) is also known as the earned value. The BCWP is calculated by multiplying the budget labor

  dollars by the percentage of work actually completed. The actual percent complete is the actual quantity divided by the forecast quantity. For account 03140, the actual percent complete is 608 lf divided by 2,880 LF, or 21.11 percent. The BCWP is $1,440 multiplied by 21.11 percent, or $304.

- The credit dollar (C$) is equal to the budgeted unit cost multiplied by the actual quantity. This is the amount that would have been spent to produce the actual quantity at the budget unit cost. The budget unit cost is the budget dollars divided by the budget quantity. For cost account 03140, the budget unit cost is $1,440 divided by 2,880 LF, or $0.50 per LF. The C$ is $0.50 per lf multiplied by 608 LF, or $304. Note that the C$ is equal to the BCWP. This will always be the case when the forecast quantity is equal to the budget quantity.

- The cost performance index (CPI) is a measure of the cost performance. It is calculated by dividing the BCWP by the ACWP. Indexes greater than one indicate good cost performance. Indexes of less than one point towards poor cost performance. For cost account 03410, the CPI is equal to $304 divided by $288, or 1.056, which indicates good performance.

- In Table 4, the estimated total dollars or workhours at completion (EAC) is computed assuming that the cost performance to-date will continue until the cost account is completed. The EAC is calculated by dividing the budget labor dollars by the CPI. The CPI is equal to 1.00 for accounts that have no actual data. For cost account 03410, the EAC is equal to $1,440 divided by 1.056, or $1,364.

- The schedule performance index (SPI) is a measure of schedule performance. The SPI is the ratio of the BCWP to the BCWS. Indexes greater than one indicate good schedule performance and indexes of less than one point towards poor schedule performance. For cost account 03410, the SPI is equal to $304 divided by $360, or 0.844, which indicates poor schedule performances; i.e., the edge forms are behind schedule.

- The unit cost index (UCI) is a measure of unit cost performance. The labor unit cost is a combination of both labor productivity and wage rates. Variances between the budget unit cost and actual unit cost are generally caused by differences in productivity. Therefore, the UCI is an indirect measure of labor productivity. The UCI is the ratio of the C$ to the ACWP. Indexes greater than one indicate good unit cost performance and indexes of less than one point towards poor unit cost performance. For cost account 03410, the UCI is equal to $304 divided by $288, or

1.056. Note that the UCI is equal to the CPI for this account. Since there is no variance between the budget quantities and actual quantities, the overall cost performance is determined solely by the unit cost variance.

UNIT RATES METHOD

The unit rates labor cost control system is another method for the project management team to compare the actual inputs and outputs to the project budget inputs and outputs. This method makes comparisons at the cost code level, total project level, or at any level in the WBS. In the unit rates labor cost control system, actual dollars or workhours to-date are used to calculate actual unit rates (dollars per unit or workhours per unit). The actual unit rates are then analyzed to forecast the unit rates at the completion of the account. The estimated total dollars or workhours at completion (EAC) is calculated by multiplying the estimate at completion unit rates by the forecasted quantities. The EAC is then compared to the budget dollars or workhours to determine cost performance. Note that at the account level, to-date unit rates can be compared directly to the budget unit rates to determine performance.

The estimated total dollars or workhours at completion (EAC) is analogous to finding the EAC in the earned value method. It is determined by predicting the overall unit rates at the completion of the cost account. The three basic approaches for determining EAC are restated here for the unit rates method.

Method 1: assumes that work from this point forward will progress at budget unit rates whether or not these rates have prevailed to this point. (See Equation 15.)

(equation 15)

Estimate at Completion (EAC) = (actual dollars or workhours to-date) + [(to go quantity) (budget unit rate)]

Method 2: assumes that the unit rate prevailing to-date will continue to prevail. (See Equation 16.)

Estimate at Completion (EAC) = (total quantity) x (actual unit rate)

Method 3: utilizes historical curves that show the normal variation in unit rates as the cost account progresses. The forecaster simply makes the best extrapolation possible using the typical shapes of such curves and whatever other information may be available to the forecaster to make the projection.

As with the earned value method, it is recommended that no single forecasting method be used. Rather, include a forecast by each of the above methods in order to provide a range of possibilities.

The labor cost report using forecasted unit rates, which analyzes labor cost performance using the forecasting unit cost method, can be found in Table 23.5. The detailed description of each field in the labor cost report using forecasted unit rates for cost account 03140 follow:

- The actual quantity is transferred to this report from the actual quantities provided in Table 21.1, or from the quantities calculated on the daily production report, Table 21.2. Note that some cost accounts appear in more than one work package. The cost account total on this report is the summary of all work packages. For cost account 03140, the actual quantity is calculated at 608 LF. See the daily production report in Table 21.2.

- The budget quantity is transferred to this report from the labor estimate. For cost account 03140, the budget quantity is 2,880 LF.

- The forecasted quantity is the budget quantity plus or minus changes or corrections. There are no changes or corrections for cost account 03140.

- The percent complete is the actual quantity divided by the forecast quantity. For account 03140, the actual percent complete is 608 lf divided by 2,880 LF, or 21.1 percent.

- The actual cost of work performed is gathered from the daily time cards. For cost account 03140, the actual cost of work performed is $288.

- The budget labor dollars is transferred from the labor estimate. For cost account 03140, the labor budget is $1,440.

- The actual unit cost is the actual dollars divided by the actual quantity. For cost account 03140, the actual unit cost is $288 divided by 608 LF, or $0.4737 per LF. Note that the report is formatted to show only two decimal places.

- The budget unit cost is the budget dollars divided by the budget quantity. For cost account 03140, the budget unit cost is $1,440 divided by 2,880 LF, or $0.5000 per LF . By comparing the budget unit cost to the actual unit cost, the project management team can determine the cost performance of the account. The project management team has to take into account that cumulative to-date unit rates at the beginning of an account are typically higher than the unit rate at completion.

- In Table 21.5, the estimated total dollars or workhours at completion (EAC) is computed assuming that the actual unit cost to-date will continue until the cost account is completed (Method 2). Therefore, the forecasted unit cost is equal to the actual unit cost. For cost account 03410, the forecasted unit cost is $0.4737 per LF. Method 2 is just one of the methods used to forecast the final unit cost. The accuracy of the forecast generally improves as more information is used in the forecast.

- The EAC is calculated by multiplying the forecast quantity by the forecast unit cost. For cost account 03410, the EAC is equal to 2,880 lf multiplied by $0.4737 per LF, or $1,364.

TWO-WAY VARIANCE ANALYSIS

A frequent question is what or who is responsible for the total difference between the budget and the EAC? Variance analysis is one method for answering this question. The project

Table 23.5—Labor Cost Report Using Unit Rates

WAREHOUSE PROJECT BUILDING CONCRETE

COST CODE	DESCRIPTION	UNIT	% COMPL	ACTUAL QUANTITY	BUDGET QUANTITY	FORECAST QUANTITY	ACTUAL COST OF WORK PERFORM.	LABOR BUDGET	ESTIMATE AT COMPL.	ACTUAL UNIT COST	BUDGET UNIT COST	FORECAST UNIT COST
03110	ANCHOR BOLTS	EA	82.5%	132	160	160	$285	$320	$346	$2.16	$2.00	$2.16
03120	FORM FOOTINGS	SF	73.9%	1,922	2,548	2,602	$3,200	$3,822	$4,332	$1.66	$1.50	$1.66
03130	FORMS WALLS	SF	20.0%	356	1,485	1,782	$682	$3,713	$3,416	$1.92	$2.50	$1.92
03140	FORM EDGE OF SLAB	LF	21.1%	608	2,880	2,880	$288	$1,440	$1,364	$0.47	$0.50	$0.47
03150	CONTROL JOINTS	LF	6.0%	520	8,640	8,640	$267	$4,320	$4,436	$0.51	$0.50	$0.51
03160	EXPANSION JOINTS & COLUMN DIA.	LF	10.0%	180	1,800	1,800	$205	$1,800	$2,050	$1.14	$1.00	$1.14
03210	REBAR #3 TO #7	LBS	75.7%	5,184	6,599	6,851	$805	$990	$1,064	$0.16	$0.15	$0.16
03220	WELDED WIRE FABRIC	SF	14.0%	18,150	129,600	129,600	$2,425	$16,848	$17,316	$0.13	$0.13	$0.13
03310	PLACE FOOTING CONCRETE	CY	92.6%	313	334	338	$1,670	$1,670	$1,804	$5.34	$5.00	$5.34
03320	PLACE WALL CONCRETE	CY	0.0%	0	42	50	$0	$294	$350		$7.00	$7.00
03330	PLACE SLAB ON GRADE CONCRETE	CY	10.0%	240	2,400	2,400	$1,375	$12,000	$13,750	$5.73	$5.00	$5.73
03340	FINISH TOP OF FOOTINGS	SF	87.1%	4,525	5,086	5,194	$638	$763	$732	$0.14	$0.15	$0.14
03350	FINISH TOP OF WALLS	SF	0.0%	0	203	244	$0	$51	$61		$0.25	$0.25
03360	FINISH SLAB ON GRADE	SF	10.0%	12,960	129,600	129,600	$3,522	$32,400	$35,220	$0.27	$0.25	$0.27
03370	PATCH & RUB WALLS	SF	0.0%	0	1,485	1,782	$0	$223	$267		$0.15	$0.15
							$15,363	$80,653	$86,507			

manager allocates the total difference between the budget and the EAC to the appropriate variance category, quantity, or rate. This is an important step in determining the appropriate corrective action for attaining budget performance for the account. Corrective actions to correct quantity variances are different than the corrective actions to correct rate (dollars per unit or workhours per unit) variances. Table 21.6 contains the necessary formulas to carry out the variance analysis. The following example illustrates a variance analysis of a pipe installation account.

Table 21.6—Variance Analysis Formulas—Two-Way

Variance Analysis Example

Estimated Total at Completion (EAC)	$Q_F \times P_F$
Budget	$Q_B \times P_B$
Quantity Variance	$C_Q \times P_B$
Rate Variance (Production Rate or Unit Cost)	$Q_F \times C_P$

LEGEND
Q_B Budget Quantity
Q_F Forecast Quantity
P_B Budget Production Rate or Unit Cost
P_F Forecast Production Rate or Unit Cost
C_Q Change in quantity $= Q_B - Q_F$
C_P Change in production rate or unit cost $= P_B - P_F$

SUMMARY

Which method, earned value or unit rates, is best for controlling construction labor dollars or workhours? Each method analyzes the construction project and identifies the deviations from the budget for corrective action by the project management team. Using the assumptions stated in this chapter yields identical estimates at completion for each method. While both methods, when diligently applied, will control project costs and produce identical estimated total at completion, each one has a unique advantage. The earned values in the earned value method can be compared to the value of work scheduled as part of an integrated project control system. The advantage of the unit rates method is that the unit costs and production rates are used for estimating and are therefore familiar to most managers.

Labor cost control is best achieved by using a feedback loop. As construction activities proceed, both actual dollars or workhours and actual progress are measured. The actual performance is compared to the budgeted or planned performance. The project manager concentrates corrective efforts on those activities whose actual performance deviate from the budget. The effectiveness of the corrective action is monitored by the feedback loop. This chapter presented an integrated system for implementing a feedback loop control system for labor cost control.

COST CODE	DESCRIPTION	ACTUAL QUANTITY LF		BUDGET QUANTITY LF	FORECAST QUANTITY LF	LABOR BUDGET WH		ACWP WH
15170-20	Chilled Water, large bore welded	221		365	395	256		140
		Quantity		WH/LF		Workhours		
Budget		365	LF	0.701	WH/LF	256.0	WH	
EAC		395	LF	0.633	WH/LF	250.2	WH	
Change -		30	LF	0.068	WH/LF	5.8	WH	
Quantity Variance =		-30	LF	0.701	WH/LF -	21.0	WH	
Production Rate Variance Check =		395	LF	0.068	WH/LF	26.8	WH	
Check						5.8	WH	OK

PRACTICE PROBLEMS AND QUESTIONS

1. You have summarized all control accounts in Area A of a project to the end of the reporting period. You note that you had scheduled 28,000 work hours, have earned 26,000 work hours, and have paid for 25,000 work hours. Analyze the cost and schedule status in Area A at the end of the reporting period by calculating SV, SPI, CV, and CPI.

2. Given the data below in Practice Table 1, complete the worksheet from a project's status reports at the end of a reporting period. Refer to the text for the method to calculate earned value (BCWP) and percent complete for multiple accounts.

3. In planning and budgeting a fixed price project, a given work package was estimated to include 200 units of work. Estimators further utilized a unit rate of 4 work hours per unit of work so they budgeted for 800 work hours in this account. In the field, it was subsequently determined that there were really 240 units of work to be performed. This was strictly an estimating error, and, with no contingency fund available, the budget remained at 800 work hours. At the end of the latest reporting period, work was 50 percent complete (120 units) and 432 work hours had been paid for. Is this package overrunning or under running cost, and is productivity better or worse than planned?

4. Find the ACWP, BCWP, BCWS, CWH, CPI, SPI, PI, and EAC in Practice Table 2. Estimate the cost of this account at completion (EAC) assuming that the cost performance to-date will continue until the end of the project. Monday through Friday are the project workdays.

5. Given the rules of credit and work completed for fabricated pipe spools below in Practice Table 3, find the equivalent linear feet of pipe in place. This pipe spool account is estimated and controlled using the total lineal feet of pipe as the summary unit of measure. The summary unit of measure is the characteristic that represents the total of all subtasks. For the formwork example in the text the summary quantity is the total square feet of all of the formwork. Note that for the formwork example the subtask total quantity is equal to summary quantity.

Practice Table 1

Code	U/M	Quantity Total	Quantity To-Date	Budget WH	Earned WH	Percent Complete
03110	SF	5,000	5,000	5,000	_____	_____
03210	Ton	10	9	1,000	_____	_____
03110	CY	1,000	750	10,000	_____	_____
Subtotal Slabs at Grade				16,000	_____	_____
03120	SF	5,500	550	6,000	_____	_____
03220	Ton	10	2	1,000	_____	_____
03320	CY	2,500	0	15,000	_____	_____
Subtotal Elevated slabs				22,000	_____	_____
Total Concrete (slabs at grade plus elevated slabs)				38000	_____	_____

Practice Table 2

Account 09200 Gypsum board, walls			Cutoff: Friday, February 15 at 5 PM	
Quantity	Budget: 2,000 SF	Forecast: 1,800 SF	Actual: 720 SF	
Workhours	Budget: 600 WH		Actual: 180 WH	
Schedule:	Start: Wednesday, February 6	Duration: 16 work days		

Practice Table 3

Allowed Credit	Subtask	Unit of Measure	Total Quantity	To-Date Quantity	Equivalent Quantity
0.40	Erect pipe	LF	3,030	1,800	
0.40	End connections	Each	180	75	
0.10	Pipe hangers/supports	Each	290	116	
0.10	Pipe trimmed	%	100	30	

6. See the quantity take-off for four hydronic piping accounts. The estimator made two errors in taking off the length of the hydronic piping. To correct these errors, add 30 LF to the chilled water large bore pipe (also, 12 joints & 4 hangers) and add 32 LF to the heating hot water large bore pipe (also, 12 joints & 3 hangers). Use the forecasted quantities for the hydronic piping daily production report.

Complete the hydronic piping daily production report for the Hydronic piping for the project to-date as of day 30. Account 15170-20, chilled water, large bore welded steel has been completed for you. Use the following rules of credit:

Subtask	Large Bore	Small Bore
Erect pipe	0.25	0.10
Connect pipe, joints	0.65	0.70
Pipe hangers	0.10	0.20

Practice Table 4—Hydronic Piping Take-off

Cost Code	Description	Budget Quantity	Unit of Measure
15170-10	Chilled Water, small bore copper pipe * 30 ea. hangers & 247 ea. joints	238	lf
15170-20	Chilled Water, large bore welded steel pipe * 34 ea. hangers & 112 ea. joints	365	lf
15170-40	Heating Hot Water, small bore copper pipe * 65 ea. hangers & 851 ea. joints	519	lf
15170-30	Heating Hot Water, large bore welded steel pipe * 55 ea. hangers & 414 ea. joints	758	lf

Example: Chilled water large bore pipe

The forecast quantity is equal to the budget quantity +/- any adjustments

Pipe forecast quantity	= 365 LF + 30 LF = 395 LF
Hangers forecast quantity	= 34 ea + 4 ea = 38 ea
Joints forecast quantity	= 112 ea + 12 ea = 124 ea

Use the forecast quantity for both the subtask total quantity and the summary quantity.

Equivalent Quantity = Allowed Credit x (Subtask to-date quantity/Subtask total quantity) x Summary quantity

Pipe equivalent quantity = 0.25 x 230 lf/395 LF x 395 LF =
Pipe equivalent quantity = 0.25 x 0.58 x 395 LF =   57.3 LF

Joints equivalent quantity = 0.65 x 68 ea/124 ea x 395 LF =
Joints equivalent quantity = 0.65 x 0.55 x 395 LF = 141.2 LF

Hanger equivalent quantity = 0.10 x 22 ea/38 ea x 395 LF =
Hanger equivalent quantity = 0.10 x 0.58 x 395 LF =   22.9 LF
Total   221 LF

7. Complete the BCWS report on page 21.22, and earned value labor cost report for the hydronic piping project to-date as of day 30. Assume that performance to-date will continue. Account 15170-20, chilled water, large bore welded steel has been completed for you. You need to use some of the data and the solution for Problem 6 to complete Problem 7.

8. Complete the BCWS report, and earned value labor cost report for the formwork project to-date as of day 30. Assume that performance to-date will continue. Refer to the text for directions on completing these worksheets. For some accounts you must add work packages together to get the account totals.

Practice Table 5—BCWS Report

Cost Code	Description		Unit of Measure	Day 24	Day 25	Day 26	Day 27	Day 28	Day 29	Day 30	Task Total @day 30	Task Forecast Total	Task % Complete	Rules of Credit	Total
15170-10	Chilled Water, small bore copper														
		Erect	LF						20	30					
		Joints	EA						30	20					
		Hangers	EA						4	4					
		Total													
15170-20	Chilled Water, large bore welded steel														
		Erect	LF			30	40	60	40	60	230	395	58%	0.25	57.3
		Joints	EA			15	14	15	12	12	68	124	55%	0.65	141.2
		Hangers	EA			6	5	4	3	4	22	38	58%	0.1	22.9
		Total													221.4
15170-40	Heating Hot Water, small bore copper														
		Erect	LF						20	30					
		Joints	EA						40	40					
		Hangers	EA						6	5					
		Total													
15170-30	Heating Hot Water, large bore welded steel														
		Erect	LF	30	40	40	30	20	40	50					
		Joints	EA	12	18	20	15	20	15	15					
		Hangers	EA	3	2	3	2	2	3	3					
		Total													

REFERENCES

1. Halpin, Daniel W. 1985. *Financial and Cost Concepts for Construction Management*. New York: Wiley.

Chapter 22

Leadership and Management of Project People[1]

Dr. Ginger Levin

INTRODUCTION

It has been recognized for some time that cost professionals, and other professionals, are faced with an unprecedented rate of technological change and growing competitiveness in the marketplace. However, it also is recognized that technology and competition can be more easily managed than the human element of the enterprise. Some have noted that the managing change would present few problems if it were not for the people who create and are affected by the change (Conference Board, 1969). This presents even greater challenges for today's leaders. This chapter examines different approaches to leadership—one of the most important aspects of project management.

LEARNING OBJECTIVES

After completing this chapter, readers should be able to

- recognize some of the key contributions to the field of leadership and management,
- describe the challenges of working with multicultural teams and identify advantages they afford,
- recognize some theories of motivation and some critical motivation mistakes to avoid, and
- appreciate the challenges associated with business ethics at the individual and organizational levels.

LEADERSHIP STYLES

Today's leaders must work to promote a team culture and establish partnerships with customers and suppliers. This is done through communication and information sharing among all stakeholders. Leaders now are considered team players. The leader does not work to control team members, but instead works to obtain commitment from them to support goals and objectives by fostering open communication, increased productivity through group efforts, and participatory decision making. The leader may not be necessarily a technical expert, as his or her expertise is in leading the team to reach success on each endeavor as measured by its goals and objectives. A number of theories and writings of behavioral scientists have influenced the development of leadership styles. Five key contributions are discussed in this section.

Douglas McGregor

In *The Human Side of Enterprise* [19], Douglas McGregor was an early proponent of management as a profession. McGregor stated that management demands a scientific base of research and application to make it a successful profession. He said that to develop the professional manager, first the manager should examine how he or she saw himself or herself in relation to the job of managing human resources. The starting point is a set of fundamental beliefs or assumptions of what people are like. He developed two theoretical constructs of the nature of man in relation to his work, known as Theory X and Theory Y. Theory X includes the following assumptions:

- The average person has an inherent dislike of work and will avoid it if possible.
- The average person must be coerced, controlled, directed, or threatened with punishment to put forth adequate effort toward achievement of organizational objectives.
- The average person prefers to be directed, wishes to avoid responsibility, has relatively little ambition, and wants security.
- Control should be externally imposed.

Theory Y assumptions include the following:

- People are self-motivated and will exercise self-direction and self-control toward achieving objectives to which they are committed.

---

[1]This chapter includes modified excerpts from Flannes, Steven W., and Ginger Levin. 2001. *People Skills for Project Managers*. 2001. Management Concepts, Inc. Reprinted with permission.

- Average people learn to not only accept but also seek responsibility.
- People are capable of a high degree of imagination, ingenuity, and creativity in solving organizational problems.
- The average person's intellectual potential is only partially used.

Central to a discussion of McGregor's two theories is the matter of control. Under Theory X, control is externally imposed, while Theory Y emphasizes self-control or an internal control. Theory Y implies that within a climate of trust and respect, the employee is capable of putting forth willing effort and controlling work habits. Theory Y presented a flexible view and opened up a wide range of possibilities for new managerial policies and practices.

Frederick Herzberg

Frederick Herzberg [12] studied the relationship between the role of work and working conditions. He developed a motivation-hygiene theory based on the concepts of satisfiers and dissatisfiers. He found that real motivation resulted from the worker's involvement in accomplishing an interesting task, not from the working conditions or environmental factors that are peripheral to the job. The hygiene factors, though, must be adequately provided if a person is to rise above them and be able to involve oneself in meaningful tasks. Managers need to recognize the disparate nature of hygiene factors and motivators and increase the challenging content of the job. Herzberg's emphasis on job enrichment stated that increasing the challenging content of the job would cause the employee to grow both in skill and in a feeling of accomplishment.

Chris Argyris

Chris Argyris [2] advanced some of McGregor's theories and said that the organization may be the source and cause of human problems. He felt that individual needs and organizational needs were not met effectively in most organizations, as he described the dichotomy between these two sets of needs. Part of the problem, Argyris noted, was due to the bureaucratic nature of organizations and their hierarchical structures; he was an early proponent of the concept of ad hoc work groups, or project teams, that cross-cut organizational lines. Argyris felt that the organization must change to conform to human needs, and that the organization should offer meaningful challenges and opportunities for responsibilities. A climate of open communication and trust is needed in all interpersonal relationships. Argyris advocated the development of interpersonal competence and authenticity in relationships as the first step in dealing with any personal differences that may block information flow and understanding of objectives at the individual, unit, and organizational levels.

Rensis Likert

Well-known for the development of an attitude measurement approach known as the Likert-type scale, Rensis Likert [15] also developed the concept of the linking pin—a person who belongs to two groups in the organization. The linking pin shows that the entire organization is viewed as a set of overlapping and interacting groups. Likert advocated open communication within groups, development of mutual trust, consensus decision-making, group goal setting, definition of roles, and shared responsibility. He said that real authority is not just official or formal authority, but is dependent on how much authority a manager's subordinates allow the manager to exert over them, regardless of formal authority position. As Likert stated, the amount of influence a manager exerts over subordinates is determined by how the manager allows himself or herself to be influenced by them. The degree of group commitment and involvement is based on the extent to which the manager considers the opinions of subordinates in reaching a decision whose outcome has impact upon the group. Likert [16] further developed four basic styles of leadership related to a wide range of organizational variables:

- exploitive-authoritative,
- benevolent-authoritative,
- consultative, and
- participative group.

These four styles exist in everyday practice, but he directed his attention toward the participative group, which he felt was ideal for a human-concerned organization.

Robert Blake and Jane Mouton

In 1962, Dr. Robert Blake and Dr. Jane Mouton developed a concept called the managerial grid [4]. They felt there was an unnecessary dichotomy in the minds of most managers between concern for people problems and concern for production problems. These concerns are complementary. They said that each manager has a discernible style of management based on the degree of concern for production and people. At one end is the manager who is only concerned with production; at the other end is the manager who coddles people at the cost of lost production. There are 81 possible positions on their managerial grid representing leadership styles; of these, though, there are five key styles. Ideally, on the grid, a manager should be a 9,9. This manager stresses team management. Concern for people and production are interdependent. The manager's job is one of a coach, an advisor, or a consultant.

TEAMS

It has long been recognized that teams out-perform individuals acting alone, especially when performance involves multiple skills and areas of expertise. However, groups of people do not become a team merely because they are assigned to one. They must be collectively committed to each other and mutually accountable. As noted by Katzenbach and Smith [13], "the wisdom of teams comes with a focus on collective work products, personal growth, and performance results. However meaningful, 'team' is always a result of pursing a demanding performance challenge."

A team begins as a group of individuals with different motivations and expectations. Some people are pleased to be part of the team; others are not. Some people want to have significant responsibility on the team and want to lead it, while others want to follow. People also bring views as to how teams should operate and stereotypes that reflect one's views and attributes toward members of various groups. Not everyone will view the project with the same attitudes.

These conditions create an environment in which individuals determine the conditions on the team. Individual accountability must be merged with mutual accountability. Team members must be committed to a common approach as to how they might best work together. Performance challenges should energize teams, as a team's performance goals must always relate to its overall purpose [13]. Clear goals can help reduce the potential for future disruptive conflicts and minimize any past differences among the various people represented on the team. As Parker [22] notes, the people who come together to be part of the team will be effective to the extent that they agree on a common goal, set aside their individual priorities and agendas, develop a plan to reach that goal, and then commit to work together to attain it.

CROSS-CULTURAL CONCERNS

Culture, as defined by the American Heritage Dictionary [1], is "The totality of socially transmitted behavior patterns, arts, beliefs, institutions, and all other products of human work and thought." It includes political, economic, demographic, educational, ethical, ethnic, religious, and other areas, including practices, beliefs, and attitudes, that affect the way people and organizations interact [24].

All organizations are becoming more culturally diverse with each passing business day. People working on teams in the field of cost management, for example, often consist of members representing many different nationalities, languages, and cultures. This cultural richness brings many advantages to a team in the form of different backgrounds, values, norms, and perspectives. However, the characteristics that add richness to a team also increase its complexity. With multicultural teams, the team leader must create vehicles to bridge the cultural gap and bring the team together. A manager working with a multicultural team needs to be aware of these cultural differences and take special care to avoid the potential risks associated with them.

GLOSSARY TERMS IN THIS CHAPTER

culture ◆ empowerment ◆ ethics
hierarchy of needs ◆ leadership ◆ management
motivation ◆ motivation-hygiene theory ◆ team
Theory X management ◆ Theory Y management

Culture affects our work in many ways. Research has shown that birth culture has a greater effect on a worker's frame of mind than does organizational culture. A worker, no matter how well he or she adopts the organization's culture, is still motivated primarily by the cultural environment in which he or she was raised.

In such a multicultural world, the manager or team leader faces a variety of issues, such as managing the team member who may be bicultural and dealing with a culture that may be different from that of the organization. This includes a wide range of challenges from language barriers and time differences to religious diversity and differences in food preferences. For example, in some cultures that value harmony, indirectness, and shared identify, conflict is seen as a loss of face. Open discussion and resolution of conflict is viewed as negative, and a direct approach to conflict resolution, such as a confrontational style, is considered threatening. Here, conflict is best handled behind the scenes, using a smoothing or compromising method. Other cultures that value confrontation see conflict as a positive force as it allows ideas to be aired and insights to be shared in an open fashion. As another example, some cultures view risks as only the responsibility of the executives in the organization, while others view it as the team's responsibility.

For a manager working in settings that involve multicultural issues, it is important to recognize the effect of cultural factors. In the area of communications, the manager must be aware of verbal and nonverbal differences, and recognize that cultural differences can result in misunderstandings. The manager should remain conscious of the fact that cultural differences do exist and try to accommodate these differences if possible. Diversity itself, although a challenge, is also the source of many creative issues. A multicultural team does have greater potential for higher productivity and innovation. Cultural differences should not be ignored or minimized, and if a cultural difference does cause a problem, it should be addressed. Awareness of cultural differences among team members may even make the difference between success and failure.

LEADING, MANAGING, FACILITATING, AND MENTORING

Similar to many leaders, cost engineers and other professionals are often promoted into leadership roles for reasons related to technical competency, not demonstrated leadership and management skills. This technical professional then must acquire functional knowledge of basic leadership and management skills, because ultimately the success and failure of all projects can be traced to the "people" component. Carr, Hard, and Trahant [6] and Fitz-Enz [8] offer resources related to generic managerial and leadership skills. The importance of this elusive, people component remains constant in today's complex world in which sophisticated technology and software resources are available to manage the intricate processes of any project.

Working with a team of people, the manager faces many challenges. These include the following:

- uncertain organizational resource support for the project,
- extreme time pressures,
- first-time challenges to solve unique and complicated problems,
- a wide variety of personnel and other resource interdependencies, and
- challenges of obtaining resources from senior managers who may not totally support the project.

As a result, the successful manager must bring special skills and abilities to the organization. He or she must be able to

- apply both technical and managerial skills in addition to operating as a generalist;
- motivate the team toward the goals and objectives of the project while still attempting to meet each individual's professional goals;
- create group cohesion without succumbing to "group think;"
- think and thrive under pressure while integrating and resolving conflicting priorities and goals of other stakeholders;
- drive the team toward excellence;
- work with the emotional, intellectual, and physical challenges in the start-up and close-out phases of the project;
- think in terms of three dimensions– timely delivery, cost compliance, and task performance; and
- create mechanisms within the team that encourage the discussion of conflict and balance the process through methods that motivate the team toward decisive action.

The role of the project manager is multifaceted. During a project, the project manager then must be able to assume four different roles: that of leader, manager, facilitator, and mentor.

Leadership

Being a leader of a project is a more subtle, complicated role than simply being the person who is in charge of the project and is supposed to deliver it on time and within budget. True leadership involves the ability to conceptualize the vision and direction of the project and then be able to communicate and sell this vision to the team members and other stakeholders. In this context, vision is not an idealistic, amorphous concept of the project, but involves identifying the purpose of the project. This involves listening to the customer to determine the added value the project will bring and recognizing what the customer is not saying.

Once the project manager has discussed the purpose of the project, the next step is to create a personal vision of its purpose. The key point is to create a personal representation of the true purpose of the project, noting subtle goals and the customer's true requirements. This then enables the project manager to be confident and motivated to begin the project and to determine how to best sell this process to the team and required stakeholders.

The next step is to begin a dialogue with the team members on the subject of the project's purpose. The project manager must create an atmosphere in which all team members are encouraged to ask questions about the purpose of the project and to offer opinions and clarification. Additionally, the project manager must gain credibility and must demonstrate managerial actions and behaviors that are consistent with verbally espoused values. Congruence in actions and stated values is crucial because it creates a state of comfort and trust for team members that enables the person to take the leader at face value and become involved in the task without holding any reservations, doubts, or hesitation. Leadership also involves an active role in being the team's voice to the outside world. The leader needs to communicate actively with outside participants who affect the success of the project to address stakeholders in terms of supporting and buying into the project goals, obtaining needed project resources, providing updates and progress reports, and addressing conflict in a productive and forthright manner. Active communication between the project manager and various stakeholders maintains sponsor support, creates needed ongoing liaisons, and helps reduce the risk of unexpected obstacles hindering the project.

Management

The manager role ensures the project is completed on time, within budget, and at acceptable levels of performance. It involves creating the administrative procedures and structure to monitor completion of the work. The manager role, viewed from the perspective of people challenges, involves creating an administrative system with enough structure and discipline to complete the project without the structure stretching into the realm of excessive bureaucracy. It is important to balance the need for structure and the need for autonomy and flexibility.

Facilitation

Facilitation is one of the more subtle, yet profound roles for the project manager. Facilitation is those behaviors and attitudes that help others get their work done and is often achieved through the art of influencing others. It involves communication abilities, conflict resolution, the ability to actively procure necessary supplies and resources for the team as a hole, and the ability to motivate both individual team members and the team ass a unit. Team-focused motivation involves the creation of strategies that unite the team in common action and rewards that are realistic. The goal is to provide team members with choices, options, and a conductive setting and then trust that the team members will create the desired outcome. A project manager who is adept at helping team members address and resolve conflict in a productive manner promotes facilitation.

Mentor or Coach

The roles of mentoring and coaching are becoming increasingly important areas in the workplace. They can be defined as those processes in which one person (the mentor or coach) assists another person, either formally or informally, in various tasks related to the general purposes of professional growth and development. This assistance takes the form of guidance and encouragement, which may or may not be directly tied to an actual project issue being faced by the individual but instead may be directed at assisting the individual in attaining a broader view of future career directions or advancement. The role of mentoring and coaching involves the following:

- being a role model who demonstrates desired skills, behavior, and attitudes whose adoption may benefit team members;
- demonstrating a genuine, personal interest in the welfare and professional growth of team members;
- offering suggestions, possibilities, resources, problem-solving approaches, and opportunities to think-out-loud with team members regarding current or future issues;
- providing feedback that is supportive and also frank and accurate; and
- offering motivation directed toward assisting team members in identifying and achieving long-term professional goals.

The Four Key Roles

Thus, the most effective project manager is able to assume these four roles—leader, manager, facilitator and mentor—throughout the project and has competency in each of the four areas. Additionally, the project manager needs the skill of timing to determine when to move from one role to another, since projects have different needs at different times.

MOTIVATORS AND DEMOTIVATORS

What is Motivation?

Used in the context of this chapter, motivation is defined as "That process, action, or intervention that serves as an incentive for a project team member to take the necessary action to complete a task within the appropriate confines and scope of performance, time, and cost"[10].

The impetus for taking action may come from either intrinsic or extrinsic sources of motivation. Intrinsic motivation is that which arises from a source within a team member, such as a desire to obtain new skills or the need to confront a stimulating personal challenge. Extrinsic sources of motivation involve a force outside of the individual, such as recognition from one's peers in a professional association or at a conference or a manager providing a sizeable pay increase for a job well done. Members of a high-performance team tend to be motivated by both sources. The manager or leader, working with his or her team, should strive to search for both intrinsic and extrinsic sources of motivation when working with each team member.

Motivational Challenges

Motivation is particularly difficult because of three strong forces and trends: the continuing ongoing reductions in force; the unspoken contract between the employee and employer, which has changed dramatically over the past 20 years; and the increase in the number of team members that are from different backgrounds and viewpoints.

Organizations in both the public and private sectors continue to downsize. Even organizations that are experiencing growth in one sector of their operations may downsize in other sectors. Nearly all downsizing results in situations in which those who survive are required to do more with less. Frequently, the survivors have experienced feelings of anger and guilt that clearly decrease motivation [21]. It is not unusual to find pervasive cynicism and skepticism among the surviving employees, which creates an environment that makes motivation difficult at best.

The contract between the employer and the employee in today's operating environment primarily focuses on the organization owning the job with the employee owning the career. This differs from the era before the 1970s, in which employees often perceived an unspoken contract between themselves and their employer, grounded in the belief that quality job performance and loyalty would be in turn rewarded by job security. In today's environment, the manager must instead be creative in developing motivational approaches and processes that are part of the current reality.

The richness of team members from different backgrounds, as noted in the previous section, brings many positive contributions to the work environment. However, it can be a richness that also complicates the process of motivating team members, since the "norms" for what is viewed as motivating can be so different across the different cultural groups and locations involved. Greater sensitivity is required of the manager who is responsible for motivating people from different cultural backgrounds. Knowledge must be acquired as to what is motivating for each individual, while at the same time avoiding the pitfall of generalizing as to what will be motivating for specific cultural groups.

Other Motivational Considerations

It is important to recognize that people bring with them a certain amount of "baggage" that will affect their motivation. This baggage can be feelings, attitudes, or expectations that have a negative tone and are the result of previous negative personal or professional experiences of the individual involved. The baggage then becomes an impediment to the person's positive engagement with the work to be done. Sources of such baggage include the following:

- previous or ongoing organizational problems,
- industry changes,
- health issues,
- career stalling, and
- personal problems.

It is also important to be aware of some motivational mistakes. The following are some examples:

- what motivates me will probably motivate others,
- people are primarily motivated by money,
- everyone wants to receive a formal award,
- team members are motivated by quotas,
- each person needs a rally slogan,
- the best leader is a strong cheerleader,
- people who are professionals do not need motivating,
- people only need to be motivated if there is a problem,
- everyone should be treated the same, and
- just find one thing that motivates each person and then stay with it.

Motivation of project team members is one of the most challenging tasks of managers. It must address individual issues as well as organizational issues. Sources of motivation are both fluid and dynamic. As a manager, a good practice to follow is to ask each person what he or she finds to be particularly motivating. This practice, although simplistic, will provide the manager with a wealth of current and specific information that cannot be obtained through any other method.

Theories of Motivation

Traditionally, theories of motivation have characterized the subject from the perspective of evolution, biology, drives, needs, and social influence. Each of these perspectives is in agreement that individuals display a wide range of motives. An overview of these theories of motivation begins with the premise that motivation involves goal-directed behavior.

- **Biological perspective** is considered an evolutionary approach. It asserts that actions or behaviors that contribute favorably to the preservation and expansion of the species will produce motivation. It is appropriate when confined to the more basic aspects of human behavior, such as hunger and thirst, reproduction, and the need for affiliation for the goal of basic survival.

- **Drive theories** state that certain behaviors are the result of individuals meeting the requirements of specific drives. Drives are considered complex combinations of internal stages of tension that cause the individual to take action to reduce the level of tension. The goal of reducing tension is to achieve an internal state of equilibrium or balance or "homeostasis." Individuals in this model are believed to desire homeostatic states in their lives, and behavior is motivated because of attempts to maintain this balance. Similar to evolutionary theories, these drive theories work best when applied to the most basic human behaviors. They are often insufficient when trying to explain the complex behavior and skills involved in management.

- **Incentive theories** state that individual behavior is pulled in certain directions based on the external conditions in the specific setting. Much of the field of learning theory and instrumental learning work conducted by the noted psychologist, B.F. Skinner, is based on the incentive type of motivation. These approaches can work in settings when the manager and team member have the ability and the resources to identify a desired behavior that can be awarded by providing the identified incentive. The incentives must be valued by the group and may need to come directly from the group members. The incentives also need to be appropriate to the culture of the organization.

- **Theory of needs** is another approach to motivation primarily based on work done by David McClelland [18], who developed the concept that people who value the need for achievement are often those people who are the leaders in the areas of creativity and economic growth. This approach is based on premises that, as humans, challenging environments provide us with an opportunity to achieve excellence, or to compete against others successfully will provide motivation. The need to achieve and compete within one's own professional discipline can self-motivate many individuals.

- **Fear of failure** can describe another motivational basis to act and succeed. This approach can be a strong motivator in situations when the consequences for failure are especially distasteful or catastrophic. However, it should be employed only in unusual circumstances, such as if a project is headed for crisis, and immediate action is required. If it is employed too frequently, it may create a crisis management, disaster-avoiding environment, which will easily lead to employee burn out and dissatisfaction.

- **Hierarchical theory** of motivation was set forth by Abraham Maslow [17]. It adopts the premise that the basic physical needs and more subtle social or psychological needs will motivate people. Maslow states that people are motivated by the desire to satisfy these various needs according to a hierarchy, with the most basic needs placed at the bottom of a "needs pyramid." When one need is satisfied, the individual will then move upward to the next need. Maslow's hierarchy of needs can be described as follows:

  -**Level 1**—physiological needs (food, thirst),
  -**Level 2**—security and safety needs (stability, survival),
  -**Level 3**—belonging needs (affiliation, love),
  -**Level 4**—esteem needs (achievement and the acquisition of recognition),
  -**Level 5**—cognitive needs (knowledge),
  -**Level 6**—aesthetic needs (beauty, order), and
  -**Level 7**—self-actualization needs (the realization of one's personal potential).

- **Career stages** is a different approach presented by Schein [25] through a model that describes major stages in a person's career. An understanding of an individual's current career stage by the leader can be used in developing tangible approaches to individual motivation. This model has 10 career stages.

  -**Stage one and stage two** occur in the person's life before entering the world of work and involve early years of career exploration followed by formalized career preparation, such as higher education and specialized training.
  -**Stage three** is the first formal entry into the workplace where real world sills of the profession are acquired.
  -**Stage four** refers to training in the concrete application of skills and professional socialization, which occur as the identity of being a professional is becoming established.
  -**Stage five** occurs when the individual is observed as having gained full admission into the profession based on competency and performance.
  -**Stage six** is the point at which the individual gains a more permanent membership in the profession.
  -**Stage seven** is the natural mid-career assessment or crisis period during which questions are asked as to the value of the career and what has been accomplished.
  -**Stage eight** is the challenge of maintaining momentum as the career starts to move into its final chapters.
  -**Stage nine** is when the individual beginning to disengage from the profession and the world of work.
  -**Stage ten** is the retirement stage in which the individual must come to some form of closure of employment with a

specific organization or membership in a certain profession.

Schein also stated that our personal values affect our enjoyment and pursuit of various tasks in the workplace, and, as a result, the more we understand our own values in specific areas, the better we are able to achieve work satisfaction. Therefore, our motivation will be greatest when we pursue tasks and functions consistent with our values. Schein identified eight of these values, which he describes as career anchors; the word anchor suggesting a person's self-image of what is important for them as they consider the aggregate of their skills, motives, and values. These eight values are as follows:

  -technical-functional,
  -general managerial,
  -autonomy and independence,
  -security and stability,
  -entrepreneurial creativity,
  -service and dedication to a cause,
  -pure challenge, and
  -lifestyle.

- **Empowerment** is another approach suggested by Meredith and Mantel [20] in which a team environment be established in which the members experience a strong sense of empowerment through the use of participatory management methods. Empowerment is defined as an approach that stresses individual initiative, solution creation, and accountability. The team is then motivated by the opportunity to be self-determinative in creating the structure and methods to achieve its goals.

ETHICAL THEORIES AND APPLICATIONS

For any professional, in any discipline, ethics is an emotionally and intellectually charged word. It prompts images of moral responsibility and obligation, scholars debating the intricacies of profound issues, and arguments between professionals and social commentators about right and wrong behavior. Other images are those such as a professional oversight board ruling on professional conduct or misconduct; discussions about financial or corporate malfeasance, and the like [9].

Business ethics is considered a management discipline because of the social responsibility movement that began in the 1960s. During the 1960s, social awareness movements emphasized the expectations of businesses to use their influence to address social problems. People asserted that since businesses were making profits, it was also their responsibility to work to improve society. Many replaced the word "stockholder" with "stakeholder," including employees, customers, suppliers, and the wider community. By the 21st century, 90 percent of business schools provide some type of training in business ethics. However, philosophers, academics, and social critics traditionally have handled the field of business ethics. Much of the literature that is available is not geared to the practical requirements for the behavior of leaders and managers. And, while there is no shortage of differing opinions about what businesses should do in various situations, there is little information on ways to actually implement ethical practices.

One definition is that ethics "is the science of judging specifically human ends and the relationship of means to those ends" or "the art of controlling means so that they will serve specifically human ends." It, therefore, involves techniques of judging and decision making, as well as tools of social control and personal development. Accordingly, it is or should be involved in all human activities. In terms of business, ethics is concerned with the relationship of business goals and techniques to human ends. It studies the impacts of acts on the good of the individual, the organization, the business community, and society as a whole [11]. Another definition is that it is "the guidelines or rules of conduct by which we aim to live" [5]. As Cadbury explains, while it is difficult enough to resolve dilemmas when one's personal rules of conduct conflict, the real difficulties arise when one must make decisions affecting the interests of others. Often it is necessary to balance the interests of employees against those of shareholders and the differing views that exist among the shareholders. What matters most is how one behaves when faced with decisions that involve combining ethical and commercial judgments.

Most organizations have ethics programs, but many are unaware of them. These ethics programs typically are composed of values, policies, and activities that affect the propriety of organization behavior. Ethics is a matter of values and associated behavior. Several principles have been set forth for highly ethical organizations:

- They easily interact with diverse internal and external stakeholder groups. The ground rules of these firms make the good of the stakeholder groups part of the organizations' own good.
- They are obsessed with fairness. The ground rules emphasize that other peoples' interests count as much as their own.
- Responsibility is individual, not collective; individuals assume personal responsibility for the actions of the organization. The ground rules state that individuals are responsible to themselves.

- Activities are viewed in terms of purpose; this purpose is a way of operating that members of the organization value highly. The purpose ties the organization to its environment [23].

There are few, if any, ethical truths or standards that can be memorized and applied in a concrete fashion in all settings applicable to cost and project management. Ethical behavior is difficult to qualify and operationalize. It can be viewed as a process that one goes through, a method to consider the conflicting and often contentious agendas of those involved. It is not an action taken after the consideration of memorized rules of conduct. It is, instead, the actions that are taken as a result of the individual having engaged in a process of considering the needs of the various stakeholders, thinking through the consequences of various actions, and arriving at an action that is grounded in a good faith approach to respect the rights of those involved [10].

The difficulty of establishing sound ethical norms for an organization cannot be underestimated, as the ethical climate of an organization is extremely fragile. The task requires unremitting effort, and ethical codes can be helpful, although not decisive [3]. In the end, society sets the ethical framework within which those who run companies must work out their own codes of conduct. Business must take into account its responsibilities to society in reaching its decisions, but society must accept its responsibilities for setting the standards against which decisions are made [5].

SUMMARY

The challenges associated with management of project people are numerous and complex. But as a leader or manager, one must establish direction, communicate this direction to others, and motivate and inspire people to achieve goals and objectives. This involves the necessity of developing a leadership style that is appropriate to the specific organizational situation, working more frequently with diverse groups of people representing many different cultures, using the most appropriate motivational approaches, and also taking professional responsibility for one's actions.

REFERENCES

1. *American Heritage Dictionary of the English Language.* Third Edition. 1992. Boston: Houghton Mifflin.
2. Argyris, C. 1964. *Integrating the Individual and the Organization.* New York: Wiley.
3. Badaracco, J. L., and A. P. Webb. 1995. Business Ethics: A View from the Trenches. *California Management Review.* Winter.
4. Blake, R., and J. Mouton. 1964. *Corporate Excellence Through Grid Organization Development.* Houston: Gulf Publishing Co.
5. Cadbury, A. 1987. Ethical Managers Make Their Own Rules. *Harvard Business Review.* September–October.
6. Carr, D. K., K. J. Hard, and W. J. Trahant. 1996. *Managing the Change Process: A Field Book for Change Agents,*

Consultants, Team Leaders, and Reengineering Managers. New York: McGraw-Hill.

7. The Conference Board. 1969. *Behavioral Science Concepts and Management Applications.* New York.

8. Fitz-Enj, J. 1997. *The 8 Practices of Exceptional Companies: How Great Organizations Make the Most of Their Human Assets.* New York: American Management Association.

9. Flannes, S. 2001. *Ethics and Professional Responsibility.* Unpublished paper.

10. Flannes, S. and Levin, G. 2001. *People Skills for Project Managers.* Vienna, Virginia: Management Concepts.

11. Garrett, T. 1996. *Business Ethics.* New York: Meredith Publishing Company.

12. Herzberg, F. 1968. "One More Time: How Do You Motivate Employees?" *Harvard Business Review.* January-February.

13. Katzenbach, J. R, and D. K. Smith. 1994. *The Wisdom on Teams.* New York: HarperBusiness.

14. Kotter, J. P. 1990. *A Force for Change: How Leadership Differs From Management.* New York: The Free Press.

15. Likert, R. 1961. *Patterns of Management.* New York, 1961, McGraw-Hill Book Company.

16. Likert, R. 1967. *The Human Organization.* New York: McGraw-Hill Book Company.

17. Maslow, A. 1970. *Motivation and Personality.* New York: Harper & Row.

18. McClelland, D. 1961. *The Achieving Society.* New York: The Free Press.

19. McGregor, D. 1960. *The Human Side of Enterprise.* New York: McGraw-Hill.

20. Meredith, J. R. and Mantel S. J. 2003. *Project Management: A Managerial Approach.* New York: John Wiley & Sons.

21. Noer, D. 1993. *Healing the Wounds: Overcoming the Trauma of Lay-Offs and Revitalizing Downsized Organizations.* San Francisco: Jossey-Bass.

22. Parker, G. M. 1994. *Cross-Functional Teams. Working with Allies, Enemies, and Other Strangers.* San Francisco: Jossey-Bass.

23. Pastin, M. 1986. *The Hard Problems of Management: Gaining the Ethics Edge.* San Francisco: Jossey-Bass.

24. Project Management Institute. 2000. *A Guide to the Project Management Body of Knowledge. PMBOK® Guide.* Newtown Square, Pennsylvania: Project Management Institute.

25. Schein, E. 1990. *Career Anchors: Discovering Your Real Values.* San Francisco: Jossey-Bass/Pfeiffer.

Chapter 23

Quality Management

Gary Cokins

INTRODUCTION

The quality management movement has evolved considerably over the past two decades. This chapter introduces quality management concepts and current trends (such as Six Sigma) and their implications for cost professionals.

LEARNING OBJECTIVES

After completing this chapter, readers should be able to

- understand a brief history of the quality management, continuous improvement, and benchmarking movements;
- appreciate why there is renewed interest in quality management now emerging as Six Sigma;
- learn why traditional managerial accounting has failed the quality management movement;
- get oriented to the COQ categories—error-free, conformance related, and nonconformance related;
- understand how activity-based cost management (ABC/M) provides a foundation for repetitively and reliably computing COQ; and
- appreciate the goals and uses of COQ and benchmarking data.

WAS THE TOTAL QUALITY MANAGEMENT MOVEMENT A FAD?

In the 1980s, the total quality management (TQM) movement—a vast collection of philosophies, concepts, methods, and tools—grew increasingly popular. It received substantial business media attention and was intellectually appealing.

---

[1]This chapter includes modified excerpts from Cokins, Gary. 2001. *Activity-Based Cost Management: An Executive's Guide.* New York: John Wiley and Sons.

At an operational level, TQM was effective at identifying waste and accelerating problem solving for tactical issues. However, at a more strategic level, it was felt by many that TQM was not the magic pill for which senior executives always seem to be searching.

TQM usually did not double or triple an organization's profits. In many cases, implementation of TQM probably prevented greater financial losses from customer defections caused by quality problems or from waste and inefficiencies. Unfortunately, the avoidance of reduced profits is not measured or reported by the financial accounting system. No one could easily assess TQM's benefits. As a result, in the 1990s, TQM was regarded by senior management of some organizations as another check-in-the-box improvement program that they needed to have in place along with other programs. But TQM was not viewed as foundational.

What led to the initial interest in TQM? By the 1980s it had become evident to senior executives and the federal government that Japan was winning market share with better quality. What began as a competitive nuisance quickly became feared as a serious threat. Japan's economy had miraculously transitioned from a low- to high-quality reputation. In hindsight, we now realize it was not miraculous but a result of plain commonsense business practices. What had occurred was that consumers began to recognize Japanese products as either superior or a bargain. Consumers realized they did not need to resign themselves to accepting shoddy workmanship.

North American executives countered this threat and began to realize that quality management initiatives improve productivity while concurrently defending their market share position—a win-win. Executives were learning that there is no trade-off of extra cost for greater market share.

In the 1980s, TQM got its opportunity to shine as a leading change initiative. Popular quality management consultants raised awareness and educated businesses. Joseph M. Juran, W. Edwards Deming, Phillip Crosby, and others became leading experts and guides for organizations struggling with how to turn themselves around. Quality management programs became prevalent and often institutionalized via accepted standards such as the ISO 9000 Quality System Standard. In 1987, the U.S. Congress passed a law establishing the Malcolm Baldrige National Quality Award. In 1988, the European Foundation for Quality Management (EFQM) was founded, and in 1992, it introduced the European Quality Award. It appeared as if industry was solving its "quality crisis."

In the early 1990s, skepticism about TQM began to take the bloom off the TQM rose. A disappointing pattern from past TQM projects had emerged. Results from TQM were below possibly inflated expectations. Regardless of the explanation, after initial improvements from TQM, executives began to question if there were enough results. In October 1991, *Business Week* ran a "Return on Quality" cover article questioning the payback from TQM. In short, there was an ominous disconnection between quality and the bottom line, as increasingly more companies adopted quality programs yet few could validate much favorable impact on profitability.

At about this same time, other change initiatives, such as just-in-time production management and business process reengineering (BPR), began capturing management's attention. TQM settled in as a necessary-but-not-sufficient back-seat program.

Renewed Emphasis on Quality Management
A historical perspective on the role of quality in business and commerce may be helpful. During the Middle Ages many guilds of craftsmen were established to guarantee the quality of workmanship and to define standards by the purchaser. During the Industrial Revolution, many of the technological advances, such as the development of the steam engine, were made possible through developments in metrology and the standardization of engineering components such as screw threads.

The advent of mass production during the twentieth century increased the demands for control of product quality. During the 1940s and 1950s, the techniques of quality control became an increasingly important element of business management as organizations sought to gain competitive advantages. The success of Japanese manufacturers during the 1960s and 1970s changed the emphasis from a quality control approach to a quality assurance approach that involved more of an organization's functions.

Organizations worldwide began recognizing that quality management need not operate in isolation from other change initiative programs. Managements admitted to themselves that there had been drawbacks that had harmed quality management's reputation, such as nonverifiable measures, claimed but unrealized cost savings, and small projects that

were too local and tactical. However, these same executives realized that with corrections, what was earlier referred to as TQM could be repositioned with new branding.

In the face of increasing pressures, organizations have often launched massive, but usually uncoordinated, change initiatives that may or may not achieve their goals. Each effort in isolation may have shown results, but collectively, the initiatives can fall well short of their potential. Despite the temptation for management to continue this search for that special improvement program, system, or change initiative to cure their ills, pragmatic executives realized that there is no single program. Multiple concurrent change initiatives are needed, and they require integration.

A variety of programs and management systems began to emerge. Balanced scorecards became accepted as a solution to aligning organizational execution with strategy. Information systems such as ERP and advanced planning and scheduling (APS) improved execution, compressed lead times, and reduced unused capacity. Customer relationship management (CRM) systems connected the sales force to customer needs, value, and satisfaction. Activity-based cost management (ABC/M) systems improved the visibility and understanding for management to infer things, understand and believe their profit margins, draw conclusions, and make better decisions.

The rate of change began to accelerate. The strong force of recognizing customer satisfaction as being essential moved organizations from hierarchical structures toward process-based thinking. The reengineering message was to worry about the outputs, not the functions: Do not get entangled in the politics of the hierarchical organization chart. Power was shifting from sellers to buyers, and organizations had to shift their orientation.

Quality management qualified as one of the essentials in the new suite of management tools and methodologies. Corporate role models emerged. Six Sigma programs with "black belt" quality training at General Electric and Motorola were heralded as keys to their successful performance. To validate an organization's claim to having achieved high quality, quality assessment mechanisms have been developed. The Malcolm Baldrige Award, established in 1987, has become coveted as a sign of excellence in the U.S. Europe honors its winners of the European Quality Award (EQA), and Japan has honored winners of the Deming Application Prize. Figure 23.1 illustrates the stages of maturity that quality programs have progressed through. The figure emphasizes that the benefits for any program stem from when customer and/or shareholder value are created.

There have been and will continue to be endless debates about which management techniques matter and are effective—and which don't matter. There is an increasingly prevailing consensus that strategy and mission are essential; after strategy and mission are defined by senior management, the core business processes take over to execute the strategy. The core business processes are now accepted as the mechanism to deliver the value (both customer and stockholder value) defined by the strategy. Time, flexibility, quality, service, and cost are all derivatives of the business process. They are inextricably braided together and should not be addressed in isolation from each other. (Programs such as "core competencies," "organizational learning," and cycle time compression are considered to be important enablers.)

At the same time that management tools and methodologies were being blended, new thinking about how to achieve competitive advantage began displacing old thinking. Quality management has a golden opportunity to be part of this new managerial thinking. As an example, at some companies the Michael Porter "competitive advantage" strategy model is being abandoned. Companies can no longer compete by concentrating on "low price versus high product or service-line differentiation." This is because companies that are successfully sustaining their competitiveness have achieved competencies in new product development. Those "first-to-market" suppliers are quickly met by competitors with rapid "me-too" capabilities—and with lean cost structures. There is no place left to stake out a competitive edge. The only option that competitors have is to adopt aggressive, confrontational management styles.

This is a major challenge for executives, and it involves increasing value. *Value* is an ambiguous term and can be highly subjective. A primary responsibility for executives is to create value for the customer while increasing economic wealth for employ-

> ### GLOSSARY TERMS IN THIS CHAPTER
>
> benchmark indexes ◆ benefit cost analysis
> chart of accounts ◆ cost ◆ cost of quality
> cost of quality conformance ◆
> cost of quality nonconformance ◆
> cost of lost business advantage ◆ functional worth
> indirect costs ◆ overhead ◆ prevention ◆ quality
> quality performance tracking aystem ◆
> total quality management (TQM) ◆ value activity

ees and shareholders—all at the same time! The capability of producing value is a prerequisite to growth, and pressure is mounting to increase the rate of value creation.

A simple equation for value is value = performance/cost, where performance loosely refers to the right type of results aligned with the organization's strategy. With this math, value increases if the numerator goes up or the denominator goes down.

In some ways, executives feel boxed-in given that pricing is market-driven. They are realizing that profit margin management will require visibility and relentless management of costs. Quality management will be essential for managing costs.

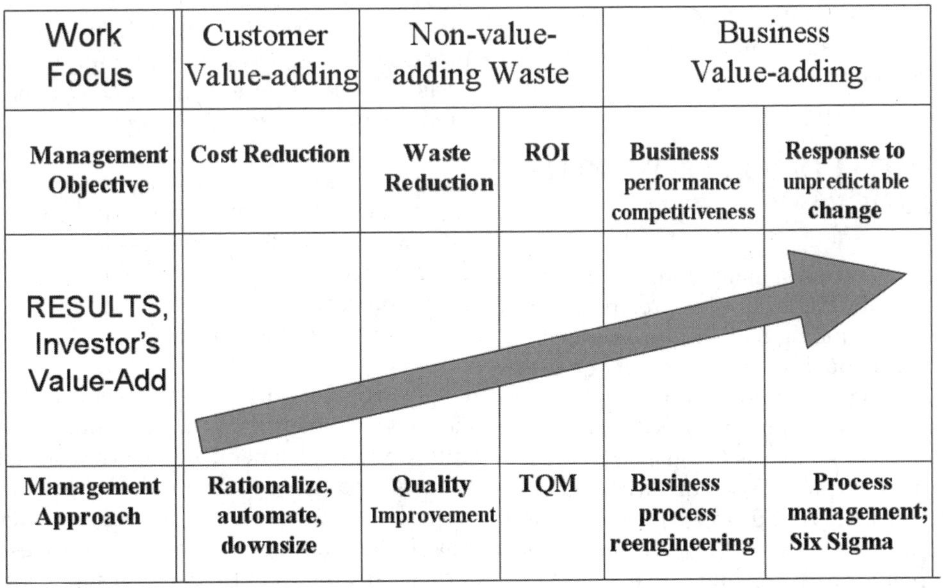

Work Focus	Customer Value-adding	Non-value-adding Waste		Business Value-adding	
Management Objective	**Cost Reduction**	**Waste Reduction**	**ROI**	**Business** performance competitiveness	**Response to** unpredictable **change**
RESULTS, Investor's Value-Add					
Management Approach	**Rationalize, automate, downsize**	**Quality** Improvement	**TQM**	**Business process reengineering**	**Process management; Six Sigma**

Figure 23.1—Evolution of Value Realization

PRODUCTIVITY PARADOX

To complicate matters, some companies that have been "reengineered" may have become leaner and smaller from downsizing, but not necessarily fitter. It may have helped them to survive, but they may still not have a distinct competitive or quality advantage. In many cases, you cannot simply remove bodies if you do not also reduce the work; otherwise, service levels erode and deteriorate. In addition, the old methods and old systems usually remain in place. Management may have met some short-term objectives, but the surviving workforce is hopefully operating with the long term in mind.

As a result of these types of changes, so-called improvements in productivity do not always translate into a more profitable business. This has been referred to as the productivity paradox.

Some organizations have invested in improving processes that were not critical to their strategic success. Such processes may have been improved, sometimes dramatically, but they did not turn out to be sufficiently relevant to the organization's long-term performance and success. Process performance improvement, cost reduction, and the like are managerial terms, but they are not necessarily indicative of value added. Value is an economic concept. However, with an advanced managerial accounting system, increases or decreases to shareholder wealth can be traced to the changes in features, functions, and processes aimed at altering customer satisfaction.

In addition, simply being lean and agile will no longer be sufficient for success. Companies' success will depend on all the trading partners in their supply chains behaving similarly. Waste and redundancy created by interorganizational mistrust must be removed via collaboration. Ideally quality management can be a shared experience among trading partners and a basis for communications.

THE ROLE OF CONTINUOUS IMPROVEMENT PROGRAMS

Quality management encompasses many tools and techniques under the umbrella of what is popularly referred to as continuous improvement, including statistical process control (SPC), quality control, quality improvement, quality assurance, and benchmarking. The emphasis in this chapter is on measuring the financial accounting aspects, because Six Sigma's key differentiator is its emphasis on financial returns justification (in contrast to its predecessor quality management programs) and because AACE International is an organization that approaches problem solving and management from a cost viewpoint. There are substantial materials about continuous improvement tools and techniques at the Web site of the American Society for Quality at www.asq.org.

WHY IS TRADITIONAL ACCOUNTING FAILING QUALITY MANAGEMENT?

One of the obstacles affecting quality management initiatives, and other initiatives as well, has been the shortcomings of the financial accounting field. Part of the problem is the traditional emphasis of accounting on external reporting.

A significant reason why traditional accounting fails quality managers is that the initial way in which the financial data are captured is not in a format that lends itself to decision making. It is always risky to invest in improving processes for which the true cost is not well established, because management lacks a valid cost base against which to compare the expected benefits of improving or reengineering the process. Gabe Pall, in *The Process-Centered Enterprise*, states:

> Historically, process management has always suffered from the lack of an obvious and reliable method of measurement that consistently indicates the level of *resource consumption* (expenses) by the business processes at any given time—an indicator which always interests executive management and is easily understood. The bottom line is that most businesses have no clue about the costs of their processes nor their processes various outputs [5].

Another part of the problem involves attitudes. For some quality professionals, using quality to connect with the bottom line or with executive thinking may seem irrelevant or, worse yet, destructive. These quality professionals fear the danger of managers who myopically focus on short-term results.

In short, understanding the economic contribution toward increasing shareholder wealth from individual business processes is a significant concern for management. When the costs of processes and their outputs can be adequately measured financially, two things can happen:

1. The data can gain management's attention and confidence that they can depend on these managerial accounting data as reliable business indicators.
2. Management can more reliably assess the different worth of processes and how they contribute to the overall performance of the business.

Finally, another part of the problem is accountants and deficiencies with their financial accounting system. The accountants' traditional general ledger is a wonderful instrument for what it is designed to do: post and bucketize (i.e., categorize) transactions into their specific account balances. But the cost data in this format (e.g., salaries, supplies, depreciation) are structurally deficient for decision support, including measuring cost of quality (COQ). The accounting community has been slow to understand and accept this problem.

The quality professional's focus should be on the quality of cost as well as the COQ. That is, focusing on the quality of cost ensures that any money spent on the business produces its equivalent in value for the customer and the supplier's employees and shareholders. The COQ measures how much cost is caused by poor quality. Both are important. This is a before-investment view in contrast to an after-the-fact view.

The next section discusses the issues related to measuring the financial dimensions of quality.

BRING FACTS, NOT HUNCHES

To some people, it is obvious that better management of quality ultimately leads to goodness that, in turn, should lead to improved financial health of an organization. Perhaps some of these same people have difficulty imagining a bridge of linkages that can equate quality improvements with exactly measured costs or profits. However, for them this does not matter very much. These types of people operate under the belief that if you simply improve quality, good things, such as happier customers and higher profits, will automatically fall into place.

Other types of people prefer having fact-based data and reasonable estimates with which to evaluate decisions and prioritize spending. These types of people do believe in quality programs, but in complex organizations with scarce idle resources, they prefer to be more certain they know where it is best to spend the organization's discretionary money.

Some quality managers have become skeptical about measuring the COQ. They have seen increasing regulations and standards, such as the ISO 9000 series, where installing any form of COQ measurement was perceived as more of a compliance exercise to satisfy documentation requirements to become "registered" rather than a benefit to improve performance.

Some perceive quality and cost as an investment choice, implying that there is a trade-off decision. This thinking assumes that achieving better quality somehow costs more and requires more effort. This is not necessarily true. If quality programs are properly installed, productivity can be improved while also raising customer satisfaction. These two combined eventually lead to increased sales, market penetration, and higher profits and returns.

Managers in the quality field have seen a number of quality programs and tools come along. Some have fallen short of their initial promise. The ISO 9000 series is the popular international standard. It addresses not only products and service lines but also the processes and policies of an organization. The benefits of the ISO 9000 accreditation included relieving buyers of redundant supplier assessments, expansion of assessments to the suppliers' suppliers, protection against

product liability litigation, and a firm foundation upon which organizations could potentially further develop their quality development. However, a disadvantage of ISO 9000 is that it represents only a minimum standard, perhaps insufficient to induce competitive-advantage behavior. Also, due to its being written in general terms, with a manufacturing origin, it is open to interpretation with ambiguities for service sector organizations. Some complain that ISO 9000 serves as a documentation tool with little extension to apply as a managerial tool.

Now, Six Sigma is vying to exhibit staying power as a quality management program. Will it succeed, or is there an inherent flaw? Six Sigma is viewed as a paradigm shift in the quality arena. Veterans of quality management believe that quality just for quality's sake—meaning conformance to standard—is not good. This sounds paradoxical. Quality is obviously needed to capture and retain customers, but quality must also be applied to the business itself. Six Sigma ensures that there is emphasis on the conversion and the paperwork-related transaction processes as well. But Six Sigma goes much farther and also suggests consideration of the business' financial health.

A popular definition of quality preferred by Six Sigma advocates is quality is a state in which value entitlement is realized for the customer and the supplier (i.e., employees and shareholders) in every aspect of the relationship. It is predictable that there will be debates about trade-offs among shareholders, customers, employees, taxpayers, and the environment. The methods of COQ measurement will be useful to convert debates into agreements [3].

This new perspective acknowledges that investing additional capital intended to reduce defect rates will not be sustained unless shareholders and lenders feel assured of high-quality financial returns to them. In Six Sigma, financial data to support manager proposals for projects are absolutely required. So, just like customers who demand utility-value, owners, investors, and lenders have a rightful expectation of profit-value and wealth creation.

This broader notion of quality is well beyond the more narrow TQM of the 1990s. For producers, it is no longer enough to just make and deliver quality goods and services. A quality business must exist as well. The intent of Six Sigma is to refocus on business economics as the driver of quality improvements.

WHAT IS QUALITY?

Before discussing the various costs of quality and how to measure them, one should have a definition of quality itself. To some the term *quality* might mean durability or richness in a product or a pleasurable experience. This is a "fitness for use" definition that relates to a customer's needs. In the 1980s, a predominant supplier-oriented view defined quality as being a high conformance to the buyer's requirements or specifications, usually measured at the time of final product test. One of the risks of limiting the definition of quality to a supplier "doing things right" is that it can miss the customers' real needs and preferences.

More recently, quality has been considered from a customer satisfaction orientation to meet or exceed customer requirements and expectations. This shifts the view from the sell side to the buy side. There has been substantial research about customer preferences, both stated and subconscious, with elaborate survey questionnaires, diagnostics, and conjoint statistical analysis. For example, "food" may be a customer's stated need, but "nourishment" or a "pleasant taste" are the real primary needs. A customer's ultimate perception of quality involves many factors. In short, the universally accepted goals of quality management are lower costs, higher revenues, delighted customers, and empowered employees.

IMPACT OF POOR QUALITY

Almost every organization now realizes that not having the highest quality is not even an option. High quality is simply an entry ticket for the opportunity to compete. Attaining high quality is now a must. Anything less than high quality will lead to an organization's terminal collapse. In short, high quality is now a prerequisite for an organization to continue to exist. The stakes are much higher.
The quality techniques that have been applied in the past,

however, are still relevant. One of leaders in the quality movement, Joseph M. Juran, has described managing for quality by using three managerial steps, called the Juran Trilogy [4, p. 2–7]:

1. **Quality planning**—translating customer needs into characteristics of products and service lines (e.g., quality function deployment analysis).
2. **Quality control**: measuring quality levels and comparing them against desired levels (i.e., removing *sporadic* deficiencies).
3. **Quality improvement**: implementing incremental improvements to attain better levels of control (i.e., removing *chronic* deficiencies).

Figure 23.2 shows that each step leads to a result used in the next step.

In the figure, sporadic problems are those that periodically occur and are dealt with shortly after they happen. In effect, the problem is quickly corrected until the process or off-spec output is returned to an acceptable level. Sporadic problems will likely continue to recur because the solution is usually more a bandage than a real cure.

Chronic problems, in contrast, have usually existed for an extended period of time and may be accepted or tolerated by the organization as known but unresolvable. Examples include poor communications or inadequate tools for work-

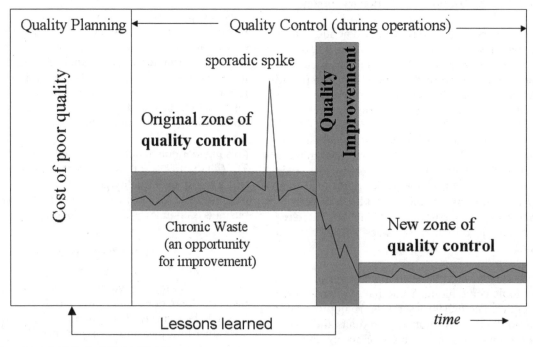

Source: Juran's Quality Handbook; McGraw-Hill; 1999.

Figure 23.2—Juran's Trilogy

ers. Employees are often resigned to the existence of chronic problems. They are undesirable but expected to persist because they have been subconsciously designed and planned into the processes and procedures.

Organizations tend to concentrate on sporadic problems because when they occur there is usually an adverse consequence, such as a customer complaint or a missed delivery date. But the fix may not necessarily be lasting. In contrast, the elimination of chronic problems requires greater effort. The solution may be the result of forming a project team that produces an innovative solution. The problem analysis will likely be more intent on truly understanding the root cause. When root causes of chronic problems are removed, improvements in performance and costs can be substantial.

In Figure 23.2, sporadic problems can spike from an unplanned event, such as a power failure. Immediately following these events teams troubleshoot and "put out the fire," which restores the error level back to the status quo—the planned chronic level. The figure also reveals that after a quality improvement initiative addresses the process, the level of error is driven downward.

Another leader in the quality movement, W. Edwards Deming, advocated a similar and now well-accepted set of steps with his "Plan-Do-Check-Act" (PDCA) cycle, an iterative approach to achieving preventive and corrective solutions [4, p. 41.3–41.5]. Some now have reduced PDCA to a more simple "Do-and-Reflect." Regardless of the quality techniques applied, financial measures will be increasingly relevant as organizations move from decisions based on instinct and intuition toward fact-based decisions.

CATEGORIZING QUALITY COSTS

To some people quality costs are very visible and obvious. To others, quality costs are understated; and they believe that much of the quality-related costs are hidden and go unreported.

There are several levels of non-error-free quality costs, as illustrated in Figure 23.3. The following discussion of scope is restricted to the inner concentric circles, although there are additional quality costs.

Figure 23.3 begins to reveal that there are other hidden financial costs and lost income opportunities beyond those associated with traditional obvious quality costs. Examples of obvious quality-related costs are rework costs, excess scrap material costs, warranty costs, and field repair expenses. These

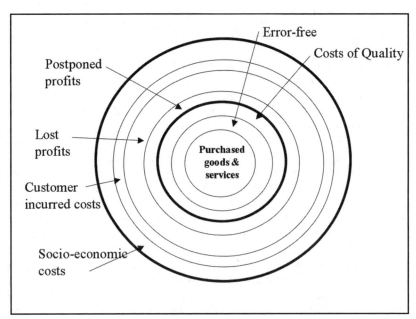

Figure 23.3—Levels and Scope of Quality Costs

typically result from errors. Error-related costs are easily measured directly from the financial system. Spending amounts are recorded in the accountant's general ledger system using the "chart-of-accounts." Sometimes the quality-related costs include the expenses of an entire department, such as an inspection department that arguably exists solely as being quality-related. However, as organizations flatten and de-layer, and employees multitask more, it is rare that an entire department will focus exclusively on quality.

The hidden poor quality costs, represented in the figure's outer circle, are less obvious and are more difficult to measure. For example, a hidden cost would be those hours of a few employees' time sorting through paperwork resulting from a billing error. Although these employees do not work in a quality department that is dedicated to quality-related activities, such as inspection or rework, that portion of their workday was definitely quality-related. These costs are not reflected in the chart-of-accounts of the accounting system. That is why they are referred to hidden costs.

The lack of widespread tracking of the COQ in practice is surprising because the tools, methods, and technologies exist to accomplish reporting COQ. A research study [6] investigating the maturity of COQ revealed that the major reason for not tracking COQ was lack of management interest and support in tracking COQ and their belief that quality costing is "paperwork" that does not have enough value to do. Other major reasons for not tracking COQ were a lack of knowledge of how to track costs and benefits of COQ as well as a lack of adequate accounting and computer systems. Given the advances in today's data collection, data warehousing, data mining, and ABC/M system implementations, these reasons begin to appear as lame excuses—the technology is no longer the impediment for reporting COQ that it once was.

Providing employee teams with visibility of both obvious and hidden quality-related costs can be valuable for performance improvement. Using the data, employees can gain insights into causes of problems. The hidden and traditional costs can be broadly categorized as follows:

- **Error-free costs** are costs unrelated to planning of, controlling of, correcting of, or improving of quality. These are the did-it-right-the-first-time (nicknamed "dirtfoot") costs.
- **COQ** are costs that could disappear if all processes were error-free and if all products and services were defect-free. COQ can be subcategorized as
  -**costs of conformance**—the costs related to prevention and predictive appraisal to meet requirements.
  -**costs of noncomformance**—the costs related to internal or external failure, including detective appraisal work, from not meeting requirements. The distinction between internal versus external is that internal failure costs are detected prior to the shipment or receipt of service by the customer. In contrast, external failure costs result usually from discovery by a customer.

An oversimplified definition of COQ is the costs associated with avoiding, finding, making, and repairing defects and errors (assuming that all defects and errors are detected). COQ represents the difference between the actual costs and what the reduced cost would be if there were no substandard service levels, failures, or defects.

Simple examples of these categories for a magazine or book publisher might be as follows:

- **Error-free**—"first time through" work without a flaw;
- **Prevention**—training courses for the proofreaders, and preventive maintenance on the printing presses;
- **Appraisal**—proofreading;
- **Internal failure**—unplanned printing press downtime, and correction of typographical errors; and
- **External failure**—rework resulting from a customer complaint.

There are other quality-related costs depicted in the outer levels that are somewhat more difficult to measure but may be relevant in decision analysis. These additional concentric rings of costs are supply chain-related:

- **Postponed profits (current)**—profits that could not be formally recognized during a specific financial accounting period because the goods and services did not satisfy all of the customer's requirements. The impact is deferred cash inflow.

- **Lost profits (permanent)**—the sales and profit opportunity permanently lost when a customer elects to switch to a competitor or substitute or no longer purchase due to a bad experience.
- **Customer incurred costs**—all of a customer's COQ (plus postponed and lost profits from the customer's customers) caused by the supplier's nonconformance. Examples include the customer's own rework, its equipment repair, or its tarnished name due to reduced service levels.

Some people may argue that an additional level of socioeconomic costs exists where the public and community are affected, such as when an oil spill or pollution occur. This is represented in Figure 23.3 as the most outside concentric ring of costs.

Figure 23.4 uses a pie chart to portray, in financial terms, how an organization's sales, profits, purchased materials, and COQ expenses might exist. In principle, as the COQ expenses are reduced, they can be converted into higher bottom line profits.

Figure 23.5, titled "ABC/M's Attributes Can Score and Tag Costs," illustrates how "attributes" can be tagged or scored into increasingly finer segments of the error-free and COQ subcategories. Attributes are tagged to individual activities

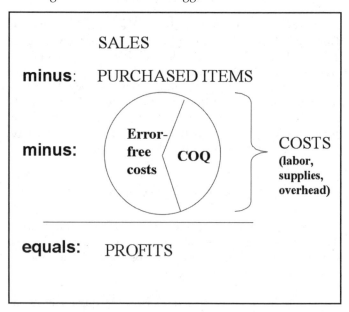

Figure 23.4—Sales, Costs, and Profits

for which the activities will already have been costed using activity-based cost management (ABC/M). Hence, the subcategory costs can be reported with an audit trail back to which resources they came from. Each of the subattributes can be further subdivided with deeper "indented" classifications.

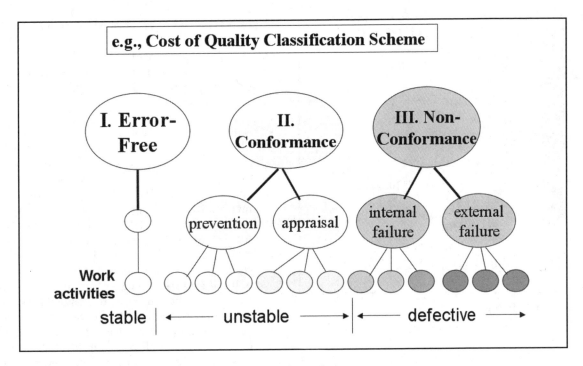

Figure 23.5—ABC/M's Attributes Can Score and Tag Costs

Because 100 percent of the resource costs can be assigned to activities, 100 percent of the activities can be tagged with one of the COQ attributes, since the activities have already been costed by ABC/M. The attribute groupings and summary roll-ups are automatically costed as well.

Life would be nice in an error-free world, and an organization's overall costs would be substantially lower relative to where they are today. But all organizations will always make mistakes and errors. They will always experience some level of errors. However, the goal is to manage mistakes and their impact. Cost quality serves to communicate fact-based data—in terms of money—to enable focusing and prioritizing to manage mistakes.

As previously mentioned, unless an entire department's existence is fully dedicated to one of the COQ subcategories, or an isolated chart-of-account expense account fully applies to a COQ category, most of the COQ spending is hidden. That is, the financial system cannot report those costs.

A danger exists if only a fraction of the quality-related costs are measured and their amount is represented as the total quality costs—this is a significant understating of the actual costs. Unfortunately, there are as many ways of hiding quality costs as there are people with imagination. Organizations that hide their complete COQ from themselves continue to risk deceiving themselves with an illusion that they have

effective management. ABC/M is an obvious approach to making visible the missing COQ amount of spending.

WHERE DO QUALITY COSTS RESIDE IN THE ACCOUNTANT'S FINANCIAL STATEMENT?

It may make it easier to think of the sum total of all of the cost categories (i.e., error-free or COQ) as equating to the total expenditures during a time period, less purchased material costs, that make up a company's budget statement. For any nonprofit organization, their budget-funded expenditures "equals" error-free costs "plus" COQ. (If there are fees or revenues, then these are simply added to the budget-funded amount.)

One hundred percent of the total expenditures can be accounted for and included. Figure 23.6 illustrates the distribution of quality costs using the subcategories that were described in Figure 23.5. An example of a commercial company will be used to demonstrate how quality can be measured financially. The parallels to a government or nonprofit organization are high.

In this example, a fictitious manufacturer with revenues of $200,000 enjoys a healthy 5 percent profit-to-sales rate and purchases roughly half of its expenditures, $90,000, from its suppliers. The remaining expenses of $100,000 were not directly purchased from external suppliers; 80 percent of

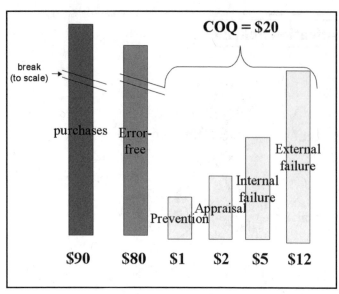

Figure 23.6—COQ Histogram

these were error-free, but 20 percent involved quality-related work. (In advanced COQ analysis, portions of the external purchases, such as for contract labor, can also be included for segmentation as error-free versus COQ. Externally purchased services are rarely perfect.)

Sales	$200,000	
Expenses		
Purchased direct material	< 90,000>	
Labor, supplies, and overhead	<100,000>	this equates to the total expenses not purchased from suppliers (i.e., error-free + COQ)
Profit	$10,000	(5% of sales)

In Figure 23.6, the majority of the costs of $20,000 quality-related costs are classified as external failure ($12,000). That is, the product or service-line was unsuccessful after being received by the end-customer. In theory, if half of that type of COQ expense (i.e., $6,000) could be eliminated, and presuming the freed-up capacity can be redeployed elsewhere, then the profits would rise by $6,000 from $10,000 to $16,000—a 60 percent jump! The profit rate would increase from 5 to 8 percent of sales.

Figure 23.7 displays how the COQ histogram from Figure 23.6 could ideally appear after both prevention and appraisal spending is initially increased, and then process efficiencies are applied to drive all of the COQ costs down.

BENEFITS FROM INCLUDING TOTAL

EXPENDITURES WHEN MEASURING QUALITY

Starting the measurement by assuming a 100 percent inclusion of the total expenditures, then subsequently segmenting those expenses between the error-free costs and the COQ has the following results:

- **reduces debate**—With traditional COQ measures, people can endlessly debate whether a borderline activity is a true COQ, such as scrap produced during product development that may arguably be expected. Including such a cost as COQ may inflate a measure that is of high interest. By excluding it, that expense melts away without any visibility into all the other total expenditures of the organization. It can be tempting for controversial costs to be excluded as a quality-related cost category. By starting with the 100 percent expenditure pool, *every* cost will fall into *some* category and always be visible. Each type of cost can always be reclassified later on, as people better understand how to use the data.

- **increases employee focus**—By developing classifications into which all costs can be slotted, organizations will hopefully focus much less on their methods of measurement and focus much more on their organization's problems and how to overcome them.

- **integrates with the same data used in the boardroom**—When traditional and obvious COQ information is used, only portions of the total expenditures are selected for inclusion. This invites debate about arbitrariness or ambiguity. However, when 100 percent of expenditures are included, the COQ plus error-free costs exactly reconcile with the same data used by executive management and the board of directors. There is no longer any

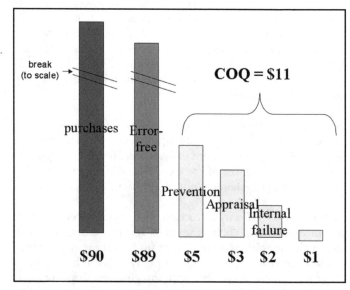

Figure 23.7—Getting Efficient with Conformance-Related COQ

suspicion that some COQ has been left out or that the COQ data are not anchored in reality. By starting with 100 percent expenditures, the only debate can be about misclassification, not omission.

The capture of COQ can be further refined if it is worthwhile for the organization.

When making decisions, the universally popular costs-versus-benefits test can be applied with COQ data. If either subcategory of COQ is excessive, it draws down profits for commercial companies or draws down resources in government agencies that could have been better deployed on higher-value-added activities elsewhere.

GOALS AND USES FOR THE COQ INFORMATION

If an organization makes the effort to collect data, validate the information, and report it, it might as well use the information. In fact, to state the obvious, the amount of use of and utility in the information will be proportional to the length of life of the COQ measurement system. In short, the uses of a COQ measurement system can range from favorably influencing employee attitudes toward quality management by quantifying the financial impact of changes to assisting in prioritizing improvement opportunities.

The rationale for implementing COQ is based on the following logic:

- For any failure, there is a root cause.
- Causes for failure are preventable.
- Prevention is cheaper than fixing problems after they occur.

If you accept the logic that it is always less expensive to do the job right the first time than to do it over, the rationale and goal for quality management and using COQ to provide a quality program with concrete and fact-based data should be apparent.

Implementation involves the following steps:

- Directly attack failure costs with the goal to drive them to zero.
- Invest in the appropriate prevention activities, not fads, to effect improvements.
- Reduce appraisal costs according to results that are achieved.
- Continuously evaluate and redirect prevention efforts to gain further improvement.

Figure 23.8 on page 23.12 illustrates the direction in which quality-related costs can ideally be managed. Ideally, all four COQ

cost categories should be reduced, but one may initially need to prudently increase the cost of prevention to dramatically decrease the costs of and reduced penalties paid for nonconformance. This makes COQ more than just an accounting scheme; it becomes a financial investment justification tool.

A general corrective operating principle is that as failures are revealed, for example via customer complaints, the root causes should be eliminated with corrective actions. A general rule-of-thumb is that the nearer the failure is to it being used by the customer, the more expensive it is to correct. The flip side is that it is less expensive—overall—to fix problems earlier in the business process. As failure costs are reduced, appraisal efforts can also be reduced in a rationale manner.

QUANTIFYING THE MAGNITUDE OF THE COSTS OF QUALITY

The formal COQ measurement system provides continuous results. In contrast to a one-time assessment, it requires involvement by employees who participate in the business processes. More important, these employees must be motivated to spend the energy and time, apart from their regular responsibilities, to submit and use the data.

Commercial ABC/M software products were designed for frequent repeated updating. For such a COQ system to be sustained longer-term, the system requires senior management's support and interest as well as genuinely perceived utility by users of the data to solve problems.

Regardless of the collection system selected, it is imperative to focus analytical and corrective time and energy on the area of failure costs. As Dr. Joseph Juran discussed in his highly popular article, "Gold in the Mine," there is still much "mining" that can be performed [4, p. 8.1–8.11]. This mining should be considered a long-term investment, because failure costs, when starting a quality management program, usually constitute 65 to 70 percent of a corporation's quality costs. Appraisal costs are normally 20 to 25 percent, and prevention costs are 5 percent.

CONTINUOUS IMPROVEMENT WITH BENCHMARKING AND UNIT COSTS

Tagging attributes onto costs is obviously a secondary purpose for measuring costs. The primary purpose for costing is to simply know what something costs. This data allows you to measure profit margins, to focus on where the larger costs are that may be impacted, or to estimate future costs to justify future spending decisions (e.g. ROI). In short, managerial accounting transforms expenses into calculated costs. That is, expenses are postings to the general ledger bookkeeping sys-

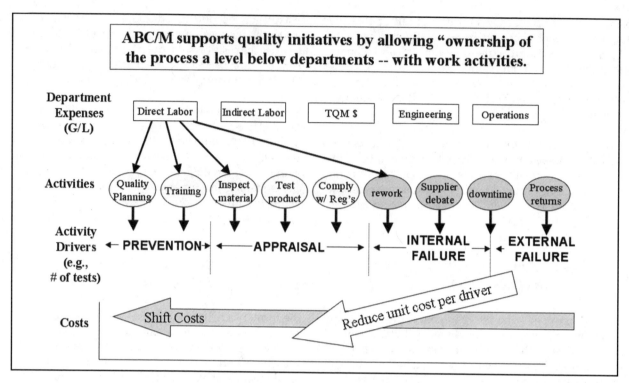

Figure 23.8—Driving Cost-of-Quality Downward

tem to recognize exchanges of money to vendors and employees. Expenses are purchases of resources. In contrast, costs are the uses of that spending. Costs are always calculated. Many organizations arbitrarily "allocate" costs based on broadly-averaged volume factors, but the proper rule is to trace and assign the expense based on a one-to-one cause-and-effect relationship.

When an organization has good costing, then it can use calculated costs, such as the cost per processed invoice, as a basis for comparison. In short, the unit cost per each output of work is computed and then this data is usable for benchmarking—either internally or with other organizations.

The use of ABC/M data is becoming more popular as a metric for benchmarking. Often in benchmarking studies, there can be a bad case of apples-to-Oreo's. That is, there is lack of unrecognized comparability amongst the participating organizations. There is lack of consistency among what work activities or outputs are to be included or excluded in the study. An ABC/M methodology and system introduces rigor and is sufficiently codified and leveled for relevancy as to remove this nagging shortcoming of benchmarking.

In practice, the vast majority of ABC/M is applied to subsets of the organization for process improvement rather than revenue enhancement and profit margin increases. An example of a subset is an order processing center or equipment maintenance function. These ABC/M models and systems are designed to reveal the cost structure to the participants in the

main department and related areas. In ABC/M's cost assignment view, the cost structure is seen from the orientation of how the diversity and variation of the function's outputs cause various work to happen, and how much. The costs of the work activities that belong to the processes are also revealed in the ABC/M model as they relate in time and sequence. However, it is ABC/M's powerful revealing of the costs of various types of outputs that serves as a great stimulant to spark discussion and discovery. For example, if an order processing center learns that the cost per each adjusted order is roughly eight times more costly than for each error-free or adjustment-free entered order, that would get people's attention. This result happens even if the order entry process has been meticulously diagrammed, flowcharted, and documented.

DECONSTRUCTING COQ CATEGORIES

In effect, the technique to calculate a reasonably accurate COQ is to apply ABC/M and ABC/M's attribute capability. Figure 23.9 shows categories for work activities that are one additional level below the four major categories of COQ. This figure reveals how each of these subcategories can be tagged against the ABC/M costs. This provides far greater and reliable visibility of COQ without the great effort required by traditional cost accounting methods.

The quality movement has been a loud advocate for measuring things rather than relying on opinions. It would make sense that measuring the financial implications of quality will become an increasingly larger part of the quality management domain.

SUMMARY

The reputation of quality management movement has experienced a few waves of ups and downs. It has become almost religious-like for some years and then ridiculed. Hopefully, the addition of valid costing data will give the quality movement more legitimacy. In a recent publication from one of the key sanctioning quality societies, The American Society for Quality (ASQ), there was a key definition. ANSI/ISO/ASQ Q9004-2000 suggests financial measurement as an appropriate way to assess "the organization's performance in order to determine whether planned objectives have been achieved [1]. Hopefully there will be increased coordination amongst the quality, managerial accounting, and operations system.

REFERENCES

1. American Society for Quality. 2000. ANSI/ISO/ASQ 9004-2000. Milwaukee, Wisconsin: ASQ Quality Press.
2. Cokins, Gary. 2001. *Activity-Based Cost Management: An Executive's Guide*. New York: John Wiley & Sons.
3. Harry, Mickel J. 2000. New Definition Aims to Connect Quality with Financial Performance. *Quality Progress*. January. p. 65.
4. Juran, Joseph M. 1999. *Juran's Quality Handbook*. New York: McGraw-Hill.
5. Pall, Gabe. 2000. *The Process-Centered Enterprise*. New York: St. Lucie Press. p. 40.
6. Sower, Victor E., and Ross Quarles. 2002. *Cost of Quality Usage and Its Relationship to Quality Systems Maturity*. Working Paper series. Center for Business and Economic Development at Sam Houston State University. Lucie Press, 2000), p. 40.

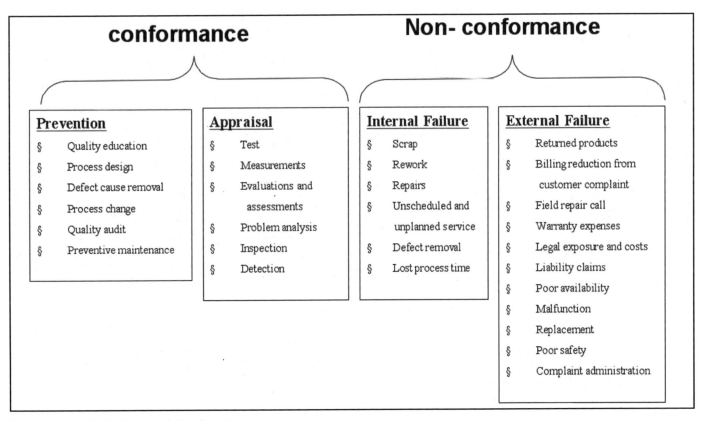

Figure 23.9—Typical Cost-of-Quality Components

Chapter 24

Value Analysis

Del L. Younker, CCC

INTRODUCTION

The objective of the value analysis (VA) study is to improve the value for the intended project objectives. This VA practice chapter covers a procedure for defining and satisfying the requirements of the user/owner's project. A multidisciplinary team uses the procedure to convert design criteria and specifications into descriptions of project functions and then relates these functions to revenues and costs.

All examples of costs presented are relevant costs over a designated study period, including the costs of obtaining funds, designing, purchasing/leasing, constructing/installing, operating, maintaining, repairing, and replacing and disposing of the particular item, design or system. While not the only criteria, cost is an important basis for comparison in a VA study of a building. Therefore, accurate and comprehensive cost data is an important element of the analysis.

The following are guidelines for developing alternatives that meet the project's required functions:

- Estimate the costs for each alternative.
- Provide the user/owner with specific, technically accurate alternatives, appropriate to the stage of project development, which can be implemented.
- The user/owner then selects the alternative(s) that best satisfies the needs and requirements.

This methodology can be applied to an entire project or to any subsystem. The user/owner can utilize the VA methodology to improve the element or scope of the project to be studied.

LEARNING OBJECTIVES

After completing this chapter, the reader should be able to

- develop alternatives to a proposed design that best fulfills the needs and requirements of the user/owner of the project or system.

- identify the functions of the project and its systems;
- develop alternatives to fulfill the user's/owner's needs and requirements; and
- evaluate the alternatives in their ability to meet defined criteria.

VALUE ANALYSIS SIGNIFICANCE AND USE

Perform VA during the planning, design, and final phases of a project, product, program, system or technique. The most effective application of VA is early in the design phase of a project. Changes or redirection in the design can be accommodated without extensive redesign at this point, thereby saving the user/owner time and money.

During the earliest stages of design, refer to VA as value planning. Use the procedure to analyze predesign documents—for example, program documents and planning documents. At the predesign stage, perform VA to define the project's functions, and to achieve consensus on the project's direction and approach by the project team. By participating in this early VA exercise, members of the project team communicate their needs to other team members and identify those needs in the common language of functions. By expressing the project in these terms early in the design process, the project team minimizes miscommunication and redesign, which are costly in both labor expenditures and potential schedule delays.

Also, perform VA during schematic design (up to 15 percent design completion), design development (up to 45 percent design completion), and completion documents (up to 100 percent design completion). Conduct VA studies at several stages of design completion to define or confirm project functions, to verify technical and management approaches, to analyze selection of equipment and materials, and to assess the project's economics and technical feasibility. Perform VA studies concurrently with the user/owner's design review schedules to maintain the project schedule. Through the schematic design and design development stages, the VA team analyzes the drawings and specifications from each technical discipline. During the completion (such as construction or manufacturing) documents stage, the VA team analyzes the design drawings and specifications, as well as the details and equipment selection, which are more clearly defined at this later stage.

A VA study performed at a 90 to 100 percent completion stage, just prior to bidding, concentrates on buildability, economics and technical feasibility. Consider methods of construction, phasing of construction, and procurement. The goals at this stage of design are to minimize costs and maximize value; reduce the potential for claims; analyze management and administration; and review the design, equipment and materials used.

During construction or other completion means, analyze value analysis change proposals (VACPs) of the contractor. VACPs reduce the cost or duration of construction or present alternative methods of construction, without reducing performance, acceptance, or quality. At this stage, the alternatives presented to the user/owner are VACPs. To encourage the contractor to propose worthwhile VACPs, the owner and the contractor share the resultant savings when permitted by contract.

The numbering and timing of VA studies varies for every project. The user/owner, the design professional, and the value analyst determine the best approach jointly. A complex or expensive facility or a design that will be used repeatedly warrants a minimum of two VA studies performed at the pre-design and design development stages.

VALUE METHODOLOGY STANDARD FORWARD

Since 1947, the methods, technology, and application of the value methodology (VM) has greatly increased and expanded. VM includes the processes known as value analysis, value engineering, and value management. It is sometimes also referred to as value control, value improvement, or value assurance. This standard defines common terminology, offers a standardized job plan (while allowing the great diversity of individual practices that have been successfully developed), and is offered to reduce confusion to those being introduced to VM. The standard includes the approved job plan, the body of knowledge as developed by the SAVE International professional ccertification board, typical profiles of the value specialist and value manager, duties of a value organization, a glossary, and an appendix of references. Learn more about the VM by reviewing the SAVE International Web site www.value-eng.org.

VM Applicability

The VM can be applied wherever cost and/or performance improvement is desired. That improvement can be measured in terms of monetary aspects and/or other critical factors such as productivity, quality, time, energy, environmental impact, and durability. VM can beneficially be applied to virtually all areas of human endeavor.

The VM is applicable to hardware, building or other construction projects, and to "soft" areas such as manufacturing and construction processes, healthcare and environment al services, programming, management systems, and organization structure. The prestudy efforts for these soft types of projects utilizes standard industrial engineering techniques, such as flow charting, yield analysis, and value added task analysis to gather essential data.

For civil, commercial and military engineering works such as buildings, highways, factory construction, and water/sewage treatment plants, which tend to be one-time applications, VM is applied on a project-by-project basis. Since these are one-time capital projects, VM must be applied as early in the design cycle as feasible to achieve maximum benefits. Changes or redirection of design can be accomplished without extensive redesign, large implementation cost, and schedule impacts. Typically for large construction projects, specific value studies are conducted during the schematic stage and then again at the design development (up to 45 percent) stage. Additional value studies may be conducted during the final completion stages.

For large or unique products and systems such as military electronics or specially designed capital equipment, VM is applied during the design cycle to assure meeting of goals and objectives. Typically, a formalized value study is performed after preliminary design approval but before release to the build/manufacture cycle. VM may also be applied during the build/manufacture cycle to assure that the latest materials and technology are utilized.

VM can also be applied during planning stages and for project/program management control by developing function models with assigned cost and performance parameters. If specific functions show trends moving toward or beyond control limits, value studies are performed to assure the function's performance remains within the control limits.

VALUE STUDY TEAM

A key to the successful application of a value study is the skills and experience of those applying the methodology. While the methodology can, and often is, used by individuals, it has been proven that a well-organized team obtains the best value for effort performed for significant projects .
The team leader performs a key role and is a significant fac-

tor in the degree of success. The team leader must have thorough training in both the VM and team facilitation. The requirements include strong leadership, communication skills, and experience working with users/clients.

The size and composition of the team is project dependent. The members should represent a diverse background and experience that incorporates all the knowledge required to fully cover the issues and objectives of the project. Typically, these include cost, estimating, procurement/materials, and those technical disciplines unique to the project such as design, manufacturing, construction, environmental, and marketing, etc.

It is most advantageous for the team leader, or a team member, to implement the approved value proposals at study completion.

Decisions based primarily upon one technical discipline will often have significant effects on other disciplines within the project. In addition to being technically competent, team member selection should include individuals who represent the range of disciplines and end users the study results will impact. They must be individuals who generate positive attitudes and are willing to investigate new ideas and then rationally evaluate them.

GLOSSARY TERMS IN THIS CHAPTER

agenda ◆ constructability reviews ◆ cost ◆ cost-design cost-life cycle ◆ cost model ◆ cost/worth ratio Function ◆ function-basic ◆ function-secondary function models ◆ hierarchy ◆ function analysis system technique (fast) ◆ job plan ◆ performance ◆ price product ◆ scope ◆ value ◆ value-monetary value methodology ◆ value methodology proposal value study ◆ value methodology training ◆ value analyst value engineer ◆ value engineering change proposal (VECP) value specialist ◆ worth

---

THE VALUE METHODOLOGY JOB PLAN

The VM uses a systematic job plan (Table 24.1). The job plan outlines specific steps to effectively analyze a product or service in order to develop the maximum number of alternatives to achieve the product's or service's required functions. Adherence to the job plan will better assure maximum benefits while offering greater flexibility.

Table 24.1—The VM Job Plan

PRESTUDY	Creative Phase	POST-STUDY
	create quantity of ideas by function	
collect user/customer attitudes		complete changes
complete data file	*Evaluation Phase*	implement changes
determine evaluation factors	rank and rate alternative ideas	monitor status
scope the study	select ideas for development	
build data models		
determine team composition	*Development Phase*	
	conduct benefit analysis	
VALUE STUDY	complete technical data package	
	create implementation plan	
Information Phase	prepare final proposals	
complete data package		
modify scope	*Presentation Phase*	*The VM Job Plan covers three major periods of activity: prestudy, the value study, and post-study. All phases and steps are performed sequentially. As a value study progresses new data and information may cause the study team to return to earlier phases or steps within a phase on an iterative basis. Conversely, phases or steps within phases are not skipped.*
	Present Oral Report	
Function Analysis Phase	Prepare Written Report	
identify functions	Obtain Commitments for	
classify functions	Implementation	
develop function models		
establish function worth		
cost functions		
establish value index		
select functions for study		

PRESTUDY

Preparation tasks involve six areas: (a) collecting/defining user/customer wants and needs, (b) gathering a complete data file of the project, (c) determining evaluation factors, (d) scoping the specific study, (e) building appropriate models, and (f) determining the team composition.

a. **Collect User/Customer Attitudes**—The user/customer attitudes are compiled via an in-house focus group and/or external market surveys. The objectives are to

1. determine the prime buying influence;
2. define and rate the importance of features and characteristics of the product or project;
3. determine and rate the seriousness of user-perceived faults and complaints of the product or project;
4. compare the product or project with competition or through direct analogy with similar products or projects.

For first time projects such as a new product or new construction, the analysis may be tied to project goals and objectives.

The results of this task will be used to establish value mismatches in the information phase.

b. **Gather a Complete Data File**—There are both primary and secondary sources of information. Primary sources are of two varieties: people and documentation. People sources include marketing (or the user), original designer, architect, cost or estimating group, maintenance or field service, the builders (manufacturing, constructors, or systems designers), and consultants. Documentation sources include drawings, project specifications, bid documents and project plans.

Secondary sources include suppliers of similar products, literature such as engineering and design standards, regulations, test results, failure reports, and trade journals. Another major source is like or similar projects. Quantitative data is desired.

Another secondary source is a site visitation by the value study team. "Site" includes actual construction location, manufacturing line, or office location for a new/improved system. If the actual "site" is not available, facilities with comparable functions and activities may prove to be a valuable source of usable information.

c. **Determine Evaluation Factors**—The team, as an important step in the process, determines what will be the criteria for evaluation of ideas and the relative importance of each criteria to final recommendations and decisions for change. These criteria and their importance are discussed with the user/customer and management and concurrence obtained

d. **Scope the Study**—The team develops the scope statement for the specific study. This statement defines the limits of the study based on the data-gathering tasks. The limits are the starting point and the completion point of the study. Just as important, the scope statement defines what is not included in the study. The study sponsor must verify the scope statement.

e. **Build Models**—Based on the completion and agreement of the scope statement, the team may compile models for further understanding of the study. These include such models as cost, time, energy, flow charts, and distribution, as appropriate for each study.

f. **Determine Team Composition, Wrap-Up**—The value study team leader confirms the actual study schedule, location and need for any support personnel. The study team composition is reviewed to assure all necessary customer, technical, and management areas are represented. The team leader assigns data gathering tasks to team members so all pertinent data will be available for the study.

Value Study

The value study is where the primary VM is applied. The effort is composed of six phases: (a) information, (b) function analysis, (c) creativity, (d) evaluation, (e) development, and (f) presentation.

a. **Information Phase**—The objective of the information phase is to complete the value study data package started in the prestudy work. If not done during the pre-study activities, the project sponsor and/or designer brief the value study team, providing an opportunity for the team to ask questions based on their data research. If a "site" visitation was not possible during prestudy, it should be completed during this phase.

The study team agrees to the most appropriate targets for improvement such as value, cost, performance, and schedule factors. These are reviewed with appropriate management, such as the project manager, value study sponsor, and designer, to obtain concurrence.

Finally, the scope statement is reviewed for any adjustments due to additional information gathered during the Information Phase.

b. **Function Analysis Phase**—Function definition and analysis is the heart of VM. It is the primary activity that separates VM from all other "improvement" practices. The objective of this phase is to develop the most beneficial areas for continuing study. The team performs the following steps:

1. Identify and define both work and sell functions of the product, project, or process under study using active verbs and measurable nouns. This is often referred to

as random function definition.

2. Classify the functions as basic or secondary.
3. Expand the functions identified in step 1 (optional).
4. Build a function model—function hierarchy/logic or function analysis system technique (FAST) diagram (see Figure 24.1).
5. Assign cost and/or other measurement criteria to functions.
6. Establish worth of functions by assigning the previously established user/customer attitudes to the functions.
7. Compare cost to worth of functions to establish the best opportunities for improvement.
8. Assess functions for performance/schedule considerations.
9. Select functions for continued analysis
10. Refine study scope

c. **Creative Phase**—The objective of the creative phase (sometimes referred to as speculation phase) is to develop a large quantity of ideas for performing each function selected for study. This is a creative type of effort, totally unconstrained by habit, tradition, negative attitudes, assumed restrictions, and specific criteria. No judgment or discussion occurs during this activity. The quality of each idea will be developed in the next phase, from the quantity generated in this phase.

There are two keys to successful speculation: first, the purpose of this phase is not to conceive ways to design a product or service, but to develop ways to perform the functions selected for study. Secondly, creativity is a mental process in which past experience is combined and recombined to form new combinations. The purpose is to create new combinations which will perform the desired function at less total cost and improved performance than was previously attainable.

There are numerous well-accepted idea generation techniques. The guiding principle in all of them is that judgment/evaluation is suspended. Free flow of thoughts and ideas—without criticism—is required.

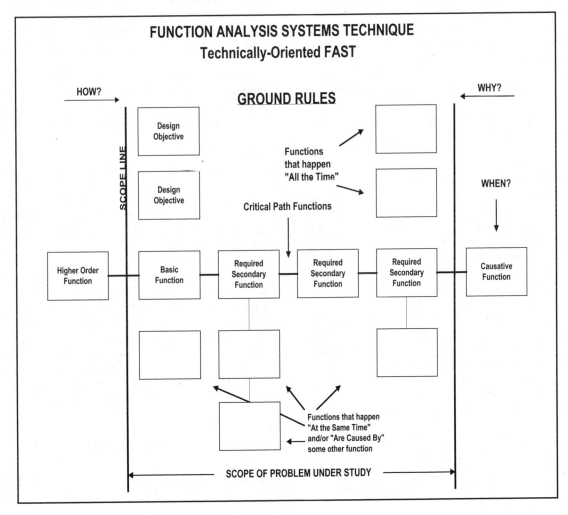

Figure 24.1—FAST Diagram Example (other examples are found at SAVE International's Web site www.value-eng.org

d. **Evaluation Phase**—The objectives of the evaluation phase are to synthesize ideas and concepts generated in the creative phase and to select feasible ideas for development into specific value improvement.

Using the evaluation criteria established during the pre-study effort, ideas are sorted and rated as to how well they meet those criteria. The process typically involves several steps:

1. Eliminate nonsense or "thought-provoker" ideas.
2. Group similar ideas by category within long-term and short-term implications. Examples of groupings are electrical, mechanical, structural, materials, special processes, etc.
3. Have one team member agree to "champion" each idea during further discussions and evaluations. If no team member so volunteers, the idea or concept is dropped.
4. List the advantages and disadvantages of each idea.
5. Rank the ideas within each category according to the prioritized evaluation criteria using such techniques as indexing, numerical evaluation, and team consensus.
6. If competing combinations still exist, use matrix analysis to rank mutually exclusive ideas satisfying the same function.
7. Select ideas for development of value improvement.

If none of the final combinations appear to satisfactorily meet the criteria, the value study team returns to the creative phase.

e. **Development Phase**—The objective of the development phase is to select and prepare the "best" alternative(s) for improving value. The data package prepared by the champion of each of the alternatives should provide as much technical, cost, and schedule information as is practical, so the designer and project sponsor(s) may make an initial assessment concerning their feasibility for implementation. The following steps are included:

1. Beginning with the highest ranked value alternatives, develop a benefit analysis and implementation requirements, including estimated initial costs, life cycle costs, and implementation costs, taking into account risk and uncertainty.
2. Conduct performance benefit analysis.
3. Compile technical data package for each proposed alternative.
4. Write descriptions of original design and proposed alternative(s).
5. Include sketches of original design and proposed alternative(s).
6. Calculate cost and performance data, clearly showing the differences between the original design and pro-

posed alternative(s).
7. Provide technical back-up data, such as information sources, calculations, and literature.
8. Assess Schedule impact.
9. Prepare an implementation plan, including a proposed schedule of all implementation activities, team assignments, and management requirements.
10. Complete recommendations, including any unique conditions to the project under study, such as emerging technology, political concerns, impact on other ongoing projects, marketing plans, etc.

f. **Presentation Phase**—The objective of the presentation phase is to obtain concurrence and a commitment from the designer, project sponsor, and other management to proceed with implementation of the recommendations. This involves an initial oral presentation followed by a complete written report.

As the last task within a value study, the VM study team presents its recommendations to the decision making body. Through the presentation and its interactive discussions, the team obtains either approval to proceed with implementation, or direction for additional information needed.

The written report documents the alternatives proposed with supporting data and confirms the implementation plan accepted by management. Specific organization of the report is unique to each study and organization requirements.

POST STUDY

The objective during post-study activities is to assure the implementation of the approved value study change recommendations. Assignments are made either to individuals within the VM study team, or by management to other individuals, to complete the tasks associated with the approved implementation plan.

While the VM team leader may track the progress of implementation, in all cases the design professional is responsible for the implementation. Each alternative must be independently designed and confirmed, including contractual changes if required, before its implementation into the product, project, process or procedure. Further, it is recommended that appropriate financial departments (accounting, auditing, etc.) conduct a post audit to verify to management the full benefits resulting from the value methodology study.

SUMMARY

In conclusion, value analysis is an important part of competing in today's marketplace. The value improvement process takes shape by following the SAVE International recommended job plan, consisting of information, function analysis, creative, evaluation, development, and presentation/reporting.

The main benefit from conducting such VA studies on a program, project, product, process, system, or technique is that the managers of value improvement programs have a valuable tool in value analysis for managing the value objectives for which they have control and are expected to produce. The managers' goals are to produce the best product with the greatest amount of value improvement in the timeframe, allowed and within or under budget according to the customer's expectations. VA is only one effective tool to help the manager meet and exceed the project goals. Side benefits from conducting the study are numerous, including better team relations and better project identification and understanding of the customer's goals, as well as more improved group dynamics and cohesiveness focused on managing value objectives.

REFERENCES

1. Dell'Isola, Alphonse J. 1988. *Value Engineering in the Construction Industry*. Construction Publishing Co. Van Nostrand Reinhold Co.
2. Miles, Lawrence D. *Techniques of Value Analysis and Engineering*. Eleanor Miles Walker (publisher).
3. SAVE International Web site. www.value-eng.org.
4. Younker, Del L. *Value Engineering, Analysis and Methodology*. New York: Marcel Dekker, Inc.

Chapter 25

Contracting for Capital Projects

James G. Zack, Jr.

INTRODUCTION

The purpose of this chapter is to discuss the elements of a contract, various contracting arrangements, changes to contracts, and disputes arising under contracts. Cost management is an integral part of good contract administration. Thus, practicing cost professionals must learn fundamentals of contracts in order to fulfill their role properly.

LEARNING OBJECTIVES

After completing this chapter, readers should be able to

- understand the basic requirements of a contract;
- understand how contracts may become defective and, possibly, unenforceable;
- understand the types of contracts typically employed in capital projects, their requirements, and the potential advantages and disadvantages of each;
- understand typical project delivery methods and how contracts are employed in each method;
- understand various key clauses in contracts;
- understand what sorts of claims may arise on contracts for capital projects; and
- understand how disputes arising under contracts may be resolved.

DEFINITION OF CONTRACT

A contract is simply an agreement between two or more persons that is enforceable at law. It is a business agreement (as opposed to a social transaction), whereby one party agrees to perform work or services for the other party for some consideration. Depending upon the nature of the business to be transacted and the jurisdiction in which the work or services are to be performed, contracts may be either written or oral. That is, in some jurisdictions certain types of contracts must be in writing, otherwise they are not enforceable (for example, in California all contracts for sales of property must be in writing by statute).

The difference between a contract and an agreement is the element of legal enforceability. Whenever two parties have a meeting of the minds on a subject, there exists an agreement. It is only when the two parties agree and intend to be legally obligated to perform to the terms and conditions of an agreement, does a contract arise.

REQUIREMENTS OF A CONTRACT

Regardless of the type of contract or the nature of the contractual arrangements, to be enforceable, the following basic elements of contract formation must be met:

- **Offer**—To be enforceable, there must be a clear, unequivocal offer to perform the work or services by one party. The offer to perform must be definite, seriously intended and communicated to the other party.

- **Acceptance**—Once an offer has been clearly communicated to a party, and that party, or someone authorized to act on their behalf, accepts the offer, a contract can be formed. As with the offer, the acceptance must be communicated to the party making the offer. Counteroffers do not constitute acceptance. If a party receives an offer and agrees to accept the offer with a condition not included in the original offer, this is a rejection of the original offer and a counteroffer. In such a case, the offer has not been accepted and no contract exists. Of course, the party receiving the counteroffer may accept the counteroffer and thus form a contract.

- **Legality of Purpose**—To be an enforceable contract, the work or service to be performed must involve legal activities. For example, a contract to design and construct a laboratory to manufacture illegal drugs is likely to be considered unenforceable, even if it's in writing and meets all other conditions.

- **Competent Parties**—In order to have an enforceable contract, all parties to the contract must be competent – that is, possess the legal and mental capacity to form a contract. Typically contracts with minors, insane individuals, intoxicated persons, convicts (in some states in the U.S.) and enemy aliens are not legally binding. These are, however, fairly rare situations. What is more common is the issue of whether both parties executing a contract have the legal authority to do so. In private contracts, the person asking for an offer is presumed to have the legal authority to contract (apparent authority). A party dealing with such an individual has the legal right to assume authority and competency to contract on the part of that individual. In public contract, however, the risk is shifted by statute to the party making the offer. That is, there is no apparent authority doctrine applicable to public contracts. The party making the offer has an affirmative obligation to determine whether the public official asking for the offer has the authority to execute a contract and legally bind their public agency to the terms and conditions of the contract.

- **Consideration**—Courts will enforce contracts only when there is consideration. Consideration is another differentiating factor between mere agreements and contracts. Consideration, under the law, is whatever one party demands and receives in exchange for the work or services performed. Typically, of course, consideration for most contracts is monetary in nature. That is, "We will design and construct the specified processing facility for $205,000,000." However, consideration may be anything the receiving party perceives as having sufficient value to warrant performing the work or services offered.

MISTAKES THAT MAKE CONTRACTS DEFECTIVE

Despite all of the above, certain mistakes may occur during the contract formation stage that will render a contract unenforceable. These mistakes include the following:

- **Mistakes as to the Nature of the Transaction**—A mistake as to the nature of the transaction will render a contract void if the mistake was brought about by fraud by one of the contracting parties (e.g., express misrepresentation or concealment of material facts). For example, if the parties agree to the design and construction of a facility at a specific location, and it turns out that the property is not zoned for such a facility, then a mistake as to the transaction has arisen. However, to raise this defense, the party asserting fraud must demonstrate that they, themselves, were not negligent during contract formation (e.g., never read the terms and conditions of the contract).

- **Mistakes as to the Identity of a Party**—Freedom to contract brings with it the right to refuse to contract with some parties. The law cannot compel any party to contract with another party they have chosen not to do business with. If one party is mistaken as to the identity of the party they are contracting with, then the contract is unenforceable. It is, however, incumbent upon contracting parties to perform some due diligence during the contract formation stage to determine who they are dealing with and deciding whether they will, in fact, execute a contract.

- **Mutual Mistakes as to the Identity of the Subject Matter**—Unlike the mistakes set forth above (which were unilateral mistakes or mistakes on the part of only one party), mistakes as to the identity of the subject matter must be mutual—made by both parties. For example, a party may plan to design, construct, and operate two similar facilities in two different locations. During the bidding process, engineering drawings may be inadvertently switched such that drawings for facility A may be substituted for those of facility B, a location at which facility A cannot be constructed. Any contract arising under these circumstances will be unenforceable.

- **Mutual Mistakes as to the Existence of the Subject Matter**—If two parties contract for the remodeling of an existing facility but, unknown to either party, the facility is destroyed by fire, the contract is unenforceable.

MISTAKES THAT DO NOT MAKE CONTRACTS DEFECTIVE

There are other mistakes, again arising during the contract formation stage, which do not make the contract unenforceable. These include the following:

- **Mistakes as to Value, Quality, or Price**—A contract is not rendered unenforceable simply because one of the parties was mistaken about value, quality, or price of the contract. If a contract clearly requires full compliance with a particular building code, for example, and one of the parties is not knowledgeable of the requirements or expense involved with conforming to such code, this type of mistake does not render the contract unenforceable.

- **Mistakes as to the Terms of the Contract**—Mistakes such as this typically result from a failure to read the terms and conditions of the contract or a failure to understand the meaning of the provisions of the contract. For example, a party, after contract execution, learns that they are required to provide weekly project schedules (at a cost of $1,000,000 over the life of the contract). That party's failure to understand the requirement at the time of contract execution or include the cost in their bid will not excuse them from compliance nor render the contract unenforceable.

OTHER FACTORS EFFECTING CONTRACT ENFORCEABILITY

Depending upon the nature and type of contract and the jurisdiction (location) where the work is to be performed, there may statutory or regulatory provisions applicable to contracts, the effect of which may determine the enforceability of a contract. For example, in many states in the U.S., to be a legally enforceable construction contract, the contractor must possess a valid contractor's license at the time the contract is executed and throughout the entire duration of the project. Failure to do so may render the contract unenforceable and compensation otherwise owed unrecoverable. Likewise, to enforce design contracts, in some states, a design professional may be required to possess a valid professional registration in the state where the project is to take place.

Other jurisdictions may have other statutory or regulatory requirements that must be complied with fully in order to have an enforceable contract. It is, therefore, incumbent upon contracting parties to be fully aware of the laws affecting various types of contracts in the jurisdiction where the work is to be performed. To quote John Selden, "Ignorance of the law excuses no man; not that all men know the law, because 'tis an excuse every man will plead, and no man can tell how to confute him."

PARTIES TO A CONTRACT

As described above, there must be a minimum of two parties in a contractual arrangement. The first, for the purposes of this chapter, will be referred to as the owner. The owner is the party who wants a capital project completed (i.e., design and construction of a petrochemical processing facility, airport, bridge, aircraft, missile, power plant, etc.). The owner is typically the party issuing the invitation to bid (ITB) or request for proposal (RFP)—that is, asking other parties to make offers to perform the project. The second party will be referred to in this chapter as the contractor. The contractor is the party offering to perform the work or service the owner is seeking. The contractor may be an architect or engineer (A/E) who offers to perform design and design related services. The contractor may be a constructor who offers to physically build the facility or a manufacturer who offers to fabricate the items requested.

That is the simplest form of contracting. Contracting may, however, be considerably more complex and may involve many more parties. The owner may be a consortium of individual companies who have joined together as an operating entity, or the owner may be a subsidiary or special purpose entity established by a parent company for the purposes of accomplishing this project. Contractors may also act in consortiums, joint ventures, prime contract arrangements with multiple subcontractors, etc.

Due to the potential complexity of parties to contracts, to avoid any possibility of mistake as to the identity of a contracting party, contracting parties have an obligation to perform some due diligence to determine everyone involved and decide whether they want to contract with the other parties. Failure to perform some level of due diligence may put one of the contracting parties at risk.

WHY HAVE WRITTEN CONTRACTS?

In some cases, a written contract is a legal requirement of the jurisdiction in which the project is being performed. Such a legal requirement is typically found in a state's statute of frauds, wherein specific types of contracts must be in writing in order to be enforceable (i.e., sales of property, contracts of more than one year's duration, etc.). In more general terms, however, a written contract is necessary to record the conditions of the contract, the commercial terms and pricing arrangements, the scope of work to be performed and other necessary project execution provisions. That is, the contract sets forth the duties, obligations, and responsibilities of the parties involved as well as the commercial terms and conditions under which the project is to be performed.

In the event of a disagreement during the performance of the work, the parties must be able to look to a written document to determine what is, and what is not, required of each party to the contract. And, if the disagreement grows into a legal dispute, then the trier of fact (an arbitrator, judge or jury) should have a written document framing the original agreement of the parties in order to render a decision on the dispute.

CONTENTS OF A CONTRACT

The term *contract* is typically a defined term in most contracts. That is, in the definitions section of a contract, the term

---

GLOSSARY TERMS IN THIS CHAPTER

contract completion date ◆ contract documents
direct cost ◆ indirect cost ◆ scope

---

is defined to include, generally, the following:

- invitation to bid or request for proposal,
- instructions to bidders,
- addenda issued during the bid period,
- bid or proposal,
- contract,
- bonds,
- general conditions,
- special or supplemental conditions,
- scope of work (plans, drawings, specifications, special provisions, etc.), and
- change orders or contract modifications.

In some contracts (generally engineering and construction contracts) other items that may be included in the definition of the term *contract* include the following:

- permits,
- operating licenses,
- environmental agreements,
- codes,
- geotechnical or subsurface conditions reports, and
- other technical requirements incorporated by reference.

It is important for the contracting parties to define the term *contract* carefully at the outset so everyone involved in the project clearly understands what documents make up the contract. Poor definition of this term often leads to disputes.

SCOPE OF WORK

Perhaps the most critical part of a contract is the scope of work. This is most often referred to as the "technical requirements" of the contract. The work scope should define, in fairly precise terms, what work is to be accomplished by which party, when, and to what level of quality. Disagreement over what is in or out of scope is one of the most frequent causes of disputes. The number of disputes, typically, is in inverse proportion to the amount of time spent defining, negotiating and recording the scope of work. That is, the more time and effort spent on defining and understanding the scope of work, the lower the number of disputes over work scope.

While contract form, contractual terms and conditions, and commercial arrangements are frequently "off the shelf items" and often not subject to a great deal of negotiation, the scope of work is almost always individually crafted and often subject to a great deal of negotiation. Even in public contracting (the hard dollar, low bid form of contracting) plans, specifications and technical requirements of the contract are individually drafted. Thus, the more time and effort expended on defining scope clearly and properly, the less likely it is that a scope dispute will arise. Proper scope definition requires that the

project owners clearly determine and articulate their needs prior to or during the drafting of the scope of work. Owners who do not make up their own minds on what it is they want are much more likely to face multiple changes during the construction or fabrication of the project. Such "scope creep," in turn, often leads to cost overruns and later disputes.

UNIFORM COMMERCIAL CODE (UCC) CONTRACTS

Every state in the U.S. has adopted the uniform commercial code (UCC) in one form or another. The UCC is intended to be a common set of legal principles governing the sale of goods. In capital projects, the UCC rarely applies to the prime contract between the owner and the contractor since the transaction in this contract deals with a capital project. However, procurement of materials or equipment, for example, either by the owner or the contractor on a capital project is likely to be subject to the terms of the UCC in the state where the capital project is to take place. While it is beyond the scope of this chapter to discuss the UCC in any detail at all (especially since the UCC differs to some extent in every state), the reader is cautioned that contracts for goods (materials or equipment) may be subject to this statute. In such situations, the reader would be well advised obtain appropriate legal information on the application of the UCC to the transaction the reader is involved with.

TYPES OF CONTRACTS

Generally, there are four basic types of contracts (with an almost unimaginable number of variations) used on capital projects. The basic types of contracts are the following.

Fixed-Price/Lump-Sum Contracts

Under this contractual arrangement, the scope of work is well defined, the contracting risks are clearly identified, the price is fixed, and the time of performance is typically also fixed. The contractor is generally free to select their own means and methods to perform the work provided that the final result conforms to the technical, quality, and cost requirements of the contract. This results from the fact that under a fixed-price contract, the contractor assumes risk for the fixed price. That is, if the bidding documents are accurate but the fixed price too low, it is the contractor who suffers the penalty. To balance this out somewhat, contractors are most often allowed the freedom to select their own means and method of performing the work. Some variations of lump-sum, fixed-price contracts follow:

- **Fixed Price with Economic Adjustment**—Under this form of contract, some portions of the fixed price may be adjustable under certain conditions. For example, if the price of asphalt, copper tubing, computer chips, electronic boards, etc. increases or decreases more than 15 percent from the bid price, payment for the specified item(s) will be adjusted in accordance with the terms and conditions of the economic price adjustment clause of the contract.

- **Fixed Price with Incentives**—In this variation, while the base price of the contract itself is fixed, certain incentive clauses may be inserted into the contract related to time, cost savings, project performance, etc. For example, the contractor may be entitled to additional payment for every day the project is completed prior to the contract completion date. Or, a contractor may be entitled to keep fifty percent of costs saved on a completed project when such costs are compared with the original budget. The concept is to provide an economic incentive for the contractor to meet or exceed certain baseline objectives.

Fixed-Price/Unit-Price Contracts

This is another form of a fixed-price contract. The distinction between this contract form and the lump sum form discussed above is that the price is fixed for each unit of work rather than the entire scope of work—thus the name, unit price. The total value of the contract is a function of the number of units fabricated, delivered, installed, etc. Similar to the lump-sum form of contract, a unit-price contract may also be incentivized. Unit-priced contracts generally also contain a quantity variation clause to the effect that if any of the unit quantities vary by +/- 15 percent, say, from the estimated quantities, then the unit price is subject to adjustment on that portion of the work. The risk of changes to units provided is, therefore, shared between the owner and the contractor under such a clause. Since the total quantity of units may not be known at the outset of the contract, the final cost of the contract is generally subject to adjustment once the final quantity is known at the end of the contract.

Cost Reimbursable Contracts

As opposed to fixed-price contracts, cost reimbursable contracts are not fixed. Rather, the essence of a cost reimbursable contract is the contractor is paid for their legitimate actual cost incurred in performing the work plus a stipulated amount for profit. Such a contract is often referred to as a cost plus fixed fee (CPFF) contract or a time and material (T&M) contract. Costs are ordinarily classified as either direct or indirect costs under such contracts.

- **Direct Costs**—These are costs incurred for the direct and sole benefit of the project and can be associated directly with work scope items or activities under the contract (such as labor, materials, equipment, subcontractors, or subconsultants, consumables, etc.).

- **Indirect Costs (Overhead Costs)**—These are associated with the management of the work (field overhead or general conditions costs), which cannot be allocated to specific items of work or costs allocated by the contract-

ing organization's headquarters (i.e., salaries of corporate executives) as a cost of doing business (home office overhead). Home office overhead costs are usually calculated as a percentage of direct costs.

Cost reimbursable contracts may also be incentivized for meeting or exceeding selected project objectives—time or costs, for example. Incentivizing, in capital projects, typically takes the form of the owner offering to pay additional money to the contractor in the event of early delivery of the project, underruns on the budget, performance of the completed project above specified standards, etc. Such contracts are often referred to as cost plus incentive fee (CPIF) contracts.

Target Contracts

Target contracts are generally intended to provide an economic inducement to the contractor to entice completion of work at the lowest possible cost and least amount of time. Often, the contractor will perform the early part of the work (i.e., planning and design) on a cost reimbursable basis. At some point, the contractor will prepare and negotiate with the owne, a detailed estimate with not-to-exceed cost and time of performance. Once agreement on time and cost is reached, these become the contractor's targets. (Such contracts are also referred to as guaranteed maximum price [GMP] contracts.) At the end of the work the contractor's actual costs are compared to target cost and underruns, if any, are shared between the owner and the contractor on whatever basis the contract stipulates. Overruns, unless caused by owner intervention or other excusable events set forth in the contract, are generally assessed to the contractor. Similarly, a comparison of targeted versus actual schedule is made and early completion bonuses are often paid to the contractor for beating the target schedule.

REQUIREMENTS, ADVANTAGES, AND DISADVANTAGES OF CONTRACT TYPES

The following list of requirements, advantages and disadvantages for each of the contract types has been extracted from Chapter 19, "Contract Packages—Contracting Arrangements," by James A. Bent, CCC, from AACE International's *Skills & Knowledge of Cost Engineering*, 4th Edition.

Fixed-Price/Lump-Sum Contracts

In this type of contract, the contractor is generally free to employ whatever methods and resources it chooses in order to complete the work. The contractor carries total responsibility for proper performance of the work, although approv[al] of design drawings and the placement of purchase o[rders] and subcontracts can be monitored by the owner to [ensure] compliance with specifications. The work to be p[erformed] must be closely defined. Since the contractor will [not perform] unspecified work without requiring addition[al] fully developed specification is vitally important. The work has to be done within a specified period of time, and the owner can monitor status/progress to ensure that completion meets the contractual requirements.

The lump-sum/fixed-price contract presents a low financial risk for to the owner, and the required investment level can be established at an early date. This type of contract allows a higher return to the contractor for superior performance. A good design definition is essential, even though this may be time consuming. Further, the bidding time can be twice as long as that for a reimbursable contract bid. For contractors, the cost of bidding and the high financial risk are factors in determining the lump sum approach.

Requirements

- good definition (of work scope) and stable project conditions;
- effective competition in a buyer's market;
- several months for bidding and appraisal; and,
- minimum scope changes.

Advantages

- low financial risk to owner since maximum risk is on the contractor;
- cost and project viability are known before a commitment is made;
- minimal owner supervision—mostly quality assurance and schedule monitoring;
- contractor will usually assign its best personnel to the work;
- maximum financial motivation of contractor—maximum incentive for the contractor to achieve early completion at superior performance levels;
- contractor has to solve its own problems and do so quickly; and,
- contractor selection by competitive bidding is fairly easy, apart from the deliberate low price.

Disadvantages

- variations (changes) are difficult and costly—the contractor, having quoted keenly when bidding, will try to make as much as possible on extras;
- an early start is not possible because of the time taken for and for developing a good design basis;
- choose the cheapest and hnical monitoring and vner essential (schedule
- interest in completing the a damage to local union ings as setting poor prece-

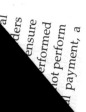

- bidding is expensive for the contractor, so the bid invitation list will be short (technical appraisal of bids by the owner may require considerable effort);
- contractors will usually include allowances for contingencies in the bid price and they might be high; and,
- bidding time can be twice that required for other types of contracts.

Fixed-Price/Unit-Price Contracts

These require sufficient design definition or experience in order to estimate the unit/quantities for the work. Contractors then bid fixed prices for each unit of work. The time and cost risk is shared, with the owner responsible for total quantities, and the contractor assumes the risk of a fixed unit price. A quantity increase greater than 10 percent can lead to increases in unit prices.

Requirements

- an adequate breakdown and definition of the measured units of work;
- a good quantity surveying/reporting system;
- adequate drawings and/or substantial experience for developing the bill of quantities;
- financial/payment terms that are properly tied to the measured work and to partial completion of work;
- owner-supplied drawings and materials must arrive on time;
- quantity sensitivity analysis of unit prices to evaluate total bid price for potential quantity variations;
- ability to detect biased bidding and/or front end loading; and,
- Contractor experience with this contracting arrangement.

Advantages

- good design definition is not essential—typical drawings can be used for the bidding process;
- very suitable for competitive bidding and relatively easy contractor selection subject to sensitivity evaluation;
- bidding is speedy and inexpensive, and an early start is possible; and,
- flexibility—depending on the contract conditions, the scope and quantity of work can be varied.

Disadvantages

- final cost is not known at the outset, since the bills of quantities have been estimated on incomplete engineering;
- additional site staff are needed to measure, control, and report on the cost and the status of the work; and,
- Biased bidding and front end loading may not be detected.

Cost Reimbursable Contracts

These require little design definition, but need to be drawn in a way that allows expenditures to be properly controlled.

The major advantage of a reimbursable cost contract is time, since a contract can be established during the early stages of a project. This type of contract presents a disadvantage to an owner, however, since poor performance by the contractor can result in increased costs and because final costs are the owner's responsibility. Further, the final or total investment level is not known until the work is well advanced.

Reimbursable cost contracts can contain lump-sum elements, such as the contractor's overhead charges and profit, which is usually preferable to calculating these costs on a percentage basis. Reimbursements may be applied to such items as salaries, wages, insurance and pension contributions, office rentals, and communication costs. Alternatively, reimbursement can be applied to all-inclusive hourly or daily rates for time spent by engineers on the basis that all office support costs are built into these rates. This form of contract is generally known as a fixed-fee or reimbursable-cost contract, and can be used for both engineering and other office services as well as for construction work.

Such arrangements give the owner greater control over the contractor's engineering work, but reducing the lump sum content of the contractor's remuneration also reduces its financial incentive to complete the work economically and speedily. Further, it lessens the owner's ability to compare and evaluate competitive bids, since only a small percentage of the project cost is involved. Finally, it is possible that the "best" contractor may not quote the lowest price.

Requirements

- a competent and trustworthy contractor;
- close quality supervision and direction by the owner; and,
- detailed definition of work and payment terms covered by lump sums and by all-inclusive rates.

Advantages

- flexibility in dealing with changes (which is very important when the job is not well defined), particularly if new technology development is proceeding concurrently with the design;
- an early start can be made;
- useful where site problems such as trade union actions like delays or disruptions may be encountered; and,
- owner can control all aspects of the work.

Disadvantages

- final cost is unknown;
- difficulties in evaluating proposals—strict comparison of the amount quoted may not result in selecting the "best" contractor or in achieving the lowest project cost;
- contractor has little incentive for early completion or cost

economy;
- contractor may assign its "second division" personnel to the job, make excessive use of agency personnel, or use the job as a training vehicle for new personnel;
- owner carries most of the risks and faces the difficult decisions; and,
- biased bidding of fixed fees and reimbursable rates may not be detected.

Target Contracts

Target contracts are intended to provide strong financial incentive for the contractor to complete the work at minimum cost and within minimum time. In the usual arrangement, the contractor starts work on a reimbursable cost basis. When sufficient design is complete, the contractor produces a definitive estimate and project schedule for owner review, mutual negotiation, and agreement. After agreement is reached, these become targets. At the end of the job, the contractor's reimbursable costs are compared with the target and any saving or overrun is shared between the owner and the contractor on a prearranged basis. Similarly, the contractor qualifies for additional payment if it completes the work ahead of the agreed upon schedule. The main appeal this form of contract has to the contractor is that it does not involve competitive bidding for the target costs and schedule provisions.

Requirements

- a competent and trustworthy contractor;
- quality technical and financial supervision by the owner; and,
- competent estimating ability by the owner.

Advantages

- flexibility in controlling the work;
- almost immediate start on the work, even without a scope definition;
- encourages economic and speedy completion (up to a point); and,
- contractor is rewarded for superior performance.

Disadvantages

- final cost initially unknown;
- no opportunity to competitively bid the targets;
- difficulty in agreeing on an effective target for superior performance;
- variations are difficult and costly once the target has been established—contractors tend to inflate the costs of all variations to increase profit potential with easy targets; and,
- If the contractor fails to achieve the targets, it may attempt to prove that this was due to owner interference or to factors outside the contractor's control; hence, effective control and reporting are essential.

Summary of Risks by Contract Type

Figure 25.1 depicts the allocation of risk between owners and contractors under the types of contracts discussed above.

PROJECT DELIVERY METHODS AND RESULTING CONTRACTING ARRANGEMENTS

Project Delivery Methods

Contracting arrangements between a project owner, the architect/engineer (A/E) and the contractor are substantially influenced by the project delivery system chosen which, in turn, is frequently driven by the time available in which to accomplish a project. That is, some project delivery systems are inherently faster than others, and as owners perceive the time available to deliver a project shortening, they are more likely to choose some project delivery methods over others.

Design-Bid-Build Method—First, some comments concerning project delivery method. In most industries, there are three general project delivery methods applicable to almost all projects. The first and perhaps, most common, is known as the design-bid-build method. This methodology is depicted in Figure 25.2 .

The fundamental concept involved in the project delivery method is that the project is fully designed prior to the time the contractor is employed. Owners who employ a lump-sum, fixed-fee or a lump-sum, unit-price contracts as the contracting vehicle, frequently opt for the design-bid-build project delivery method in order to get some assurance that the total project cost is a known quantity prior to the start of construction.

Design-Build Method—The other project delivery method used on many projects is generally referred to as the design-build method. This project delivery method is also referred to by many other names, including the engineer-procure-construct (EPC), fast track, flash track, or turnkey methods. This delivery method is depicted in Figure 25.3.

The essence of this project delivery method is to shorten the timeframe between the planning and the construction process, thus allowing for a faster project delivery. Since the same team that designs the project will construct the project, then construction can start prior to the completion of the design as the owner is not at risk for coordination between the designer and the contractor. This method also eliminates the need for the bid/award phase of the contract, again shortening the timeframe for project delivery. Of course, the total project cost is not known to the owner at the time the design/build team is selected and may not be known for sometime after.

Indefinite Quantity Contract Method—The third project delivery method is generally referred to as the indefinite quantity ccontract method. This project delivery method has also been referred to as **Task Order Contracting,** or **Job Order Contracting.** The method is depicted in Figure 25.4.

This project delivery method is typically utilized on repetitive, non-capital projects, such as routine repair and maintenance projects. Under this method, the owner and contractor establish set prices up-front for labor, equipment, markups, etc. As a result, the

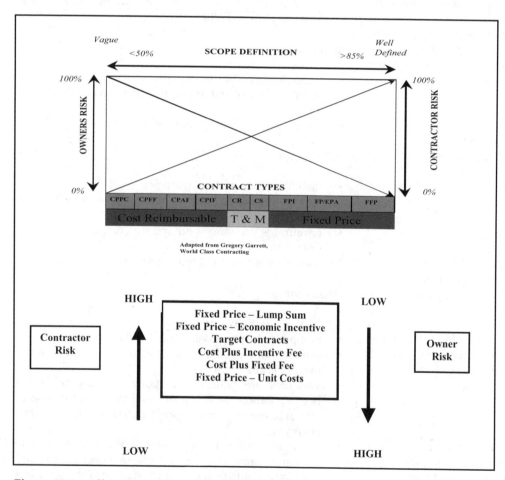

Figure 25.1—Allocation of Risk Between Owners and Contractors

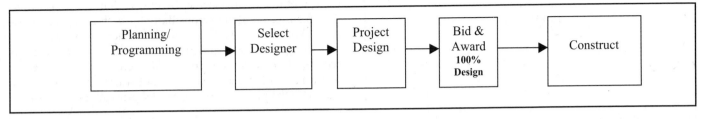

Figure 25.2—Design-Bid-Build Method

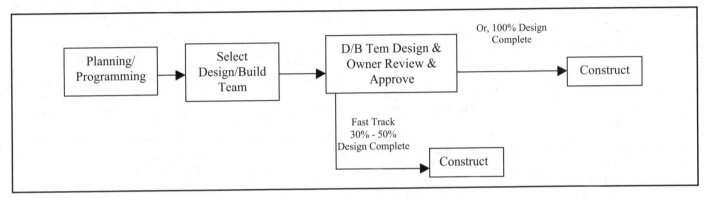

Figure 25.3—Design-Build Method

scope of each work assignment does not need to be fully known prior to commencing work. Since work is performed on a set price basis, scope can be developed as work proceeds. Accordingly, project delivery time can be significantly shortened once the contractor is selected and terms negotiated because there is no need to design and bid subsequent work.

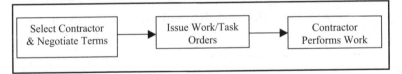

Figure 25.4—Indefinite Quantity Contract Method

While there are some variations of these three project delivery methods, the above three generically describe the most common project delivery methods.

Contracting Arrangements

As with project delivery methods, there are five basic contracting forms or arrangements used in most industries to develop and deliver projects. Not addressed in this chapter is whether the owner staffs project with internal staff personnel or hires outside personnel to perform such functions.

Single Prime Contractor—The first arrangement is referred to most often as single prime contractor and is most often used with the design-bid-build project delivery method.

Under this arrangement, the owner first contracts with a design professional to perform the requisite planning and design work. Once design is complete, the owner then contracts with a single contractor to deliver the project. All procurement and subcontracts are with the single prime contract, thus insulating the owner, to a limited extent, from claims or disputes arising from vendors, suppliers and/or subcontractors. The arrangement is depicted in Figure 25.5.

In this contracting arrangement, the owner has a single relationship for project design and a separate, single contractual relationship for construction or project delivery. The owner's liability exposure for coordination is substantially reduced under this arrangement.

Multiple Prime or Independent Prime—The second basic contracting arrangement is most often referred to as the multiple prime or independent prime contractors arrangement. Under this contracting model, the owner still retains a design professional as the single point of responsibility for planning and design of the project. However, the owner then issues a series of contracts to several prime contractors. The multiple prime contracting arrangement may be organized by craft or trade (i.e., civil/structural, mechanical, electrical contracts) or may be organized by project phase (i.e., site grading, prep and utilities; building A, Building B, Parking Structure, etc.). In either event, the concept is that project delivery can be

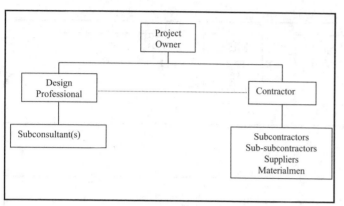

Figure 25.5—Single Prime Contractor Arrangement

build method are to shorten the project delivery time and to have a single point of responsibility for both design and project execution. A variation of the typical design-build contract is a turnkey contract. A turnkey contract is a design-build contract, but most often is more comprehensive in its scope of work. For example, in a turnkey contract, the contractor may purchase the property for the capital project, may finance the contract, etc.

Agency Construction Management—The fourth generic contracting arrangement is often referred to as the agency construction management contract approach. This contractual arrangement is also referred to as project management or program management contracting. In this arrangement, the owner still maintains a direct contractual relationship with both the design professional and the contractor, but also retains the services of an independent construction manager to coordinate between the two other entities and oversee activities of the others. The construction manager is often

sped up by allowing construction to begin prior to completion of the full design. This contracting arrangement is depicted in Figure 25.6.

While this arrangement allows the owner to get to construction more quickly than the arrangement outlined above, this arrangement puts the owner at risk for coordination problems arising between the independent prime contractors. There is no contractual relationship between the independent prime contractors. There is, however, a relationship between each contractor and the owner. Thus, any conflicts, delays or coordination problems between the multiple prime contractors may become claims to the owner.

Design-Build—The third basic contracting arrangement is the design-build contracting arrangement Refer to the previous discussion of this project delivery method. The design-build contracting arrangement is depicted in Figure 25.7.

As noted previously, the concepts underlying the design-

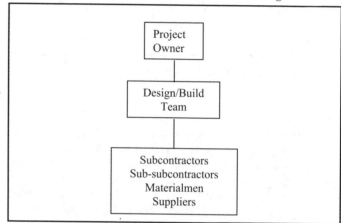

Figure 25.7—Design-Build Contractor Arrangement

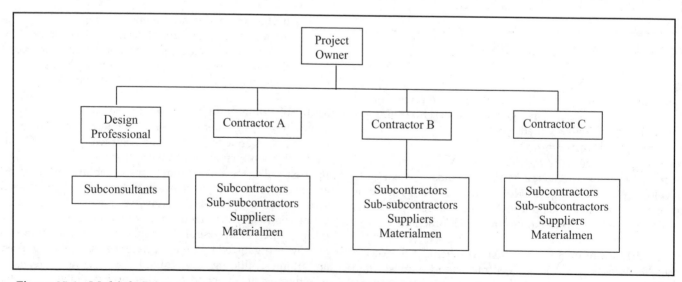

Figure 25.6—Multiple Prime or Independent Prime Contractors Arrangement

granted the authority of a limited agent of the owner. That is, they have been vested with contractual authority ot take certain actions in the name of the owner, and the owner will be bound by such actions. Other actions, however, may be reserved exclusively to the owner and its staff. This contractual arrangement is depicted in Figure 25.8.

Construction Manager at Risk—The final generic contracting arrangement is most often called the construction manager at risk model. This contractual model employs the construction manager, project manager, or program manager in lieu of a general contractor. Thus, the owner maintains a direct relationship with the design professional and a separate relationship with the construction manager. All trade contracts are then issued by the construction manager. In this manner, the owner provides for multiple prime contracting

require more than a simple low bid. Owners may find themselves in a position of having to prequalify contractors. This is especially true in situations where owners opt to utilize a design-build model and/or guaranteed maximum price or target contracts. Prequalification may be problematical for public works owners as many government procurement statutes call for award to the lowest, responsive, responsible bidder and are deliberately designed to encourage maximum public competition. Where owners have the legal ability to prequalify contractors prior to bidding, it is wise to do so. An owner benefits when there is some degree of assurance that all contractors submitting bids are qualified and capable of successfully performing.

The advantage to the contracting community is twofold. First, those bidders who are prequalified can be assured that they are bidding against relatively equal competitors and are not forced to compete against unqualified bidders who are less likely to understand the work and thus more likely to bid artificially low. The other advantage is to bidders deemed unqualified to bid. While such a decision will obviously be a disappointment, it saves the cost of bidding (which can be very high) and protects unqualified bidders from major mistakes in bidding work they are not truly qualified to perform, thus jeopardizing their financial ability to survive in business.

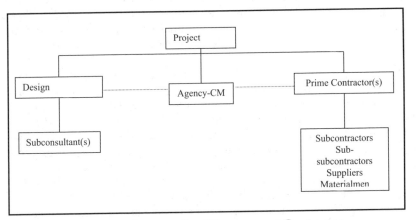

Figure 25.8—Agency Construction Management Contractor Arrangement

to speed up the project delivery cycle while at the same time, sheds some potential liability with respect to the multiple primes. The constrcution manager holds all trade contracts and the liability for the same. The construction manager typically executes a contract with a firmfixed price/lump sum or a guaranteed maximum price with the owner. The construction manager is able to take economic advantage of the difference between his/her contract value with the owner and the sum total of all contracts with trade contractors. This contractual agreement is depicted in Figure 25.9.

There are variations of each of the five generic contracting arrangement models set forth above. However, these five models generically address the majority of typical contracting arrangements.

Contractor Prequalification

As noted earlier, many forms of contract

If an owner chooses to prequalify contractors, an objective, rational system should be established such that all potential bidders can easily determine whether they are, in fact, qualified. Such objective measures may include the following:

- past experience on projects with similar size, complexity, and technical and schedule requirements;
- past experience with the design-build team proposed on

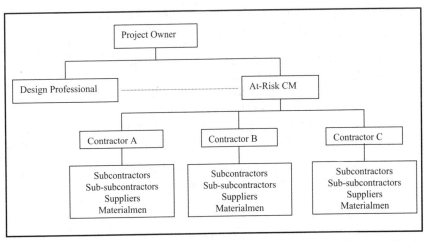

Figure 25.8—Agency Construction Management Contractor Arrangement

this project;
- current financial capability;
- safety ratings on past projects; and
- experienced project team, etc.

Some owners (particularly in the design-build arena) have held open competitions to prequalify potential contractors followed by preliminary design competitions among pre-qualified contractors (with limited remuneration for those invited to the design competition).

DECISION TO BID

Perhaps one of the toughest decisions in contracting is the bid/no bid decision that every contractor must make once an opportunity to bid on a project is identified. The contractor needs to carefully examine each potential bidding opportunity. Some of the factors the contractor must consider include the following:

- **Expertise**—When considering submitting a bid, a contractor has to determine whether its organization has the expertise to perform the work. A review of past projects will determine whether the contractor has done anything like this project in the past. If not, some thought should be given to whether they are truly capable of performing the work. In the alternative, a contractor might consider teaming with another through a joint venture, in order to assure sufficient expertise to perform the work and to spread the risk of the project.

- **Financial Capability**—A contractor considering a bid must look at insurance and bonding requirements, payment provisions, and potential project cash flow scenarios to determine if they have the necessary financial capability to perform the work and successfully complete the project.

- **Bonding Capacity**—Many capital projects require both performance and payment bonds to protect the interests of the owner in the event of contractor failure to complete the work or failure to pay subcontractors and vendors. In such cases, part of the contractor's decision to bid involves their bonding capacity. If a contractor has a bonding capacity of $100 million and already has $85 million in active projects underway, the contractor may not be able to bid a new $50 million capital project unless they can successfully convince their surety (bonding company) to increase their bonding coverage limits.

- **Personnel**—A contractor considering as bid must look to its own staffing to determine whether it has sufficient experienced personnel to perform the work during the period of anticipated performance.

- **Equipment**—If a project requires specialized equipment in order to perform the work, a potential bidder determine whether ther have or can acquire the equipment through purchase, lease, or rental arrangements.

- **Specialized Knowledge**—Along with all of the above, a potential bidder should review pre-bid information to determine whether their organization has the requisite skills and knowledge to successfully perform the work under the known terms and conditions.

- **Risk Analysis**—A contractor considering bidding on a potential project should review the general and supplemental or special provisions of the contract to determine how project risk is allocated under the contract. For example, if there is a no damage for delay clause in the contract, or if the contract has no differing site condition clause, then the contractor's risk if increased substantially in the event of delay or it encounters materially different conditions. This being the case, a potential bidder needs to determine if their company can survive if such situations occur during performance of the work.

- **Workload and Other Potential Projects**—Finally, a contractor considering bidding on a project needs to think about their current workload to see how that may impact equipment, key personnel, logistics, bonding and financial capabilities. Further, a contractor needs to consider what other projects are likely to be bid in the same timeframe that they may want to bid on. A potential problem faced by many contractors is multiple projects being bid at the same time. If a contractor bids on three projects simultaneously, serious consideration must be given to what happens if they are the successful bidder on all three projects. If this event occurs, can they perform?

KEY CONTRACT CLAUSES

In the administration of contracts, all clauses in the contact are important and must be adhered to to avoid breach of contract situations. However, some clauses are more important than others. Among the more important clauses, in alphabetical order, are the following:

- **Audit**—This clause typically outlines an owner's right to perform reviews (audits) of contractor costs or records. Such clauses ordinarily outline what costs or records are subject to audit, when, and under what circumstances.

- **Changes**—This clause is critical. This is the clause that allows the owner to direct changes to the work, including plans, specifications, time of performance, means, and methods. Absent a change clause, an owner is precluded from making changes to the work. Of particular importance in this clause is whether the clause allows the owner to unilaterally direct changes to the work (in which case, if the contractor refuses to comply with the directive, they are in breach of the contract). Alternatively, the clause may require the owner and the contractor to mutually agree on the change (a bilateral change).

- **Contractor Responsibilities**—This clause lays out, in general form, the duties, obligations and responsibilities of the contractor in performance of the work. This clause assigns specific risks to the contractor, including customarily the risk of adequate labor and equipment to accomplish the work within the required timeframe, the obligation to perform work safely, to perform work in strict accordance with the terms and conditions of the plans and specifications, and to be responsible for the work of subcontractors and suppliers; etc.

- **Delays**—This is, ordinarily, a risk allocation clause with respect to delays in the work. "Excusable delay" under a contract results in time extensions but no time related damages. That is, a contractor's performance time is extended because of an excusable delay situation, but the contractor is not entitled to collect time extension costs nor is the owner entitled to impose late completion damages for this time. "Compensable delay," on the other hand, results in both a time extension as well a time related damages. Customarily, owner-caused delay is excusable and compensable to the contractor while contractor caused delay is the responsibility of the contractor (to either make up the lost time or pay the contractually stipulated late completion damages). Third-party-caused delay (sometime referred to as force majeure delay) is, most often, excusable and noncompensable to the contractor.

- **Differing Site Conditions or Changed Conditions**—Another risk allocation clause, the differing site or changed conditions clause, routinely allocates risk of latent site conditions to the owner. The clause normally provides an equitable adjustment to the contract in the event the contractor encounters a materially different condition at the site during performance of the work.

- **Dispute Resolution**—This clause customarily sets forth the mechanism to resolve disputes during the performance of the work. Most dispute clauses contain some form of a stepped resolution system. For example, the clause may require on site negotiation between project managers, followed by an appeal to project executives, followed by 3 days of mediation, followed by binding arbitration under a formal set of rules. Often, the location (jurisdiction) of the disputes resolution will be set forth (i.e., arbitration hearings shall be held in New York City).

- **Force Majeure**—Some contracts contain a force majeure clause or a clause dealing with delays to the work caused by unforeseeable events beyond the control of both the owner and the contractor. Such clauses often provide lists of examples of force majeure events—acts of God, acts of the government, civil disorder, acts of war, adverse weather, fires, floods, strikes, etc. Other contracts provide for such events in the excusable delay clause.

- **Governing Law**—Many contracts involve parties from differing locations with subcontractors and suppliers from even more locations. Accordingly, contracts often specify which law applies to a dispute, regardless of where the dispute is handled. For example, a contract executed in Mississippi may specify that Texas law applies because the owner is a Texas corporation. The trier of fact (a judge or an arbitrator) is then bound by this contractual stipulation regardless of where the hearings are held.

- **Indemnification**—To indemnify another is to protect them against loss or damage either by paying for the loss or standing in their place in the event of a legal dispute. An indemnification clause in a contract typically requires a contractor to indemnify the owner against all loss resulting from contractor errors, omissions, accidents, third party property damage, etc.

- **Insurance**—Most contracts have lengthy and complicated clauses requiring owners and contractors to furnish multiple insurance policies prior to commencing work, among which are the following: builder's risk/all risk; workman's compensation; automobile, aircraft, and/or marine liability; general liability; bodily injury; broad form property damage; completed operations; personal injury; etc.

- **Late Completion Damages**—Since time is of the essence with most contracts, contracts often contain a clause specifying damages for late completion. In general terms, there are two types of late completion damages – actual and liquidated. Actual damages are those damages an owner actually suffers when a contract is completed late and may include loss of revenue, increased engineering, architectural or inspection services, increased financing costs, etc. Liquidated damages, on the other hand, is a pre-agreed upon amount the contractor will pay the owner in the event the project is completed late due to no excusable delay causes—that is, due solely to the contractor's fault. Such damages are typically expressed in terms of a daily cost (i.e., $250,000 per day) and need not be proven as actually incurred if the project is completed late.

- **Limitation of Liability**—In order to cap (or limit) a contractor's risk exposure from late completion damages, performance penalties, etc., under a contract, many contracts contain a clause limiting maximum liability to a percentage of the value of the contract. For example, total aggregate damages shall in no case exceed 35 percent of the value of the contract. Or a contract may limit damages to a maximum dollar value, for example, such that total damages shall not exceed $75.0 million.

- **No Damage for Delay**—Many contracts contain a clause limiting a contractor's recovery for any and all delays to a time extension only, no delay damage costs. While some states have adopted statutes precluding no damage for delay clauses in public works contract, others strictly enforce such clauses provided they are clearly written and the delay involved should have been within the contemplation of the parties at the time of contract execution (owner review of contractor submittals, for example).

- Order of Precedence –Contracts often recognize that the potential for conflicting provisions in a contract is fairly high. Accordingly, most contracts contain an order of precedence clause, intended to provide guidance to both the owner and the contractor in the event of conflicting provisions. Typically, specifications have precedence over drawings, details over general, special provisions over general provisions, and so on and so forth. The legal concept is to provide guidance to people on projects in the event there are two or more conflicting provisions relating to a topic.

- **Owner Responsibilities**—Similar to a contractor responsibility clause, an owner responsibility clause ordinarily sets forth the obligations of the project owner, including adequate project financing, all required and necessary permits, appropriate site access, etc.

- **Payments**—This is a key contract clause in terms of project cash flow. This clause sets forth how often the contractor is to be paid, in what manner, and what are the conditions precedent to the issuance of payment.

- **Quantity Variations**—Many contracts contain estimated quantities to be installed. In the event as-bid quantity estimates vary substantially (+/- 10 percent or more) many contracts (both unit price and lump sum) contain a quantity variation clause which allows either the owner or the contractor to request a redetermination of the as-bid unit price on affected portions of the work.

- **Schedules**—A schedule clause typically sets forth the requirements for contractor scheduling, including format (bar chart vs. CPM), level of detail, submittal requirements, frequency of schedule updating, damages for failure to submit, delay or time extension analysis requirements, actions to be taken in the event of forecasted late schedule, etc.

- **Suspension of Work**—This clause habitually allows a project owner to suspend or stop all or some of the work,

with or without cause. Such clauses normally provide for some adjustment to the terms of the contract in such events, including a time extension and payment of delay costs. However, recovery of time and cost may be limited by the terms of the contract. Often, if the actual cause of the suspension order is something for which the contractor is responsible (i.e., unsafe work conditions, work not in compliance with contract requirements, etc.) no recovery of time or cost is allowed.

- **Termination**—Almost all contracts have a provision allowing the owner to end, in whole or in part, performance of the work prior to project completion. There are, typically, two types of termination: termination for convenience and termination for default. Termination for convenience usually occurs when a project owner decides, for their own reasons, not to complete the project as designed. Such situations might arise if the owner's needs change, if project financing fails, or if the underlying project economics change substantially. In such a circumstance, the owner may elect to terminate the contractor's performance for the convenience of the owner and pay off the contractor in accordance with the terms of the clause. Termination for default arises only when a contractor is found to be in material breach of the contract, has been provided with a cure notice from the owner outlining the material breach, and has failed to remedy the breach in a timely manner. (For example, failing to man the project in such a manner as to assure timely project completion.) Usually the owner will terminate the contractor from the project and call upon the contractor's financial guarantees to complete the work (i.e., letter of credit or surety bond). Some contracts also provide a contractor the right to terminate their participation in a project. Under certain carefully proscribed circumstances (such as, failure to make payments, bankruptcy of the owner, suspension of work for more than a defined period of time, etc.) the contractor is allowed to terminate their own involvement in the project.

- **Time of the Essence/Time of Performance**—If project completion by a time or date certain is important to an owner, then they must say so in the contract. As timely project completion is normally important, most contracts contain a clause stating that "Time is of the essence of this contract." Such a clause must be included to make enforceable a time of performance clause and collection of late completion damages. Absent such a clause, the time of project completion is considered unenforceable. The time of performance clause, typically expressed either in work or calendar days after issuance of the notice to proceed, sets forth when the work must be completed and the consequences of failure to meet these dates.

- **Warranty**—A warranty clause, which ordinarily continues in existence for some specified period of time after project completion, guarantees the contractor's work after project acceptance. It is not uncommon for warranty clauses to require a warranty for 1 year after project completion, during which time, if any portion of the project fails, the contractor is obligated to return to the project and make it right or agree to some commercial settlement of the issue.

As noted above, all clauses in a contract are important and must be complied with in order to avoid any allegation of breach of contract. Good contract administration requires knowledge of and compliance with all clauses. Some clauses, especially those identified above, are more important than others. Cost engineers and project controls personnel must become intimately familiar with the terms and conditions of any contract they work on. In reading and interpreting contracts, it is a fundamental rule of law that contracts must "be read as a whole." That is, it is a rare situation for a single clause in a contract to be definitive of an issue. Therefore, people dealing with contracts must read the entire document many times in order to fully understand and appreciate all terms and conditions.

CHANGES

A frequent occurrence on almost all contracts is change. All contracts contemplate the probability of changes to the work. It is incumbent upon both the owner and the contractor to establish formal systems to identify change as soon as it arises, and to estimate and negotiate the full time, cost, and impact of the change as quickly as possible. Projects that do not deal adequately with change as it occurs are destined to end up with major end of job disputes. On almost all contracts, changed work involves cost and may involve time (as in a delay to the end date of the job). Of equal importance, and perhaps at even greater cost, is the impact of change including such things as follow on work being delayed into bad weather periods, increased labor or material costs, and impact to unchanged work. All such elements of change should be dealt with as promptly as possible in order to avoid later disputes.

CLAIMS

It is not infrequent that disputes arise on projects that cannot be resolved easily. Typically, such disputes are referred to under the rubric of a "claim." Claims, like changes, should be addressed promptly and resolved in accordance with the terms of the contract and as soon as possible. It is almost a certainty that the longer a claim remains unresolved on a project the harder and more expensive it will be to resolve later.

- **Definition**—The term *claim* is generally defined in law as a written demand or assertion by one of the contracting parties seeking, as a matter of legal right, payment of

additional money, an adjustment to the time of performance, or some other change to the terms of the contract arising under or related to the contract.

- **Universe of Claims**—Under most contracts, there is a finite number of claim types possible. While the causes of claim situations are numerous, the clauses of the contract under which relief may be sought are limited. Typically, there are only eleven types of claims in most contracts. They are the following.

- **Directed Changes**—Claims resulting from directed changes ordinarily involve a dispute over the time and/or cost of an owner directed change. That is, while a change to some aspect of the work has clearly been directed by the project owner there is a dispute concerning the time and cost impact of the changed work.

- **Constructive Changes** [1]—Unlike directed changes, a constructive change is an owner action, which has the unintentional effect of requiring the contractor to do more than is required by the contract and results in additional cost or time being incurred. It is an accidental or unintended change to the work. Owner comments pertaining to a contractor submittal, not intended to be a change, may bring about a change to the work and result in time and/or cost impacts.

- **Differing Site Conditions**—These are classically described as encounters with latent (hidden) physical conditions at the site differing materially from the conditions indicated in the contract documents or conditions normally encountered and reasonably anticipated in work of this nature in this area.

- **Suspension of Work**—This is an owner directive to stop some or all of the work of the project for a limited period of time.

- **Constructive Suspension of Work**—This is an accidental or unintended work stoppage caused by some owner action or inaction which, while not intended to cause a work stoppage, has the effect of doing so. For example, a failure by the owner to act on a contractor submittal concerning a piece of equipment that is on the project's critical path. While the owner probably did not intend to stop work, their failure to approve the submittal may unwittingly cause the contractor to not purchase, deliver and install the equipment in a timely manner.

- **Force Majeure**—Force majeure events are usually described as unforeseeable events brought about or caused by third parties over which neither the owner nor the contractor exercise any control. For example, an areawide strike of operating engineers may shut down work for a period of time.

- **Delays**—Delay is a term of art in that there are numerous ways to define the term. In the broadest sense, a delay may be defined as any event that causes the project to complete later than planned and beyond the current contract completion date. Most contracts identify and deal with four generic causes of delay—owner, contractor, third-party and concurrent delay. Many contracts also deal, in general terms, with seven types of delay—float consumption, inexcusable, excusable, compensable, concurrent, pacing, and early completion delays [2].

- **Acceleration** – Acceleration is a directive from the owner to the contractor to complete work earlier than required under the contract or earlier than scheduled.

- **Constructive Acceleration**—This is an inadvertent owner action or failure to act, which results in a contractor being required to complete work earlier than required under the contract and causes a cost impact. For example, issuing change orders while refusing to examine delay related issues may bring about constructive acceleration.

- **Termination for Convenience**—This is an action on the part of the owner to end, in whole or in part, the work of the contract prior to completion through no fault of the contractor.

- **Termination for Default**—This is an action to end the work of the contract prior to completion due to a material breach of the contract. Failing to mobilized to the site to commence work after the notice to proceed was issued constitutes such a material breach, for example.

For each of the above eleven types of claims there are a myriad of rules and case law. Each particular situation is quite fact-intensive and is highly dependent upon the exact wording of the contract clause being relied upon. Additionally, there is normally written notice requirement, which must be fulfilled or the contractor may risk losing their legal right to an equitable adjustment. It is, therefore, important for a cost engineer to study the field of claims to learn the basics of each type of claim and then examine carefully the terms and conditions of each contract.

The basic equation of a successful claim is summarized below:

- **Liability**—An event or circumstance has occurred during project performance, which gives rise to a legal right to an adjustment to the contract. For example, a change, delay or differing condition.

- **Causation** – The event or circumstance causes something which otherwise would not occur. For example some portion of the work is revised and performed differently than originally planned and work has to be resequenced

as a result.

- **Damages**—The work costs more and/or takes longer than planned.

The burden of proof of all three elements of a claim rests squarely on the shoulders of the party making the claim. That is, the claimant bears the burden of affirmatively proving all three elements of the claim based upon a preponderance of the evidence. To successfully recover in a claim situation, the claimant must document and prove all three parts before becoming eligible to recover any damages at all. Thus, notice of claim, clear documentation of facts (including both liability and causation), and concise tracking of damages (both cost and time) are a necessary prerequisite to a successful claim.

Dispute Resolution

A contract traditionally includes a disputes clause. This is the clause that details, to a greater or lesser degree, the process by which all contract disputes will be prosecuted. While there are numerous variations on the theme, there are four basic methods of resolving disputes on project, as follows.

- **Negotiation**—Face-to-face negotiation may be accomplished in the field between project teams or elevated in both the owner's and the contractor's organizations. In either case, the concept is for the project participants to discuss the disputed issue and mutually arrive at an acceptable business solution to the problem. Outsiders are rarely involved in negotiation. The process and the outcome are entirely under the control of the parties to the dispute and the outcome is confidential.

- **Mediation**—Mediation is a form of a structured negotiation between the parties utilizing the services of an outside, neutral facilitator—the mediator. It is a voluntary submission of the dispute to a process, which is largely controlled by the parties. The mediator's only power is the power of persuasion, and the mediator's role is generally to help bring the parties closer together until agreement on a solution can be reached. The parties, not the mediator, control both the process and the outcome of the mediation.

- **Arbitration**—Arbitration is a more formalized and legalistic proceeding, whereby the dispute is heard by an outside organization typically operating under a national or international set of rules, such as the American Arbitration Association (AAA), the Judicial Arbitration and Mediation Service (JAMS), or the International Chamber of Commerce (ICC). There may be a single arbitrator or a panel appointed by one of these organizations. Formal hearings are generally held with testimony, examination, cross examination, submittal of evidence, etc. At the end of the hearing(s) the arbitrator "rules" on the outcome of the dispute. In most arbitration proceedings, the arbitrator's ruling is enforceable at law in a court of competent jurisdiction and may be appealed only for very limited causes. While all of the rules governing a formal court case do not apply in an arbitration, most arbitrators are skilled trial attorneys, and, therefore, an arbitration hearing is much more formalized and legalistic than a mediation hearing. Additionally, the parties no longer control either the process or the outcome and, generally, are not free to quit the process of their own volition.

- **Litigation**—This is a formal lawsuit in a state or federal court pursuant to the terms of the contract and under the rules of the jurisdiction where the lawsuit is filed. Lawsuits are time consuming, lengthy, and very expensive. And, the outcome may rest more on legal technicalities than on fact or circumstance. A party submitting a dispute to litigation retains no control over process or outcome.

There are numerous forms of alternative dispute resolution (ADR) available to parties involved in a dispute. Most are voluntary and need not be mandated by contract. It is almost axiomatic that the sooner the owner and the contractor get an issue to a dispute resolution forum, the less expensive it will be for both sides, almost regardless of the outcome. And, likewise, the more involvement actual project participants maintain in the dispute resolution process, the more likely it is that the outcome will be driven by facts and not legal tactics and shenanigans.

CONCLUSION

Involvement in the administration of contracts is one of the central roles of cost engineers and practicing project controls professionals. Contract administration is a skill, which should be mastered by professionals who practice cost engineering or project controls. Contract administration lies at the heart of what most cost engineers do on a daily basis. Cost engineering is also an integral part of contract administration. The two areas are inextricably intertwined and to be good at one skill one has to master the other.

NOTES

1. *Constructive* is a legal term standing for the proposition that courts may construe or interpret facts based upon conduct and circumstance and look past the technical legal arguments and contract language to determine intent and impact of one's actions.
2. While it is beyond the scope of this chapter to deal with the issue of delay in any depth, it is strongly recommended that all cost engineers become thoroughly familiar with the subject of delay and review every contract carefully to determine how delay is handled.

Portions of this chapter are from previous editions authored by James A. Bent, CCC.

Chapter 26

Strategic Asset Management

John K. Hollmann, PE CCE

INTRODUCTION

The objective of this chapter is to show how the skills and knowledge of cost engineering work from an asset owner's perspective (as opposed to a project team perspective). For the asset owner, the concepts, tools, and resources of cost engineering are applied in an integrated way through the strategic asset management subprocess of total cost management (TCM). This chapter describes strategic asset management and provides examples of how it works in practice.

LEARNING OBJECTIVES

After completing this chapter, the reader should understand

- how cost engineering practices can be applied in an integrated way using the strategic asset management process,
- how strategic asset management is applied in different industries and for different asset types, and
- typical roles and responsibilities of cost engineers in strategic asset management.

TCM AND STRATEGIC ASSET MANAGEMENT

AACE International's TCM Framework [1] defines TCM as the sum of the practices and processes that an enterprise uses to manage the total life-cycle-cost investment in its portfolio of strategic assets. The practices are called cost engineering; the process through which the practices are applied is called TCM. The framework further defines a "strategic asset" as any physical or intellectual property that is of long-term or ongoing value to an enterprise. Strategic assets may vary from industrial plants to transportation systems to software programs; essentially anything that an enterprise makes significant investments in can be considered a strategic asset.

Each asset has a "life cycle." For example, a building owner evaluates, designs, builds, leases, maintains, renovates, and eventually demolishes a building during its life cycle—at each stage of the building's life the owner makes cost investments in it that must be managed. As part of the cost management process, the building owner monitors the operating cost and profitability of the existing building, evaluates the performance of competitors' buildings, assesses alternate building investment opportunities, and initiates, plans, and controls new building construction and/or building maintenance projects. The building owner may manage a large portfolio of operating building assets as well as construction and maintenance projects in various stages of their life cycles.

In the building example, strategic asset management is the process where the building owner measures their building operating performance, assesses improvement ideas, and conceives, evaluates, and initiates building investment projects. Project resources and costs are managed through the project ccontrol process (see the "integration" chapter in the text introduction). The strategic asset management and project control subprocesses are linked in TCM.

The bridge or link between the owner's strategic asset management and project control processes is called its "project system." The project system is a subset of the strategic asset management process that includes the steps for planning asset investments, implementing investment decisions, and then measuring project system and asset performance. In a stages-and-gates or "gated" project system, the performance of planning tasks is done in successively more definitive stages. At the completion of each planning stage, plan deliverables (e.g., scope description, designs, estimates, schedules, etc.) are reviewed by the asset owner at a "gate review." If the project is meeting its stated objectives at the review, the asset owner approves sufficient funds to complete the next stage of plan development or to complete the project. If the project is not meeting objectives, it can be cancelled, rescoped or redirected.

Because business conditions and objectives are in constant flux and projects do not always go as planned, asset owners use gated project systems to ensure that their project portfolio is always aligned with current objectives and that limited resources are invested judiciously. After a project is completed and the asset has been in use for some time, a final gate review is held to assess the operational performance of the asset. A project system that results in fast, low-cost projects, but assets that don't function properly, is not a successful project system; project and asset performance must be measured and assessed together. This last review or "measurement" step closes the link between the strategic asset management and project control processes.

Figure 26.1 illustrates the steps above as a process map (i.e., TCM). In strategic asset management on the left half of the TCM process map, the asset owner performs the following steps for each asset in their portfolio, and for their project system.

1. **Performance Measurement**—Measurements (e.g., safety, cost, operability, etc.) are taken of how well existing assets and the project system are performing.
2. **Performance Assessment**—Performance measurements of assets and the project system are compared to strategic plans. Corrective, mitigating, or improvement actions are taken as needed. Ideas are considered for new or improved assets or project systems.
3. **Planning**—Considering the enterprise's objectives and requirements, asset portfolio and project system improvement ideas are conceptualized, evaluated, and converted into plans for investing resources in new or improved assets or project systems.
4. **Implementation**—Investment plans and requirements are communicated to and executed by project teams. Project teams request resources as needed. Project performance is measured and reported, thus continuing the strategic asset management cycle.

In the Project Control process on the right of Figure 26.1, strategic asset investments are implemented through the execution of projects or programs. The role of contractors (and others that contribute to the process but do not own the asset) on project teams increases as projects get larger and require more resources; however, the asset owner, not the project team or contractors, remains accountable for overall TCM process performance.

The asset owner's "project system" is the subset of the strategic asset management planning, implementation, and measurement steps, as well as the project control performance assessment step; i.e., the bridge between strategic asset management and project control.

Figure 26.2 breaks the strategic asset management process map into more detailed steps that are recognizable as cost engineering practices. The next few paragraphs walk through these steps starting with asset and project system performance measurement on the right hand side of the figure.

ASSET AND PROJECT SYSTEM PERFORMANCE MEASUREMENT

In the first step of strategic asset management (on the right hand side of Figure 26.2), the asset owner measures the performance of existing assets and operations as well as the performance of projects that have been implemented. Measures for the project system may include, but are not limited to, safety, cost, and schedule. Measures for assets in use may include, but are not limited to, safety, operations efficiency, and resource consumption (e.g., materials, labor, energy, etc.). Existing assets and ongoing projects demand from and return resources to the owner, the most common resource being money. Information about the flow of resources is captured in the accounting element of the performance measurement step. Traditionally, accounting systems have focused on

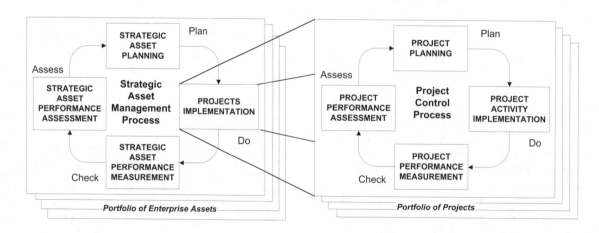

Figure 26.1—The Total Cost Management Process

monetary transactions. However, accounting systems have expanded to enterprise resource planning (ERP) systems that, as the name implies, capture information about the input and output of resources for the entire enterprise (e.g., procurement, inventory, etc.).

TCM requires that ERP implementations measure both asset costs (e.g., cost by asset to support depreciation calculations and profitability assessment) and project costs (e.g., costs by activity to support earned value assessment). Unfortunately, many owner ERP system implementations account for project costs as a type of asset ledger "work-in-progress" holding account. Using that approach, the ERP system is useless for assessing project system performance; project system information must be captured and assessed using a separate information system.

Fortunately, ERP systems now offer "project modules" to better meet project management needs. The ERP system is a key interface point between cost engineering and accounting/finance. Working together, owner cost engineers and accountants need to ensure that their ERP systems address both asset and project information needs. Interestingly, ERP

GLOSSARY TERMS IN THIS CHAPTER
asset, capital ◆ asset, strategic ◆ asset life cycle benchmarking ◆ capital budget ◆ enterprise enterprise resource planning (ERP) ◆ front-end loading (FEL) influence curve ◆ project system ◆ project system gated ◆ strategic asset management total cost management (TCM) ◆ value improving practice (VIP) ◆

software system implementations have become a major class of project themselves in the last decade.

Asset Performance Assessment

Continuing the process to the left side of Figure 26.2, the asset owner evaluates the asset and project system performance measures in comparison to performance plans, as well as internal and external historical performance data. The asset owner looks for variances between measurements and plans

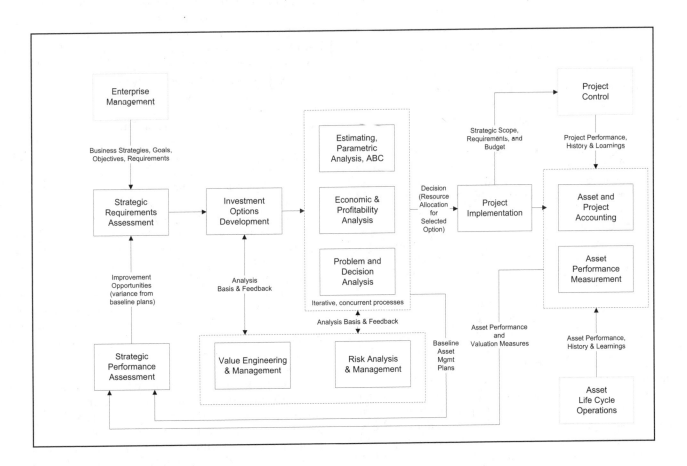

Figure 26.2—The Strategic Asset Management Process

for performance aspects, such as safety, quality, reliability, schedule, operability, and, of course, cost. The owner investigates any variances found to determine if they are caused by isolated events or systematic problems. In many cases, the immediate user of the asset, or the manager of the project system, identifies the cause of the variance and fixes it through an immediate corrective action. In other cases, the problem requires further assessment.

At the highest level of abstraction, owners assess the total long-term economic return or financial profit from its asset investments and project system performance. Return-on-investments (ROI) and return-on-assets (ROA) are common financial measures. The pressure to improve financial performance is relentless, while the availability of resources to make improvements is limited. Various parts of the enterprise will be competing for those resources. Because the business environment is dynamic, competitive, and uncertain, the strategic asset management performance and requirement assessment steps attempt to balance opportunities and risks against demand and supply for resources in such a way that the enterprise's objectives are met.

The enterprise's objectives are inputs to the strategic asset management requirements assessment step. These objectives are determined in the enterprise's strategy formation process (e.g., what is our mission?; what business should we be in?; etc.). For those with interest in the topic, one source identifies at least 10 schools of strategic management thought [2]. Cost engineers should be aware that strategic asset management, as defined in TCM, is related to, but not synonymous with, strategic management as a general field of study.

A key requirements assessment tool for the asset owner is "benchmarking." Benchmarking compares the enterprise's asset and project system performance measures to external peer enterprise measures. Benchmarking also identifies internal and external best practices that have been shown to improve performance. Internal benchmarking recognizes that there is diversity in practices and performance within most enterprises. External benchmarking helps ensure that performance is not only on plan, but competitive with industry.

When asset or project system performance problems cannot be fixed without the investment of significant resources, investment opportunities for improving performance must be identified and evaluated. The effort to identify and develop improvement ideas can itself be a project that consumes considerable resources; therefore, the owner needs to reassess their overall business objectives, requirements, and resource constraints in the strategic requirements assessment step. In this step, constantly changing regulations, industry standards, competitive positions, and market strategies are monitored and evaluated. External benchmarking can help identify competitive positions and strategies.

With their analytical skills and knowledge of both the technical and cost characteristics of the owner's assets and projects, cost engineers are often called upon to lead or support performance assessment endeavors, such as benchmarking and profitability evaluations.

ASSET PLANNING

In the performance assessment step, the owner identified asset or project system improvement challenges that required the investment of significant resources to resolve. In the asset planning steps, the owner identifies asset investment and project system options, defines and evaluates them, and decides upon which option(s) to pursue. Every investment decision is made in consideration of strategic objectives and requirements. Once an investment decision is made, owner management communicates the decision to the asset operator and/or the project team, making sure that the scope of the decision and performance objectives for the asset and/or project are clearly understood.

The investment options identification step in the top left center of Figure 26.2 finds ways to improve asset or project system performance. This step is highly creative; it seeks to understand both the nature of the opportunity, as well as the entire range of alternative solutions. A major challenge in this step is to get fresh ideas from both partial and impartial perspectives. Options identification includes a wide variety of continually evolving practices, such as benchmarking, cost driver analysis, brainstorming, problem solving, market research, business process analysis, and so on.

Larger enterprises often have centralized asset planning departments; common department titles include strategic planning, capital planning, facility planning, or product planning. Whether there is a planning department or not, the asset owner's business management creates special teams to tackle specific challenges identified by the assessment step. The planning team thus formed includes a cross-section of personnel with technical, operating, and finance experience. The asset planning effort is generally business-driven (i.e., led by business managers, not technical personnel) because of the need to keep a close eye on enterprise business objectives and strategies at this phase. Owner cost engineers are key participants (though generally not leaders of) the planning effort because of their skills in key planning practices and their knowledge of asset and project system technology and life cycle costs.

In brainstorming or other option identification sessions, the planning team generates improvement ideas; most are discarded out of hand, while others pass subjective evaluation tests of their potential. For those ideas that look promising, the planning team further develops the scope and definition to a point where their feasibility in terms of potential cost, risk, value, and profitability can be quantitatively analyzed and measured. At some point, the measures reach a level of confidence such that business management can make a decision to discard or continue developing the ideas.

The options analysis and decision steps are in the top center of Figure 26.2. Analysis is an iterative process—i.e., if an idea is still feasible after initial analysis, it is refined and evaluated again and again until it is either discarded or selected for implementation. Many ideas are going through this process simultaneously. Therefore, a gated project system is desirable, so that planning resources are regularly redirected to those concepts that have the most potential.

At some point, the cost of every improvement option is estimated because cost is a component of most decision-making criteria (e.g., ROI). Because the scope definition at early planning stages is minimal, early estimating techniques are stochastic in nature (i.e., parametric analysis, conceptual estimating, ballpark estimating, etc.). The owner cost engineer, with thorough knowledge of the owner's assets and project system, prepares these estimates using the cost estimating and analysis tools described in chapters 8 and 9. Owner cost engineers that initiate and improve on ideas rather than just analyze them (hence the term "engineer") are highly valued members of the planning team. The cost engineer also analyzes the options using risk analysis, value engineering, and economic analysis including profitability. These practices all provide quantitative measures upon which owner business management can base its go/no-go decisions.

While go/no-go decisions during the earliest phases of idea generation are usually made subjectively, decisions on options in later stages of definition are usually based on quantitative decision analysis techniques. These techniques include decision tree analysis and other decision-making tools.

IMPLEMENTATION

Once owner business management makes a decision to implement an asset or project system improvement idea, a project team is formed to implement it. While management is represented on the project team, project responsibility is handed off to a project team manager who often has an operating or technical background depending on the nature of the improvement idea. The planning focus is now on developing the technical scope and execution plans.

At the responsibility hand-off, management conveys formal documentation to the project team of the project's business objectives, conceptual scope, and performance requirements. Objectives and requirements include both the expected conduct of the project (e.g., use the established project system) and the performance of the final asset to be delivered back to the owner. At this point, the project is added to the enterprise's capital budget (or operating budget if costs are not capital). However, the project team is not authorized to spend the full budgeted amount; only enough funds are authorized to carry project definition to the next project system gate review.

The scope of the project at the hand-off is still conceptual in nature. For example, the scope of a chemical plant may include little more than the desired production capacity of the plant, the chemical product specifications, the location for the plant, and the expected date of first production. During implementation, the project team further evaluates and defines the technical scope and project execution plan until they are well enough defined (and the project estimate is considered reliable enough) to ask management for full funding for project execution.

The project definition phase is often called the front-end loading (FEL) phase. It is called FEL because the goal is to remove significant uncertainties about the project scope and execution plan during the "front-end" of the project (i.e., before full-funds are authorized by management). Good early definition practices result in more competitive and predictable project outcomes in terms of safety, cost, schedule, and asset performance. With good FEL, late changes in scope are minimized. At the completion of FEL, the project has a detailed budget and schedule that serve as the basis for project control during project execution.

Some project systems call the asset planning phase "business FEL," and the implementation phase "project FEL." The most effective business and project FEL systems not only define the scope and reduce the uncertainties of options, they use practices, such as value engineering, to improve their value (value improving practices or VIPs). The potential to influence the value of an asset diminishes as asset planning and implementation progress. Figure 26.3 illustrates this basic principle known as the "influence curve".

As projects are implemented and fully authorized (at which point the project team is in full control), the owner asset planning department measures the project portfolio's performance as part of the project system. The owner also continues to measure the performance of its existing assets and operations as well. Asset and project system performance measurement is where we began our discussion of the Strategic Asset Management cycle. Having closed the theoretical loop, some basic examples are provided below of how the theory might work in practice for various types of strategic assets.

APPLICATION—CAPITAL OR FIXED ASSETS

Capital or fixed assets include such items as manufacturing plants and equipment, buildings, roads, and similar items that are not easily moved and have significant useful life spans. Fixed assets are generally created, modified, and retired through a project process rather than a manufacturing process. When determining the profit of an enterprise, the costs of capi-

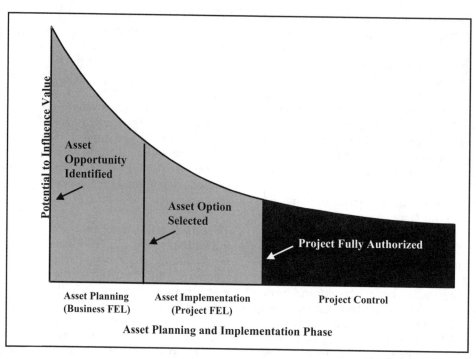

Figure 26.3—The Influence Curve

tal assets are generally depreciated rather than being deducted as a current expense. Some things, such as commercial airplanes, may be capital assets but not fixed assets; the process of creating something as complex as an airplane is a cross between a project process (i.e., a temporary endeavor with a defined beginning and end) and an ongoing manufacturing process.

As an application example of strategic asset management for capital assets, consider the case of a company that produces photographic film. One of the company's existing assets at location X is a machine that coats rolls of specially prepared plastic sheet with photosensitive chemicals and then dries the coating before winding the coated sheet back up for later conversion to a finished product (i.e., rolls of consumer film). This large film-making machine, housed in a light-tight and environmentally controlled building, continually coats, dries, and winds up thousands of square meters of film per day.

The production planning department of the film manufacturing plant continually monitors film production costs using the company's ERP system. The system tracks the inventory, usage, and cost of the rolls of plastic sheet material, the scores of different coating chemicals, the labor of the plant operating personnel, and many other resources. For costs that are difficult to associate with any particular product (such as the cost of planning department personnel), the production planning department uses activity-based costing methods to allocate these costs to specific products. The production planning department includes people with a mix of operations, busi-

ness (e.g., accounting, finance, etc.), and engineering (e.g., industrial, chemical, etc.) backgrounds. Because this plant is large and makes frequent (though individually small) capital investment decisions, the planning department staff includes a cost engineer.

The consolidated cost and resource measurements of film production for plant X and other company plants are reported through the ERP system to the company's film manufacturing division strategic planning department. In addition to ERP information about the company's internal plant operating costs, the strategic planning department monitors external film technical, business, and cost trends. The internal and external measurements are constantly in flux. The strategic planners observe and assess problems with film production quality and costs that cannot be readily dealt with at the plant level. The planners also observe and assess the market actions of competitors in the film business, and they measure the competitor's cost performance through industry benchmarking. Finally, the planners flag division management when their assessment shows that there are significant threats to, or opportunities for, greater profit. Like the plant level planners, the division level planners work on a team that has personnel with operations, business, and engineering backgrounds. Cost engineers, depending on their knowledge of a particular class of assets, are part of this team as well.

At any time, the list of opportunities and challenges identified by the strategic planning department is long. There is constant cost pressure, because silver prices (a key coating ingredient) and operating labor costs are escalating while consumer film market prices are dropping. The technology used by competitors is also improving. In this case, through market intelligence and benchmarking, the strategic planners determine that a competitor will probably lower their prices when a film plant they are constructing is completed. In order to match the expected market price while keeping profits at least level, the planning group's profitability analysis indicates that the unit manufacturing cost component of the product cost must be decreased by about 10 percent within 18 months. Division management agrees with the planning group's assessment and directs the planning team to present them with several feasible improvement options and a decision analysis within 30 days.

The strategic planning team, including cost engineering, holds several days of brainstorming sessions to identify alternative solutions. Most of the alternatives were considered in the past, but the previous analyses are out-of-date and must be revised. Among the ideas considered: make changes in how the film machine at plant X is operated to cut waste and increase uptime; increase the line speed of the film machine at plant X; move some production to plant Y that has some available capacity at lower unit manufacturing costs; build a new production line at either plant X or Y; or build a new film making facility at a very low operating cost location Z. The new plant Z idea is discarded because there is no reasonable way that a complete new facility, with its effects on the entire companies strategies, could be analyzed, designed and built in 18 months. However, the other ideas cannot be discarded out of hand.

At this point, the cost engineer's role becomes significant because each option requires conceptual cost estimating, schedule analysis, risk analysis, value engineering, and ultimately decision analysis; all the tools in the owner cost engineer's skill set. The planning team now starts outlining the conceptual scope of each option and assigns team members to analyze various scope components. Operational specialists consider enterprise and manufacturing resource elements, design engineers consider technical approaches, and cost engineers tie the analysis together with their understanding of both plant design and the cost, schedule, and risk of capital projects.

The cost engineer is prepared for this role. The cost engineering department has an extensive historical database of the cost and schedule of capital projects for film manufacturing. Through benchmarking, they also know what similar projects and facilities cost for their competitors. In addition, they have used the internal and external historical data to develop conceptual estimating, scheduling, and risk analysis tools that permit the cost engineer to rapidly analyze the many technical approaches that the design engineers develop. The cost engineer works closely with the operations specialist and the design engineers to refine approaches and discard unworkable options. The strategic planning team, including

the cost engineer, works with the plant planners and engineers to get additional ideas and work out options. However, because coordination with the plant is difficult (some options adversely affect the jobs of plant personnel), it is important that strategic planning team be very familiar with the plants.

During the course of several weeks of analysis, the team narrows the ideas down to two that meet business objectives: operational changes to cut waste and increase uptime of the machine at plant X, or increase the line speed of the film machine at plant X. In the final week of analysis, the team documents the scope of each option and conducts an early value engineering session for each. The cost engineer prepares a final conceptual estimate and schedule for each and conducts a risk analysis to determine the range of possible cost and schedule outcomes. The team then performs decision tree analysis that weighs the risks and ROI of each option. At the end of 30 days, division management holds a review meeting, and based on the decision analysis, decides to increase the line speed of the film machine at plant X. The divisions capital budget is then updated, and funding for further project scope definition is approved.

After the management decision, the division planning team documents the conceptual scope and objectives and holds a kick-off meeting with a newly formed project team. From there, the project team begins to further define the technical aspects of the speed-up in accordance with the company's project system/FEL process. The cost engineer from the division planning team continues to support the project team. The cost engineer is an important knowledge-bridge from business to technical FEL.

Many design decisions still need to be made; for example the X machine dryer length needs to be extended to accommodate the speedup and there are a number of equipment layout options for the drying area. The layout options involve building options as well. One option saves on plant real estate by using a multi-story layout with a costly heavy structure. The other option is spaced out on a single floor level that needs only a low cost building shell. Value engineering sessions are again held to optimize the function and cost of the process flow, layouts, and building additions. Again, the owner cost engineer has a cost database, estimating, and risk evaluation tools to support these planning efforts.

Eventually, the project team completes the equipment layouts, piping, and instrumentation diagrams, and other project definition deliverables. A project control-level cost estimate and a critical path, resource-loaded schedule are also prepared to serve as the basis for a management review session and approval of full project funding. The project execution plan serves as the basis for project control during project execution. At this point, the owner cost engineer's role is as advisor and consultant to the owner project manager. Cost engineers for the project contractors, with owner oversight, take the lead role for day-to-day project control.

APPLICATION—PRODUCTS

Products include such items as manufactured goods and similar things that have a limited useful life span and are not fixed in place. Products are generally created through an ongoing, discrete, or continuous manufacturing or production process rather than a project process. When determining the profit of an enterprise, the costs of creating products are generally deducted as a current expense rather than being depreciated over a number of years as with a capital asset.

As an application example of strategic asset management for products, consider an expansion of the film company case previously described. At the same time that the division planning team was informing management that a 10 percent manufacturing cost reduction within 18 months was needed, they also noted that the competitor's new film plant was likely going to be able to make film with better image capture capability. The division management was appraised of the product technical challenges, and they direct the planning group to present them with several feasible options and a decision analysis within 30 days that will meet the cost, time, and product improvement objective.

Fortunately, a program had been underway in the research and development laboratories that offered the company two alternative coating formulations that would provide comparable or better capabilities. One formulation adds an additional coating layer, while the other changes the chemistry of an existing coating layer. Furthermore, the additional layer option requires a modification to the company's one-hour film developing machine product used by photo shops. The product improvement is such that the planning department thinks it can support a premium price. As the division planning team enters the asset planning phase, they now have to deal with product decisions as well as capital asset decisions, and, as they so often are, the capital and product planning are highly intertwined.

The planning team now includes personnel with operations, business, and engineering backgrounds, as well as a representative from the research department, specialists in product planning, and a design engineer from the one-hour developing machine group. Subteams are formed to concentrate on the manufacturing cost alternatives, the film product alternatives, and the developing machine alternatives. They all report to a lead planning manager and regularly meet as a group to integrate the assessment of the many alternative branches.

The film product subteam considers consumer perception of the images produced by the alternative formulations. They also evaluate marketing, sales, distribution, inventory, and other considerations for the new alternative products. The developing machine subteam considers the implications of modifying the several models of machines in their customer's photo shops. The manufacturing team considers the

alternatives discussed previously, but now they also must deal with modifications to the film coating process to address the formulation options.

Eventually the team performs a decision tree analysis that weighs the risks and ROI of each option. At the end of 30 days, division management holds a review meeting, and based on the decision analysis, decides to increase the line speed of the film machine at plant X and upgrade its coating and drying process to handle the extra coating layer, and to modify the one-hour developing machines as needed. The divisions capital budget is then updated, and funding for further program definition is approved (the decision initiates both capital and product development projects that will be managed as a program).

After the management decision, the division planning team documents the conceptual scope and objectives and holds a kick-off meeting with the newly formed program team. Capital and product project teams are formed within the program. The capital project team begins to further define the technical aspects of the speedup and modified coating process. The film product development team begins to further define the business plans (sales, marketing, inventory, distribution, price, etc.) for the new film. The one-hour developer machine product team begins to further define both the technical aspects of the modified machine design, as well as the business aspects of dealing with its customers in whose shops the machines are used.

As the teams continue with scope development, cost engineering practices are used for capital and product planning, including cost estimating, risk analysis, and value engineering. The basic processes are the same for both capital assets and products, but the details of how they are used differ. Product estimates deal with the assembly process versus the construction process for capital estimates. Product value engineering focuses on product (e.g., the one-hour developer machine) functions that can be combined or eliminated as opposed to plant manufacturing process (e.g., the film dryer) functions for capital project value engineering. The owner cost engineer's major role has traditionally been to support capital planning; however, the more the cost engineer understands both the product and capital planning aspects, the more valuable their input will be to the program.

APPLICATION—SOFTWARE

Software is difficult to classify as either a capital asset or a product. As a manufactured good, it is captured in the form

---

[1] Software's ambiguous nature (is it an asset or product?) is reflected in wide variations in how companies expense or depreciate software development costs.

of a plastic disk or a silicon chip, but the value and cost of the software has little relationship to the manufactured good (i.e., the disk or chip). Software may or may not have a limited useful life span depending on its function; some software is quickly outdated while other software is used for decades. Finally, software may or may not be fixed in place depending on the device it is installed in.[1] In any case, many things need software in order to perform their functions, and software is a "strategic asset" of long-term or ongoing value to the enterprise holding the software copyright or patent.

As an application example of strategic asset management for software, consider a final extension of the film company case. Previously, the case described how the one-hour developing machine subteam had to consider the implications of modifying the several models of machines in their customer's shops. Beyond this, this subteam has to consider both the developer machine operating software and user interface associated with the machine.

The existing operating software is based on coding and a chipset for a now defunct machine model, and the software's capabilities for modification and improvement are limited. Also, the planning department has received feedback that shop owners are complaining about the hard-to-understand user interface. So now, the overall planning team includes a one-hour developing machine subteam design engineer and a software engineer as well. The developing machine subteam must now consider the implications of modifying the several models of machines in their customer's shops and the known software limitations and user interface complaints.

Eventually, the overall planning team performs a decision tree and other analyses that weigh the risks and return on net assets of each option. At the end of 30 days, division management holds a review meeting, and based on the decision analysis, decides to increase the line speed of the film machine at plant X, upgrade its coating and drying process to handle the extra coating layer, and design and manufacture a new developing machine model using the latest software and user interface (a modified version taken from the prototype of a different, but related model that had been in research and development).

As the developing machine subteam continues with scope development, cost engineering practices are used for software development. Software estimates deal with software configuration and coding activities versus the construction or assembly activities for capital and product estimates. Software value engineering focuses on software and interface functions that can be combined or eliminated or developed as object code modules. Again, the more the cost engineer understands the capital, product, and software planning aspects, the more valuable their input will be to the program.

SUMMARY

This chapter outlines the basics of strategic asset management with its measurement, assessment, planning and implementation steps. Gated project systems that link the strategic asset management and project control are described. Examples were provided of how the asset management steps could be applied to three types of strategic assets: a capital asset, a product, and software. The examples show that the same basic asset management steps and systematic approach apply to all strategic asset types. The examples also show that while the approach is basic, strategic asset management implementation can be complex because the assets in an enterprise's portfolio are often interrelated in a myriad of ways. More example applications can be described by simply substituting specific descriptors of a given asset type and asset management organization. The strategic asset management process of TCM is universal.

The application example also illustrates the typical roles and responsibilities of cost engineers in strategic asset management teams. The teams include personnel from all parts of the enterprise, such as operations, business, engineering, research and development, product planning, software development and so on. While there may not be anyone on the team with the title of cost engineer, someone on the team must practice the cost engineering skills of estimating, planning and scheduling, value engineering, and so on. Few cost engineers will perform each skill for each asset; however, it is important to understand the strategic asset management process so that no matter what your role is, you can communicate and work effectively with the asset management team.

PRACTICE QUESTIONS

1. **Question**: What are the four basic steps of asset management?
   Answer: measurement, assessment, planning, and implementation.

2. **Question**: List two ways that a cost estimate prepared by an owner during asset management might differ from a cost estimate prepared by a contractor during project control?
   Possible Answers: (owner during asset management considers the asset life cycle, based on more limited scope information, less accurate, more likely to address alternate scenarios, more parametric methods)

3. **Question**: What is a common assessment technique used by companies to find out if their asset performance is competitive with other enterprises in their industry?
   Answer: benchmarking

4. **Question**: Is a strategic asset always a capital asset?
   Answer: no

5. **Question**: Can a product be a strategic asset?
   Answer: yes

6. **Question**: In a "stages and gates" project system, why are gate reviews usually held?
   Possible Answers: to consider or make a decision to proceed to the next phase, or to ensure that funds being expended are always in alignment with business or project objectives.

7. **Question**: What is "front-end loading" in reference to asset management and project systems?
   Answer: a process to reduce scope uncertainties and perform value improving practices early (i.e., at the front-end) in the planning and implementation steps)

8. **Question**: What is the principle that states the potential to influence the value of an asset diminishes as asset planning and implementation progress?
   Answer: influence curve

DISCUSSION CASES

1. Consider an enterprise that has significant capital assets, but no one trained in the skills and knowledge of cost engineering to support asset management. Discuss how asset management at such an enterprise might be less effective than otherwise.

2. Consider the case of the strategic assets that are owned by an enterprise that you are familiar with (company, department, school, church, home, etc.). Discuss how an integrated strategic asset management process might apply in that situation.

3. Consider the case of a contractor cost engineer working on a project (e.g., project control, estimating, etc.). Discuss how having an understanding of the client owner's asset management process might help that cost engineer be a more valuable contributor to successful project execution.

4. Consider an asset implementation decision (e.g., build a building, create a software program, etc.) that you are familiar with that either did or did not meet its objectives. Discuss the reason that it was or was not successful and whether an integrated asset management process that applied cost engineering skills and knowledge would have or did make a difference in its success.

REFERENCES

1. *AACE International's Total Cost Management Framework.* www.aacei.org/technical.
2. Mintzberg, Henry, Bruce Ahlstrand, and Joseph Lampel. 1998. *Strategy Safari; A Guided Tour Through the Wilds of Strategic Management.* New York: The Free Press.
3. *The International Association of Database Professionals Dictionary.* www.teamdatabase.com/dictionary.

Section 6

Economic Analysis

Chapter 27

Basic Engineering Economics

Dr. Scott J. Amos, PE

INTRODUCTION

Engineering economic analysis is a technique that assists in the solution of substantial engineering problems where economic aspects dominate over a considerable period of time. Industry is frequently confronted with the need to select from among multiple alternatives. This decision-making process can be greatly simplified if the alternatives can be quantified objectively and equated in some numerical value, such as money. The objective of this chapter is to establish a framework for the modeling and subsequent comparison of engineering problems in terms of the time value of money.

LEARNING OBJECTIVES

After completing this chapter, readers shoud be able to

- calculate simple and compound interest rates and solve interest problems using basic single payments, uniform series, and gradient formulas;
- calculate present value, future value, and equivalent uniform annual value of a cash flow series; and
- determine the discounted rate of return of a cash flow series.

SYMBOLS

The following symbols are used in this and the following chapter:

A	Annual amount or annuity. A uniform series of end-of-period payments or receipts.	$
B	Benefits or income	$
C	Cost or expenses	$
e	The base of natural logarithms (2.71828)	decimal
EOY	End-of-year, usually followed by a number indicating which year, i.e., EOY4 indicates end of year 4	-
$EUAW$	Equivalent uniform annual worth	$
F	Future value, a single lump sum value occurring at the end of the last of n time periods	$
G	Uniform or arithmetic gradient amount, a constant increase in funds flow at the end of each period	$
i	Interest rate per period	decimal
k	Number of compounding periods per year	decimal
$MARR$	Minimum attractive rate of return	decimal
n	Total number of compounding periods, or life of asset	decimal
P	Present value, a single lump sum occurring at time zero, the first of n time periods.	$
r	Nominal annual interest rate	decimal
S_n	Expected salvage value at end of year n	$
ϕ	(Effective interest rate (r/k)	decimal

EQUIVALENCE

An essential concept in engineering economic analysis is that of equivalence or the ability to compare cash flows at different points in time. Equivalence is based on the time value of money, and the cardinal rule is that two cash flows or alternatives only can be compared at a common interest rate. For example, if a person is indifferent to the acceptance of $110 one year from now in lieu of $100 today, we can say that the two sums of money are equivalent at an interest rate of 10 percent. If however, the interest rate is something greater than 10 percent, we can no longer say the sums are equivalent and would thus prefer the $100 today.

Suppose two alternatives are available. Alternative one has a lower initial cost and higher operating cost, while alternative two has a higher initial cost and lower operating costs. Because of the time value of money, the sums of money at different times cannot be added up directly. Using equivalence calculations, these streams of money, or cash flows, can be converted to either lump-sum values at any point in time or a series of uniform benefits/costs. The conversion of dissimilar cash flows to similar lump-sums or uniform series at a particular interest rate and a common point in time provides values with a valid basis for comparison.

The model used for engineering economic analysis is based on the conversion of an existing cash flow to an equivalent cash flow at a particular interest rate through the application of predefined factors. The cash flow can be represented in tabular or graphical format. The conversion factors are called discount factors and are readily available in either algebraic form or in tables. Many hand-held calculators have been programmed with these factors in addition to most computer spreadsheet applications. A thorough understanding of the structure and development of the model and its components will permit the solution of engineering economic problems using any of three approaches: tabular, calculator, or computer spreadsheet application.

CONVENTIONS

Cash Flow Representation—Cash flow occurs whenever cash or something of monetary value flows from one party to another. It can be either cash flow in, for example cash receipts, or when payments or disbursements are made, which is a cash flow out. This can be shown in a tabular format as in Table 27.1 or in the case of relatively simple problems, a cash flow diagram similar to figure 27.1(a) can be developed. The cash flow diagram consists of two basic parts: (1) the horizontal or time line, and (2) the vertical arrows or cash flow lines. The horizontal line is divided into periods appropriate for the specific problem under consideration. Each vertical line represents an interest period based on an end of period convention. Thus, the points in Figure 27.1(b) represent interest periods 1 through 5. These periods could be daily, monthly, quarterly, semi-annually, or annually depending on the problem statement. All transactions will be assumed to occur at the end of the interest period.

The vertical lines represent cash flow and are placed according to the timing and direction of the cash flow. Receipts or income are represented by an upward arrow, while disbursements and expenditures are downward arrows representing cash out. Although the arrows are not usually to scale, a longer line will distinguish a large cash flow from a smaller one. The arrows also will be labeled with the monetary value of the transaction. Other labels that might be used on arrows are P, A, F, G, and S, as shown in Figure 27.1(c). These terms have been previously defined in the list of symbols.

Table 27.1—Cash Flow Table

YEAR	INCOME	EXPENSE
0		$20,000
1	$5,000	500
2	5,000	600
3	5,000	700
4	5,000	800
5	5,000	900

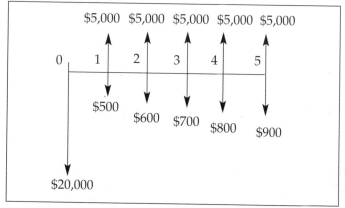

Figure 27.1(a)—Cash Flow Diagram

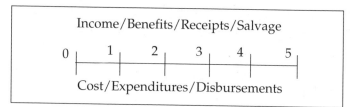

Figure 27.1(b)—Cash Flow Convention

Salvage Value—In many studies there may be a residual value resulting in income at the end of the useful life of an alternative. The resale or salvage value may be associated with the anticipated market value of the asset at that point in time. It is shown as an upward arrow on the cash flow diagram. If the salvage value is low with respect to other cash flow, it is usually omitted. Any significant costs associated with disposal at the end of useful life also can be shown on the diagram as a downward arrow.

INTEREST

Time Value of Money—When monetary consequences of a problem occur over a substantial period of time there is usually a cost associated with the use of the money. Since money is a valuable asset, people are willing to pay to have it available for their use. This could be likened to paying rent for the use of money just as one would pay rent for the use of an apartment. With money, the charge for its use is called interest rather than rent.

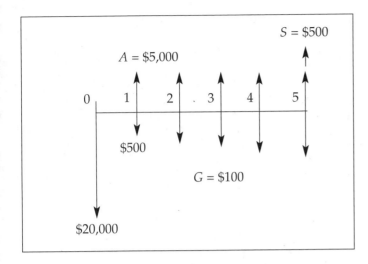

Figure 27.1(c)—Cash Flow Notation

Simple Interest—The interest due is proportional to the length of time the principal is outstanding and does not accrue or compound on previous interest. Each subsequent interest payment is calculated based on the total principal, ignoring accumulated interest to date, as shown in example 27.1.

Example 27.1—Simple Interest

$(i = 10\%)$

Principal	$1,000
Interest accrued EOY1	100
Interest accrued EOY02	100
Total @EOY2 with simple interest	$1,200

Compound Interest—The interest is considered an increased increment of principal earning additional interest with time. Each subsequent interest payment is calculated based on the total principal plus accumulated interest to date, as shown in example 27.2.

Example 27.2—Compound Interest

$(i = 10\%)$

Principal	$1,000
Interest accrued EOY1	100
New principal with accrued interest	$1,100
Interest accrued EOY02	110
Total @EOY2 with compound interest	$1,210

Nominal Interest Rate—The annual interest rate, r, disregarding the effects of compounding periods that are more frequent than annually. Common practice is to express interest rates at the nominal rate even though there is compounding such as quarterly, monthly, or daily. The nominal rate, r, is not the same as the annual rate, i, except in the case of annual compounding.

Effective Interest Rate—If the effective interest rate per period, ϕ, is given it can be converted easily to the effective annual interest rate, i, which includes the effects of compounding over k periods per year by using equations 27.1 or 27.2. In general, it can be assumed that the rate given in a problem is annual unless stated otherwise. If compounding is annually, the rate given is the effective rate. If compounding is anything other than annual, the rate given is the nominal rate.

$$i = \left(1 + \frac{r}{k}\right)^k - 1 \qquad \text{(equation 27.1)}$$

$$i = \left(1 + \phi\right)^k - 1 \qquad \text{(equation 27.2)}$$

Example 27.3—

Given an interest rate of 12 percent, find the effective and annual rates for yearly, semi-annual, and monthly compounding.

Solution—The nominal rate, r, is given as 12 percent. The effective rate per period can be found by dividing the nominal rate, r, by the number of compounding periods per year, k. The annual rate then can be found through the application of equation 27.1 or 27.2.

For yearly compounding, the annual rate is the same as the effective rate of 12 percent.

For semi-annual compounding:

$$\phi = \frac{r}{k} = \frac{.12}{2} = .06 \text{ or } 6\%$$
$$i = (1 + \phi)^k - 1$$
$$= (1 + .06)^2 - 1 = .124 \text{ or } 12.4\%$$

For monthly compounding:

$$\phi = \frac{r}{k} = \frac{.12}{12} = .01 \text{ or } 1\%$$
$$i = (1 + \phi)^k - 1$$
$$= (1 + .01)^{12} - 1 = .127 \text{ or } 12.7\%$$

Continuous Compounding—Discrete compounding occurs when interest payments are made at the end of finite compounding periods such as annually, monthly, quarterly, or daily. As the duration of the interest period becomes infinitely short, the number of compounding periods per year becomes infinite and is referred to as continuous compounding. It can be shown that the limit of equation 27.1 as k approaches infinity is the continuous compounding rate:

$$i = e^r - 1 \qquad \text{(equation 27.3)}$$

For continuous compounding (example 27.3):

$$
\begin{aligned}
i &= e^r - 1 \\
&= e^{0.12} - 1 \\
&= .128 \text{ or } 12.8\,\%
\end{aligned}
$$

Due to this relationship the formulas and factors to be developed for discrete compounding are not directly applicable to problems involving continuous compounding.

Minimum Attractive Rate of Return—The interest rate used in feasibility studies is often called the minimum attractive rate of return, or MARR. This represents the minimum rate of return at which the owner is willing to invest. Investments yielding less than the MARR are therefore not considered worthwhile. The selection of a suitable rate of return can be quite complex and could vary from problem to problem. Simply stated, it involves the analysis and selection of the highest one of the following three values:

- cost of borrowed money from banks, insurance companies, etc.;

- cost of capital or the composite value for the capital structure of the firm; and
- opportunity cost or the rate-of-return of the best project that is rejected.

When there is risk or uncertainty in a project, a commonly used method is to increase the MARR, thus diminishing the effect of future costs and benefits. Care should be taken since a MARR that is unrealistically low will magnify the importance of future costs and benefits, leading to the erroneous conclusion that a project is either too costly or too beneficial.

Example 27.4—

A firm is evaluating the feasibility of a design and construction project and needs to know what interest rate should be used in the study. The following data has been compiled:

cost of borrowed money, loan A = 9 percent; investment opportunity, project B = 16 percent; and cost of capital = 20 percent.

Solution—The MARR should be equal to or greater than the highest of the three values. Choose 20 percent.

DISCOUNT FACTORS

Discount factors that have been derived for discrete compounding are summarized in Table 27.2. The algebraic form of the various factors can become quite complex. The functional notation illustrates a standardized notation that simplifies the calculations and permits the use of tabulated fac-

Table 27.2—Discount Factors for Discrete Compounding

Factor	Converts	Notation	Formula
Single Payment Compound Amount	P to F	$(F/P, i, n)$	$(1 + i)^n$
Single Payment Present Worth	F to P	$(P/F, i, n)$	$(1 + i)^{-n}$
Uniform Series Sinking Fund	F to A	$(A/F, i, n)$	$\dfrac{i}{(1+i)^n - 1}$
Uniform Series Capital Recovery	P to A	$(A/P, i, n)$	$\dfrac{i(1+i)^n}{(1+i)^n - 1}$
Uniform Series Compound Amount	A to F	$(F/A, i, n)$	$\dfrac{(1+i)^n - 1}{i}$
Uniform Series Present Worth	A to P	$(P/A, i, n)$	$\dfrac{(1+i)^n - 1}{i(1+I)^n}$
Arithmetic Gradient Present Worth	G to P	$(P/G, i, n)$	$\dfrac{(1+i)^n - 1}{i^2(1+i)^n} - \dfrac{n}{i(1+i)^n}$
Arithmetic Gradient Uniform Series	G to A	$(A/G, i, n)$	$\dfrac{1}{i} - \dfrac{n}{(1+i)^n - 1}$

A = Annual Amount/Annuity

G = uniform gradient amount, constant increase in...

tors as shown in Tables 27.3 and 27.4. The notation is in the form

$$(X/Y,i,n) \qquad \text{(equation 27.4)}$$

which can be read as "to find the equivalent amount X given amount Y, interest rate i, and the number of discounting or compounding periods n." These factors can be used to simplify cash flows or convert cash flows for comparison purposes.

In most types of engineerin mary calculation is determini lent uniform annual cost of a analysis. This section will application for each of the di

Present Worth—The presen computed given a lump-sum future value, a un or an arithmetic gradient series, as shown in the following examples.

MEASURES OF EQUIVALENT WORTH

Table 27.3—Compound Interest Factors at 5 Percent

	Single Payment			Uniform Payment Series			Gradient	
n	F/P	P/F	A/F	A/P	F/A	P/A	A/G	P/G
1	1.050	.9524	1.000	1.0500	1.000	0.952	0	0
2	1.102	.9070	.4878	.5378	2.050	1.859	0.488	0.907
3	1.158	.8638	.3172	.3672	3.152	2.723	0.967	2.635
4	1.216	.8227	.2320	.2820	4.310	3.546	1.439	5.103
5	1.276	.7835	.1810	.2310	5.526	4.329	1.902	8.237
6	1.340	.7462	.1470	.1970	6.802	5.076	2.358	11.986
7	1.407	.7107	.1228	.1728	8.142	5.786	2.805	16.232
8	1.477	.6768	.1047	.1547	9.549	6.463	3.244	20.970
9	1.551	.6446	.0907	.1407	11.027	7.108	3.676	26.127
10	1.629	.6139	.0795	.1295	12.578	7.722	4.099	31.652

Table 27.4—Compound Interest Factors at 6 Percent

	Single Payment			Uniform Payment Series			Gradient	
n	F/P	P/F	A/F	A/P	F/A	P/A	A/G	P/G
1	1.060	.9434	1.0000	1.0600	1.000	0.943	0	0
2	1.124	.8900	.4854	.5454	2.060	1.833	0.485	0.890
3	1.191	.8396	.3141	.3741	3.184	2.673	0.961	2.569
4	1.262	.7921	.2286	.2886	4.375	3.456	1.427	4.945
5	1.338	.7473	.1774	.2374	5.637	4.212	1.884	7.934
6	1.419	.7050	.1434	.2034	6.975	4.917	2.330	11.459
7	1.504	.6651	.1191	.1791	8.394	5.582	2.768	15.450
8	1.594	.6274	.1010	.1610	9.897	6.210	3.195	19.841
9	1.689	.5919	.0870	.1470	11.491	6.802	3.613	24.577
10	1.791	.5584	.0759	.1359	13.181	7.360	4.022	29.602

ntractor is considering the acquisition of a piece of quipment with anticipated financial impact as shown in Table 27.5. If the contractor's minimum attractive rate of return (MARR) is 6 percent, should the investment be made?

Solution—There are two approaches that can be taken to this problem. Due to the small number of compounding periods, the simple approach would be to compute the present value of the net cash flow for each year at 6 percent as shown in the table. If summation of the present values results in a positive number, the investment is desirable.

Although the income and expense were equal, the application of an interest rate, or the time value of money, resulted in a negative present value of $4,830. This investment is therefore not desirable.

A second approach to the problem would be to use a cash flow diagram as shown in Figure 27.2.

From the diagram it can be seen that the cash flow is comprised of a lump-sum expense of $38,000, an arithmetic gradient expense of $1,000, and a uniform series income of $11,000. Application of the discount factors gives the following:

$$P = P_0 + P_1 + P_2$$

Where

P_0 = -$38,000

P_1 = -G (P/G,i,n)=-$1,000 (P/G, 6 %, 4)=-$1,000 (4.945) = -$4,945

P_2 = A (P/A,i,n)=$11,000 (P/A, 6 %, 4)=$11,000 (3.465)=$38,115

P = -$38,000-$4,945+ $38,115 = -$4,830

Which agrees with the previous solution.

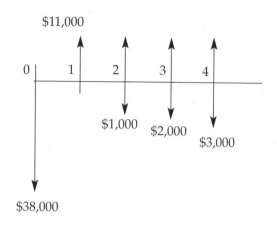

Figure 27.2—Cash Flow Diagram

Future Worth—The future worth method uses the end of the planning horizon as a reference point. Typical applications would include investment growth and equipment replacement costs.

Example 27.6—

Using the cash flow of the previous example calculate the future worth at EOY4.

Solution—As before, we will first use a tabular solution based on the net cash flow as shown in Table 27.6.

As in the previous example, the future worth is negative, and the investment would be not be acceptable. This problem also can be solved using the cash flow diagram of figure 27.2 Notice that in table 27.4 there are no discount factors that convert from G to F. To solve this problem, the gradient series first can be converted to a present worth and then to a future worth.

Table 27.5—Present Worth Analysis

YEAR	EXPENSE	INCOME	NET	FACTOR	P
0	$38,000	0	($38,000)	1.000	(38,000)
1	0	11,000	11,000	.9434	10,377
2	1,000	11,000	10,000	.8900	8,900
3	2,000	11,000	9,000	.8396	7,556
4	3,000	11,000	8,000	.7921	6,337
Total	$44,000	$44,000	0		($4,830)

Table 27.6—Future Worth Analysis

YEAR	NET	FACTOR	F
0	($38,000)	1.262	($47,956)
1	11,000	1.191	13,101
2	10,000	1.124	11,240
3	9,000	1.060	9,540
4	8,000	1.000	8,000
Total	0		($6,075)

$$F = F_0 + F_1 + F_2$$

Where,

$F_0 = -P \ (F/P, i, n) = -\$38,000 \ (F/P, 6\%, 4) = -\$38,000 \ (1.262)$

   $= -\$47,956$

$F_1 = -G \ (P/G, i, n) \ (F/P, i,n) = -\$1,000 \ (P/G, 6\%, 4) \ (F/P, 6\%, 4)$

   $= -\$1,000 \ (4.945) \ (1.262) = -\$6,241$

$F_2 = A \ (F/A, i, n) = \$11,000 \ (F/A, 6\%t, 4) = \$11,000 \ (4.375) = \$48,125$

$F \ = -\$47,956 - \$6,241 + \$48,125 = -\$6,072$

The slight difference in results can be attributed to rounding errors.

Annual Worth—The basis of this method is the conversion of all cash flows to an equivalent uniform annual worth (EUAW). It is often expressed as either EUAC or EUAB to distinguish between costs and benefits. Typical applications for this method are in the calculation of loan payments and determining the cost of capital recovery.

Example 27.7

Referring again to the cash flow of example 27.5, calculate the equivalent uniform annual worth.

Solution—In order to compute an annual worth, it is first necessary to convert the lump sum at time 0 and the gradient to equivalent uniform series then add them to the existing uniform series.

$$A = A_0 + A_1 + A_2$$

Where,

$A_0 = P \ (AA/P, i, n) = -\$38,000 \ (A/P, 6\%, 4) = -\$38,000 \ (.2886) = -\$10,967$

$A_1 = G \ (A/G, i,n) = -\$1,000 \ (A/G, 6\%, 4) = -\$1,000$

   $(1.427) = -\$1,427$

$A_2 = \$11,000$

$A \ = -\$10,967 - \$1,427 + \$11,000 = -\$1,394$

Another approach would be to convert the lump sum, either P or F as determined in the previous examples through application of the appropriate discount factors.

From example 27.5, $P = -\$4,830$

and,

$A = P \ (A/P, i, n) = -\$4,830 \ (A/P, 6\%, 4) = -\$4,830$

   $(.2886) = -\$1,394$

Or, using example 27.6, $F = -\$6,075$

and,

$A = F \ (A/F, i, n) = -\$6,075 \ (A/F, 6 \text{ percent}, 4) = -\$6,075$

   $(.2286) = -\$1,389$

If a purely algebraic approach had been taken, these three numbers would have been equal. As before, the difference can be attributed to rounding errors from the tabular factors.

Portions of this chapter are from previous editions authored by Julian A. Piekarski, PE CCE.

Chapter 28

Applied Engineering Economics

Dr. Scott J. Amos, PE

INTRODUCTION

In the previous chapter, the basic tools for economic analysis were developed. These tools allow us to manipulate cash flows in many ways and give us the power to compare and evaluate cash flow against specified criteria. Application of these tools is the subject of this chapter. In general, economic selection criterion will be either maximization of benefits, minimization of costs, or maximization of the net profits. Techniques will be presented for evaluation of single as well as multiple alternative type problems.

LEARNING OBJECTIVES

After completing this chapter, readers should be able to

* evaluate and select the best alternative using present value, future value, equivalent uniform annual value, and discounted rate of return; and
* compare alternatives using the benefit-cost ratio.

CASH FLOW ANALYSIS

There are two fundamental approaches to the analysis of a given cash flow, equivalent worth, and rate-of-return.

Equivalent Worth—The equivalent worth method simply converts to one of the basic forms, i.e., the equivalent present worth, or annual worth, using previously-developed techniques and the required MARR. A negative result means the proposed cash flow is unacceptable because it does not provide the required return-on-investment. Positive results are desirable and indicate an investment that will meet the prescribed criteria. This technique has been previously illustrated in examples 27.5 through 27.7.

Rate-of-Return—The fundamental concept behind rate-of-return (ROR) analysis is that the ROR is the interest rate at which benefits are equivalent to costs. Thus the cash flow is solved for the unknown value, i. This technique is also known as internal rate of return and can be used with either present worth or annual worth equivalents.

Example 28.1—

A $10,000 investment returned $2,342 per year over a 5-year period. What was the rate of return on this investment?

Solution—Set the present worth of benefits equal to the present worth of costs, then algebraically isolate the discount factor and treat it as an unknown.

$$\$2,342 \, (P/A, i, 5) = \$10,000$$
$$(P/A, i, 5) = \frac{\$10,000}{\$2,342} = 4.27$$

Now look at the compound interest factors in the tables 27.2 and 27.3 for the value of i where $(P/A, i, 5) = 4.270$; since no tabulated value is given, find the values on either side of the desired value and interpolate to find the rate of return i.

From the tables find

i	$(P/A, i, 5)$
5.0 %	4.379
?	4.270
6.0 %	4.212

In this example, the rate of return for the investment was found to be 5.5 percent.

MULTIPLE ALTERNATIVES

Many projects will require a selection from among several mutually-exclusive alternatives. The selection of one alternative will preclude the selection of any other alternative. Two simple rules will help identify the preferred alternative:

- compute the net present worth (annual worth or future worth) of each alternative at the required minimum attractive rate of return (MARR); and
- select the alternative having the highest net present worth (annual worth or future worth).

Example 28.2—

Given the following mutually-exclusive alternatives and an minimum attractive rate of return (MARR) of 5 percent, which one would be chosen?

YEAR	A	B	C
0	($2,500)	($2,700)	($3,000)
1	0	650	0
2	0	650	350
3	0	650	700
4	0	650	1,050
5	3,100	650	1,400
Total	$600	$550	$500

Solution—Compute the net present worth for each alternative and select the highest value. Notice the values on the total line would suggest that alternative B would be favored. Remember, this does not consider the time value of money.

PW_A = - $2,500 + $3,100 (P/F, 5 %, 5) = -$2,500 + $3,100 (.7835) = -$71

PW_B = - $2,700 + $650 (P/A, 5 %, 5) = -$2,700 + $650 (4.329) = $114

PW_C = - $3,000 + $350 (P/G, 5 %, 5) = -$3,000 + $350 (8.237) = -$117

This provides an interesting result. Alternative A, which had the least initial cost and apparently the most return, is in fact not the preferred alternative based on maximization of the net present worth at 5 percent. Alternative B is preferred in this case.

We have illustrated the solution of problems by the two major methods, equivalent worth and rate-of-return. Notice that the equivalent worth procedure can be applied to multiple alternatives. In order to use rate of return analysis on two or more alternatives, it is necessary to evaluate the increment of investment between the alternatives.

Analysis Period—When comparing alternatives using present worth methods, it is necessary to analyze over a common planning horizon. In the event that alternatives do not have equal lives, consideration must be given to the difference. A common technique is to select an analysis period equal to the least common multiple of the alternative lives. Another approach is to select an analysis period and determine the salvage value for each alternative at that point in time. When using annual worth methods there is no need to establish equal lives.

Capitalized Cost—Problems occasionally arise involving extremely long analysis periods. For example, in governmental analysis of permanent structures such as roads, dams, and pipelines, the required maintenance can be spread over an infinite period ($n = \infty$). In these cases the analysis is called capitalized cost or more. Simply stated, capitalized cost is the present sum of money that would have to be set aside now, at a given interest rate, to provide a perpetual uniform cash flow. In equation form,

$$P = \frac{A}{i}$$ (equation 28.1)

INCREMENTAL ANALYSIS

Assume that the rate-of-return on two alternatives is known. Investment A yields 100 percent, and investment B yields 20 percent. Do we select A as the preferred alternative? Given further information we find that investment A was $1 returning $2 at the end of year 1, and investment B was $10,000 returning $12,000 at the end of year 1. The profit for A is $1 and B is $2,000. The lower rate of return (ROR) alternative in this case is probably the better investment if the minimum attractive rate of return (MARR) is 20 percent or less. This illustrates the need for a procedure to evaluate the return on the increment of initial investment if one alternative requires a higher initial investment than the other. This process should also apply to multiple alternatives. By examining the differences between alternatives, we can determine whether or not the differential costs are justified based on the differential benefits.

Rate of Return—This technique is based on the paired comparison of alternatives. The following steps should be followed in an incremental rate-of-return analysis:

1. Identify all alternatives. Be sure to consider the option of maintaining the status quo or what is often called "do nothing;"

2. compute the rate-of-return for each alternative and discard any alternative with ROR < MARR;
3. arrange remaining alternatives in ascending order of initial cost;
4. calculate the rate-of-return on the difference between the first two (lowest initial cost) alternatives. If this ΔROR $\geq$ MARR, retain the higher cost alternative, otherwise retain the lower cost alternative;
5. take the retained alternative from the previous step and compare it to the next higher alternative; and
6. repeat this process until all alternatives have been evaluated.

Example 28.3—

Given the following mutually-exclusive alternatives and a minimum attractive rate of return (MARR) of 5 percent, which one should be chosen? Use the incremental rate-of-return method and assume the "do nothing" alternative is not available.

YEAR	A	B	C
0	($2,500)	($2,738)	($3,000)
1	0	650	0
2	0	650	350
3	0	650	700
4	0	650	1,050
5	$3,191	650	1,400

Solution—The first step is to compute the rate-of-return for each alternative.

For alternative A:

$2,500 = $3,191 (P/F, i, 5)$

$(P/F, i, 5) = \dfrac{\$2,500}{\$3,191} = .7835$ and from table 27.3, $i = 5\%$

For alternative B:

$2,738 = $650 (P/A, i, 5)$

$(P/A, i, 5) = \dfrac{\$2,738}{\$650} = 4.212$ and from table 27.4, $i = 6\%$.

For alternative C:

$3,000 = $350 (P/G, i, 5)$

$(P/G, i, 5) = \dfrac{\$3,000}{\$350} = 8.571$

From the tables find:

Table 27.3	Table 27.4
(P/G, 5 %, 5)	(P/G, 6 %, 5)
8.237	7.934

Since 8.571 > 8.237, $i < 5\%$ and alternative C can be rejected.

The remaining alternatives are already ranked in ascending order. The next step is to compute the difference by subtracting the lower initial cost from the higher initial cost as shown below:

YEAR	A	B	B-A
0	($2,500)	($2,738)	($238)
1	0	650	650
2	0	650	650
3	0	650	650
4	0	650	650
5	$3,191	650	(2,541)

Next, calculate the rate-of-return by setting present worth of benefits equal to present worth of costs.

$650 (P/A, i, 4) = $238 + $2,540 (P/F, i, 5)$

Since we have two unknown discount factors in this equation, it must be solved by trial and error by using the appropriate factors for varying values of i. The first try should be the MARR of 5 percent, which results in:

Year 0 cost:		($ 238)
Year 5 cost:	$2,541 (0.7835) =	($1,991)
Total cost	=	($2,220)
Year 1-4 benefits	$650 (3.546) =	$2,305
Total cost less benefits	=	$ 76

Since the benefits are greater than the costs, or in other words, the net present worth of the increment is greater than 0, the rate-of-return on the increment must be something greater than 5 percent and we therefore accept the increment and retain the higher cost alternative, B.

Benefit-Cost Ratio—This analysis technique is based on the ratio of benefits to costs. An alternative is considered acceptable if the following criteria are met:

PW of benefits - PW of costs ≥ 0 or $EUAB - EUAC \geq 0$

Another way of stating this in terms of ratios is:

$$\dfrac{B}{C} = \dfrac{PW \text{ of benefits}}{PW \text{ of costs}} = \dfrac{EUAB}{EUAC} \geq 1$$

The incremental approach for the analysis of two or more alternatives will follow the same procedure as that for rate-of-return analysis.

Example 28.4—

Given the following mutually-exclusive alternatives and a MARR of 5 percent, which one should be chosen? Use the benefit-cost method and assume the "do nothing" alternative is not available.

YEAR	A	B	C
0	($2,500)	($2,738)	($3,000)
1	0	650	0
2	0	650	350
3	0	650	700
4	0	650	1,050
5	$3,191	650	1,400

Solution—The first step is to compute the benefit-cost ratio for each alternative.

For alternative A:

$$\frac{B}{C} = \frac{\$3{,}191\ (P/F,\ 5\%,\ 5)}{\$2{,}500} = \frac{\$3{,}191\ (.7835)}{\$2{,}500} = 1,\ \text{which is acceptable}$$

For alternative B:

$$\frac{B}{C} = \frac{\$650\ (P/A,\ 5\%,\ 5)}{\$2{,}738} = \frac{\$650\ (4.329)}{\$2{,}738} = 1.03,\ \text{which is also acceptable}$$

For alternative C:

$$\frac{B}{C} = \frac{\$350\ (P/G,\ 5\%,\ 5)}{\$3{,}000} = \frac{\$350\ (8.237)}{\$3{,}000} = 0.96,\ \text{which is not acceptable}$$

Alternative C is then rejected and we can proceed with the incremental analysis between A and B. These alternatives are already ranked in ascending order, and the difference is computed by subtracting the lower initial cost from the higher initial cost as shown below:

YEAR	A	B	B-A
0	($2,500)	($2,738)	($238)
1	0	650	650
2	0	650	650
3	0	650	650
4	0	650	650
5	$3,191	650	($2,541)

Next, calculate the ratio of the present worth of benefits and costs.

$$\frac{B}{C} = \frac{\$650\ (P/A,\ 5\%,\ 4)}{\$238 + \$2{,}541\ (P/F,\ 5\%,\ 5)} = \frac{\$650\ (3.546)}{\$238 + \$2{,}541\ (.7835)} = 1.03$$

As in the previous example, the ratio on the increment is favorable and we retain alternative B.

TAX CONSIDERATIONS

The effects of taxes on investments are a significant part of all real problems and should be considered. Because taxes have been ignored in our analysis, the results are considered a before-tax cash flow. If the consequences of income tax and other tax effects are incorporated into the economic analysis we will have an after-tax analysis. The following relationships are involved:

- before-tax cash flow;
- depreciation;
- taxable income = (before-tax cash flow) - (depreciation)
- income taxes = (taxable income) x (incremental tax rate); and
- after-tax cash flow = (before-tax cash flow) - (income taxes).

Tax laws are complex and changing. It is not our purpose to explain them in this text. All of the principles and techniques that have been developed can be applied to an after-tax analysis.

RECOMMENDED READING

1. Fleisher, G.A. 1994. *Introduction to Engineering Economy.* PWS Publishing Co.
2. Park, C.S. 1997. *Contemporary Engineering Economics.* 2nd Ed. Addison Wesley Publishing Co.
3. Steiner, H.M. 1992. *Engineering Economic Principles.* New York: McGraw-Hill Inc.

Portions of this chapter are from previous editions authored by Julian A. Piekarski, PE CCE

Section 7

Statistics, Probability, & Risk

Chapter 29

Statistics & Probability

Dr. Elizabeth Y. Chen and Mark T. Chen, PE CCE

INTRODUCTION

Statistics is the field of study where data are collected for the purpose of drawing conclusions and making inferences. Descriptive statistics is the summarization and description of data, and inferential statistics is the estimation, prediction, and/or generalization about the population based on the data from a sample

Four elements are essential to inferential statistical problems:

1. **Population** is the collection of all elements of interest to the decision-maker. The size of the population is usually denoted by N. Very often, the population is so large that a complete census is out of the question. Sometimes, not even a small population can be examined entirely because it may be destructive or prohibitively expensive to obtain the data. Under these situations, we draw inferences based upon a part of the population (called a sample).
2. **Sample** is a subset of data randomly selected from a population. the size of a sample is usually denoted by **n**.
3. **Statistical inference** is an estimation, prediction or generalization about the population based on the information from the sample.
4. **Reliability** is the measurement of the "goodness" of the inference.

Only the first two elements will be discussed in this chapter. Numerical characteristics of a population are called parameters of the population. The corresponding numerical characteristics calculated from a sample are called sample statistics.

LEARNING OBJECTIVES

After completing this chapter, readers should be able to

- understand basic definitions and terminologies in probability and statistics, and
- apply statistical techniques in decision making.

DESCRIBING DATA

In general, data can be classified as either qualitative or quantitative.

Qualitative Data
Qualitative data can be categorized or summarized.

Example:
As of September 2, 2003, the total membership of AACE International is 4,307. This can be classified according to member types:

members and associates	4,036
students	147
honorary	124
total	4,307

Or according to geographical distribution:

U.S.	3,509
Canada	480
Caribbean	28
Asia	158
Africa	29
Europe	48
Australia	55
total	4,307

Quantitative Data
The description of quantitative data is more complex. It can be described graphically or numerically.

Some graphic methods for describing quantitative data include the following:

- frequency distribution and relative frequency (f/n),
- stem and leaf plots, and
- histogram.

Numerical methods for describing quantitative data include the following:

- measures of location (central tendency),
   -mean (average),
   -median, and
   -mode;
- measures of dispersion,
   -range,
   -variance, and
   -standard deviation;
- relative standing,
   -percentile, and
   -Z-score.

Example:
Many companies invest on training their employees. The following average training hours for every employee are selected from "The 100 Best Companies to Work For" (*Fortune*, January 20, 2003). Numbers are rounded to the nearest 5 for convenience.

145	50	35	50	25	160	30	40	40	20
40	20	30	95	40	50	30	50	20	35
70	35	40	45	30	45	70	45	40	140
50	70	20	30	40	40	30	60	40	50
60	55	50	35	40	30	45	75	20	40

The data will first be divided into smaller equal intervals (classes). The number of observations that fall into each class, the frequency, is then counted. These classes should not overlap and there should be enough classes to include all the data. There may be open-ended intervals when the first class contains no lower limit or the last data class contains no upper limit. The number of classes depends on the number of observations in the data set. In practice, a frequency distribution usually has from five to twenty classes.

The stem and leaf plot is developed by first determining the *stem* and then adding *leaves*. In this example, the stem is formed by the "tens" digit and the leaves are the "ones" digit. Note that the stem values are placed to the left of the vertical line and the leaves on the right.

Example: 45 is shown as:

Stem	Leaf
4	5

Stem	Leaf	f frequency	f/n relative frequency
2	5, 0, 0, 0, 0, 0	6	6/50
3	5, 0, 0, 0, 5, 5, 0, 0, 0, 5, 0	11	11/50
4	0, 0, 0, 0, 0, 5, 5, 5, 0, 0, 0, 0, 0, 5, 0	15	15/50
5	0, 0, 0, 0, 0, 0, 5, 0	8	8/50
6	0, 0	2	2/50
7	0,0,0,5	4	4/50
8		0	0
9+	95, 145, 160, 140	4	4/50
		50	50/50

Figure 29.1—Stem, Leaf, Frequency and Relative Frequency Distributions

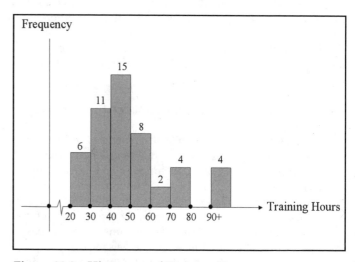

Figure 29.2—Histogram of Training Hours

The sum of the training hours from the above 50 companies is

$$145 + 50 + 35 + 50 + \ldots + 20 + 40 = 2{,}445 \text{ hours}$$

Mean (average): Mean is the sum of measurements divided by the number of measurements.
Population mean is denoted by μ = sum of all numbers in population/N
Sample mean is denoted by x = sum of all numbers in sample/n
The mean of this example is 2,445/50 = 48.9 hours

Median: Median is the middle number when the data observations are arranged in ascending or descending order. If the number *n* of measurements is even, the median is the average of the two middle measurements in the ranking. The median of this example is 40 hours.

For symmetric data set, the mean equals to the median.

If the median is less than the mean, the data set is skewed to the right.
If the median is greater than the mean, the data set is skewed to the left.

Mode: Mode is the measurement that occurs most often in the data set
The mode of this example is 40 hours.

If the observations have two modes, the data set is said to have a bimodal distribution.
When the data set is multi-modal, the mode(s) is no longer a viable measure of the central tendency.
In a large data set, the modal class is the class containing the largest frequency. The simplest way to define the mode will then be the midpoint of the modal class.

Comparison of the Mean, Median, and Mode

The mean is the most commonly used measure of central location. However, it is affected by extreme values. For example, the high incomes of a few employees will influence the mean income of a small company. Under such situation, the median maybe a better measure of central tendency.

The median is of most value in describing large data sets. It is often used in reporting salaries, ages, sale prices, and test scores.

The mode is frequently applied in marketing. For example, the modal men's shirt neck size and sleeve length, shoe size, etc.

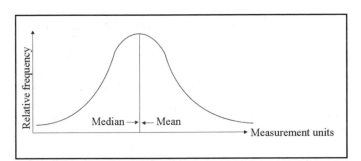

Figure 29.3—Symmetry

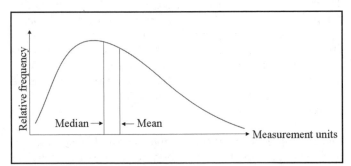

Figure 29.4—Rightward Skewness

Numerical Measures of Variability

Measures of central tendency do not describe the spread of the data set, which may be of greater interest to the decision-maker.

The simplest measure of the variability of a data set is its range.

Range: The difference between the largest and the smallest values of the data set.
The range of this example is 160 - 20 = 140 hours.

The range only uses the two extreme values and ignores the rest of the data set. One instinctive attempt to measure the dispersion would be to find the deviation of each value from the mean and then calculate the average of these deviations. One will find that this value is always zero, an answer which is no accident. The alternative might be to calculate the average absolute deviation. However, this measure is rarely used because it is difficult to handle algebraically and does not have the nice mathematical properties possessed by the variance.

Variance: The average of the squared deviations from the mean.

The population variance is denoted by

$$\sigma^2 = \frac{(x - \mu)^2}{N} = \frac{x^2 - N\,\mu^2}{N}$$

The sample variance is denoted by

$$s^2 = \frac{(x - \bar{x})^2}{n - 1} = \frac{x^2 - n\bar{x}^2}{n - 1}$$

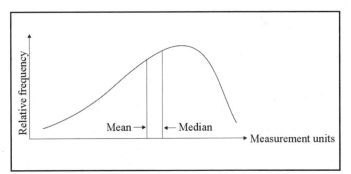

Figure 29.5—Leftward Skewness

Note the divisor $(n-1)$ is used instead of the more obvious n. This will make the sample variance, s^2, a better estimate of the population variance, σ^2. The explanation for this practice is beyond the scope of this text but can be found in many statistics textbooks.

The variance of this example is:

$$s^2 = \frac{162{,}825 - 50(48.4)^2}{50 - 1} = 882.95 \text{ hours}$$

The variance has a squared unit and is in a much larger scale than that of the original data. To offset these, the square root is used.

Standard Deviation: The positive square root of the variance.
The population standard deviation is denoted by σ.
The sample standard deviation is denoted by s.

The sample standard deviation s of this example is

$$\sqrt{882.95} = 29.71 \text{ hours}$$

The standard deviation can be approximated by range/6. Some may prefer to use range/4.

Measures of Relative Standing
Another measure of interest is the description measurement of the relative location of a particular observation within a data set.

pth percentile: In any data set, the pth percentile is the number with exactly p percent of the measurements fall below it and (100-p) percent fall above it when the data are arranged in ascending or descending order.
The first (lower) quartile: the 25th percentile
The third (upper) quartile: the 75th percentile

And you guessed it; the second (middle) quartile is the median.

For the above training hours example, the 80th percentile is 60 hours.

Another measure of relative standing is the famous z-score.

A z-score is the number of standard deviations a point is above or below the mean of a set of data.

The population z-score for a measurement x is $z = (x - \mu)/?$

The sample z-score for a measurement x is $z = (x - \bar{x})/s$

RANDOM VARIABLES AND SOME IMPORTANT PROBABILITY DISTRIBUTIONS

Analyzing frequency distribution for every decision-making situation would be very time consuming. Fortunately, many physical events that appear to be unrelated have the same underlying characteristics and can be explained by the same laws of probability. The mathematical model used to represent frequency distributions is called a probability distribution. To understand the concept and know which distribution to use in a particular situation will save considerable time and effort in the decision-making process. We will start from the concept of a random variable.

Random Variable: A random variable is a variable whose numerical value is determined by the outcome of a random experiment. A random experiment is the type of experiment that may produce different results in spite of all efforts to keep the conditions of performance constant.

If a random variable can take on only countable number of values, then we call it a discrete random variable. For example, the number of sales made by a salesperson in a given day

Random variables that can assume any value within some interval or intervals are called continuous random variables. For example, the length of time an employee is late for work

Probability Distribution: Probability Distribution is expressed in a table listing all possible values that a random variable can take on together with the associated probabilities.

Notice that the random variable itself will be denoted by X, while the small x denotes a particular value of X. The symbol $p(x) = \Pr(X=x)$ means the probability that the experiment yields the value x.
In a discrete probability distribution, each p(x) 0 for all values of x and p(x)=1.
Example: Two coins are tossed. Let X be the number of heads appeared.

Probability distribution of X

x	0	1	2
p(x)	1/4	2/4	1/4

The probabilities p(x) can be interpreted as long-run relative frequencies. For instance, if two coins were flipped many, many times, we could anticipate obtaining two tails (X=0) about one-fourth of the time, one head and one tail (X=1) one half of the time and two heads one-fourth of the time. Therefore, the probability distribution for a random variable is a theoretical model for the relative frequency distribution of a population.

Like the frequency distribution, the mean and standard deviation of a probability distribution need to be calculated to describe the central location and spread of the probability distribution.

The predicted long-range average of a discrete random variable X, often called the expected value (or mean) of X, is defined by

$$\mu = E(x) = \ xp(x)$$

The population variance is defined as

$$\mu = E(x-\mu)^2 = \ (x-\mu)^2 p(x)$$

The standard deviation σ is the square root of the variance.

In the above two-coin example, the expected value of X is

$$\mu = \ xp(x) = 0^*p(x=0) + 1^*p(x=1) + 2^*p(x=2) = 0^*(1/4) + 1^*(1/2) + 2^*(1/4) = 1$$

It is very important to remember that the expected value is not a number we "expect" to get at a given experiment. What this expected value tells is that if we were to toss two fair coins many, many times, carefully record the number of heads appeared in each toss, and at the end calculate the average number of heads, then this average would be 1.

The variance and the standard deviation of X is respectively,

$$\sigma^2 = (0-1)^2 (1/4) + (1-1)^2 (1/2) + (2-1)^2 (1/4) = 1/2$$

$$\sigma = \sqrt{\tfrac{1}{2}}$$

Another example of expected value is the following:

Suppose you work for an insurance company and sell an individual 10-year $100,000 term life insurance coverage at an annual premium of $240. Actuarial tables show that the probability of death during the next year for a person of your customer's age, sex, health, etc., is .001. What is the expected gain to the company for a policy of this type?

Gain(X)	Event	Probability
$240	customer lives	.999
$240–100,000	customer dies	.001

If the customer lives, the company keeps the $240 premium. If the customer dies, the company must pay $100,000 and will have a net "gain" of $(240-100,000). The expected gain is therefore

$$\mu = E(X) = (240)(.999) + (240 - 100,000)(.001) = 240(.999 + .001) - 100,000(.001) = \$140$$

Please note that for each policy sold, the insurance company is taking a risk of either gaining $240 or losing $99,760. However, if the company were to sell a very large number of such insurance policies to customers possessing the characteristics described above, the company would on the average net $140 per policy written.

DISCRETE RANDOM VARIABLES

There are several theoretical discrete probability distributions that have extensive applications in decision-making. One will be introduced in this section.

Binomial Distribution

Many decisions are of the either/or variety. A company bidding for a contract may either get the contract or it won't. The responses to a public opinion poll may be either "favor" or "oppose". Many experiments (situations) have only two possible alternatives, such as yes/no, pass/fail, or acceptable/defective.

Consider a series of experiments which have the following properties:

- The experiment is performed n times under identical conditions.
- The result of each experiment can be classified into one of two categories, say, success (S) and failure (F).
- The probability of a success, denoted by p, is the same for each experiment. The probability of a failure is denoted by q. Note that $q = 1-p$.
- Each experiment is independent of all the others.
- The binomial random variable X is the number of successes in n experiments. Probability of x successes in n experiments:

$$p(x) = \binom{n}{x} p^x q^{n-x} \qquad x = 0,1,2,\ldots,n$$

The name *binomial* arises from the fact that the probabilities p(x), x = 0,1,2,...,n, are terms of the binomial expansion, $(q+p)^n$.

Mean, Variance, and Standard Deviation for a Binomial Random Variable:

Mean: $\mu = np$
Variance: $\sigma^2 = npq$
Standard Deviation: $\sigma = \sqrt{npq}$

Several extensive tables of the binomial distributions for some values of p and n have been published. Either one of the cumulated probabilities $\Pr(X \ x)$ or $\Pr(X \ x)$ is listed.

Example: Suppose your company ships electrical fuses in lots, each lot containing 10,000 fuses. Your quality control plan requires that you will randomly sample twenty-five fuses from each lot and accept the lot if the number of defective fuses, x, is less than 2. If x 2 you will reject the lot and will conduct a complete re-inspection. What is the probability of accepting a lot (x=0,1) if the actual fraction defectives in the lot is (a) .1? (b) .01?

Solution:

$n = 25$

(a) If p = 0.1; q = 1-p=1-0.1=0.9

Pr (Accepting the lot) = Pr(x < 2) = Pr (x ≤ 1) = Pr(x = 0) + Pr(x = 1)

$$= \binom{25}{0} (.1)^0 (.9)^{25} + \binom{25}{1} (.1)^1 (.9)^{24}$$

$$= .27121$$

(b) If p = .01; q = .99

$$Pr(x \leq 1) = \binom{25}{0} (.01)^0 (.99)^{25} + \binom{25}{1}$$

$$(.01)^1 (.99)^{24} = .77782 + .19642$$
$$= .97424$$

The two measurements indicate that, under the proposed quality control plan, there is 73 percent chance that you will reject the lot if in fact 10 percent (p=0.1) of the fuses are manufactured are defective. If only 1 percent of the fuses are defective, the chance of re-inspection is very small (less than 3 percent).

Continuous Random Variables

The probability distribution for a continuous random variable is often denoted by $f(x)$ and is variously called a probability density function. The primary difference between probabilities for discrete and continuous random variables is that while probabilities for a discrete random variable are defined for specific values of the variable, the probabilities of a continuous random variable are defined for a range of values of the variable. The graphic form of $f(x)$ is a smooth curve and the area under the curve corresponds to probabilities for x. For example, the area A beneath the curve between the two points a and b, is the probability Pr($a<x<b$).

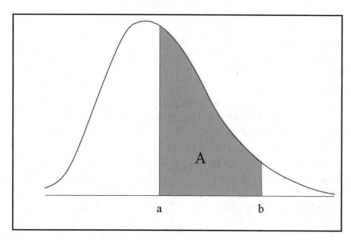

Figure 29.6—Continuous Distribution

Because there is no area over a point, the probability associated with any particular value of x, say, x=a, is equal to zero. Hence, Pr(a x b)=Pr($a<x<b$). In other words, the probability is the same regardless of whether the endpoints of the interval are included. The total area under the curve, which is the total probability for x, equals to 1.

The areas under most probability density functions are obtained by the use of calculus or other numerical methods. This is often a difficult procedure. However, as with commonly used discrete probability distributions, there are tables exist for finding probabilities under commonly used continuous probability distributions.

Similar to the requirements for a discrete probability distribution, we require

$$f(x) \ 0 \ \text{and} \quad f(x)dx = 1 \qquad \text{for all x}$$

The Normal Distribution

The most important continuous distribution in statistical decision making is the *normal distribution*. It is important for the following reasons:
- as odd as it may seem, many observed variables are normally distributed, or approximately, so.
- many of the procedures used in statistical inference require the assumption that a population is normal.

Probability distribution for a normal random variable X is

$$f(x) = \frac{1}{-2\check{s} \ \sigma} \ e^{-\frac{1}{2}\left(\frac{x-\mu}{-2\check{s}\ \sigma}\right)^2} \qquad \text{for } -\infty x<+\infty$$

where

μ = mean of the random variable X
σ = standard deviation of X
e = 2.71828…
š = 3.14159…

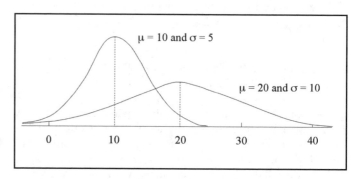

Figure 29.7—Two Normal Distributions

The graph of a normal distribution is called a normal curve and it has the following characteristics:

- It is bell-shaped and is symmetrical about the mean. The mean, median and mode are all equal. Probability density decreases symmetrically as x values move from the mean in either direction. Since the total area (probability) under the curve is 1, the area on each side of the mean is 1/2.

- The curve approaches but never touches the horizontal axis. However, when the value of X is more than three standard deviations from the mean, the curve approaches the axis so closely that the extended area under the curve is negligible.

The Standard Normal Distribution

If X is a normally distributed random variable with mean μ and standard deviation σ, the random variable Z, defined by

$$Z = (X - \mu)/\sigma$$

is a normally distributed variable with mean zero and standard deviation 1. The probability distribution of Z is called the standard normal distribution. Notice that z gives the number of standard deviations that a value of x lies above or below the mean. By using the Z score, all normal distributions can be transformed to Standard Normal Distribution. We can say that if X is $N(\mu, \sigma^2)$, then $Z = (x - \mu)/\sigma$ is $N(0,1)$.

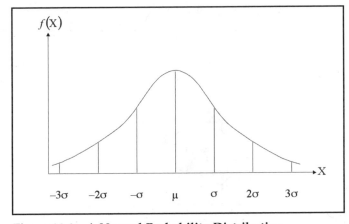

Figure 29.8—A Normal Probability Distribution

The standard normal distribution table that gives the area under the standard normal curve is available. Some tables give the area between the mean 0 and any particular value of z, where $0 < z < 3.59$. Remember that the area represents the probability that a value of z will lie between zero and the given value and it must always be positive. Further, since the normal curve is symmetric, the area between -z and zero is the same as the area between zero and z; the area between -z and +z is twice the area between zero and z.
Frequently quoted z values and the probabilities:

Table 29.1—Frequently Quoted Z Values and Probabilities

Z	Pr (-z < Z < z)	Pr(Z<-z) or Pr(Z>z)
1.00	.683	.158
1.282	.80	.10
1.645	.90	.05
1.96	.95	.025
2.00	.954	.023
2.326	.98	.01
2.576	.99	.005
3.00	.997	.0015

Example: The actual amount of coffee grounds that a filling machine puts into "6-ounce" jars varies from jar to jar, and it may be assumed as a normal random variable with a standard deviation of 0.04 ounce. If the jar contains less than 6 ounces, it is considered unacceptable. Determine the mean fill of the machine so that only 1 percent of the jars will be unacceptable.

Solution: Let x be the amount of coffee in the jar. We are given $\sigma = 0.04$

We are asked to find the average fill, μ, such that Pr(x<6)=.01

$$Px(x<6) = Pr\left(\frac{x - \mu}{\sigma} < \frac{6 - \mu}{\sigma}\right) = Pr\left(z < \frac{6 - \mu}{.04}\right) = .01$$

From the above table we find that
Pr(z < –2.326) = .01; therefore,

$$\frac{6 - \mu}{.04} = -2.326 \qquad \mu = 6.093$$

If the average fill is set at 6.093 ounces, only 1 percent of the jars will contain less than 6 ounces.

PRACTICE PROBLEMS AND QUESTIONS

1. After a long-term observation of a production line, the following productivity data are recorded.

Work-Hours/ Unit	Frequency (f)	Relative Frequency (f/N)	Cumulative Relative Frequency
6	6	6/200	6/200
7	11	11/200	17/200
8	27	27/200	44/200
9	47	47/200	91/200
10	52	52/200	143/200
11	44	44/200	187/200
12	9	9/200	196/200
13	4	4/200	200/200
Total	200 = N		

Find:
  a. mean
  b. median
  c. mode
  d. variance
  e. standard deviation

2. The average project duration to build a greenfield man-
    ufacturing plant is 26 months with a standard deviation
    of two months, assuming the project critical path follows
    a normal distribution. Your company is planning to
    build a similar greenfield manufacturing plant. The sen-
    ior management is interested in the following three
    schedule outcomes:

    a. What is the chance to complete the project between 24
       and 28 months?
    b. What is the likelihood of completing the project in 24
       months?
    c. What is the risk that the project duration would exceed
       30 months?

Solutions:

1. a. Mean is the average work-hours/unit of the 200
       observations.

$$\mu = \frac{x}{N} = \frac{(6 \times 6) + (7 \times 11) + (8 \times 27) + (9 \times 47) + (10 \times 52) + (11 \times 44) + (12 \times 9) + (13 \times 4)}{200}$$

    b. After arranging the observed 200 workhours/unit
       data in ascending order, the median is the average of
       the 100th and 101st observations. Both are 10 work-
       hours/unit, so the median is 10 workhours/unit.

    c. The mode is the observation that occurred most often.
       Ten workhours/unit was recorded 52 times, the high-
       est frequency. Thus, 10 workhours/unit is the mode.

    d. variance $= \sigma^2 = \frac{(x - \mu)^2}{N} = \frac{x2 - N\mu^2}{N}$

$$= \frac{[(6^2 \times 6) + (7^2 \times 11) + (8^2 \times 27) + (9^2 \times 47) + (10^2 \times 52) + (11^2 \times 44) + (12^2 \times 9) + (13^2 \times 4)] - 200 \times (9.58)^2}{200}$$

$$= \frac{18786 - 200 (9.58)^2}{200} = \frac{18786 - 18355.28}{200} = 2.1536$$

e. Standard deviation $\sigma = \sqrt{2.1536} = 1.47$
   workhours/unit.

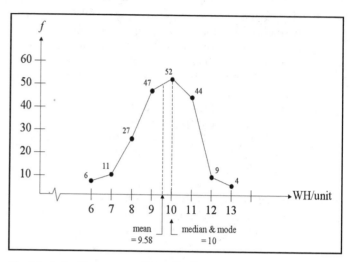

Problem 1—Frequency Distribution

2. a. The project duration between 24 and 28 months is
       within one standard deviation from the average
       (mean) duration of 26 months. Since the probability
       within one standard deviation from the mean is 0.68,
       this project has a 68 percent chance to be competed
       between 24 and 28 months.

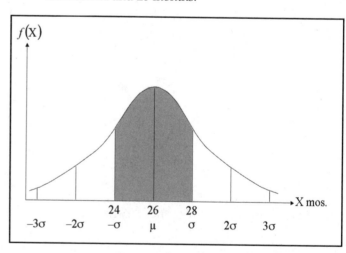

Problem 2a—Project Duration Between 24 and 28 months

    b. Twenty-four-month duration is shorter than the 26-
       month mean duration by two months. Referring to
       the standard normal distribution table, the probabili-
       ty is 0.16. This project has only 16 percent chance to
       be completed within 24 months.

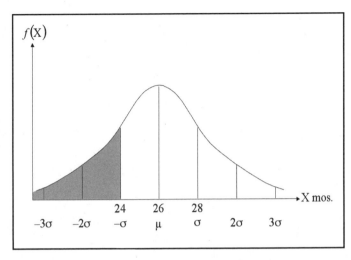

Problem 2b—Project Duration within 24 Months

REFERENCES

1. AACE International. 2003. *Certification Study Guide*. 2nd ed. Chapter 20.
2. Brockett, P., and A. Levine. 1984. *Statistics & Probability & Their Applications*. CBS College Publishing.
3. Byrkit, D.R. 1987. *Statistics Today*. The Benjamin Cummings Publishing Company.
4. Groebner, D. F., and P.W. Shannon. 1985. *Business Statistics*. Charles E. Merrill Publishing Company.
5. McClave, J.T. and F. H. Dietrich. 1985. *Statistics*. 3rd.ed. Dellen Publishing Company.
6. Smith, G. 1985. *Statistical Reasoning*. Allyn and Bacon.
7. Summers, G. W., W. S. Peters, and C. P. Armstrong. 1985. *Basic Statistics in Business and Economics*. 4th ed. Wadsworth Publishing Company.

c. Thirty-month duration is four months longer than the 26-month mean duration, which is two standard deviations above the mean. From the standard normal distribution table, the probability exceeding two standard deviations is 0.023. Thus, there is only a 2 percent risk that the project duration would exceed 30 months.

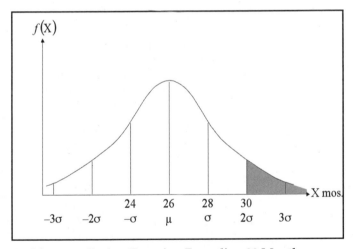

Problem 2c—Project Duration Exceeding 30 Months

Chapter 30

Basic Concepts in Descriptive Statistics

Dr. Frederick B. Muehlhausen

INTRODUCTION

The manager of the construction process must make decisions daily that affect the operation of an individual project as well as the company as a whole. Rarely does a manager have the intuition to make decisions that avoid serious or continued error without input from past field and company performance. The successful company collects information so that when analyzed, good decisions can be made. Statistics constitutes all methods useful for the analysis of this information. In general, statistical methods are of two types and subsequent purpose:

1. **descriptive statistics**, which allow the cost engineer to organize, summarize, interpret, and communicate quantitative information obtained from observations; and

2. **inferential statistics**, which allow the cost engineer to go beyond the data collected from a small sample to formulate tentative conclusions about the population from which the sample was taken.

This chapter examines some of the basic concepts and procedures that are a part of descriptive statistics.

LEARNING OBJECTIVES

After completing this chapter, the readers should be able to

- understand the basic concepts and procedures of descriptive statistics, such as frequency distributions, frequency graphs, the normal curve, and cumulative probability curve.

FREQUENCY DISTRIBUTIONS

A concrete contractor engaged in installing foundation footings and walls needs to be able to predict with some accuracy the time it takes to install formwork. Not only will a knowledge of past performance help the contractor predict future performance useful in estimating and scheduling, this knowledge also will provide an internal benchmark for cost control purposes once the project is in progress. Before these predictions can be made, the contractor must know more about past performance. Thus, data about similar forming techniques is collected from 20 projects completed over the last several years. This data is summarized in Table 30.1.

Table 30.1—Formwork Production in Hours Per Square Foot of Contact Area

JOB	HRS/SFCA	JOB	HRS/SFCA	JOB	HRS/SFCA	JOB	HRS/SFCA
1	.050	6	.050	11	.040	16	.050
2	.050	7	.065	12	.055	17	.060
3	.065	8	.060	13	.045	18	.055
4	.055	9	.050	14	.050	19	.070
5	.050	10	.045	15	.065	20	.045

The data above is hard to interpret in its present form. It must be organized so that the data yields meaning to the manager.

Frequency Distribution—A frequency distribution is an organization of measures or observations that lists the class (in this case, the productivity rate as measured in labor hours per square foot of contact area) and the frequency or the number of times this production rate was achieved. In Table 30.2, the data has been rearranged by listing the data from high productivity to low productivity (column 1), and the number of times this production rate occurred (column 2).

Note that it is much easier to get a "feel" for the measures observed when arranged by frequency (column 2) than when examining the unorganized raw data. One can easily determine the highest productivity (.040 HRS/SFCA), the lowest (.070 HRS/SFCA), and the production rate that occurred most often (.050 HRS/SFCA). In addition, one can easily observe how the measures are distributed along the entire scale; that is, whether the measures are distributed uniformly or whether gaps appear at certain points. In this case, the data is distributed uniformly.

Cumulative Frequency Distribution—Sometimes, one is not particularly interested in the number of occurrences within a particular class but in the number of occurrences that fall below or above a certain value. For example, suppose the contractor bid this type of formwork at .055 HRS/SFCA. Any value above this rate would be over budget and extend the project duration. The question arises, "How many projects failed to yield the required production rate?" The cumulative frequency distribution answers this question by adding successively from the bottom (.07 HRS/SFCA) the number of cases in each class interval. Thus, the distribution would be developed as shown in Table 30.2, column 3. Note that the topmost entry in the cumulative frequency column must agree with the total number of measures ($n = 20$). If it does not, then an error has been made in adding the frequencies.

Interpretation of the cumulative frequency distribution (col-

umn 3) indicates that 6 of the 20 productivity rates fall below (too many hours expended per square foot of contact area) the required rate of .055 HRS/SFCA. In order to be within budget and on time for more than 2/3 of the projects, the data indicates that the contractor has two choices: (1) bid future work at a higher rate per square foot of contact area, or (2) implement process changes to increase production on future projects.

Cumulative Percentage Distribution—Sometimes it is useful to show the percent of scores that fall below certain values. The contractor acknowledges the fact that variations from project to project in labor and management will prevent process changes from reducing the rate on all projects to .055 HRS/SFCA or lower. In addition, market competition will not allow the budget rate to go above .055 HRS/SFCA. The contractor will accept a 10 percent failure rate. That is, 90 percent of the projects must yield a production rate of .055 HRS/SFCA or less. The cumulative frequency distribution can be converted into a cumulative percentage distribution to readily find the failure rate. This is accomplished by dividing each cumulative frequency by the total number of measures ($N = 20$). Table 30.2, column 4, shows the cumulative percents for the production rates.

The advantage of this distribution is that it readily shows the percentage of measures falling below a certain value. Generally, it is more meaningful to know the percentage of those measures that fall below a certain value rather than to know the number of measures. In this case, 30 percent of the production rates failed to make .055 HRS/SFCA. Hence, one would conclude that the contractor would not be satisfied.

FREQUENCY GRAPHS

Table 30.2—Frequency Distributions

COLUMN 1	COLUMN 2	COLUMN 3	COLUMN 4
rate (SFCA)	frequency (f)	cum. freq. (cf)	cum. percent (%)
.040	1	20	100
.045	3	19	95
.050	7	16	80
.055	3	9	45
.060	2	6	30
.065	3	4	20
.070	1	1	5
	$n = 20$		

Once the contractor finds that 30 percent of the projects yield an unacceptable production rate, this information is conveyed to project management and labor. Rather than show the information in tabular form, the contractor decides to present the information graphically. Graphs convey the essential characteristics of a frequency distribution in a pictorial form. Graphical information is much more pleasing to view than tables, and so provides an effective medium for communicating frequency distribution information to others.

Frequency graphs have two characteristics in common: (1) one axis that represents all possible scores or classes within a distribution, and (2) one axis that represents the frequency of occurrence of that score or class. Frequency distributions are represented graphically via the histogram or the frequency polygon.

Histogram—In a histogram, the frequency of each score or class is represented as a vertical bar. For the production rate data, a histogram would be produced as shown in Figure 30.1.

When developing the histogram, the 3/4 rule should be applied. That is, the highest frequency should be laid out so that the height is approximately 3/4 the length of the horizontal axis. Otherwise, the viewer may obtain the wrong impression based on graph appearance rather than on graph data. The bar width should be the same as the "real limit" of a class. For example, suppose the production rates were rounded off to the nearest .005, then the real productivity rate for class .05 would fall between .0475 and .0525. Thus, the width of the vertical bar would be .005 and extend from .0475 to .0525 on the graph. In addition, the graph should be titled in a descriptive fashion to indicate what the graph is showing.

Frequency Polygon—For the frequency polygon, the vertical and horizontal axes are laid out the same way as for the histogram, but instead of drawing a vertical bar, a point is plot-

ted at the exact score (or midpoint of the interval) and at a height corresponding to the frequency of that score (or interval). These points are then connected by a straight line, which results in a polygon. See Figure 30.2.

The reason for constructing histograms and frequency polygons is to reveal how scores are distributed along the score scale. That is, the form of the distribution is shown. A distribution is symmetrical if one side is a mirror image of the other. If not, it is asymmetrical. Asymmetrical curves can be skewed either positively or negatively. See Figure 30.3.

For negative skewness, the tail travels to the left; for positive skewness, the tail travels to the right. The production rate frequency polygon, Figure 30.3, indicates a mild skew in the positive direction. Another noticeable feature of a polygon is the number of humps or high points. If only one high point, then the curve is unimodal. If two humps, then the curve is bimodal. For three humps, it is trimodal, and so on. The production rate frequency polygon, Figure 30.2, shows 2 humps, one much higher than the other.

The frequency graph's information should generate curiosity among the viewers. In this case, the following questions arise, "Why the second hump at .065 HRS/SFCA? What causes the variation? Can we isolate this cause and fix it?" For example, suppose that an examination of job data reveals that the projects with the lower productivity rate (higher number of hours per square foot of contact area installed) occurred where formwork was stacked. One might conclude that the stacking activity requires more hours related to square feet of contact area than if no stacking occurred. Thus, the outcome of the analysis would be to have two budget rates—one for when panels are not stacked and one for when they are. Based on the frequency distribution, viable budget rates would be .050 HRS/SFCA for no stacking and .065 HRS/SFCA for stacking. Each rate reflects a mode of the frequency distribution.

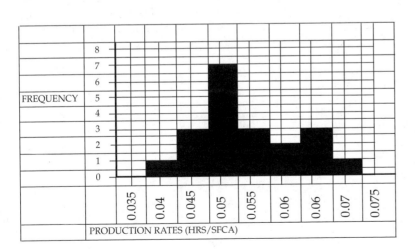

Figure 30.1—Histogram of Production Rates

MEASURES OF CENTRAL TENDENCY

The frequency distributions can be characterized by certain statistics. One type of statistic is called the index of central tendency, or average, and represents the general location of a distribution of measures on the measurement scale. There are three commonly used indexes of central tendency—the mode, the median, and the mean.

Mode—The mode is the simplest measure of central tendency. It is merely the score value or measure that occurs most often in a distribution of scores. For the production rate distribution, the score occurring most often is .050 HRS/SFCA. Hence, the mode for this distribution is .050.

Median—The median is the middle point in a distribution. Half of the distribution is above this point and half is below. To find the median one arranges the scores in order. For example, consider the following observations of concrete test cylinders: 2700 psi, 2750 psi, 2965 psi, 3100 psi, 3130 psi, 3480 psi, and 3500 psi. The score, 3100 psi, is the middle point. There are three observations above and below the median of 3100 psi.

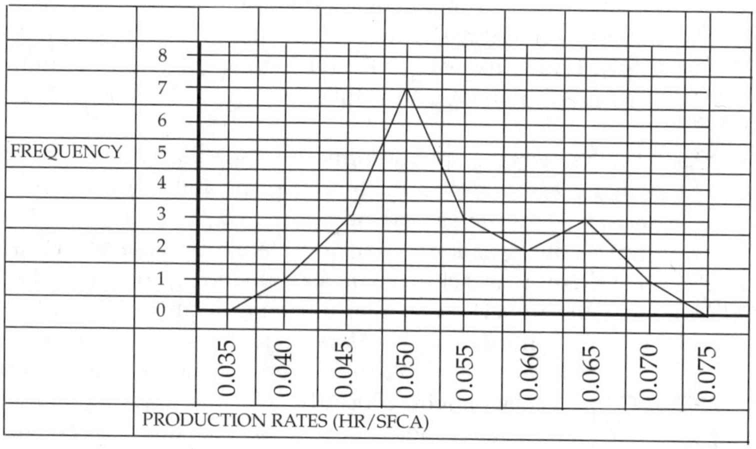

When the number of scores is even or there is a repetition of a certain score, then the location of the median requires computation. Consider the production rate distribution shown in Figure 30.4. Since there are 20 scores, the median is the point below which 10 cases fall.

If one counts from the left of the distribution, one finds that the median falls between the sixth and seventh .05 in the distribution. Since there is an additional .05 lying above the tenth score which is also .05, one cannot say that .05 is the median. Looking at the distribution, there are 4 scores that fall below .05, and 9 scores that lie above .05. Thus, .05 would not fit the definition of the median. But, one knows that the median falls somewhere within the interval .005, somewhere between .0475 and .0525. One can locate the median within an interval by applying the formula shown in Figure 30.5.

Mean—The best known and most reliable measure of central tendency is the mean. The mean is the arithmetic average of a group of scores. Thus, for the production rate distribution containing the 20 observations in Table 30.1, one would compute the mean as shown in Table 30.3.

Comparison of Mean, Median, and Mode—If the contractor wants to know what production rate occurred most often, the mode would be calculated. However, the mode is a crude and unstable measure of central tendency and is generally not used to describe a distribution. Usually the median or the mean is used. However, there is an important difference between the median and mean. The median is a rank or a position statistic unaffected by the numerical size of the individual scores, while the mean is sensitive to the size of the individual scores in a distribution, including extreme scores.

If the frequency distribution is unimodal and perfectly symmetrical, then the mean, median, and mode will fall at exactly the same point. This frequency distribution is called the *normal curve*. If a

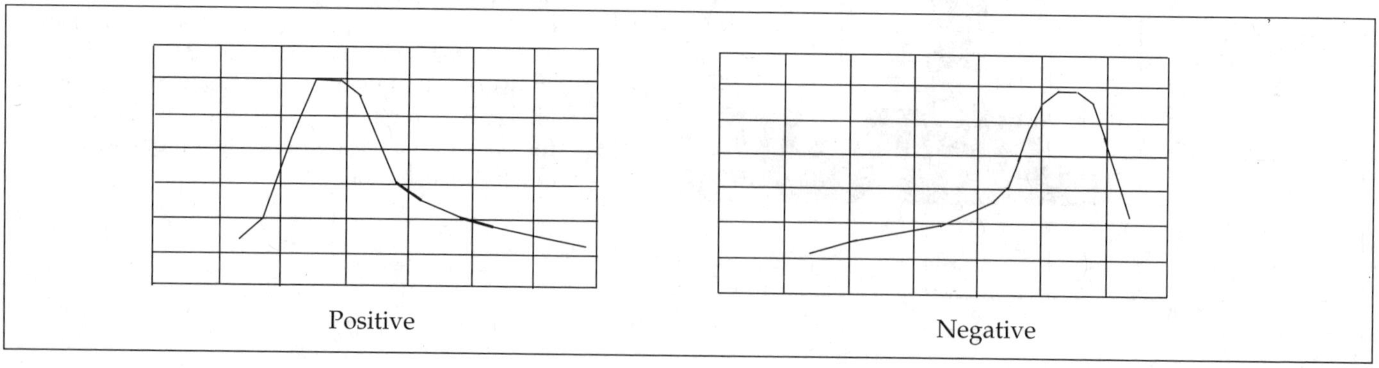

Figure 30.2—Frequency Polygon of Production Rates

Figure 30.3—Skewed Curves

04, .045, .045, .045, .05, .05, .05, .05, .05, .05, .05, .055, .055, .055, .06, .06, .065, .065, .065, .07

$|\sim\sim$

10 scores <-- | -----> 10 scores

Figure 30.4—Production Rate Distribution

Table 30.3—Calculation of the Mean Production Rate

RATE (HRS/SFCA)	FREQUENCY (F)	PRODUCT
.040	1	.040
.045	3	.135
.050	7	.350
.055	3	.165
.060	2	.120
.065	3	.195
.070	1	.070
TOTALS	20	1.075

Mean = Sum of scores/N = 1.075/20 = .05375

$Mdn = L + [(N/2-cfb)/fw]i = .0475 + [(20/2 - 4)/7].005 = .05179$

where: Mdn = the median
        N = total number of cases in the distribution
        L = lower real limit
        cfb = the cumulative frequency below
        fw = the frequency of cases within the median
        interval i = interval size

Figure 30.5—Calculation of the Median Production Rate

distribution is skewed (that is, scores are concentrated more at one end or the other), then the curve will not be symmetrical, and the three measures of central tendency will not be equal. Note that the median lies between the mode and mean in all skewed distributions. If negatively skewed, the median is higher than the mean. If positively skewed, the median is lower than the mean.

The mean is the most stable or reliable measure of central tendency. If one were to draw a sample from the total population, the mean would show less fluctuation from sample to sample than the medians. Thus, if one wanted to infer some characteristic about a population from a sample, the mean would yield the most reliable estimate of the population parameter. Or, stated another way, if the contractor wanted to bid the next job based on past experience, the best estimate (that rate with the least amount of error) of the actual production rate would be the mean of .05375 HRS/SFCA.

MEASURE OF VARIABILITY

The measures of central tendency (mean, median, and mode) provide a concise index of the average value of a set of scores or measures. However, there is more to be known about a distribution of scores than this one characteristic. The amount of variability or spread of the scores within the distribution is also an important characteristic to know about a given distribution. For example, suppose the production rates varied from .02 to .09, a spread of .07, rather than .04 to .07, a spread of .03; yet, in both instances the mean was .05375. If the contractor used the mean production rate to bid

the work, the distribution with the greater spread would yield less confidence in the accuracy of the mean rate for any one particular project than if the spread were small. In addition, the real amount of error would be greater.

The Range—The simplest measure of variability is the range. The range is defined as the difference between the lowest and highest score in a distribution of scores. Figure 30.6 shows the calculation of the range.

Range = X_h- X_1 =   .065 - .04 = .25
where: X_h = the highest score
        X_1 = the lowest score

Figure 30.6—Calculation of the Range for the Production Rates

The range is not considered a stable measure of variability because the value can change greatly with the change in a single score within the distribution--either the high or low score. In addition, there may be frequent or large gaps in the distribution, which the range does not reflect, because it only uses two scores—the high and low. Thus, the range is only useful as a quick estimate of variability.

Quartile Deviation—The quartile deviation is more stable than the range because it is based on the spread of the scores through the center of the distribution rather than through the two extremes. The quartile deviation is the measure which is half the distance between the 1st and 3rd quadrilles. The first quartile (Q1) is the score that sets off the lowest 25 percent of the scores while the third quartile (Q3) sets off the upper 25 percent of the scores. The interval from Q1 to Q3 contains the middle 50 percent of the scores in a distribution and is called the inter-quartile range. Then, this distance is divided by 2 to give the average distance from the median to each of the quadrilles. This is called the quartile deviation (QD). For the production rates, the calculations are shown in Fgure 30.7.

Since the quartile deviation is an index that reflects the spread of scores throughout the middle part of the distribution, it should be used whenever extreme scores may distort the data. Thus, the median and the quartile deviation are both insensitive to extreme scores in the distribution and should be used accordingly.

Standard Deviation—The major disadvantage of the quartile deviation is that it does not take into account the value of each of the raw scores in the distribution. A more reliable indicator of the spread of a distribution can be found by determining the amount each score deviates from the mean of the distribution. In most instances, the contractor will be computing a sample statistic rather than a population statistic. The production rates do not include the entire population of rates for every job past, present, and future. Thus, the 20 rates are a sample of all work the contractor does. The sample standard deviation can be calculated from the frequency distribution shown in table 30.4.

The standard deviation can be computed from raw scores with the use of an inexpensive hand-held calculator that has statistical functions built in. One simply enters the raw scores in the STAT mode on the calculator. Then, a few key strokes will yield such information as the sample mean and the sample standard deviation.

$Q1 = L + [(N/4 - cfb)/fw]i = .0475 + [(20/4 - 4)7].005 = .0482$
$Q3 = L + [(.75N - cfb)/fw]i = .0575 + [(.75 \times 20 - 14)2].005 = .060$
$QD = (Q3 - Q1)/2 = (.060 - .0482)/2 = .0118$

where:

$Q1$ = first quartile
$Q3$ = second quartile
L = the lower limit of the interval within which the first quartile lies or the third quartile lies
N = the number of cases
cfb = the cumulative frequency below the interval containing either the first quartile or third quartile
fw = the frequency of cases within the interval containing either the first or third quartile
i = the interval size

Figure 30.7—Calculation of the Quartile Deviation for the Production Rates

Table 30.4—Calculation of the Standard Deviation From the Frequency Distribution

Production Rate (X)	Frequency (f)	Product (fX)	fX²
.070	1	.070	.004900
.065	3	.195	.038025
.060	2	.120	.014400
.055	3	.165	.027225
.050	7	.350	.122500
.045	3	.135	.018225
.040	1	.04	.001600
	N = 20	sum of fX = 1.075	sum of fX² = .226875

$s = [\text{Sum of } fX^2 - (\text{Sum of } fX)^2/N]/(N - 1) = [.226875 - (1.075)^2/20](20-1) = .0088996 \text{ or } .009$
where: s = sample standard deviation
$\quad X$ = raw data (individual observed production rate)
$\quad f$ = frequency with which that raw data occurs
$\quad N$ = number of observations in the sample

THE NORMAL CURVE

Recall that a frequency distribution that is symmetrical is known as the normal curve. The normal curve is unimodal with mean, median, and mode at the same point. See Figure 30.8.

In actuality, the normal curve is a theoretical curve, which by definition can take many shapes, but in all of those shapes, the shape is symmetrical, and the curve is unimodal. This theoretical curve is important because many physical and psychological phenomena resemble the normal curve when shown in a frequency distribution.

Properties—The important properties of normal curves are (1) the curve is symmetrical with its maximum height at the mean; (2) the mean, median, and mode fall at the same point; (3) the height of the curve decreases to the left and to the right of the mean at an accelerated rate, which forms the convex portion of the curve until reaching one standard deviation above or below the mean at which point the decrease decelerates and the curve becomes concave; and (4) the theoretical range of the curve is plus infinity to minus infinity, but for all practical purposes so little of the curve falls below -3 standard deviations or above +3 standard deviations that for most frequency distributions these are the practical limits of the curve.

z-scores—Though two or more frequency distributions may approximate normality yet differ in terms of their means and standard deviations, any normal distribution can be transformed into a distribution of standard scores. These scores are known as z-scores. The distribution is known as the standard normal curve.

The z-score is computed from a sample score by applying the formula, $z = (X-\bar{X})/s$, where $\bar{X}$ is the mean of the distribution, X is a raw score from the distribution, and s is the sample standard deviation. For example, assume that the production rate frequency distribution approximates the normal curve. Then, a rate of .60 would yield the following:

$$z = (.060-.05375)/.009 = .694 \text{ or } .69$$

When all scores from a distribution are transformed to their corresponding z-scores, the result is a distribution of scores with a mean of 0 and a standard deviation of 1. Thus, the score above is .694 standard deviation above the mean. One can determine what this z-score indicates by entering published tables. A portion of one such table is shown in Table 30.5.

Based on the observed data, the contractor concludes that for the z-score of .69 (column 1), the area (proportion of scores) from the mean to .69 is .2549 or 25.49 percent (column 2), the area below the score of .69 is .7549 or 75.49 percent (column 3), the area above the score of .69 is .2451 or 24.51 percent (column 4), and the .69 score is found on the curve at the y-ordinate of .3144 (column 5). Thus, the contractor could interpret the score by saying that 75.49 percent of all the possible production rates will fall below .060 HRS/SFCA.

The contractor also can use the standard normal curve table to determine a specific production rate to be used in estimating and scheduling. Assume that the contractor wants to select a rate based on past experience that will be greater than 95 percent of the rates possible. From the table, the contractor finds the area in larger portion (column 3) closest to .95 or 95 percent. From the table, .9505 is found, with a corresponding z-score of 1.65. (Typically, for the kinds of analysis the contractor will perform, interpolation is not necessary.)

Solving for the unknown by applying the equation above, the production rate can be computed as follows:

$$1.65 = (X -.05375)/.009$$
$$X = .0686 \text{ } HRS/SFCA$$

When one compares this rate (.0686) with that shown on the cumulative percent frequency distribution (.07), one notices a discrepancy. The difference is that the cumulative percent is based on only those rates in the sample as compared to the rate extracted from the normal curve, which is based on all possible rates within the distribution and is an estimate of the true population rate. In addition, the assumption was made that the distribution of production rates was normally distributed. An examination of the frequency polygon reveals that it is not normally distributed. If the lower production rates (high scores) were omitted, then the curve would indeed be more normally distributed.

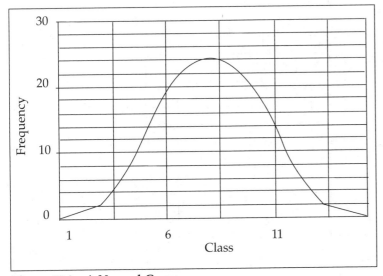

Figure 30.8—A Normal Curve

Table 30.5—Areas of the Standard Normal Curve

1	2	3	4	5
z-score	Area from mean to z-score	Area in larger portion	Area in smaller portion	y ordinate at z-score
.67	.2422	.7422	.2578	.3230
.68	.2517	.7517	.2483	.3166
.69	.2549	.7549	.2451	.3144
.70	.2580	.7580	.2420	.3123
.71	.2611	.7611	.2389	.3101
.72	.2642	.7642	.2358	.3079
1.65	.4505	.9505	.0495	.1023

CUMULATIVE PROBABILITY CURVE

One key purpose of the frequency polygon is to examine how the data is distributed. From this examination, one gets an indication of whether the scores are normally distributed or not. If they are not, then the cumulative probability curve can be applied to the data. An examination of the frequency polygon in Figure 30.2 reveals that the production rate data is not normally distributed. The curve plots the cumulative percentage distribution data (Table 30.2, column 4) as illustrated in Figure 30.9.

Note that the curve shows the percentage of scores (crude measure of probability) where the production rate will fall below a certain value. For example, the contractor may wish to know what the probability is that the production rate will not meet or exceed the acceptable rate. From the cumulative probability curve, one reads that 30 percent of the production rates are .060 HRS/SFCA or higher; thus, 30 percent of the observed rates failed to yield the acceptable rate of .055 HRS/SFCA.

It is important to note that the construction of the cumulative probability curve is dependent upon the question asked. In this case, the contractor wanted to determine the probability of failure. The contractor could just have easily asked for the probability of success. In this instance, the data in Table 30.2 would have been rearranged from low production (high score) to high production (low score). The cumulative percentage frequency would be found as shown in Table 30.6.

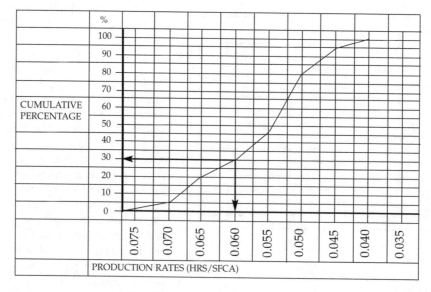

Figure 30.9—Cumulative Probability Curve

Table 30.6—Cumulative Probability

Rate (HRS/SFCA)	Frequency	Probability of Occurrence	Cumulative Probability
.070	1	5 percent	100 percent
.065	3	15 percent	95 percent
.060	2	10 percent	80 percent
.055	3	15 percent	70 percent
.050	7	35 percent	55 percent
.045	3	15 percent	20 percent
.040	1	5 percent	5 percent

The resultant cumulative probability curve is shown in Figure 30.10. Note that the successful production rate is .055 HRS/SFCA. Thus, from the curve, the probability of success is 70 percent.

RECOMMENDED READING

1. Ary, D., and L. C. Jacobs. 1976. *Introduction to Statistics: Purposes and Procedures.* New York: Holt, Rinehart and Winston.
2. DeFranco, D., and M. R. Spiegel. 1996. *Schaum's Interactive Outline of Statistics.* New York: McGraw-Hill, Inc., 1996.
3. Montgomery, D. C., and G. C. Runger. 1994. *Applied Statistics and Probability for Engineers.* New York: John Wiley & Sons, Inc.
4. Spiegel, M. R. 1989. *Schaum's Outline of Statistics.* New York: McGraw-Hill, Inc., 1989.

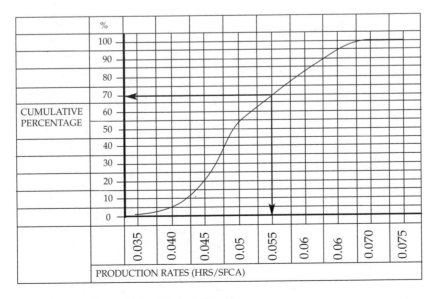

Figure 30.10—Cumulative Probability Curve

Chapter 31

Risk Management

Allen C. Hamilton, CCE

INTRODUCTION

Why Understand Risk Management

Risk management is an important tool in the management of projects. Risk is much talked about, and there are many papers in the academic and popular literature to help understand this topic. Many projects deal with uncertainty and the results of many different aspects of project performance and delivery. Risk management allows us to provide some degree of the process and approach to handling project uncertainties.

In June 1815, Napoleon met Wellington and Blucher at the Battle of Waterloo. At Waterloo it has been calculated Napoleon had an 18 percent chance of winning based on a statistical calculation of leadership, morale, troop size, intelligence and technology between the two opposing armies. Napoleon was defeated and it brought to an end his military and political career. He was exiled to St. Helena and died in 1821 [3]. Would you engage in an undertaking that had an 18 percent chance of success? Perhaps you would also ask, "If successful, what would be the benefit?"

Benefits of Risk Management

All organizations need to deal with risk. There are many examples of failed projects and companies that were unable to deal with risk. One of the greatest risks to projects is the lack of adequate and appropriate planning. An important part of project planning is risk management. Risk management in all its forms both simple and complex will potentially have a positive effect on the implementation of projects. Risk management will also assist projects where the risk was not identified or anticipated. By using risk management, projects will develop techniques and methods to deal with both anticipated and unanticipated events.

Peter L. Bernstein in his book *Against the Gods* describes the history and development of risk management. He says in the introduction, "By showing the world how to understand risk, measure it, and weigh its consequences, they converted risk-taking into one of the prime catalysts that drives modern

Western society" [2]. Much of his book is devoted to the history and development of risk as it related to society, macro economic events, and investments. However the application of the theories is just as relevant to projects and investments.

Fundamental Approach to Risk Management

When we perform risk management we should keep in mind the following:

- You don't need an advanced degree in mathematical theory to perform risk management.
- Risk management can be applied in different ways suitable to project needs from easy/simple to complex.
- One of the more important elements of risk management is to establish a process for dealing with risks

The fundamental approach to risk management is to identify the risks to project success, assess and analyze the risks, and develop plans to mitigate the risks. Risk management usually follows the following sequence:

Identification → Assessment → Analysis → Mitigation

This risk management chapter will provide an overview of the process and examples of how to apply the tools of risk management.

LEARNING OBJECTIVES

After completing this chapter, readers should

- gain a general understanding of risk management;
- learn about techniques of identifying risk items, assessing risk items in terms of occurrence and impact, and analyzing risk;
- learn about risk mitigation;
- learn about quantitative risk analysis (i.e. simulation, sensitivity analysis, and decision trees);
- learn about risk analysis software; and
- find out about the use of contingency.

A BIT OF HISTORY

Counting, Gambling, Insurance, Investments

Risk management as we know it developed as an outgrowth of the study of mathematics, specifically statistical analysis. The knowledge and science of risk management was developed to satisfy the needs of counting, gambling, insuring and investing. The 15th to 16th centuries brought us algebra, statistics, and probabilities. With probabilities we had the beginnings of risk management using probabilistic analysis.

During World War II, as Moscow was being bombed, a well known Soviet professor of statistics declined the use of the local air raid shelter and said, "There are seven million people in Moscow. Why would I expect them to hit me?" One night he showed up at the shelter and a woman asked him why he was there. He said, "There are seven million people in Moscow and one elephant (in the zoo). Last night they got the elephant"[5]. The professor was well aware of the low probability of being hit by a bomb and the association of an outcome (death) with a risk. However, we are all affected by the knowledge of a remote event occurring.

Much of the historical progress of risk management has been helped by the desire to quantify the risks of investments. Today, a lot of numerical information is available on the degree to which stocks, bonds and mutual funds move and behave. Alpha, beta, and R squared metrics are commonly available. Even Shakespeare in the *Merchant of Venice* had something to say about the risks of investments and the need to diversify:

> My ventures are not in one bottom trusted,
> Nor to one place; nor is my whole estate
> Upon the fortune of this present year;
> Therefore, my merchandise make me not sad.
> (Act I, Scene 1)

In the 18th to 19th century, we saw the development of averages, means, symmetrical distribution around the mean, normal distributions, and correlation. All of which leads us to the beginning of the 21st century and the essence of risk management, which is to

- maximize areas where we have some control, and
- minimize areas where we have no control.

And that leads us to risk management on projects.

RISK MANAGEMENT STEPS

Risk Planning

Prior to beginning risk management, it is appropriate to review the risk management plan as outlined in the project plan, project execution plan, or project coordination procedure. If nothing has been done in this regard, it should be started. Risk planning in its broadest scope should establish the approach, form, content and results of risk management. Depending on the project, this can range from one to dozens of pages of content with any number of attachments, forms, and checklists. It is important to establish what is to be covered by risk management. A mission statement and scope of work description are essential in this regard. The scope of risk management should include the basis of including external, internal, strategic, and tactical risks. Many risk management efforts focus on risks that the project management team can influence.

Risk planning should also establish criteria for risk identification items, assessment criteria for occurrence and impact, analysis approaches, and general mitigation strategies. In addition, responsibilities of risk mitigation and follow-up should be identified.

Risk Identification

Risk identification is the most common step in risk management. Everyone touches on risk issues perhaps everyday, for example, driving, writing that critical memo, and the choice of answers to an important client. Many of our actions are weighed with the calculation of which choice to make based on the most positive outcome. In risk management on projects, this is reduced to a more objective level. Risks on projects are the identification of activities that can have a negative impact on outcomes or performance. One view of risk management is to widen the approach to include both negative (risks) and positive items (opportunities). Identifying positive outcomes gives the project the opportunity to improve performance or lower costs.

The first step in risk identification is to assemble a list of project risks. There are many techniques to putting together a risk identification list:

- authored by one person;
- authored by a team with surveys and interviews;
- circulate a chart where risk items can be added by each person;
- free-form list put together by a group at a meeting, e.g., a brainstorming session; and
- a list developed by a group facilitated by a third party.

The author's experience indicates the use of a small focused group is a good approach to assembling a risk identification list. The interaction among members of the group has been shown to be very productive. Discussion about risk items leads to identifying new items that may not have been developed in an isolated setting. In risk identification, it is better to be inclusive and ensure capturing more risks rather than try and manage the risk item editing at too early a stage. An important aspect of identifying risk management items is to clearly communicate or show the scope of work by summaries or the work breakdown structure (WBS). Creativity is also helpful in ensuring the identification of risks is as complete as possible. Inclusion of people outside the project may also be helpful in making the list complete. Editing of the list occurs later rather than during identification. Identification items may be classified into groups depending on how the project is set up. It is desirable to have items that would be clearly the responsibility of an organizational group or individual.

Elements of risk identification can include the following:

- statement of the problem/issue/risk,
- short description of the risk,
- identification of the fundamental risk, and
- basis for categorizing the risk

Internal and External Risks

There are two general classifications of risk, external and internal. The classifications differentiate between the ability of the company or project team to control the risk. External risks are risks the company or project team cannot control. Frequently these risks are also strategic and may affect the economy or many companies. Examples of external risks include "force majeure" risks such hurricanes, price changes due to market forces, and major labor strikes. The company or project cannot control the occurrence of external risk but can mitigate the impact if the risk occurs. Internal risks are risks the company or project team can control. Examples of internal risks are ineffectual contractor due to flawed selection process, design errors due to using untrained personnel, and cost overruns due to excessive project changes. These risks are also tactical in the sense they can be controlled by the project team, group, or members of the team. The company or project can control the occurrence of internal risks and can mitigate the impact if the risk occurs. (See Table 31.2 on pages 31.4 and 31.5 for a list of external and internal risk categories and risk items).

Risk Assessment

Risk assessment is the next major step in risk management. The objective of risk assessment is to establish the relative importance and impact of the risk item. Assessment allows the team to prioritize the risk items. Each risk item is assessed a probability of occurrence and a potential impact. The assessment scale that has shown to be easy to understand and use is a high/medium/low scale (Table 31.1). Other more refined scales such as 1 to 5 or 1 to 10 can be used. The high/medium/low is easy because individuals and teams can come to a quicker decision on assessment with a more compact scale.

Table 31.1—Risk Identification and Assessment Chart [5]

describe risk	probability of occurence (high, medium, low)	potential impact (high, medium, low)

With the risk items in groups the assessments (occurrence and impact) can be made. The probability of occurrence is usually straight-forward. Potential criteria on occurrence could be

- **high**—very likely the risk item will occur, e.g., >75 percent;
- **medium**—the risk item may or may not occur, e.g., 25 to 75 percent; and
- **low**—unlikely the risk item will occur, e.g., <25 percent.

The percentages are only illustrative of an approach. The occurrence assessment is almost always subjective and can't usually be calculated. However, the percentages indicated would serve to distribute items across all three categories. Establishing the occurrence criteria is up to the team and may have been outlined in the risk planning documents. Assessing the probability of occurrence is best done in a group where the assessments can be discussed and challenged.

The next assessment is potential impact. Impact usually means financial impact, although other impacts can be used, such as days of delay or other important project parameters. The criteria for high/medium/low should be established instead of gauging this for each item. The impact assessment can be either subjective or calculated. Many teams provide a rough impact assessment and, if necessary, will later do further investigation or calculation. The risk plan should identify the impact criteria. Examples of potential criteria for impact are the following:

- **high**—greater than 1 percent of project cost;
- **medium**—from 0.1 to 1 percent of project cost; and
- **low**—up to 0.1 percent of project cost.

The cost impacts above are examples and the project team will need to establish the cost criteria most useful to the project. Companies have project approval and control procedures that trigger reviews or additional approvals. These trigger points may influence the choice of the impact criteria. Projects will need to establish the threshold at which impacts are judged significant. In a very cost-sensitive environment, the thresholds would be made lower. It has also been mentioned that the review can include savings or risk opportunities. These are shown as savings instead of costs.

Analysis

The first part of analysis is the review of the risk items. The review confirms the occurrence and impact assessments where completed and were consistent with the established criteria for each. There may be reasons to consider the combining or splitting of risk items. Responsibility and control of the mitigation are good reasons to consider changing items. Analysis is a good time to refine the cost impact assessments on items where the scope is unclear. Investigation of cost assessments may be helpful later.

The main objective of analysis is the selection of risk items for mitigation. Many techniques are available for this purpose. It is possible to make a selection from the list and proceed. It is also possible to perform a calculation to give each risk item a score. However, a common method, and one that is easy to understand and visualize, is the occurrence/impact matrix. The matrix uses the high/medium/low assessments for each risk item to establish the criteria for mitigation. The matrix is usually used as shown in Figure 31.1.

The risk planning document will determine the criteria for occurrence and impact. It should also determine the criteria for selection of risk items for mitigation. This is commonly

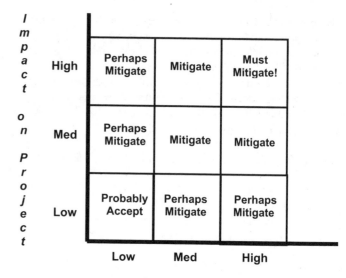

Figure 31.1—Risk Mitigation Chart [4]

Table 31.2—Risk Management-Risk Identification Categories [1]

External Risks—The company cannot control the occurrence of these risks but can mitigate their impact if they occur.

TYPE OF RISK	EXAMPLES	
Natural Hazards	• storm • flood • fire	• tornado • earthquake
New or Revised Government Regulations	• environmental issues • design standards • product specifications • facility siting issues	• product pricing • taxes • import/export issues • supply of raw materials
Market Conditions	• customer/user demand • availability/cost of raw materials • state of overall economy	• actions by competition • salvage value after useful life
Acts of Deliberate Intent	• vandalism • sabotage	• terrorism • labor strikes
Indirect Effects Occurring as a Result of the Project	• environmental impacts	• social impacts
Contractor / Vendor Performance	• Shortage of qualified contractors/vendors • quality of work	• bankruptcy • contract claims • schedule slippage
Financial	• obtaining financing • currency fluctuations • inflation	• taxes • cashflow problems
Legal	• lawsuits • contract problems • process license disputes	• patent rights • obtaining permits
Technical	• new unproven technology • technology becomes obsolete	• new technology makes project too complex

determined by how items show up on the matrix. For example a risk item that had a high impact and a high occurrence would be a high-high. As the chart shows, this item would be reviewed for mitigation. It is up to the project to determine the item approach according to the matrix. Some projects may feel it is appropriate to mitigate all items that have a high impact on the project or to probably accept all items that have a low impact on the project.

Mitigation

Once a risk item is selected for mitigation during analysis, a risk mitigation technique would be chosen. It is assumed the risk items selected will be acted upon or placed in a priority list such that they will potentially be acted upon depending on resources. Some mitigation items may require a review of different techniques to select the optimal solution. Methods of handling risk include the following:

- **avoidance**—structuring the project so that the risk is avoided. Examples include project relocation, cancellation, delay, restructure, and redesign.

- **prevention**—structuring the project so that the risk is prevented. Prevention may reduce the risk factors so that the risk does not occur, or, if it does, the severity is reduced. Examples include safety and security measures, and redesign. Hazardous operations design reviews (HAZOPS) are good examples of risk prevention in engineering and design offices. Safety inspections are also good examples of prevention activities.

- **reduction**—the occurrence of a loss may justify actions that will prevent or reduce reoccurrence.

- **transfer**—a common method of risk mitigation is to transfer the risk to an organization that is more competent or willing to assume it. The transfer is usually accomplished by contract. All owners, contractors, and subcontractors have a collective share of the total project risk. There are two parts to the assumption of these risks: the company is technically qualified and financially prepared to accept the consequences. Project claims are a good example of the misunderstanding of who is at risk

Table 31.2—(continued)

Internal Risks—The company can control the occurrence of these risks and can mitigate their impact if they occur.

TYPE OF RISK	EXAMPLES	
Management Problems	• loss of control • unresolved conflict • lack of policies/procedures • inadequate planning • inadequate personnel • changing priorities	• management turnover • goals unclear, unrealistic, or not aligned • poor definition of roles and responsibilities • not understanding the complexity of large projects
Schedule Delays Due To	• above management • problems • unrealistic schedule • regulatory approvals • labor shortages • unforeseen site conditions • lack of scope definition • project changes (scope, design, field, execution, etc.) • schedule not coordinated between design, procurement, construction and startup	• poor contractor/vendor • accidents or sabotage • work stoppages • late deliveries • material shortages • lack of access • inadequate planning & scheduling procedures • difficulties with startup turnover • design and/or field rework
Cost Overruns Due To	• above management problems • above schedule delays • inappropriate procurement or contracting strategy • contractor/vendor claims • inexperienced workforce	• labor negotiations • errors in cost estimate • unrealistic cost budget • inadequate cost control procedures
Technical/Quality Problems	• shortage of trained and experienced design personnel • new technology • design can't be built • inappropriate design standards	• facility proves unreliable • facility too expensive to operate and/or maintain • facility cannot perform to specifications

and who accepts the consequences.

- **hedging**—is a specialized part of transfer where the risk of price fluctuations is assumed by a speculator through the purchasing and selling of futures contracts. It is assumed the commodity futures contracts are covered by an organized exchange, such as the Chicago Board of Trade. Examples include crude oil, fuel oil, and foreign currency. Purchase orders for equipment or material in foreign currency can be fixed by the purchase of currency futures.

- **insurance**—part of transfer but by companies that indemnify parties against specific losses in return for premiums.

Most mitigation actions will be avoidance, prevention, and reduction. Many projects will have established the approach to project execution in the areas of transfer, hedging, and insurance by the time the project team is engaged in risk management. If risk management begins early in project development, transfer and hedging may be important considerations. A sample risk mitigation chart is shown below.

After the mitigation action is selected, the cost to mitigate and the probability of success are judged. Again, a high/medium/low category is illustrated but the calculation can be expanded and made more precise. The cost to mitigate can be relatively straightforward to estimate or calculate. A high/medium/low category is easy to assign and easy to understand. In risk mitigation we are looking for low costs to mitigate and high probability of success. In other words, getting the most money for what we spent on mitigation. The ranking of risk items in terms of cost of impact and probability of occurrence can be combined with the ranking of mitigation. For example, the highest ranking mitigation items would have the following:

- risk identification and assessment (Table 31.1),
- high impact on the project,
- high probability of occurrence,
- risk mitigation (Table 31.3),
- low cost to mitigate, and
- high probability of success.

Next in risk mitigation is to decide if the mitigation action will be taken. The priority listing may be helpful in this regard. The decision to do it can also depend on the avail-

ability of resources. Ranking mitigation items also helps in deciding to what extent the project is able to execute its mitigation actions. Table 31.3 uses a yes or no for taking mitigation action. In addition, the use of a numerical list or a high/medium/low category could be used.

It would be helpful to describe items that if mitigated would be the responsibilities of a group, department, or individual. Risk management is facilitated by reducing mitigation items to clearly defined individuals. It is also facilitated by describing the risk item as the sole or primary responsibility of one group. Risk items may span many groups, but if possible, it is helpful to divide or reduce items to more limited groups. Finally, it should be identified when the mitigation item needs to be completed, especially if the action is time dependent.

Follow-Up

Risk management is most effective if it is monitored, controlled, and adjusted as required. Taking the time to have meetings and establish the risk management plan is wasted if the work is completed, put in a notebook, and ignored until one of the risk items occurs without the mitigation being performed. Regular monitoring and updating of risk management progress should be part of a regular cycle of project activities. Monthly or quarterly reviews and status reporting of risk mitigation is recommended.

QUANTITATIVE RISK ANALYSIS

Up to this point we have used both a qualitative and a quantitative approach to risk management. The emphasis has been to provide an approach that can be readily used with limited use of quantitative tools. Some of these analytical tools can be of use to refine and focus the qualitative conclusions. Quantitative risk analysis is the use of mathematical techniques and models to numerically establish the probability of risk and the consequences of risk. The most common of these techniques are simulation, sensitivity analysis, and decision tree analysis.

Simulation

A simulation is the development of a model of the uncertainties of project in terms of cost or time and the effect on the project. The effect is usually expressed as a curve of the outcomes verses the probability. The general approach to simulation using the Monte Carlo method is:

Table 31.3—Risk Mitigation Chart [4]

describe action	cost to mitigate (high, medium, low)	probablility of success (high, medium, low)	Do it? (yes/no)	Who leads?	By when?

1. Develop a model.
   - cost estimate → work breakdown structure
   - schedule → network diagram
2. Select the group for analysis.
   - cost variables → summaries,
   - schedule → activities, high level summaries, management schedule
3. Identify uncertainty.
   - Select the probability distributions and provide inputs.
   - Identify the form of the results.
4. Analyze the model with simulation.
5. Generate reports and analyze information.

The curve shown in the simulation output curve in Figure 31.2 indicates the project cost would vary from $0.8 million with a 10 percent probability to $1.4 million with a 90 percent probability.

Sensitivity Analysis

Sensitivity analysis is the substitution of variables in a risk model to test the effects of these changes. This is easily accomplished with the wide availability of electronic tools, such as spreadsheets. Some spreadsheets have tools that facilitate sensitivity analysis. These add-on tools are available from vendors. Sensitivity analysis is also referred to as "what if" analysis. For example, in cost items, one can substitute various quantities and unit costs to test the "sensitivity" of risk items to changes. Concern would be raised if small changes result in large effects on the costs.

Table 31.4—Sensitivity Analysis Example

Base	1,000 units labor	$1 per unit material	$1 per unit	Total $2,000
Sensitivity 1 Additional 200 units	1,200 units +20%	$1 per unit labor	$1 per unit material	Total $2,400 +20%
Sensitivity 2 Labor at $1.50	1,000 units	$1.50 per unit labor +50%	$1 per unit material	Total $2,500 +25%

Decision-Tree Analysis

Decision analysis methods are techniques to evaluate and compare the probabilities and financial results of investment choices. Decision-tree analysis is a diagram that shows the costs, probability, and financial consequences of taking certain decisions with mutually exclusive options. The diagram shows the decision points and the costs for taking each decision. Decision trees are easy to set up and calculate. They are most useful when the decision costs and probabilities are established by knowledgeable individuals. Performing the calculations on all paths of the decision yields all of the expected monetary values. The value with the lowest cost or greatest savings should be given the highest priority. A sample of a simple decision tree is shown in Figure 31.3 on page 31.8.

In the example, a process is being analyzed which has a primary process (A or B) and a secondary process (C or D and E or F). The probability of each of the pairs of processes equals 1.00, A+B, C+D, and E + F. The expected monetary value of the individual process equals the value times the probability. The process and subprocess monetary values are added to arrive at value for a case. Therefore,

$$AC = \$4,000 (0.5) + \$2,000 (0.6) = \$3,200$$
$$AD = \$4,000 (0.5) + \$1,600 (0.4) = \$2,640$$
$$BE = \$5,000 (0.5) + \$1,200 (0.8) = \$3,460$$
$$BF = \$5,000 (0.5) + \$1,000 (0.2) = \$2,700$$

The lowest cost case is process AD and should be the first choice. However, case BF is $2,700 and is within a few percentage points of the cost of AD. Sensitivity analysis may be helpful to refining the judgment.

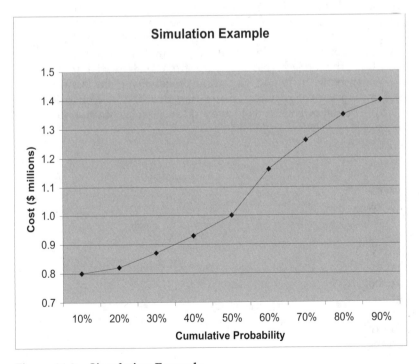

Figure 31.2—Simulation Example

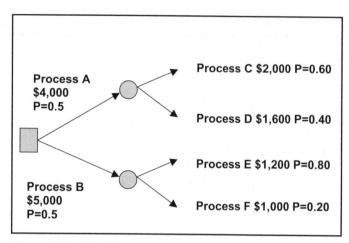

Figure 31.3—Decision-Tree Analysis

RISK MANAGEMENT SOFTWARE

The author mentions the programs below only as a guide to the audience. Neither the author nor the publisher is making a recommendation.

Cost Risk Analysis

Both of the following simulation programs are Excel add-ins. The programs integrate with Excel, and the look and feel is the same with additional functional from the simulation programs. The inputs for the model are probability distributions with additional values. The outputs of the programs are graphs and tables to show the most likely outcomes, the probability that these will fall within a range, and the dependence of inputs to outcomes. Each program features a wide array of statistical and analysis tools to facilitate the Monte Carlo simulation along with other decision support tools such as optimizing and forecasting:

1. @Risk; Palisade Corp.; Newfield, New York; (800) 432-7475; www.palisade.com, and
2. Crystal Ball; Decisioneering Inc; Denver, CO; (800) 289-2550; www.decisioneering.com

Schedule Risk Analysis

The schedule risk analysis programs below integrate with their companion scheduling programs. The risk programs can used only with the specific scheduling programs, one with Primavera Project Planner (P3) and one with Microsoft Project. Each follows the classic risk analysis approach of developing a model (network schedule), identify uncertainty (ranges & probability distribution functions), and analyze the model with simulation. The schedule risk analysis programs have the additional function of performing this analysis on the schedule activity resources, such as people, work hours and costs. Most analysis is on the results of the project completion date or project duration:

1. Monte Carlo 3.0 for Primavera; Primavera Inc.; Bala Cynwyd, PA; (800) 423-0245; www.primavera.com, and
2. @Risk for Project; Palisade Corp.; Newfield, New York; (800) 432-7475; www.palisade.com.

RELATED RISK SUBJECTS

Contingency

Contingency is an amount added to an estimate or schedule to allow for changes that experience shows will likely be required. Contingency may be derived either though statistical analysis of past project costs or schedules, or by applying experience from similar projects. It usually excludes changes in scope or unforeseeable major events such as strikes, earthquakes, etc. [1].

To reflect the view of contingency with respect to this chapter, contingency is the amount of resources added to the project, cost or schedule, which satisfies the risk approach to the business and the project.

Contingency, cost and schedule, is one of the most frequent outputs of risk management. Contingency derived from a well-executed risk analysis could be a powerful project control tool. Contingency also allows management to select the risk level appropriate to the companies approach to its business. If the business is risky and the opportunity is large, the desire to assume risk may be greater than businesses that are risk adverse and more conservative.

The use of risk management techniques and risk analysis allows projects to proceed on the basis of both a qualitative and quantitative assessment of project variability. As we explained in the simulation example shown in Figure 31.2, the project cost can vary from $0.8 to $1.4 million and between 10 and 90 percent probability. If the business environment requires greater risk, then the project budget that will be chosen will have a greater chance of variability.

REFERENCES

1. AACE International. *Standard Cost Engineering Terminology*. AACE Standard No. 10S-90. Morgantown, West Virginia.

2. Bernstein, Peter L. 1996. *Against the Gods, The Remarkable Story of Risk*. John Wiley & Sons Inc. p. 1.

3. Rotte, Ralph, and Christoph Schmidt. *On the Production of Victory: Empirical Determinants of Battlefield Success in Modern War*. Essen, Germany: Rhine-Westphalia Institute for Economic Research.

4. Westney Project Services Inc. 2000. *Profit Driven Project Management*. Course. Version 10/2000.

5. Westney, Richard E. 2000. *The Strategic Project Planner*. Marcel Dekker, Inc.

Appendices

APPENDICES

A   Glossary of Terms

B.   International System of Units (SI)

C.   Estimating Reference Material

D.   RP 11R-88—Required Skills and Knowledge of a Cost Engineer

E.   RP 17R-97—Cost Estimate Classification System

F   RP 18R-97—Cost Estimate Classification System—As Applied in Engineering, Procurement, and Construction for the Process Industries

G   RP 21R-98—Project Code of Accounts

H   Proposed Scope Graphic for PSP

I   Membership Information (Introduction, Application, Canon of Ethics)

GLOSSARY OF TERMS

This glossary includes those terms that were felt to be appropriate for discussion in this book and is intended to provide support to the book's chapters by including terms defined by the authors, by other associations, and by AACE International in reference material. Additional terminology as defined by AACE International can be found in Standard 10S-90 and other documents under development by the AACE Technical Board.

Activity—a basic element of work, or task that must be performed in order to complete a project. An activity occurs over a given period of time. (10S-90)

Activity Code—any combination of letters, numbers, or blanks which describes and identifies any activity or task shown on the schedule. (See also *Activity Identification*) (10S-90)

Activity Description—a concise explanation of the nature and scope of the work to be performed, which easily identifies an activity to any recipient of the schedule. (10S-90)

Activity Duration—the length of time from start to finish of an activity, estimated or actual, generally quantified in working or calendar day time units. (10S-90)

Activity Identification—a unique alphanumeric set of characters used for identification and computer use. (See also Activity Code) (Werderitsch)

Agenda—in the context of value, the outline and work plan the team has planned in order to accomplish the study in a given period of time. (Younker)

Allowances—additional resources included in estimates to cover the cost of known but undefined requirements for an individual activity, work item, account, or subaccount (10S-90).

Annual Value—a uniform annual amount equivalent to the project costs or benefits taking into account the time value of money throughout the study period. Syn.: Annual Worth, Equivalent Uniform Annual Value (10S-90)

Annual Worth—see *Annual Value*.

Arrow Diagramming Method (ADM)—a method of constructing a logical network of activities using arrows to represent the activities and connecting them head to tail. This diagramming method shows the sequence, predecessor, and successor relationships of the activities. (10S-90)

Asset—(1) the entire property of a person, association, corporation, or estate applicable or subject to the payment of debts; (2) a: an item of value owned, b: plural—the items on a balance sheet showing the book value of property owned. (Merriam-Webster On-Line Dictionary)

Asset, Capital (also Fixed Asset)—physical facilities or items whose costs are not accounted for as a current expense and for which depreciation is allowed. Characteristically, it cannot be converted readily into cash. (Hollmann)

Asset Life Cycle—the stages or phases of asset existence during the life of an asset. Asset life cycle stages typically include ideation, creation, operation, modification, and termination. (Hollmann)

Asset, Strategic—any unique physical or intellectual property that is of long term or ongoing value to the enterprise. As used in total cost management, it most commonly includes capital or fixed assets, but may include intangible assets. Excludes cash and purely financial assets. Strategic assets are created by the investment of resources through projects. (10S-90)

Backward Pass—calculation of the latest finish time and latest start time for all uncompleted network activities or late time for events in the ADM and PDM methods. It is determined by working from the final activity and subtracting durations from uncompleted activities. (10S-90)

Bar Chart (Gantt Chart)—a graphic presentation of project activities shown by a time-scaled bar line. (10S-90)

Base Wages—the amount of wages that will go directly to the employee (Fleishman)

Basis—documentation that describes how an estimate, schedule, or other plan component was developed and defines the information used in support of development. A basis document commonly includes, but is not limited to, a description of the scope included, methodologies used, references and defining deliverables used, assumptions and exclusions made, clarifications, adjustments, and some indication of the level of uncertainty (10S-90).

Basis of Estimate—basis documentation specifically prepared in support of a project estimate. (Dysert)

Battery Limits—Geographic boundaries, imaginary or real, enclosing a plant or (process) unit of a plant. The term is generally used to describe a process-oriented unit of a plant, and excludes facilities such as utilities, storage, auxiliary facilities, office buildings, etc. The term is sometimes used in reference to a single piece of equipment to refer to a small geographic area around the piece of equipment which includes an amount of piping, controls, foundation, etc. which are directly associated with the piece of equipment (Dysert)

Benchmark Indexes—for most manufacturing and all mining industries, indexes reflecting changes in output between census years. (10S-90)

Benchmarking—a measurement and analysis process that compares practices, processes, and relevant measures to those of a selected basis of comparison (i.e., the benchmark) with the goal of improving performance. The comparison basis includes internal or external competitive or best practices, processes or measures. Examples of measures include estimated costs, actual costs, schedule durations, resource quantities and so on. (10S-90)

Benefit/Cost—an economic analysis technique whereby benefits are divided by costs to obtain a ratio number. Both benefits and costs are discounted to a present value or uniform equivalent annual value. (Opfer)

Benefit Cost Analysis—a method of evaluating projects or investments by comparing the present value or annual value of expected benefits to the present value or annual value of expected costs. (10S-90)

Benefit-To-Cost Ratio (BCR)—benefits divided by costs, where both are discounted to a present value or equivalent uniform annual value (10S-90)

Bill of Materials—a detailed listing of all materials required for a product or a project. (Opfer)

Budget—a planned allocation of resources. The planned cost of needed materials is usually subdivided into quantity required and unit cost. The planned cost of labor is usually subdivided into the workhours required and the wage rate (plus fringe benefits and taxes). (11/90)

Budgeting—A process used to allocate the estimated cost of resources into cost accounts (i.e., the cost budget) against which cost performance will be measured and assessed. Budgeting often considers time-phasing in relation to a schedule and/or time-based financial requirements and constraints (10S-90)

Bulk Materials—material bought in lots. These items can be purchased from a standard catalog description and are bought in quantity for distribution as required. Examples are pipe (nonspooled), conduit, fittings, and wire. (10S-90)

CAD—see Computer Aided Design

Calendar Days (CD)—the number of continuous days (including holidays and weekends) to complete an activity or a project. Generally, contracts refer to calendar days from the notice to proceed through substantial completion. (Werderitsch)

CAM—see Computer-Aided Manufacturing

Capital—one of the factors of production, the wealth that makes business possible. The amount of money used within a business. (Singh)

Capital Budget—a plan for making expenditures on capital assets. (Hollmann)

Capital Budgeting—a systematic procedure for classifying, evaluating, and ranking proposed capital expenditures for the purpose of comparison and selection, combined with the analysis of the financing requirements. (10S-90)

Cash Flow—the net flow of dollars into or out of a project. The algebraic sum, in any time period, of all cash receipts, expenses, and investments. Also called cash proceeds or cash generated. The stream of monetary (dollar) values—costs and benefits—resulting from a project investment. (10S-90)

Chart Of Accounts—a systematic numeric method of identifying various categories of expenses incurred. The segregation of expenses into elements for accounting purposes. (See also Code of Accounts) (Cokins)

Chebyshev's Theorem – a statistical method of predicting the probability that a value will occur within one or more standard deviations (±) of the mean (10S-90)

Claim – a written statement requesting additional time and/or money for acts or omissions during the performance of the construction contract. The contract must set forth the facts and circumstances for which the owner or the engineer is responsible to be entitled to additional compensation and/or time (10S-90)

Code of Accounts (COA) – a systematic coding structure for organizing and managing asset, cost, resource, and schedule activity information. A COA is essentially an index to facilitate finding, sorting, compiling, summarizing, and otherwise managing information that the code is tied to. A complete code of accounts includes definitions of the content of each account. Syns.: Chart of Accounts, Cost Codes. (10S-90)

Competency (also Core Competency)—a set of skills and knowledge in an individual or in an organization that are a source of competitive advantage. Core competency represents the integration of the skills and knowledge of cost engineering in a personal or organizational context. (Hollmann)

Competitive Advantage—those individual aspects of the business that attract its customers and set it aside from its main rivals. (Singh)

Computer-Aided Design—the utilization of computer tools including computer graphics to readily develop and evaluate product or project design. (Opfer)

Computer-Aided Manufacturing—the utilization of computer tools including computer graphics to achieve and monitor manufacturing operations. (Opfer)

Constraint—an externally imposed factor affecting the scheduling of an activity. The external factor may be a resource, such as labor, cost or equipment, or, it can be a physical event that must be completed prior to the activity being restrained. Syn.: Restraint. (10S-90)

Constructability—optimum use of construction knowledge and experience in planning, design, procurement, and field operations to achieve overall project objectives (Construction Industry Institute)

Constructability Reviews—the review by a multidiscipline team improving the methods of procuring, constructing, testing, and delivering the intended project scope and goals for the owner. This review may be separate from or a part of the Value Engineering study. (Younker)

Contingency—an amount added to an estimate to allow for items, conditions, or events for which the state, occurrence, and/or effect is uncertain and that experience shows will likely result, in aggregate, in additional costs. Typically estimated using statistical analysis or judgment based on past asset or project experience. Contingency usually excludes; (a) major scope changes such as changes in end product specification, capacities, building sizes, and location of the asset or project (see management reserve), (b) extraordinary events such as major strikes and natural disasters, (c) management reserves, and (d) escalation and currency effects. Some of the items, conditions, or events for which the state, occurrence, and/or effect is uncertain include, but are not limited to, planning and estimating errors and omissions, minor price fluctuations (other than general escalation), design developments and changes within the scope, and variations in market and environmental conditions. Contingency is generally included in most estimates, and is expected to be expended to some extent. (10S-90)

Contract Completion Date—the date established in the contract for completion of all or specified portions of the work. This date may be expressed as a calendar date or as a number of days after the date for commencement of the contract time is issued (10S-90)

Contract Documents—the agreement, addenda (which pertain to the contract documents), contractor's bid (including documentation accompanying the bid and any post-bid documentation submitted prior to the notice of award) when attached as an exhibit to the agreement, the bonds, the general conditions, the supplementary conditions, the specifications and the drawings as the same are more specifically identified in the agreement, together with all amendments, modifications and supplements issued pursuant to the general conditions on or after the effective date of the agreement (10S-90)

Cost—in project control and accounting, it is the amount measured in money, cash expended or liability incurred, in consideration of goods and/or services received. From a total cost management perspective, cost may include any investment of resources in strategic assets including time, monetary, human, and physical resources. (10S-90)

Cost Category—the name, number, or both, of a function, hardware, or other significant cost category for which costs are summarized. (10S-90)

Cost Control—the application of procedures to monitor expenditures and performance against progress of projects or manufacturing operations; to measure variance from authorized budgets and allow effective action to be taken to achieve minimum costs (10S-90)

Cost, Design—a procedure which establishes an estimated cost objective for each project, then designs to that cost objective to produce a reliable product or service. (Younker)

Cost Element—a basic constituent of effort (work) and/or physical composition of an activity and/or asset. The value of a resource used to perform an activity or create an asset. (Postula)

Cost Estimate—the prediction of the probable costs of a project, of a given and documented scope, to be completed at a defined location and point of time in the future. (Dysert)

Cost Estimating—a predictive process used to quantify, cost, and price the resources required by the scope of an asset investment option, activity, or project. As a predictive process, estimating must address risks and uncertainties. The outputs of estimating are used primarily as inputs for budgeting, cost or value analysis, decision making in business, asset and project planning, or for project cost and schedule control processes. As applied in the project engineering and construction industry, cost estimating is the determination of quantity and the predicting and forecasting, within a defined scope, of the costs required to construct and equip a facility. Costs are determined utilizing experience and calculating and forecasting the future cost of resources, methods and management within a scheduled time frame. Included in these costs are assessments and an evaluation of risk. (10S-90)

Cost Estimating Relationship (CER)—in estimating, an algorithm or formula that is used to perform the costing operation. CERs show some resource (eg, cost, quantity, or time) as a function of one or more parameters that quantify scope, execution strategies, or other defining elements. A CER may be formulated in a manner that in addition to providing the most likely resource value, also provides a probability distribution for the resource value. Cost estimating relationships may be used in either definitive or parametric estimating methods. (10S-90)

Cost, Life Cycle—in the context of value, the sum of all acquisition, production, operation, maintenance, use and disposal costs for a product or project over a specified period of time. (Younker)

Cost Model—a diagramming technique used to illustrate the total cost of families of systems or parts within a total complex system or structure. (Younker)

Cost Objective—a function, organizational subdivision, contract, or other work unit for which cost data are desired and for which provision is made to accumulate and measure the cost of processes, products, jobs, capitalized projects, and so forth. (Armed Services Pricing Manual)

Cost Of Lost Business Advantage—the cost associated with loss of repeat business and/or the loss of business due to required resources and costs. (Cokins)

Cost Of Quality—consists of the sum of those costs associated with: (a) cost of quality conformance; (b) cost of quality nonconformance; and (c) cost of lost business advantage. (Cokins)

Cost Of Quality Conformance—the cost associated with the quality management activities of appraisal, training, and prevention. (Cokins)

Cost Of Quality Nonconformance—the cost associated with deviations involving rework and/or the provision of deliverables that are more than required. (Cokins)

Cost/Worth Ratio—the ratio used to determine the maximum opportunity for value improvement. (Younker)

Critical Path—sequence of jobs or activities in a network analysis project such that the total duration equals the sum of the durations of the individual jobs in the sequence. There is no time leeway or slack (float) in activity along critical path (i.e., if the time to complete one or more jobs in the critical path increases, the total production time increases). It is the longest time path through the network. (10S-90)

Critical Path Method (CPM)—a scheduling technique using arrow, precedence, or PERT diagrams to determine the length of a project and to identify the activities and constraints on the critical path. (10S-90)

Culture—totality of socially acquired behavior patterns, arts, beliefs, and institutions as well as other products of human work and thought. (Levin)

Currency Variation—the change in the value of a given currency in reference to a currency benchmark, e.g. Japanese yen versus the U.S. dollar or Euro versus Mexican peso. (Opfer)

Cycle Stock—quantity of materials required for a standard production cycle. (Opfer)

Depreciation—(1) decline in value of a capitalized asset; (2) a form of capital recovery applicable to a property with a life span of more than one year, in which an appropriate portion of the asset's value is periodically charged to current operations. (10S-90)

Direct Cost—(1) in construction, cost of installed equipment, material and labor directly involved in the physical construction of the permanent facility; (2) in manufacturing, service and other non-construction industries, the portion of operating costs that is generally assignable to a specific product or process area. (10S-90)

Direct Field Cost—The costs of all equipment, materials, and direct-hire or subcontract labor directly associated with the construction of the project. (Dysert)

Direct Labor—the labor involved in the work activities that directly produce the product or complete the installation being built. (Fleishman)

Discount Rate—the rate of interest reflecting the investor's time value of money, used to determine discount factors for converting benefits and costs occurring at different times to a base time. The discount rate may be expressed as nominal or real. (10S-90)

Distribution Costs—another operating and manufacturing cost category. These are the costs associated with shipping the products to market. They include containers and packages, freight, operation of terminals and warehouses, etc. (Humphreys)

Early Finish (EF)—the earliest time an activity can be completed based on the network relationships. (Werderitsch)

Early Start (ES)—the earliest time an activity can begin based on the network relationships. (Werderitsch)

Earned Value—the periodic, consistent measurement of work performed in terms of the budget planned for that work. In criteria terminology, earned value is the budgeted cost of work performed. It is compared to the budgeted cost of work scheduled (planned) to obtain schedule performance and it is compared to the actual cost of work performed to obtain cost performance (10S-90)

Economic life – that period of time over which an investment is considered to be the least-cost alternative for meeting a particular objective. (10S-90)

Empowerment—an approach that stresses individual initiative, solution creation, and accountability. (Levin)

Engineered or Designed Materials—materials that have undergone substantial engineering processing such as an electrical transformer, pump, or turbine. Accompanied by extensive engineering or design plans of a custom nature. (Opfer)

Enterprise—in total cost management, any endeavor, business, government, group, individual or other entity that owns, controls, or operates strategic assets. (10S-90)

Enterprise Resource Planning (ERP)—a comprehensive system tying all corporate information together, such as accounting, human resources, manufacturing, marketing, etc., and usually sharing common databases and business analysis tools. (Hollmann)

Escalation—the provision in actual or estimated costs for an increase in the cost of equipment, material, labor, etc., over that specified in the purchase order or contract due to continuing price level changes over time. (10S-90)

Estimate Accuracy—An indication of the degree to which the final cost outcome for a given project will vary from the estimated cost. (Dysert)

Ethics—the personal guidelines or rules of conduct by which one aims to live. (Levin)

Expediting—checking, tracing, and enhancing the arrival of materials and equipment to adhere to a progress schedule. (Opfer)

Fabricated materials—raw materials converted into final materials form by fundamental shop operations such as welding, cutting, brazing, bending, and shaping. Examples would be: structural steel for a building fabricated from basic steel shapes; piping spools fabricated from random lengths of pipe into finished dimensions including the welding on of pipe flanges; and electrical cable pull boxes fabricated from basic steel or alloy plate sections. (Opfer)

Fair Market Value-In-Exchange—the value of equipment in terms of money than can be expected to exchange in a third-party transaction between a willing buyer, who is under no compulsion to buy, and a willing seller, who is under no compulsion to sell, both being fully aware of all relevant facts (also referred to as Retail Value) (Chrappa)

Fair Market Value-In-Place—the amount expressed in terms of money that may reasonably be expected to exchange between a willing buyer and a willing seller with equity to both, neither under any compulsion to buy or sell, and both fully aware of all relevant facts, as of a certain date and taking into account installation and the contribution of the item to the operating facility. This value presupposes continued utilization of the item in connection with all other installed items. (Chrappa)

Fair Value—that estimate of the value of a property that is reasonable and fair to all concerned, after every proper consideration has been given due weight (10S-90)

Finish to Finish (FF)—the finishes of two or more activities are linked, i.e. one must finish before the second can finish. The delay between them, called a lag, must be defined in the same units as the activity duration. Zero lag defines no delay between the activities. (Werderitsch)

Finish to Start (FS)—the start of an activity is linked to the finish of another activity. The delay between the finish of one activity and start of the other activity is called a lag. (Werderitsch)

Fixed Cost—those costs independent of short-term variations in output of the system under consideration. Includes such costs as maintenance; plant overhead; and administrative, selling and research expense. For the purpose of cash flow calculation, depreciation is excluded (except in income tax calculations). (10S-90)

Forced Liquidation Value —the value of equipment in terms of money that can be derived from a properly advertised and conducted auction where time is of the essence (also referred to as "under the hammer" or "blow-out" value) (Chrappa)

Forward Pass—(1) in construction, network calculations which determine the earliest start/earliest finish time (date) of each activity. (2) in manufacturing, often referred to as forward scheduling, a scheduling technique where the scheduler proceeds from a known start date and computes the completion date for an order usually proceeding from the first operation to the last. (10S-90)

Free Float—the amount of time that the completion of an activity may exceed its scheduled finish time without increasing the start time of any succeeding activity. (10S-90)

Frequency Distribution—a specification of the way in which the frequencies of members of a population are distributed according to the values of the variates which they exhibit. For observed data the distribution is usually specified in tabular form, with some grouping for continuous variates. A conceptual distribution is usually specified by a frequency function or a distribution function (10S-90)

Front-End Loading (FEL)—a process in a project system by which an enterprise develops a detailed definition of the scope of a project that is required to meet enterprise objectives. (Hollmann)

Function—(1) an expression of conceptual relationships useful in model formulations (e.g., productivity is a function of hours worked). (10S-90)

Function, Basic—the primary purpose or most important action performed by a product or service. The basic function must always exist, although methods or designs to achieve it may vary. (Younker)

Function Models— a graphical depiction of the relationships of the functions within a project. There are two commonly used styles: **Hierarchy**—A vertical "tree" chart of functions. Recent practice has been to include within one branch user oriented functions such as assure convenience, assure dependability, assure safety, and attract user. Some practitioners prefer to lay out this model horizontally and refer to it as "user FAST." **Function Analysis System Technique (FAST)**—A horizontal chart depicting functions within a project, with the following rules:

- The sequence of functions on the critical path proceeding from left to right answer the questions "How is the function to its immediate left performed?"
- The sequence of functions on the critical path proceeding from right to left answer the question "Why is the next function performed?"
- Functions occurring at the same time or caused by functions on the critical path appear vertically below the critical path function.
- The basic function of the study is always farthest to the left of the diagram of all functions within the scope of the study.

Two other functions are classified: **Highest Order**—The reason or purpose that the basic function exists. It answers the "why" question of the basic function, and is depicted immediately outside the study scope to the left. **Lowest Order**—The function that is required to initiate the project and is depicted farthest to the right, outside the study scope. For example, if the value study concerns an electrical device, the "supply power" function at the electrical connection would be the lowest order function. (Younker)

Function, Secondary—a function that supports the basic function and results from the specific design approach to achieve the basic function. As methods or design approaches to achieve the basic function are changed, secondary functions may also change. There are four kinds of secondary functions:

- **Required**—A secondary function that is essential to support the performance of the basic function under the current design approach.
- **Aesthetic**—A secondary function describing esteem value.
- **Unwanted**—A negative function caused by the method used to achieve the basic function such as the heat generated from lighting which must be cooled.
- **Sell**—A function that provides primarily esteem value. For marketing studies it may be the basic function. (Younker)

Functional Worth – the lowest overall cost for performing a function. Four types are as follows:

- **Cost Value**—the monetary sum of labor, material, burden, and all other elements of cost required to produce an item or provide a service.
- **Esteem Value**—the monetary measure of the properties of a product or service, which contribute to desirability or salability but not to required functional performance.
- **Exchange Value**—the monetary sum at which a product or service can be traded.
- **Use Value**—the monetary measure of the necessary functional properties of a product or service that contribute to performance. (10S-90)

Future Value – the value of a benefit or a cost at some point in the future, considering the time value of money. Also known as future worth. (10S-90)

Future Worth—see Future Value

Gantt Chart—see Bar Chart. (10S-90)

General and Administrative Expenses (G & A Expenses)—those costs which are incurred above the factory or production level and are associated with management. This category includes marketing and sales costs, salaries and expenses of officers and staff, accounting, central engineering, research and development, etc. (Humphreys)

Hierarchy Of Needs – a theory of motivation that states that a person's needs arise in an ordered sequence. (Levin)

Indirect Costs—(1) in construction, all costs which do not become a final part of the installation, but which are required for the orderly completion of the installation and may include, but are not limited to, field administration, direct supervision, capital tools, startup costs, contractor's fees, insurance, taxes, etc; (2) In manufacturing, costs not directly assignable to the end product or process, such as overhead and general purpose labor, or costs of outside operations, such as transportation and distribution. Indirect manufacturing cost sometimes includes insurance, property taxes, maintenance, depreciation, packaging, warehousing and loading. In government contracts, indirect cost is often calculated as a fixed percent of direct payroll cost. (10S-90)

Indirect Field Cost—The costs of services and materials required in support of the field construction effort which do not contribute directly to the permanent facility. (Dysert)

Indirect Labor—labor needed for activities which do not become part of the final installation, product, or goods produced but are required to complete the project. (Fleishman)

Inflation—a rise in the general price level, usually expressed as a percentage rate. (10S-90)

Influence Curve—a conceptual diagram that shows how the potential to influence the value of an asset diminishes as asset and project planning and implementation progress. (Hollmann)

Inputs—the resources which are brought together to produce goods and services. (Singh)

Inside Battery Limits (ISBL)—In reference to a process plant, it refers to the process units of the plant or facility. In reference to a single piece of equipment, it refers to the piece of equipment and the associated bulk materials (foundation, piping, electrical, controls, etc.) directly associated with the piece of equipment. (Dysert)

Inventory – raw materials, products in process, and finished products required for plant operation or the value of such material and other supplies, ie, those for maintenance, catalyst, chemicals, and spare parts. (10S-90)

ISBL—see Inside Battery Limits.

Job Plan—a structured discipline to carry out a value study. (Younker)

Late Finish (LF)—the latest time an activity <u>must</u> be completed without delaying the project completion date. (Werderitsch)

Late Start (LS)—the latest time at which an activity <u>must</u> start without delaying the project completion. (Werderitsch)

Leadership—the use of influence to direct the activities of others toward the accomplishment of an objective. (Levin)

Life Cycle—the stages or phases that occur during the lifetime of an object or endeavor. A life cycle presumes a beginning and an end with each end implying a new beginning. In life cycle cost or investment analysis, the life cycle is the length of time over which an investment is analyzed (i.e., study period) (10S-90)

Life-Cycle Cost (LCC) Method—a technique of economic evaluation that sums over a given study period the costs of initial investment (less resale value), replacements, operations (including energy use), and maintenance and repair of an investment decision (expressed in present or annual value terms). (10S-90)

Management—consistently producing key results expected by stakeholders (Levin)

Manufacturability—utilization of manufacturing knowledge and experience in product design and production resulting in optimum consumption of resources. (Opfer)

Manufacturing Cost—the total of variable and fixed or direct and indirect costs chargeable to the production of a given product, usually expressed in cents or dollars per unit of production, or dollars per year. Transportation and distribution costs, and research, development, selling and corporate administrative expense are usually excluded. (10S-90)

Milestone—an important or critical event and/or activity that must occur when scheduled in the project cycle in order to achieve the project objective(s). (10S-90) Note: A milestone generally has a zero duration. (Werderitsch)

Motivation—the process, action or intervention that serves as an incentive for a person to take the necessary action to complete a task within the appropriate confines and scope of performance, time, and cost. (Levin)

Motivation-Hygiene Theory—two sets of factors that must be considered to satisfy a person's needs: those related to job satisfaction (motivators) and those related to job dissatisfaction (hygiene or maintenance factors). (Levin)

Must Finish On—a mandatory finish date assigned to an activity or milestone. (Werderitsch)

Must Start On—a mandatory start date assigned to an activity or milestone. (Werderitsch)

Network—a logic diagram of a project consisting of the activities and events that must be accomplished to reach the objectives, showing that shows their required sequence of accomplishment and interdependencies. (10S-90)

Not Earlier Than (NET)—a mandatory date that an activity or milestone cannot start before. (Werderitsch)

Not Later Than (NLT)—a mandatory date that an activity or project cannot finish later than. (Werderitsch)

Operating Cost—the expenses incurred during the normal operation of a facility, or component, including labor, materials, utilities, and other related costs. Includes all fuel, lubricants, and normally scheduled part changes in order to keep a subsystem, system, particular item, or entire project functioning. Operating costs may also include general building maintenance, cleaning services, taxes, and similar items. (10S-90)

Opportunity Cost—(1) the cost of something in terms of the next best thing or foregone alternative. (Singh); (2) the benefit or advantage relinquished by choosing one course of action versus another course of action. (Opfer)

Orderly Liquidation Value—the probable price for all capital assets and equipment in terms of money which could be realized from a properly executed orderly liquidation type of sale, given a maximum time of six months to conduct such sale and adequate funds available for the remarketing campaign. This value further assumes all assets will be sold upon completion of the allotted time period (also referred to as wholesale value) (Chrappa)

Original Duration (OD)—the initial accepted estimate of an activity duration used in the original baseline schedule. (Werderitsch)

OSBL—See Outside Battery Limits

Outside Battery Limits (OSBL)—In reference to a process plant, it refers to the non-process facilities of the plant (i.e., the utility generation facilities, storage facilities, office buildings, etc.), and are sometimes also referred to as offsites. (Dysert)

Overhead— cost or expense inherent in the performing of an operation, i.e., engineering, construction, operating or manufacturing, which can not be charged to or identified with a part of the work, product, or asset and, therefore, must be allocated on some arbitrary base believed to be equitable, or handled as a business expense independent of the volume of production. Plant overhead is also called factory expense.

Overhead Labor—labor portion of costs inherent in the performing of a task such as: engineering, construction, operating or manufacturing, which cannot be charged to or identified with a part of the work, and therefore must be allocated on some arbitrary base believed to be equitable, or handled as a business expense independent of the volume of production. (Fleishman)

Overlapping Scheduling Technique—allows for the development of a schedule that more closely represents how a planner visualizes actual field conditions. For example, rather than wait for an activity to complete before starting the succeeding activity, it can be said that a successor activity can start a number of days after the start of its predecessor or that it can finish a number of days after the finish of its predecessor. (Werderitsch)

Patent—a grant made by a government to an inventor assuring the grantee the sole right to produce, use and sell the invention for a specified period of time. (Opfer)

Percent Complete—a comparison of the work completed to the current projection of total work. The percent complete of an activity in a program can be determined by inspection of quantities placed as workhours expended and compared with quantities planned or workhours planned. Other methods can also be used (10S-90)

Performance—the physical characteristics required to meet the users' needs. Factors such as reliability, maintainability, quality and appearance are typical. (Younker)

PERT Diagram—an acronym for Project Evaluation Review Technique which is a probabilistic technique, used mostly by government agencies, for calculating the "most likely" durations for network activities. Most recently, however, the term PERT has been used as a synonym for CPM. (10S-90)

Planning—(1) the determination of a project's objectives with identification of the activities to be performed. Methods and resources to be used for accomplishing the tasks, assignment of responsibility and accountability, and establishment of an integrated plan to achieve completion as required. (10S-90); (2) A process for determining asset investment or project objectives with the analysis and identification of the projects, activities or other actions to be performed, methods and resources to be used for performing these actions, assignment of responsibility and accountability for each identified action, and establishment of an integrated plan to assure that performance objectives are achieved. As used specifically in the process of "planning and scheduling," planning is the subprocess of translating scope into manageable activities and determining the manner and order and in which these activities should be performed to best meet asset investment, project or other objectives. Planning includes the identification of methods and resources to be used for accomplishing the activities and the assignment of responsibility and accountability for each activity. (proposed new definition for 10S-90)

Precedence Diagramming Method (PDM)—a method of constructing a logic network using nodes to represent the activities and connecting them by lines that show logic relationships. (10S-90)

Present Value—the value of a benefit or cost found by discounting future cash flows to the base time. Also, the system of comparing proposed investments, which involves discounting at a known interest rate (representing a cost of capital or a minimum acceptable rate of return) in order to choose the alternative having the highest present value per unit of investment. (10S-90)

Prevention—quality activities employed to avoid deviations; includes such activities as quality systems development, quality program development, feasibility studies, quality system audits, contractor/subcontractor evaluations, vendor/supplier of information/materials evaluations, quality orientation activities, and certification/qualification. (10S-90)

Price—(1) the amount of money asked or given for a product (eg, exchange value). The chief function of price is rationing the existing supply among prospective buyers. (10S-90)

Price Index—the representation of price changes, which is usually derived by dividing the current price for a specific good by some base period price. (10S-90)

Price Variation—the change in price over time for a given item relative to a previously-established price. (Opfer)

Product—for the purposes of value studies, a product is the subject of the study. It may be a physical product such as a manufactured item, or a structure, system, procedure, or an organization. (Younker)

Product Design—structuring of component parts or tasks to provide the required value in one unit. (Opfer)

Production—(1) the act or process of producing; (2) the usable result of the production process: output. (Opfer); 3) the process of adding value when inputs are used to create outputs of goods and services. (Singh)

Productivity—relative measure of labor efficiency, either good or bad, when compared to an established base or norm as determined from an area of great experience. Alternatively, productivity is defined as the reciprocal of the labor factor. (10S-90) In general terms, labor productivity can be defined as the ratio of the value that labor produces to the value invested in labor. It is an absolute measure of work process efficiency, i.e., a measure of the extent to which labor resources are minimized and wasted effort is eliminated from the work process. In earned value project control practice, productivity is a relative measure of labor efficiency, either good or bad, when compared to an established base or norm as determined from an area of great experience. Alternatively, productivity is defined as the reciprocal of the labor factor. (proposed change to 10S-90)

Profitability—a measure of the excess income over expenditure during a given period of time. (10S-90)

Progress—development to a more advanced stage. Progress relates to a progression of development and, therefore, shows relationships between current conditions and past conditions. In networking, progress indicates activities have started or completed, or are in progress. (10S-90)

Project—an endeavor with a specific objective to be met within the prescribed time and dollar limitations and which has been assigned for definition or execution. (10S-90)

Project Management—the utilization of skills and knowledge in coordinating the organizing, planning, scheduling, directing, controlling, monitoring and evaluating of prescribed activities to ensure that the stated objectives of a project, manufactured product, or service, are achieved (10S-90)

Project System—a process by which an enterprise creates its strategic assets. The process is a subset of the Strategic Asset Management process. It includes the steps for planning asset investments, implementing investment decisions through projects, and then measuring project system and asset performance. (Hollmann)

Project System, Gated—(also, Stages and Gates Project System) – a project system wherein the performance of planning tasks is done in successively more definitive stages with a review by the asset owner of planning progress between each stage (i.e., a "gate" review). (Hollmann)

Purchasing—the acquisition process of materials, equipment and/or services from order through delivery. (Opfer)

Quality—conformance to established requirements (not a degree of goodness) (10S-90)

Quality Performance Tracking System—a management tool providing data for the quantitative analysis of certain quality-related aspects of projects by systematically collecting and classifying costs of quality. (10S-90)

Quantification—in estimating practice, an activity to translate project scope information into resource quantities suitable for costing. In the engineering and construction industry, a take-off is a specific kind of quantification that is a measurement and listing of quantities of materials from drawings. Syn.: Take-off (10S-90)

Rate of Return—the interest rate earned by an investment (10S-90)

Raw Materials—materials as found in their most basic state with little or no processing. Examples would be coal, logs, iron ore, and sand. (Opfer)

Reengineering—fundamental rethinking and radical redesign of business processes to achieve dramatic improvements in critical contemporary measures of performance, such as cost, quality, service, and speed (Hammer & Champy)

Relationships:
- **Finish to Finish (FF)**—the finishes of two or more activities are linked, i.e. one must finish before the second can finish. The delay between them, called a lag, must be defined in the same units as the activity duration. Zero lag defines no delay between the activities.
- **Finish to Start (FS)**—the start of an activity is linked to the finish of another activity. The delay between the finish of one activity and start of the other activity is called a lag.
- **Start to Start (SS)** - the start of two activities is linked, i.e. they start at the same time, or the second one's start will lag the first by a set amount. (Werderitsch)

Remaining Duration—the estimated work units (time) needed to complete an activity as of the data date. (10S-90)

Replacement Cost—(1) the cost of replacing the productive capacity of existing property by another property of any type, to achieve the most economical service, at prices as of the date specified; (2) facility component replacement and related costs, included in the capital budget, that are expected to be incurred during the study period (10S-90); the cost new of an item having the same or similar utility (Chrappa)

Reproduction Cost—the cost of reproducing substantially the identical item or facility at a price level as of the date specified (10S-90)

Resource—in planning and scheduling, a resource is any consumable, except time, required to accomplish an activity. From a total cost and asset management perspective, resources may include any real or potential investment in strategic assets including time, monetary, human, and physical. A resource becomes a cost when it is invested or consumed in an activity or project. (10S-90)

Risk—(1) the degree of dispersion or variability around the expected or "best" value which is estimated to exist for the economic variable in question, e.g., a quantitative measure of the upper and lower limits which are considered reasonable for the factor being estimated. (10S-90)

Risk Management—a process for identifying risk factors (assessment), analyzing and quantifying the properties of those factors (analysis), and mitigating the impact of the factors on planned asset or project performance (control) to assure that plan objectives are achieved. (proposed addition to 10S-90)

Robot—computerized equipment that can perform a variety of tasks in response to pre-programmed commands or input from vision or other systems. (Humphreys)

Safety Stock—the average amount of stock on hand when a replenishment quantity is received. Its purpose is to protect against the uncertainty in demand and in the length of the replenishment lead time. Safety stock and cycle stock are the two main components of any inventory. Also known as reserve stock. (10S-90)

Salvage Value—(1) the cost recovered or that could be recovered from a used property when removed, sold, or scrapped; (2) the market value of a machine or facility at any point in time (normally an estimate of an asset's net market value at the end of its estimated life); (3) the value of an asset, assigned for tax computation purposes, that is expected to remain at the end of the depreciation period (10S-90)

Schedule—(1) the plan for completion of a project based on a logical arrangement of activities, resources available, imposed dates or funding budgets. (10S-90); an output of the planning and scheduling process that documents planned activities and their start and finish times in a way that is logically sequenced and achieves asset investment, operation, project or other time objectives while addressing resource availability, investment objectives and constraints. A schedule may be used for projects, operations, maintenance, business planning, and other purposes. (proposed change to 10S-90)

Schedule Activity Logic—the sequence of activities including start and finish times, constraints on start and finish times, dependencies between activities, and similar logic issues. Techniques for establishing logic include arrow diagramming, precedence diagramming or PERT methods. Syn.; Network. (proposed addition to 10S-90)

Schedule Calendar—defines the calendar to be applied to the schedule, such as the workweek begins on Monday and work continues through Friday with eight hours of work per day; identifying non-workdays such as holidays. (Werderitsch)

Schedule Update—the regular review, analysis, evaluation, and reporting of progress of the project including recomputation of an estimate or schedule. (Werderitsch)

Schedule Variance—the difference between BCWP and BCWS. At any point in time it represents the difference between the dollar value of work actually performed (accomplished) and that scheduled to be accomplished (10S-90)

Scheduling—the assignment of desired start and finish times to each activity in the project within the overall time cycle required for completion according to plan. (10S-90); 2) a predictive process of estimating the duration of activities and time-scaling them in a way that achieves asset investment, operation, project or other time objectives while addressing resource availability, investment objectives and constraints. At the completion of the process, each planned activity will have determined start and finish times within the overall time cycle required. Scheduling is used for projects, operations, maintenance, business planning, and other purposes. (proposed change to 10S-90)

Scheduling Levels—various levels of the schedule used to manage the project and generally include milestone, project summary, detailed, and short interval levels of schedules. Senior management may require a very summary level referred to as a milestone schedule. Project management and key department interface may only require a summary level of the project activities while day-to-day managers require detailed and short interval project schedules. (Werderitsch)

Scope—(1) the sum of all that is to be or has been invested in and delivered by the performance of an activity or project. In project planning, the scope is usually documented (i.e, the scope document), but it may be verbally or otherwise communicated and relied upon. Generally limited to that which is agreed to by the stakeholders in an activity or project (i.e., if not agreed to, it is "out of scope"). In contracting and procurement practice, includes all that an enterprise is contractually committed to perform or deliver. Syn.: Project Scope. (10S-90)

Scrap Value—the value of equipment in terms of money that relates to the equipment's basic commodity value. For example, dollars per ton of steel or pound of copper (Chrappa)

Semivariable Costs—direct costs which are only partially dependent upon production or plant output. These include such items as direct labor, supervision, maintenance, general expense, and plant overhead. While these costs increase with production rate, they do not increase in direct proportion to production rate. When the plant is not operating, a portion of the semivariable costs continues to be incurred. At zero production or throughput semivariable costs generally total about 20 to 40 percent of the total semivariable cost at full production. (Humphreys)

Standard Deviation—the most widely used measure of dispersion of a frequency distribution. It is calculated by summing squared deviations from the mean, dividing by the number of items in the group and taking the square root of the quotient (10S-90)

Start to Start (SS)—the start of two activities is linked, i.e. they start at the same time, or the second one's start will lag the first by a set amount. (Werderitsch)

Status—the condition of the project at a specified point in time relative to its plan. An instantaneous snapshot of the then current conditions. (10S-90)

Strategic Asset—any unique physical or intellectual property that is of long term or ongoing value to the enterprise. As used in total cost management, it most commonly includes capital or fixed assets, but may include intangible assets. Excludes cash and purely financial assets. Strategic assets are created by the investment of resources through projects. (10S-90)

Strategic Asset Management—the macro process of managing the total life cycle cost investment of resources in an enterprise's portfolio of strategic assets. (Hollmann)

Statistics—the field of study where data are collected for the purpose of drawing conclusions and making inferences (Chen)

Sunk Cost—a cost that has already been incurred and which should not be considered in making a new investment decision. (10S-90)

Surplus—the amount of materials remaining after a project is complete or production is complete. May result from either incorrect over-ordering of materials or more efficient materials usage as compared to estimated materials standards. (Opfer)

System Design—design focused on organization of the system including tools, equipment and processes to produce a product or project. (Humphreys)

Take-off—a specific type of quantification that is a measurement and listing of quantities of materials from drawings in order to support the estimate costing process and/or to support the material procurement process. Syn.: Quantification. (10S-90)

Target Schedule—a static representation of the approved schedule. (Werderitsch)

Taxation—the act or process of imposing taxes by a governmental entity. (Opfer)

Taxes—contributions for the activities of a governmental entity and levied on persons and businesses within the jurisdiction of the governmental entity. (Opfer)

Team—a small number of people with complementary skills committed to a common purpose, performance goals, and approach who are mutually accountable. (Levin)

Theory X Management—the philosophy that people dislike work, will avoid it if they can, and are only interested in monetary gain from their labor. (Levin)

Theory Y Management—the philosophy that people will work best when they are properly rewarded and motivated, and that work is as natural as play or rest. (Levin)

Time Scaled Network (Time Scaled CPM)—a plotted or drawn representation of a CPM network where the length of the activities indicates the duration of the activity as drawn to a calendar scale. Float is usually shown with a dashed line as are dummy activities. (10S-90)

Time Value of Money—(1) the time-dependent value of money stemming both from changes in the purchasing power of money (that is, inflation or deflation), and from the real earning potential of alternative investments over time; (2) the cumulative effect of elapsed time on the money value of an event, based on the earning power of equivalent invested funds; (3) the expected interest rate that capital should or will earn. (10S-90)

Total Cost Management (TCM)—the effective application of professional and technical expertise to plan and control resources, costs, profitability and risks. Simply stated, it is a systematic approach to managing cost throughout the life cycle of any enterprise, program, facility, project, product, or service. This is accomplished through the application of cost engineering and cost management principles, proven methodologies and the latest technology in support of the management process. Put another way, total cost management is the sum of the practices and processes that an enterprise uses to manage the total life cycle cost investment in its portfolio of strategic assets. (10S-90)

Total Float—the amount of time (in work units) that an activity may be delayed from its early start without delaying the project finish date. Total float is equal to the late finish minus the early finish or the late start minus the early start of the activity. (10S-90)

Total Quality Management—the consistent integrated orchestration of the total complex of an organization's work processes and activities to achieve continuous improvement in the organization's processes and products. (10S-90)

Value—the lowest cost to reliably provide the required functions at the desired time and place with the essential quality and other performance factors to meet user requirements. (Younker)

Value, Activity—that portion of the contract price which represents a fair value for the part of the work identified by that activity. (10S-90)

Value Analyst—synonymous with Value Specialist. (Younker)

Value Engineering Change Proposal (VECP)—a formal proposal submitted to the customer/user which requires their approval before implementing the VA change. The result will be a modification to the submitter's contract. (Younker)

Value Improving Practice (VIP)—any project system practice that improves project outcomes and adds value (from the asset owner perspective) to the resulting assets. (Hollmann)

Value Methodology—the systematic application of recognized techniques which identify the functions of the product or service, establish the worth of those functions, and provide the necessary functions to meet the required performance at the lowest overall cost. (Younker)

Value Methodology Proposal—a proposal by the value study team to its management to provide one or more functions for financial and/or performance improvements and is within the current terms and conditions of the contract. (Younker)

Value Methodology Training—there are two levels of SAVE International approved training specifically designed to provide the minimum knowledge of VM practice. They are Value Methodology Workshop, and Value Methodology Advanced Seminar.

Value, Monetary—there are four classes of monetary value: Use Value - The monetary measure of the functional properties of the product or service which reliably accomplish a user's needs.

- **Esteem Value**—the monetary measure of the properties of a product or service which contribute to its desirability or salability. Commonly answers the "How much do I want something?" question.
- **Cost Value**—the monetary sum of labor, material, burden, and other elements of cost required to produce a product or service.
- **Exchange Value**—the monetary sum at which a product or service can be freely traded in the marketplace. (Younker)

Value Specialist—one who applies the value methodology to study and search for value improvement. (Younker)

Value Study—the application of the value methodology using the VM Job Plan, and people previously trained in VM workshops. (Younker)

Variable Costs—those costs that are a function of production, e.g., raw materials costs, by-product credits, and those processing costs that vary with plant output (such as utilities, catalysts and chemical, packaging, and labor for batch operations). (10S-90)

Variance Analysis—the process whereby differences between forecasted results and actual results are analyzed as to causation and potential corrective actions. (Humphreys)

Work Breakdown Structure (WBS)—a product-oriented family tree division of hardware, software, facilities and other items, which organizes, defines, and displays all of the work to be performed in accomplishing the project objectives.

- **Contract Work Breakdown Structure (CWBS)**—the complete WBS for a contract developed and used by a contractor in accordance with the contract work statement. It extends the PSWBS to the lowest level appropriate to the definition of the contract work.
- **Project Summary Work Breakdown Structure (PSWBS)**—a summary WBS tailored by project management to the specific project with the addition of the elements unique to the project. (10S-90)

Work Days (WD)—days (or units of time) that work is performed and is used to estimate the duration of activities. Generally, workdays begin at 8:00 a.m. and finish at 5:00 p.m.; however, days may be ten- or twelve-hour shifts and lunch may be one half-hour of non-work. (Werderitsch)

Worth—the worth of an item or groups of items, as in a complete facility, is determined by the return on investment compared to the amount invested. The worth of an item is dependent upon the analysis of feasibility of the entire item or group or items under discussion (or examination). (10S-90)

THE INTERNATIONAL SYSTEM OF UNITS (SI)

Kurt G.R. Heinze, CCE

Recognizing the value of having one common worldwide language, managers have now become quite familiar with metric conversion in North America. Because the use of metric terms is not extensive in cost management, this chapter will give only a cursory overview of the Système International d'Unites (SI).

BACKGROUND

The customary measuring system in the US is nearly the same as that brought by the colonists from England, which in turn had its origin in a variety cultures, including the Babylonian sexagesimal counting system ($360°$ circle), Egyptian (common fractions, i.e., repeated halving), and Roman (base number 12 as in dozen, hours, months). The Romans also had the abacus, while the Celts and Vikings used base number 20.

The Chinese were the first to introduce the decimal notation (ten fingers and the abacus).

Through colonization and dominance of world commerce, the English system of weights and measures spread to many parts of the world, including the American colonies. In 1585, Simon Stevin invented decimal fractions and predicted that eventually the measuring system would be based on factors of ten. His idea was realized in 1795 when the French Convention nationale passed a law establishing le système métrique décimal (the decimal measuring system), which is the basis, practically unchanged, of the metric system today.

In 1873, the British Academy for the Advancement of Science developed a system of units for the sciences, known as the cgs, or centimeter-gram-second system. It included two sets of units for electrical quantities differing by a factor of c (the speed of light) and included in their definitions factors of 4π. Engineers found the cgs units too small for engineering use. They preferred the mks (meter-kilogram-second) set of base units. They adopted a set of decimal multiples and submultiples of the electromagnetic egs units.

In 1901, Giovanni Giorgi proposed that by recognizing an electric unit (such as the ampère) as a base unit, the duality of the two sets of electric units could be eliminated, and the system could be made coherent, i.e., without conversion factors between units. Giorgi's mksA system was adopted by the Conférence générale des poids et mesures, and in 1960 the CGPM renamed it Le Système International d'Unités (SI). This involved declaring 29 old units to be obsolete and replacing them with new coherent units.

In North America, we are converting to SI, and definitely not to the old metric system.

Quantity	Base Unit	Symbol
length	meter	m
mass	kilogram	kg
time	second	s
electric current	ampere	A
thermodynamic temperature	kelvin	K
amount of substance	mole	mol
luminous intensity	candela	cd

Quantity	Derived Unit	Symbol
land surveyor's area	hectare	ha
liquid volume	liter	L
plane angle	radian	rad
solid angle	steradian	sr
frequency	hertz	Hz
force	newton	N
pressure, stress	pascal	Pa
energy, work, heat quantity	joule	J
power	watt	W
quantity of electricity	coulomb	C
electric potential, emf	volt	V
electric capacitance	farad	F
electric resistance	ohm	Ω
electric conductance	siemens	S
magnetic flux	weber	Wb
flux density, magn. induction	telsa	T
inductance	henry	H
luminous flux	lumen	lm
illuminance	lux	lx
radioactive activity	becquerel	Bq
absorbed radioactive dose	gray	Gy

Figure B.1—Base Units and Derived Units with special names

ADVANTAGES OF SI

SI Is Coherent, Absolute, Unique

SI consists of seven fundamental base units, two supplementary units, and several derived units with special names. The supplementary units were changed to derived units in October 1995, resulting in only two major categories (See Figure B.1).

SI also uses prefixes that relate to any units in intervals of one thousand (Figure B.2). In the lower range, for popular use, the intervals are ten (centi-, hecto-). Thanks to those prefixes, most measurements can be expressed with numerical values of two to four digits. The relationship to the base unit is immediately evident from the prefix. There is no need for more than one basic unit for any given quantity. Length is always expressed in meters [m] with prefix if applicable [**m**m, **c**m, **k**m (spoken emphasis on the prefix!)]. This eliminates different names for different lengths such as miles, fathoms, chains, feet, inches, etc., with many conversion factors. SI quantities relate by simply moving the decimal point.

SI Is Absolute

SI expressions are unqualified. Force is always expressed in newtons. There is no other name for force. Mass is kg, and pressure is pascal. The imperial system uses "pound" for force as in psi and also for mass as in density. "Ounces" could denote weight or volume. U.S. gallons are different from imperial gallons.

SI Is Unique

The same units are used whether we do thermal, mechanical, or electrical calculations. This is a tremendous advantage because all engineering disciplines talk the same language. One unit of power, the watt, is used now where 19 units were previously used (Btu, calories, HP, etc. . .).The pascal is replacing some 30 different pressure or stress units, including obsolete metric units.

SI Is Coherent

There are no factors relating different units; all units are related to each other by unity. One newton is the force required to give a mass of one kilogram an acceleration of one meter per

Prefix	Symbol	Factor
tera	T	10^{12} = 1 000 000 000 000
giga	G.	10^{9} = 1 000 000 000
mega	M	10^{6} = 1 000 000
kilo	k	10^{3} =1000
hecto	h	10^{2} =100
deka	da	10^{1} =10
deci	d	10^{-1} = 0.1
centi	c	10^{-2} = 0.01
milli	m	10^{-3} = 0.001
micro	μ	10^{-6} = 0.000 001
nano	n	10^{-9} = 0.000 000 001
pico	p	10^{-12} = 0.000 000 000 001

Figure B.2—Prefixes for Multiples and Submultiples of SI Units

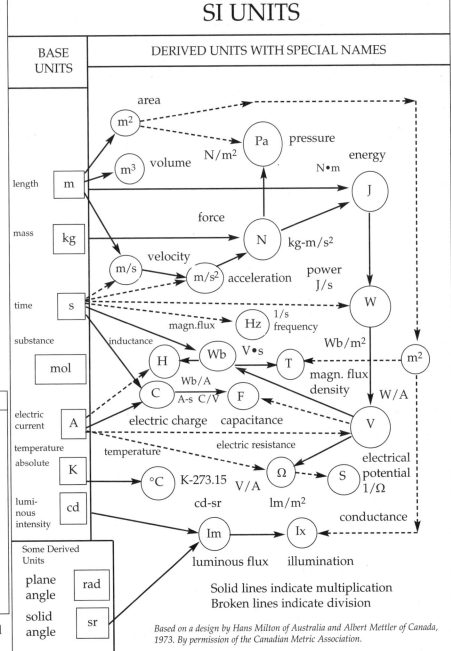

Figure B.3—SI Is Coherent

second-squared. If this force is exerted through a length of one meter, it produces the energy of one joule. If this takes place in one second, the power produced is one watt. Furthermore, if this force is distributed over an area of one square meter, it produces a pressure of one pascal. One cubic meter per second pumped against a pressure of one pascal equals one watt. A torque of one newton minus meter rotating at one radian per second equals one watt. We find the same coherence with other base units. For example, the units derived from the ampere are volt, ohm, siemens, coulomb, henry, weber, tesla, and farad (Figure B.3).

METRIC CONVERSION

Conversion Tables Do Not Teach Us SI

The advantage of SI over the customary and the old "metric" system is not necessarily appreciated by the general public. Many people still seem to be deprived of facts and may not really understand the system. It is not the learning of the new, but the unlearning of the old which is so painful.

The customary system worked in the past, but it is standing

on its own. The SI is a different improved system that also stands on its own. The two systems are incompatible. We can make it easy by using computers and conversion tables that instantly give us SI measurements. However, instant "converters" do not convert conventional units into SI units; instead, they translate the existing into the "metric" equivalent of the existing. Therefore, we are only using the old system with new numbers.

Soft Conversion

This literal approach to the changeover is called *soft conversion*. What we are doing when we soft convert is add another expression to the proliferation of expressions already in existence for each quantity of measurement. During the transition period of conversion we cannot avoid converting existing physical quantities to their SI equivalents. There is also a danger that we use an overabundance of insignificant digits. A 20-foot hydro pole should be referred as 6m, not 6096 mm. A 7 oz jar of pickled eggs is not 198 g. The liquid is probably expressed in fluid ounces and should have been hard converted into 200 cm^3 (commonly known and still accepted as 200 mL).

SI Changeover (Hard Conversion)

CONVERSION FACTORS

To convert from	to	multiply by	replacing other old units
	Length and Area:		
inch	millimeter (mm)	2.54 E+01	
foot	meter (m)	9.144 000 E-01	rod, league, pole, chain,
yard	meter (m)	3.048 000 E-01	fathom, mil, printer's pica,
mile	meter (m)	1.609 347 E+03	point, angstrom, caliber
acre	meter^2 (m^2)	4.046 873 E+03	
ft^2	meter^2 (m^2)	9.290 304 E-02	section, barn, township

Please note, that one acre (10 square chains) is 43 560 ft^2 or a square of 66 • $\overline{-10}$ = 208.710 327 feet each side, which is not a rational number. The acre (approx. 63 m • 64 m) may be compared to the derived unit hectare (ha), which is 100 m • 100 m, or approx. 2.5 acres.

	Volume and Flow:		
gallon (US dry)	meter^3 (m^3)	4.404 884 E-03	
gallon (US liquid)	meter^3 (m^3)	3.785 412 E-03	
gallon (Canada)	meter^3 (m^3)	4.546 090 E-03	barrel oil, board foot,
register ton	meter^3 (m^3)	2.831 685 E+00	bushel, cup, gill (US), gill
ounce (US fluid)	meter^3 (m^3)	2.957 353 E-05	(UK), pint, quart, cubic
fluid ounce (Canada)	meter^3 (m^3)	2.841 307 E-05	yard
gallon (US)/min	meter^3/second	6.309 020 E-05	
ft^3/second	meter^3/second	2.831 685 E-02	cubic inch per minute
	Mass:		
pound (lb avoirdupois.)	kilogram (kg)	4.535 924 E-01	
pound (troy)	kilogram (kg)	3.732 417 E-01	grain, ounce (avoir.),
ton (long)	kilogram (kg)	1.016 047 E+03	slug, ounce (troy), penny-
ton (short)	kilogram (kg)	9.071 847 E+02	weight, stone, cwt

CONVERSION FACTORS (Continued)

To convert from	to	multiply by	replacing other old units
Force (weight):			
pound-force (lbf)	newton (N)	4.448 222 E+00	
kilopond	newton (N)	9.806 650 E+00	dyne, kip, lbf thrust
poundal	newton (N)	1.382 550 E-01	

Mass is the constant property of a body. In popular speech, "weight" is used to mean mass at rest. This mass can change its weight due to acceleration to a point when it becomes "weightless." We only weigh one sixth as much on the moon than on earth, but our mass is constant.

Pressure or stress:			
psi (lb/inch^2)	pascal (Pa)	6.894 757 E+03	
atm (standard)	pascal (Pa)	1.013 250 E+05	cm Hg, cm H_2O, dyne/cm2 foot
bar	pascal (Pa)	1.000 000 E+05	of H_2O (39.2°F), lbf/ft2torr,
inch Hg (60°F)	pascal (Pa)	3.376 85 E+03	kip/in.^{2}, poundal/ft^2 etc.
inch H_2O (60°F)	pascal (Pa)	2.488 4 E+02	(approx. 30 units)
Viscosity:			
slug/ft•s	Pa•s	4.788 026 E+01	
poundal•s/ft^2	Pa•s	1.488 164 E+00	
ft^2/s	m^2/s 9.290 304 E-02		poise, stoke, lb/ft·s, rhe, etc.
Energy, work:			
Btu (international)	joule (J)	1.055 056 E+03	
calorie (international)	joule (J)	4.186 800 E+00	Various types of Btus and calories,
electronvolt	joule (J)	1.602 19 E-19	erg, ft·lbf, therm, Watthour, hp-hour
kW•h	joule (J)	3.600 000 E+06	(mech.)(approx. 19 units)
Power:			
horsepower (hp)	kilowatt (kW)	7.456 999 E-01	
Btu/h	watt (W)	2.930 711 E-01	
			hp$_{electric}$, therm/h, ftlbf/s, hp$_{metric}$

Other units:			
temperature ($^\circ$F)	celsius ($^\circ$C)	(5/9)($^\circ$F-32)	centigrade, réaumur

Kelvin ($^\circ$K) is used for absolute temperature (-273°C)

frequency (rpm)	hertz (Hz or c/s)	1.666 667 E-02 cycles per second	
Fuel consumption:			
mass (ton/h)	kg/s	2.519 958 E+04	
volume (gal/h)	dm^3/s or L/s 1.051 503 E-03 (see example below)		
automobile	L/100km	235.215 divided by US miles per gallon	

US uses fuel efficiency, i.e., miles per gallon. SI uses fuel consumption. Conversion to L/100 km is non-linear.

time (h., min., sec.)	h, s	no conversion, just spelling of symbol.	

Example

The listing above shows conversions from conventional units to SI units. When converting gal/hr into L/s, for example, 1.051 503 E-03 means 1.051 503·10^{-3} or 1.051 503/1000 = 0.001 051 503.
To convert from new to old, we divide
1/0.001 051 503 = 9.510 223 E + 02.
Converting 5000 gal/h = 5000 x 0.001 051 503 = 5.26 L/s.
We have used the prefix d (deci), where dm^3 (L) is 1/1000 of a cubic meter (m^3).
Prefixes move the decimal point back and forth.

Britain's double bed size has been 54 inches wide and 75 inches long (137 cm × 191 cm). Britain's Bedding Federation changed this into a 150 cm by 200 cm bed. This is a true changeover, taking advantage of the opportunity to increase the size of the bed at the same time. This holds true with standard door openings and other modular building components. We have the opportunity now to update, houseclean, rationalize, remove duplication, and otherwise improve the standards we use.

SI Changeover Is an Investment

As cost-conscious managers we are well aware that practical action by corporate bodies must be justified by monetary consideration. The SI changeover is a deliberate, practical move and must ultimately yield a net gain. Keeping track of costs and benefits is, therefore, an important part of metric conversion activity.

The SI changeover has an endless benefit duration, similar to the invention of the wheel. Even if we let the costs lie where they fall, benefits will accrue when conversion is complete. Therefore, it is an investment, not an expense.

The SI changeover is only a part of a larger change, the standardization of industrial products and processes. Standardization allows a rationalization of products (reduction in the total number of sizes and ranges), which is where a great deal of the benefits of conversion will occur. The benefits of rationalization remain long after the expenses of conversion are paid.

It has taken 200 years to develop a worldwide uniform measuring system, but an implementation date has not yet been established in the US. In metric conversion we have a project whose objective has not completely been defined. It has no time- or cost plan. Furthermore, it has no project leader. What would we call a project like this ?

Rules for Style and Usage

(1) Symbols and prefixes are the same in all languages.

(2) Symbols are written in lower case, except when the unit is derived from a proper name, e.g., m = meter; W = watt. The exception is the non-SI but commonly used unit for cm³, the liter (L). This is to avoid confusion between "el" and "one."

(3) Symbols and prefixes are printed in upright type. There is no spacing between prefixes and units, e.g.,

	km	cm	ng
not	*km*	*cm*	*ng*
not	k m	c m	n g

(4) Symbols are not pluralized, e.g., 100 g, 50 km not 100 gs, 50 kms

(5) There is no period after a symbol except at the end of a sentence, e.g.

$$m \quad (\text{not m.}), \qquad mL \quad (\text{not mL.})$$

(6) A sentence does not start with a symbol and prefix:
The symbol for kilogram is kg (not: kg is the symbol for . . .)

(7) Preference is given to decimal notation:
Use 3.25 percent rather than 3¼ percent;
0.75 km rather than ¾ km.
But "I walked 2 km in half an hour" (not in 0.5 h)

(8) For values less than one (1), a zero (0) is used, i.e., 0.56 (not .56)

(9) There is a space between the last digit of a number and the first letter of the symbol.

(10) The multiplication symbol is used instead of a dot or period: 5×7 (not $5 \cdot 7$ or $5 \cdot 7$)

(11) Compound prefixes must never be used:
3 mg (milligram) not 3 μkg (microkilogram)

(12) Spaces are used instead of commas to put large numbers in reading blocks of three, e.g., 23 456 789.24 not 23,456,789.24

(13) Only one unit is used to designate quantities:
5.36 m (not 5 m, 36 cm) or 3.7 kg (not 3 kg, 700 g)

(14) An oblique slash (/) with no space is used with symbols rather than the word "per":
km/h (not km / h) and (not km per h)
When writing units in full, then kilometer per hour (not kilometer/hour)

(15) ISO standard time units start with the largest unit, e.g.,

Year	Month	Day	Hour	Minute	Second
1996	07	06	18	21	08
or	1996 - 07 - 06 - 18 : 21 : 08				

Europe is committed to change from DDMMYY to the ISO standard. The US still uses MMDDYY, which can be very confusing and legally costly in international trade. The adverse effect will have great repercussions around the year 2000. If we have a commitment with China for example (it uses ISO dating) for 02 - 03 - 01 (ISO date), we will probably make payments earlier than necessary. (Feb. 3, 2001 instead of March 1, 2002).

(16) SI units are pronounced with the accent or emphasis on the first syllable: <u>cen</u>timeter, <u>kil</u>ometer, <u>Cel</u>sius, <u>mi</u>crometer, <u>meg</u>ahertz; never ki<u>lo</u>meter.
Instruments are pronounced mi<u>cro</u>meter, ther<u>mo</u>meter, spe<u>do</u>meter, o<u>do</u>meter.
(The spelling in Canada is different:, e.g., <u>kil</u>ome<u>tre</u> vs. ther<u>mo</u>me<u>ter</u>)

(17) Numeral and symbol should not be on separate lines nor should a number and symbol be hyphenated:

(18) The choice of the appropriate multiple of an SI unit is governed by the application,
preferably having values between 0.1 and 1000.
3.94 mm instead of 0.003 94 m

(19) The symbol is placed behind the numeral:
15.7 km or 350 mL; (not km 15.7 or mL 350)
(Prefixes may also apply to dollars, e.g., 250 k$ or 5 M$)

(20) Temperature will be expressed in "degrees Celsius" or °C with a space after the numeral (not centigrade or degrees C), e.g., 40 °C and (40 °C; (not + 40 °C, or minus 40 °C or 40 °C minus)

Please note, that there is no warmer or cooler temperature. It can only be higher or lower (how do we warm up a temperature?) Furthermore, 20 °C is not "half as cold" as 40 °C.

(21) Number and symbol should not be separated by an adjective.
Write   You get "200 km free" with your car rental.
not   You get "200 free km" with your car rental"

(22) If a presentation in dual values is unavoidable, give preference to the SI value:
20 kg (44 lbs.); not 44 lbs. (20 kg)

(23) Former units of area and volume will be changed as follows: Square meter (formerly sq.m) now becomes m^2, pronounced square meter, not meter square. Similarly, cubic centimeter is now cm^3, not cu.cm. or c.c. (It is acceptable to use mL instead of the SI unit cm^3 in case of liquids and gases).

(24) In order not to confuse quantity symbols in engineering with SI symbols, the ISO recommends using italic type lettering where practical.
Examples of quantity symbols are:
m = mass;
d = depth or diameter;
M = bending moment; and
A = area.

Examples of SI symbols are:
m = meter;
d = deci-;
M = mega-;
A = ampere

Equations using quantity and SI symbols are:

Gravity = g = 9.8 m/s^2; and
Force = F = m (kg) x a (m/s^2).

SOURCES OF SI INFORMATION

This chapter is based on information in the public domain and established international standards. In addition, the following sources have been used:

- AACE International *Cost Engineers' Notebook*, 209 Prairie Avenue, Suite 100, Morgantown, WV 26501.
- AACE International *Cost Engineering* Dec.1980, Vol.22/No.6 and Nov. 1986, Vol.28/No.11, p.26.
- Heinze, Kurt. *Cost Management of Capital Projects.* New York: Marcel Dekker, 1996.

Additional Information May Be Obtained By Contacting:

- American National Metric Council (ANMC), Publications Department, 4330 East West Highway, Suite 1117, Bethesda, MD, 20814 - 4408.
- American National Standards Institute (ANSI), IEEE/ASTM SI 10-10 997, 11 W 42nd St., New York, NY 10036.
- American Society of Civil Engineers (ASCE), *Metric Units in Engineering - Going SI,* Revised Edition 1995, 345 East 47th Street, New York, NY 10017-2398.
- Bureau international des poids et measures, The International System of Units, Pavillon de Breteuil, F--92310 Sevres, France.
- American Society for Testing and Materials (ASTM), *IEEE/ASTM 10, Standard for Use of the International System of Units (SI): The Modern Metric System and Units in Building Design and Construction,* 100 Bar Harbor Drive, West Conshohocken, PA 19428-2959.
- Canadian Metric Association (CMA), *Metric Fact Sheets* (no longer published, but back copies still available for nominal charge), 481 Guildwood Pkwy., Scarborough, ON, Canada M1E 1R3.
- Canadian Standards Association (CSA), *Canadian Metric Practice Guide,* CAN/CSA Z2341, 178 Rexdale Blvd., Toronto, ON, Canada M9W 1R3.
- National Institute of Standards and Technology (NIST), NIST SP 811, *Guide for the Use of the International System of Units (SI),* Gaithersburg, MD 20899-0001.
- National Research Council of Canada, Manual on Metric Building Practice, Otttawa, ON Canada K1A 0R6.
- R.S. Means Co. *Building Construction Cost Data,* Metric Edition, R.S. Means Co., Box 800, Kingston, MA 02364.
- U.S. Metric Association, 10245 Andasol Ave., Northridge, CA 91325-1504. Web site: http://www.metric.org

METRIC CONVERSION EXERCISES

Problem #1

A European furniture manufacturer calls for quotes on 10,000 cabinet drawers. His specification requires different dimensions for each set of 1,000 drawers, one of which needs boards to be cut as follows:

> depth: 450 mm outside dimension
> width: $1/2$ depth minus $1/2$ of 4 mm cut
> material thickness is 9 mm
> tolerance: up to 1.6 mm

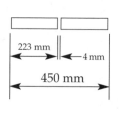

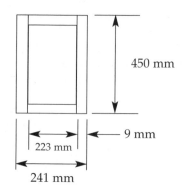

A. U.S. supplier A is the best, most reliable and inexpensive on the continent, but has no intention to convert to metrics. His shop foreman does not even have a metric scale. He needs to convert all measurements into fraction of inches.

B. U.S. supplier B has updated his shop for export and is familiar with SI dimensions.

Question: Compare the effort of supplier A with supplier B.

Answer: Supplier A converts for tolerance first:
1.6 mm = 0.0016 m/(3.048 E-01/12) = 0.0016/0.0254 = 0.063 inches. This translates into 63/1000 = x/32. x = 2.02/32 or $1/16$ of an inch. This is a generous tolerance! They now need to cut the 450 mm board. Using the same procedure, 450 mm = 17.72 inches or 17 $23/32$ of an inch, which is close to 17 $3/4$ inches. This translates into 450.8 mm, having a tolerance limit of 1.5 mm.

The foreman started to convert $1/2$ of 17 $3/4$ inches minus the equivalent of 2 mm, then planing the board to the equivalent of 9 mm thickness, when the cost optimization engineer noticed that there may be discrepancies with final tolerances by adding up several rounded figures. He suggested to start with the overall wide dimensions of 241 mm = 9.49 inches or (9 $1/2$ inches, where the tolerance on 9.5 inches = 241.3 mm is 0.3 mm. Very close indeed!

Subtracting the thickness of the side boards:
9 mm each = 0.354 inches or
(354 x 32)/1000 = $^{11.3}/32$, rounded to
$3/8$ or 9.5 mm, which is very close to
the tolerance limit again. Therefore,
the fitting piece is 9 $1/2$ - (2 x $3/8$) = 8 $3/4$ inches.
This is now the final "A" shop drawing specification
for the first 1,000 drawers. There are 9 more to go.

Supplier B measures the cut the saw blade makes.
It measures $1/8$" = 3.2 mm. Cutting 450 mm in half results in two
short pieces of 223.4 mm each, out by 0.4 mm or the thickness of this line ———— ,
which is 1.13 points or $1/72$ of an inch, which is well within the tolerance.

Comparing the Effort

To convert drawings from millimeter to inches (or vice versa) takes time and mathematical skills. This would not be necessary if workers were trained to use a metric measuring tape. Reading from this scale is simple, and no fractions are needed.

Problem #2

Please convert the following text into appropriate SI units (either soft or hard conversion).

Tom and Mary live near Boston on a 1½ acre lot. They decided to drive to New York City to attend a convention on 03-07-1998. It is a 249-mile drive. With a speed of about 50 miles per hour, they should be there in 5 hours.

"They predict fair weather, about 80 degrees. The barometer reads 29.5 inches Hg and falling, not the best time to travel" said Mary. Tom replied, "I made sure that the car is in good working order. I added a quart of oil and made sure that the tire pressure is 26 psi (pound force per square inch), then added 12 gallons of gasoline to fill the tank. Since the 195 horsepower car engine has a fuel economy of 14 miles per gallon, a full tank should get us to New York." "I will go to

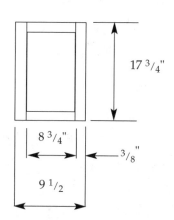

the store for I want to make some sandwiches for the trip" said Mary. She bought ½ lb. butter, 7 oz. cold cuts, and six 12 fl.oz. cans of soft drinks and a quart of milk.

When they left the next morning, there was a strong wind of 31 miles per hour. A rainfall of ½ inches was predicted. Coming out of the driveway, they barely missed a 20 ft telephone pole. In spite of this, they safely and happily arrived in New York City.

Translation

Tom and Mary live near Boston on a 0.6 ha (or 6000 m²) lot. They decided to drive to New York City to attend a convention on 1998-03-07. It is a 400 km drive. With a speed of about 80 km/h, they should be there in 5 hours.

"They predict fair weather, about 27 °C. The barometer reads 100 kPa and falling, not the best time to travel" said Mary. Tom replied, "I made sure that the car is in good working order. I added a liter of oil and made sure that the tire pressure is 180 kPa, then added 45 L gasoline to fill the tank. Since the 145 kW car engine has a fuel consumption of 18 L/100 km, a full tank should get us to New York." "I will go to the store for I want to make some sandwiches for the trip" said Mary. She bought 230 g butter, 200 g cold cuts, and six 355 mL cans of soft drinks and 500 mL (soft converted) milk.

When they left the next morning, there was a strong wind of 14 m/s (even though km/h is commonly used for longer distance driving, it is easier to visualize wind speed in terms of m/s). A rainfall of 13 mm was predicted. Coming out of the driveway, they barely missed a 6 m telephone pole (never convert to 6096 mm, because 20 ft is a rough height estimate and should be rounded to the proper degree of estimate reliability). In spite of this, they safely and happily arrived in New York City.

Problem #3
Question:
A specific type of mineral oil was tested to have a density of 7.74 lb/gal. Labeling of this product will have to be done in metric units. What should the label read?

Answer: One kilogram equals 2.205 pounds and one cubic meter equals 264.2 US liquid gallons. Therefore, the conversion is (7.74 lb/gal) x (kg/2.205 lb) x (264.2 gal/m³). The label should read

Density = 927.4 kg/m³

Since oil is a liquid, the label may also be expressed in terms of liter:

Density = 927.4 g/L

It is also acceptable to convert as follows:

One pound equals 453.6 grams; one US liquid gallon contains 3.785 liters. Therefore, 7.74 lb/gal = 7.74 x 453.6 /3.785 g/L = 928 g/L.

Problem #4
Question:
To convert Fahrenheit degrees to Celsius, we use the following formula
$$°F = 9/5 °C + 32$$
Using the above formula, at what point are °F numerically equal to °C in both scales?

Answer:
At minus 40.
If °F = °C, then °F - °C = 0, but from the above formula:
°C = 5/9 (°F - 32) and °F - 5/9 °F + 160/9 = 0, solving for °F
°F and °C are numerically equal at -40 degrees

Problem #5
Question:
A farmer in the US wants to fence in a square area containing 2.5 acres of land. He needs 4 x √2.5 x 66 x 660 or 4 x 330 = 1320 ft of fence. How would a farmer in the rest of the world who never heard of "acres" deal with this problem?

Answer:
Land areas are measured in ha (hectares), which are 10 000 m² or approximately 2.47 acres. He would therefore need 4 x √10 000 or 4 x 100 m = 400 m of fence.

ESTIMATING REFERENCE MATERIAL

This section is excerpted from Chapter 1 of *Skills and Knowledge of Cost Engineering*, 4th Edition, by

Charles P. Woodward, PE CCE, and Mark T. Chen, PE CCE

Table C.1—Construction Job Indirects Checklist

Salaries, Supervision
project director
construction manager
general superintendent
excavation superintendent
concrete superintendent
carpenter superintendent
rigging superintendent
welding superintendent
electrician superintendent
chief warehouseman

Salaries, Engineering
chief engineer
office engineer
cost engineer
schedule engineer
materials engineer
draftsmen
field engineers
survey party chiefs
instrument person

Salaries/Wages, Other
QA engineers
safety engineers
mechanics
plant operators
first aid workers
secretaries and clerks
computer operators
warehousemen
guards
janitors
runners

Automotive
automobiles/cars
pickups
ambulances
tractor-trailers
special-purpose vehicles
fuel/lube trucks

Buildings and Major Equipment
project office
warehouses
brass alley
change house
carpenter shop
pipe fabrication shop
welder test facility
electrical shop
rigging loft
first aid station
tool sheds
powder house
cap house
resteel fabrication
machine shop
equipment and maintenance shop
concrete batch plant
quarry
hoisting equipment
training building

Temporary Horizontal Construction
access roads
construction bridges
drainage structures
rail spurs
laydown areas
fencing and gates
parking areas
environmental protection

Support Systems
water supply
compressed air
electrical site
site communication
inert gas
oxygen

General Expenses
office furniture
engineering supplies
engineering equipment
printing/reproduction
computer terminal
CPM scheduling
phone/telegraph/radio
utilities
portable toilets
signs
safety equipment
permits and licenses
advertising
contributions
job travel expenses
testing and laboratory
legal fees
audit fees
medical supplies
progress photos
sanitary facilities
building rental
building and grounds
maintenance
exterior lighting
drinking water and ice
taxes
bonds
insurance
payroll burden costs
backcharges from others
consultants
weather protection

DIRECT AND INDIRECT COST ITEMS

Estimates must segregate direct and indirect costs. Many estimates are based on a historical database compiled from cost data derived from previous projects. The less that direct cost data is encumbered with indirect costs, the more reliable the direct cost data will be for use on the new project. Keeping indirects separate allows the unique conditions that will be encountered in the new project to be more accurately reflected in the estimate.

Table C.1 contains a list of indirect cost items [3] normally seen on construction projects.

ELEMENTS OF EQUIPMENT, LABOR, AND MATERIAL COSTS

Figure C.1 contains a hierarchical chart showing the components of a construction cost estimate. Other types of project cost estimates will take a similar form but may include more or less information than contained in the construction cost estimate.

Direct Costs

Labor Costs—Labor costs are a total of the actual amounts paid to field personnel who perform actual project work, e.g., carpenters, common laborers, masons, painters, etc. They can be divided into three main components:

- the basic wage (the wage rate multiplied by the number of hours worked);
- fringe benefits negotiated between employers and employees, either individually or collectively; and

- labor burden, including items such as taxes and insurance, that employers are required by law to pay.

The labor burden portion of the total labor cost is not always treated as a direct cost element. Normally, the labor burden will be treated in accordance with company practice unless actual project conditions dictate otherwise.

Material Costs—The costs for everything of a substantial nature that is essential to constructing or operating a facility, both direct and indirect. Manufactured equipment items generally comprise a large part of material costs.

Equipment Costs—This refers to the cost of equipment that a contractor uses to perform a contract (such as backhoes, cranes, or bulldozers) and not to equipment that is installed permanently as part of a contract. Equipment costs may be calculated in various ways, depending on whether the contractor leases or owns the equipment. If the equipment is leased, the costs consist of the lease costs and the cost of fuel. If the contractor owns the equipment, the costs include ownership costs (investment, maintenance and depreciation) and operating costs (such as fuel or repairs). Most contractors include the costs of equipment operators in direct labor costs, even though they are actually part of the operating costs.

Subcontract Costs—These are prices furnished by subcontractors for performing a specific portion of the work that the general contractor will not perform with its own forces.

Indirect Costs

Taxes—These vary significantly from location to location and by the tax status of the owner; thus, they are usually

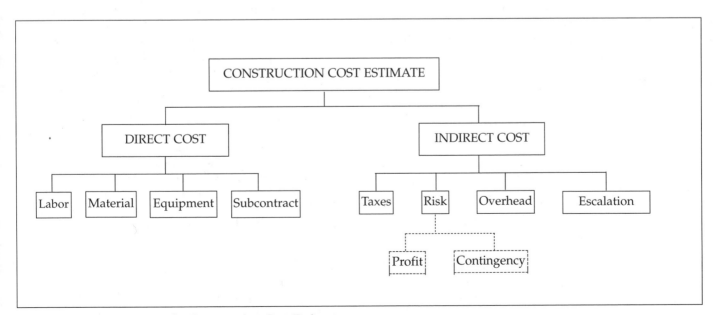

Figure C.1—Components of a Construction Cost Estimate

cataloged separately to facilitate accounting.

Risk—Elements of risk may be considered in two categories:

Profit—The amount of money included by a contractor in its price as compensation for risk, efforts, and endeavor in undertaking a project. Profit is actually the "residue" of money left after a contractor has met all costs (both direct and indirect) on a project. The amount of profit to be added is very subjective and depends on considerations such as competition, how badly the project is needed, the job market, local market conditions, and the economy.

Contingency—An amount added to an estimate to allow for changes or project cost growth that experience shows will likely be required. Contingency may be derived either through statistical analysis of past-project costs or by applying experience gained on similar projects. It usually does not include changes in scope or unforeseeable major events such as strikes or earthquakes.

Risk Analysis—Where the estimator's experience leads to conventional contingency application based on a history of project cost growth, risk analysis principles attempt to quantify this potential for direct cost elements. The members of the project team then review these elements and identify the likelihood of increases and decreases in the cost of the element, along with probabilities of deviations from the estimate. For example, they may place a 70 percent likelihood of the earthwork cost increasing because soil borings are not available. Thus the earthwork cost might increase by as much as $100,000. The cost might also be $30,000 less than the estimate due to competitive market conditions.

After the project team establishes the highest and lowest possible values for each element in the estimate, these numbers are entered into a computerized risk evaluation program that performs a Monte Carlo simulation. In this process, a random sample value for each element is taken, and the resulting total estimates are arranged in order from highest to lowest. The deviations of each total value from the original estimate are presented in a table similar to Table C.2. The certainty column represents the likelihood that the actual cost will not exceed the original estimate after the indicated amount of contingency has been added.

This information is provided to management to determine the risk they are willing to take on the project. For instance, in this example, if management selects a 70 percent risk level, the estimate would be $1,306,100 ($1,225,000 + $81,100).

Overhead Costs—These may also fall into two categories:

Home Office Overhead—The fixed costs and expenses incurred in this course of doing business, regardless of the amount of work completed or contracts received. Home office overhead includes items such as home office rent or lease, utilities, communications equipment (telephones and fax machines), advertising, salaries of home office employees (e.g., executives, estimators, and support staff), donations, legal costs, and accounting expense. In other words, home office overhead represents expenses that are not chargeable to any specific project.

One method of calculating home office overhead is to use a percentage method in which the percentage is the ratio of a specific project's total cost to the entire company/division's total projects' costs.

Job Site Overhead—Provisions contained in a contract, purchase order, or specification that are not specific to the particular transaction but which apply to all transactions. Usually, these items cannot be charged to a specific element of work. They include, for example, supervision, temporary facilities, office trailers, toilets, utilities, transportation, testing, permits, photographs, small tools, and clean-up and similar items. It also may include the costs of bonds and insurance associated with the particular project.

Escalation—Escalation is defined as being an increase in the cost of goods and services over time. Escalation has the same effect on project costs as interest does on the value of a savings account; each year becomes a new base for calculating escalation for the following year. Thus, escalation is compounded, not added, for multiple years. For example, if the escalation rate is predicted to be 5 percent per year for the next five years, an item costing $1.00 today would cost $1.28 five years from now.

$$\$1.00 \times 1.05 \times 1.05 \times 1.05 \times 1.05 \times 1.05 = \$1.28$$

Table C.2—Risk Evaluation

Target Estimate = $1,225,000

Certainty	Contingency
90	162,600
80	108,400
70	81,100
60	49,400
50	21,500
40	900
30	-28,900
20	-54,200
10	-200,950
0.5	-268,947

If a project will be completed within a given year, escalation calculation is relatively easy: simply escalate from the base year of the cost estimate to the year of construction. When a project is constructed over multiple years, however, the situation becomes more complicated, since the material, equipment, and labor in different years will be subject to different escalation rates. In such situations, the most accurate method of applying escalation to the project cost is to develop a project cash flow and calculate escalation for each year. For example, assume a project is estimated to cost $10,000,000 in 1995 dollars. The cash flow for the project may be:

$$1997—\$1,000,000$$
$$1998—\$6,000,000$$
$$1999—\$3,000,000$$

Assuming the escalation rate to be 5 percent per year, the escalation would be calculated as follows:

1997 — $1,000,000 x ((1.05 x 1.05) -1)	= $102,500	
1998 — $6,000,000 x ((1.05 x 1.05 x 1.05) -1)	= $945,750	
1999 — $3,000,000 x ((1.05 x 1.05 x 1.05 x 1.05) -1)	= $646,519	
Total escalation	$1,694,769	
Say	$1,695,000	

As can be seen by the above example, escalation is frequently one of the largest elements in a project cost estimate; yet it often receives much less attention than many smaller items. If time and detail permit, the project cost estimate should be analyzed for elements that are volatile in price. For example, in recent years, copper, aluminum, and petroleum products have seen significant price swings. If possible, this information should be considered when preparing the project risk analysis.

Most companies develop their own escalation forecasts, but they also use commercial forecasting services that provide short and long-term escalation trends. In addition, *Engineering News Record* often predicts escalation trends in its quarterly cost reports.

Estimate Documentation—An estimate should always include written documentation on how it was developed, and what is included or excluded. Whether an estimate is order-of-magnitude, definitive, a bid, or a study, it almost always becomes a benchmark against which future estimates or costs are measured. If litigation should develop, a court case can be won or lost based on the information that was used to develop an estimate; it is often difficult to know what information was used and what assumptions were made when comparing against an estimate that was developed months or even years before. To avoid such situations, the following should be included in all written documentation of an estimate's preparation.

Estimate Purpose—Since estimates may be prepared to different standards depending on their intended purpose, clarify whether the estimate is to be used for a study, a bid, a budget, or other purpose.

Scope—Provide a brief overview of what is included in the estimate. If it is a study, emphasis should be placed on the fact that the estimate may only include certain parts of the overall system cost. If the estimate is for only one of many contracts within a larger project, this fact should be noted as well.

Assumptions and Exclusions—If design information is incomplete, identify the basis for the estimate. For example, if the boring logs for the site are not available, and piling of a certain length was assumed, note the risk of a significant change occurring when the soil reports are received. Anything in the project that is excluded from the estimate should be stressed, even if this seems redundant of the scope statement.

Time/Cost Association—Indicate the project schedule that was assumed when applying escalation to the estimate. Identify the assumed escalation rates.

Contingency Development—Explain the method used to develop contingency and the rates that were applied. Contingency often can be the largest single line item in an estimate, and it deserves special attention.

Significant Findings—Note any items of significant risk that were discovered either in developing the estimate or in performing a formal risk analysis. If costs are available for a similar project, provide a comparison to those costs. Include any item that may help the project team improve the project or the estimate, or that may help sell the project, if this is the objective.

Review Credits—Identify individuals who have reviewed the estimate and scope, especially project team members and clients.

REFERENCES

1. *Cost Engineer's Notebook.* Morgantown, West Virginia: AACE International.
2. Morgantown, West Virginia: AACE International. 1998. Cost Estimate Classification System—For The Process Industry. *Recommended Practice No. 18R-9.*
3. Neil, James N. 1992. *Construction Cost Estimating for Project Control.* Englewood Cliffs, New Jersey: Prentice-Hall, Inc.

RECOMMENDED READING

1. Humphreys, K. K., ed. 1991. *Jelen's Cost and Optimization Engineering. 3rd edition.* New York: McGraw-Hill Book Co.
2. Humphreys, K.K., and L.M. English. 1993. *Project and*

Cost Engineers' Handbook. 3rd edition. New York: Marcel Dekker, Inc.

3. Vernon. *Realistic Cost Estimating for Manufacturing. Society of Manufacturing Engineers.*

4. Ostwald, P.F. 1974. *Cost Estimating for Engineering and Management.* Englewood Cliffs, NJ: Prentice-Hall, Inc.

5. Guthrie, K.M. 1974. *Process Plant Estimating, Evaluating and Control.* Solana Beach, CA: Craftsman Book Co.

6. Lorenzoni, A.B., and Forrest D. Clark. 1996. *Applied Cost Engineering.* New York: Marcel Dekker, Inc.

7. Humphreys, K.K., and Paul Wellmann. 1996. *Basic Cost Engineering.* New York: Marcel Dekker, Inc.

8. Bent James A. 1982. *Applied Cost and Schedule Control.* New York: Marcel Dekker, Inc.

9. Bauman, H.C. 1964. *Fundamentals of Cost Engineering in the Chemical Industry.* Florence, Kentucky: Reinhold Publishing Co.

10. Siddens, Scott, ed. 1995. *The Building Estimator's Reference Book.* 25th ed. Lisle, IL: Frank R. Walker Co.

11. Page, J.S. 1977. *Cost Estimating for Pipelines and Marine Structures.* Houston, Texas: Gulf Publishing Co.

12. Popper, H. Modern. 1970. *Cost Engineering Techniques.* New York: McGraw-Hill Book Co.

13. Curran, M., and W. March. Range Estimating: Measuring Uncertainty and Reasoning with Risk. *Cost Engineering.* Morgantown, West Virginia: AACE International.

14. Golden, L. Learning to Live With Probable Outcomes. *AACE Transactions.* Morgantown, West Virginia: AACE International.

15. Krumsky, S.J., and McMahon. Rules for Describing Estimates. *AACE Transactions.* Morgantown, West Virginia: AACE International.

SAMPLE PROBLEMS

1. True or false.

T F (a) Order-of-magnitude estimates can sometimes be called bid estimates.

T F (b) Definitive estimates are accurate within a range from 10 percent to 30 percent.

T F (c) Design development estimates also can be called semi-detailed estimates.

T F (d) Direct costs include the cost of labor, materials, and equipment.

T F (e) Project indirects include home office overhead and jobsite overhead.

T F (f) Changes in scope are to be covered by contingency.

2. Fill in the blanks.

   (a) Estimates accurate to within 5 percent of the actual project costs are known as _____

   (b) _____ are like change orders but they are issued before the bid date.

   (c) Unknowns in an estimate are covered by the use of _____

3. Describe the difference between costing and pricing ____

   _____

   _____

   _____

4. Describe the difference between allowance and contingency _____

   _____

   _____

   _____

5. Identify whether the following are direct or indirect costs:

   (a) D   I   Permanent foundation

   (b) D   I   Steam piping

   (c) D   I   Drafting

   (d) D   I   Permanent roofing

   (e) D   I   Permits

   (f) D   I   Surveyor

   (g) D   I   Payroll taxes for carpenter doing direct work

   (h) D   I   Janitor
   (i) D   I   Dewatering

   (j) D   I   Electrician superintendent

6. True or false

   (a) T   F   Indirect costs are sometimes called distributable costs.

   (b) T   F   A cost index is used to adjust costs for time and location.

(c) T   F   Escalation is applied using a simple interest formula.

(d) T   F   Escalation includes productivity changes in cost over time.

7. Identify whether the following are field or home office costs

(a) F   H   Carpenter superintendent

(b) F   H   Company president

(c) F   H   Profit

(d) F   H   Construction equipment

(e) F   H   Bonds

8. True or false

(a) T   F   Labor cost includes base salary plus all fringe benefit costs and labor burdens that can be directly assigned to an item of work.

(b) T   F   Productivity is defined as the reciprocal of the labor factor.

(c) T   F   The elements of risk may be used to determine both contingency and profit.

(d) T   F   Monte Carlo simulation is a term used to compare the contracting business with casino gambling.

(e) T   F   Monte Carlo simulation is a method of calculating contingency based on the elements of project risk.

9. Given the following output from a risk analysis program, what contingency would you add to the project to be 75 percent certain of not exceeding the budget.

Certainty	Contingency
90	100,000
75	_____
50	30,000
25	5,000
10	-20,000

10. You purchased an item of equipment for $100,000 in January of 1995 and plan to purchase an identical item of equipment in January of 2000. Given an escalation rate of 5 percent per year, what will you pay for the equipment in 2000?

ANSWERS TO SAMPLE PROBLEMS

1   (a) F   (b) F   (c) T   (d) T   (e) T   (f) F

2.   (a) definitive estimate

     (b) addendum

     (c) contingency

3. Costing is the assignment of cost values to the elements of the estimate, while pricing is establishing the price to be charged including contingencies and profits. Pricing can vary depending on project risk, market conditions, or even the desire of the contractor or supplier to provide the product or service.

4. An allowance is included to cover the cost of a known, but undefined, element of the estimate. (e.g., an allowance for carpeting which has not yet been selected by the owner). The contingency is included to cover unknown changes in the project, which experience has shown will be likely to occur.

5.   (a) D   (b) D   (c) I   (d) D   (e) I   (f) I   (g) D   (h) I   (i) D   (j) I

6.   (a) T   (b) T   (c) F   (d) T

7.   (a) F   (b) H   (c) H   (d) F   (e) F

8.   (a) T   (b) T   (c) T   (d) F   (e) T

9.   70,000

10. (1.05) ^5 * $100,000 = $127,628

This section is excerpted from Chapter 3 of *Skills and Knowledge of Cost Engineering,* 4th Edition, by

Charles P. Woodward, PE CCE, and Mark T. Chen, PE CCE

INTRODUCTION

Construction firms constitute only about 8 percent of all businesses in the US, yet they make up more than 17 percent of all business failures. While some of the failures may be attributed to causes such as over-extension, poor management, or lack of proper financial controls, most failures result from unrealistic bids based on poor estimates. Consequently, accurate and realistic estimates are needed by contractors who bid competitively, as well as by those who obtain jobs through negotiation.

Accurate estimates are crucial to any contractor's survival. If the estimates are too high, the bids will be noncompetitive, leaving little or no chance of getting jobs. Conversely, if estimates are too low, the jobs obtained may have little or no chance of making a profit. In other words, the estimate has to be low enough to get the job but high enough to generate a profit.

Unit cost (or line item) methods are the most common ones used to produce definitive estimates. The line item content reflects the high degree of detail in the scope and design documents and the unit quantity is usually based upon drawing take-off. Parametric estimating methods can be used for all or part of a definitive estimate, but their use is generally limited to highly repetitive type projects using little new technology.

The following paragraphs discuss the orderly development of a complete estimate based on fairly complete scope documents. While the examples used apply to a construction project, the underlying themes and techniques are not limited to contractors bidding on construction projects, and can be used by all parties to prepare detailed estimates on any type of project.

ORGANIZING THE ESTIMATE

Proper estimating requires a comprehensive, systematic approach because a detailed estimate is not only needed for bidding, but it will also be useful during construction and for future reference. The approach involves five steps:

1. **Conducting a thorough review of all contract documents, including addenda, to get a clear understanding of the project.** This is important because the documents dictate how the estimate should be prepared and how the project will be executed. During the review, empha-

sis should be placed on ensuring that the documents are complete (checking for missing pages or paragraphs), and that they do not contain unusual or unfamiliar items. The estimator should have access to and/or develop checklists to ensure that "gotcha" items are not overlooked.

2. **Generating an estimate preparation schedule to ensure that the estimate will be completed on time.** The individuals responsible for each section of the estimate should be shown by name.

3. **Preparing the project summary of estimate**—After reviewing the bid documents, the estimator must segregate the project into its cost elements. This may be done by preparing a summary sheet which will serve as a check list and help in identifying items to be performed by the firm's own forces and those that will be assigned to subcontractors. At this point, it is a good practice to contact all potential subcontractors for bids. Sometimes it may be necessary to mail bid documents to potential bidders who have no access to the bid documents by other means. The summary sheet normally has three sections—direct costs, indirect costs, and a summary of alternates (if applicable).

4. **Preparing a bid file**—The next step in organizing an estimate is to set up a portfolio so that project-related information can be stored in an organized fashion and in a single location. Since computerized databases are now in common use, it is desirable to implement and maintain an electronic database where the bid data may be incorporated for ease of use at a later date. Typically, a bid portfolio should include a folder for each of the following:

- bid documents (including plans, specifications, and addenda);
- quantity take-off and pricing sheets;
- correspondence related to the project;
- telephone or written quotes for the job, preferably arranged in order (in accordance with the Construction Specification Institute (CSI) MASTERFORMAT, current edition);
- project summary sheet (including cut/add sheets);
- owner's proposal forms;
- bonds; and
- bid form.

5. **Preparing for the take-off.**—Once the summary sheets

and the project bid file are organized, certain preparations should be made before beginning the take-off. These include:

- Conducting a further review of the contract documents, and paying particular attention to items such as wage rates, insurance and bonding requirements, general and special conditions, and any other items in the plans or specifications that may seem problematic and have cost implications.

- Assembling all reference materials such as detailed construction plans (including start-up/check out), system equipment list, engineering drawings, and division of responsibility matrix.

- Assembling all required forms such as the ones needed for the take-off or for telephone quotations. Each form should be properly identified and should state the name of the project, the architect/engineer's name, the bid date, section of the job (usually by specification section), date of the estimate and the name of the estimator, page number, and other pertinent information.

Forms and formats used in estimating vary from one company to another, but each firm should have standardized forms that are used by all estimators. As a minimum, the following forms should be available:

- summary sheets;
- pads for note taking;
- take-off and costing forms;
- work sheets; and
- general conditions sheets.

WORK BREAKDOWN STRUCTURE

Work breakdown planning is necessary at the outset of any major project, and is an ongoing process as new projects are added to the scope of work. The work breakdown structure (WBS) is a basic project management tool which defines the project along activity levels that can be clearly identified, managed and controlled. Each level of the WBS usually shows specific deliverables and responsibilities, and a carefully planned and effectively developed WBS provides the proper level of information to each individual involved in cost and schedule control. The WBS has four functions:

- segmenting the project into identifiable and manageable units;
- identifying contracted, projected, and actual costs and the associated schedule components of the entire project;
- integrating cost and schedule for planning and controlling project progress; and
- permitting summarization of cost and schedule status for management reporting.

Certain basic elements of information are associated with each WBS, including a brief work description, status, task order number, and other data necessary to facilitate sorting and selecting.

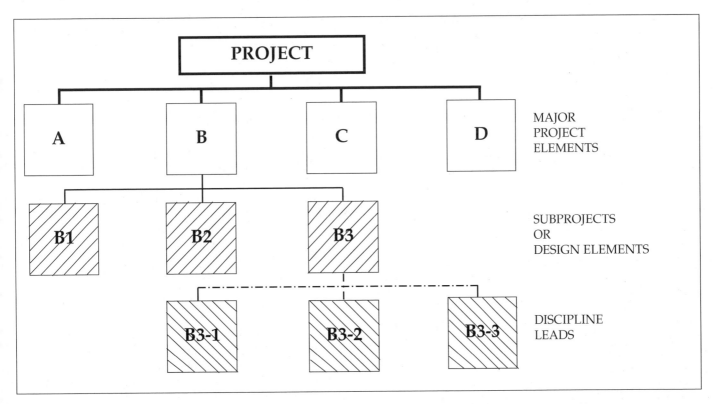

Figure C.2—Work Breakdown Structure

The numbering system used to identify each work item is structured in a way that allows easy visual recognition of the type of work to be done and its basic location. Each work item has a unique number, which can be used as the actual contract task order or purchase agreement number. This allows easy roll-up of like cost categories to various summary reports. Figure C.2 illustrates how a typical WBS is arranged.

The four basic levels of activity to be monitored are:

- total project;
- major project elements;
- subprojects or design elements; and
- disciplines.

These levels summarize the total project to allow cost and schedule performance to be monitored.

SITE VISIT

After the proposed cost estimate is organized and the plans and specifications are thoroughly reviewed, but before the take-off is begun, a visit should be made to the proposed construction site. A site investigation checklist should be used during the visit. Appendix A to this chapter contains a comprehensive example of such a checklist.

ESTIMATING WORK ITEMS

The Quantity Take-Off—After the estimate is organized, the contract documents reviewed, and the site visited, measurement of work can begin. The process of using the specifications as a guide for measuring quantities from a set of plans is called performing the take-off. This involves four main steps:

- classifying the work;
- describing items of work;
- determining dimensions of items of work; and
- extending the dimensions.

The take-off should be organized in a manner similar to the general sequence in which the project will be built since this will:

- help the estimator learn the project;
- help eliminate gross error;
- permit more than one estimator to work on the take-off;
- simplify the job planning and scheduling process; and
- facilitate the process of cost feed back and cost comparison at a later date.

The following is a suggested sequence for performing a take-off:
- earth work/site work;
- foundations;
- structural;
- piping/electrical;

- major equipment;
- finish work;
- start-up and turnover;
- general conditions; and
- subcontracts.

In addition to developing an estimate for work that will be performed in-house, it is important to develop an estimate for subcontracted work as well, even though the estimate may not be in great detail. This has several benefits. First, it serves as a check on the adequacy and responsiveness of the potential subcontract bids received. Second, to save costs, it may become prudent for the contractor to do the work instead of having a subcontractor do it. Finally, the contractor has ultimate, although not first-hand, responsibility for subcontracted work. Therefore, it must plan and manage that work within its total responsibility.

Costing for Labor and Material—When the take-off is complete and the dimensions extended and checked, the next step involves costing labor and material. While material costs are usually obtained from suppliers and/or pricing catalogs, determining the cost of labor is probably the most difficult portion of the estimate. Depending on the contractor and the contract involved, a variety of crafts and trades may be directly hired by the contractor and have their work directly supervised by the contractor's staff members. The contractor may choose to subcontract those work items it cannot perform efficiently or that involve risks it may not wish to assume.

Wage rates may be established either in the specification as part of the contract documents (as in government standards), or in current local wage agreements (on a union project). It is imperative for the estimator to know these rates before starting the estimate, since they may vary considerably from what the firm has been paying.

The labor estimate normally has two parts:

- the gross amount of paychecks to be issued to field employees (including both regular and premium pay); and
- the labor burden (fringe benefits, taxes and insurance, paid by the employer on behalf of the employee).

Since the cost of labor can be a substantial part of the total project costs, care and accuracy in costing labor are a necessity. Most estimators use unit costs (cost per unit of work), which may be determined from the estimator's experience, from historical productivity data, and from crew size calculations. However, determining unit costs by experience should be used only if the estimator has extensive field experience in either performing or observing the task to be costed.

Information for deriving unit costs from historical productivity data may be obtained from two main sources—the firm's historical cost records or published reference books. The following example illustrates the calculation of a unit price from productivity data.

To form a 10 m^2 of wall requires 6 hours of carpenter time and 5 hours of common laborer time.

The wage rate with burdens for carpenters is $21.00/hr. The wage rate with burdens for common laborers is $17.00/hr.

The unit cost may be calculated as follows:

Carpenter - 6 hours at $21.00/hr	= $126.00
Laborer - 5 hours at $17.00/hr.	= $ 85.00
Total labor cost for 10m^2	= $211.00
Labor cost per square meter = $211.00/10 m^2 = $21.1/m^2	

The worker-hour rate (WH/m^3, WH/TON, WH/m^2, etc.) is derived from the company's historical productivity data by dividing the total worker-hours required to perform a specific task by the total units of work accomplished. The following cautionary notes are in order when using the resultant data:

- Under what job conditions was the data generated—ideal, average, other?

- What elements of work are included in each rate? For example, are the 100 tons of steel erected on one project and 250 tons erected on another comparable in scope? Does one project include miscellaneous steel and scaffolding and the other not?

The estimator should be aware that both unit cost and worker-hour unit rates have their place. Still, the worker-hour unit rate calculation should be used if possible, since it eliminates problems caused by labor cost variability. After the worker-hours are calculated, the labor rates for the particular project can be applied. An additional benefit created by using this method is that the estimate is now in a form that can be easily transferred to the project control estimate for project management purposes.

To determine unit costs, using crew size calculations requires experience as well as the ability to visualize construction operations, site conditions, material quantities involved, crew size needed to accomplish the task, and the amount of time needed to perform the task. To illustrate this method, assume the following situation:

57 cubic meters of concrete needs to be placed. Site conditions dictate that the safest and best method of placement is to use a crane and a 1 1/2-cubic-meter bucket. It is determined that to perform the task efficiently, four laborers are needed—one at the concrete truck, two at the point of placement, and one on the vibrator. No finishing is required. It is assumed that supervision is done by the superintendent.

Wage rate for laborers is $17.00/hr.
Time needed:

set-up	=	30 min.
cycle		
load	=	3 min.
swing, dump and return	=	5 min.

	=	8 min.
No. of cycles = $\frac{57}{1.5}$	=	38
Total cycle time = 38 x 8 min.	=	304 min.
disassembly	=	15 min.
subtotal		349 min.
inefficiency (labor, delays, etc.) 20 %	=	70 min.
total operation time: 349 + 70	=	419 min.
amount of time needed	=	419 min. = 7 hours
laborers—4 for 7 hours at $17.00/hr.	=	$476.00
cost per 57 m^3	=	$476.00
Cost per cubic meter	=	$\frac{\$476.00}{57 \text{ m}^3} = \$8.35/m^3$

The estimator has many sources from which to obtain cost information. Estimating handbooks are printed by numerous professional societies and publishing companies, as well as by contractor, subcontractor, trade, and governmental organizations. Whichever source is used, the estimator should be judicious in matching the specifics of a particular project, since all sources are based on averages and/or other situations that may not be applicable universally. The estimating aids-reference materials section of this chapter lists a number of available estimating aids and sources of information.

Estimating Other Cost Elements—Beyond labor and material costs, the estimate includes the following elements:

Equipment—The cost of equipment to be used in performing the job is usually obtained from equipment rental firms or a company's equipment division. In addition, many vendors, equipment associations, and others publish reference books that enable the estimator to determine equipment costs.

Costs of subcontractor-supplied items—These costs are usually furnished by subcontractors and vendors either by telephone (in which case the estimator records them on a telephone bid form) or in writing (via written quotations). Related costs, such as freight charges, should be included as part of the direct material costs. As stated earlier, the estimator must be able to develop, if not a detailed subcontract estimate, at least an estimate with which the potential subcontractor bids may be compared.

Job Indirects—As defined in chapter 1, job indirects are those items of cost that cannot be directly attributed to a particular item of work or endeavor. Job indirects can logically be classified as either jobsite or home office overheads.

    Job Site Overhead—It is a good practice to develop a master list of job site overhead items based on the indications contained in the specifications and on other items that may not be indicated anywhere, but which are needed by the contractor to perform the work. Once this master list is developed, the estimator can assign costs to only the items that pertain to a specific project. The master list should include, but not be limited to, items under the broad headings of:

- bonds;
- permits;
- mobilization;
- professional services (such as scheduling);
- safety equipment;
- small tools;
- supervision;
- temporary facilities;
- travel and lodging;
- miscellaneous costs (e.g., clean-up, punch list); and
- demobilization.

All items under the above headings that pertain to a specific project should be costed, extended, and summarized to obtain the total cost of job site overhead.

Home Office Overhead—Every contractor has certain fixed costs that are incurred regardless of the volume of contracts performed. The costs of these items are normally estimated for a year and then reduced to a percentage based on estimated total volume per year. Home office overhead costs may include, but are not limited to, the following:

- salaries (home office);
- employee benefits;
- professional fees;
- insurance;
- office lease or rent;
- office stationery and supplies;
- depreciation;
- maintenance;
- procurement and marketing;
- home office travel and entertainment; and
- advertising.

For example, if a contractor has an overhead of $480,000 per year and annual volume is approximately $6,000,000 then overhead is about 8 percent of annual volume.

Alternates and Allowances—Some projects may have alternates (either additive or deductive) in addition to the base bid. The owner normally has the option of accepting or rejecting any or all alternates. Care should therefore be taken in pricing alternates, particularly where subcontractor costs are involved. Any mark-up should be added to or deducted from the subcontractor's price for an alternate price as applicable.

At times, an owner/client may specify certain lump sum amounts in the bid documents for items such as landscaping,

light fixtures, hardware, or carpet. These predetermined amounts are called allowances and should be included in the contractor's estimate. However, unless it is specifically indicated otherwise, these amounts may include only the cost of materials, and the estimator should add the cost of labor for installation, overhead, and profit to the given allowance to obtain the total price.

Mark-Up—It is the role of the estimator to identify all potential cost elements of a project and to estimate a cost associated with each. The estimator should also identify any risk elements in the contract so they can be evaluated during the bid review. However, it is not the estimator's job to cost the risk elements or to add the profit—these items are discretionary and are determined by management. Hence, the term *mark-up* is usually applied to the pricing operation of adding an amount for contingency and for profit.

Contingency—A contingency mark-up should be based on a structured evaluation of the risks identified in the contract. Although no reasonable rules-of-thumb exist for determining contingency mark-up, it can be done in numerous ways. One popular method is to evaluate the composite effect of those elements in the contract subject to significant variability through a Monte Carlo approach. Some contractors use a "gut feel" approach for handling contingency, although this is a dangerous practice.

Profit—A mark-up for profit may be taken as a percentage of either labor costs or all direct and indirect costs—each contractor has its own system. This mark-up can vary anywhere from 0 percent to 15 percent, depending on the size of project, competition, the economy, the client, and so forth. Occasionally a contractor will "buy" a project. In other words, the contractor will anticipate not making a profit or may even anticipate a loss. This is not uncommon on a project where the project involves multiple, sequential contracts of the type the contractor can perform well. If the contractor gets onto the site during the early stages of a project, its mobilization costs will have been absorbed, it will have a better handle on real costs at the location, and it will be in a position to be very competitive while still making a profit on subsequent contracts. In times of economic downturn, a contractor may knowingly accept a loss on project, since that loss will surely be less than the loss of maintaining a company without work. Nevertheless, a contractor must make a profit in the long run, and the dollar value of the company's investment should yield a return that reflects current investment yields. Ultimately, the contractor deserves additional profit as a reward for the risks assumed.

BID WRAP-UP

The final form a bid will take is determined by the type of project and the form of the contract. Many private projects are based on negotiated proposals from a select few, pre-qualified bidders. Due to state and federal regulations, most public projects are competitively bid, open to all, and have a set time and place for "bid opening." Unfortunately, the construction industry traditionally puts many hours and dollars into an estimate before bid wrap-up, only to see its efforts jeopardized on "bid day" by hectic last-minute cuts, adds, and misplaced decimal points. To minimize this confusion, scramble, and panic, the following procedure is suggested:

- The final bid should be tabulated no later than the day before the bid date, if this is at all possible. To enhance the possibility of achieving this goal, the take-offs must be extended, costed, and transferred to the summary sheet. Subcontractor bids should be evaluated to select the most appropriate and responsive bids, and the selected subcontractor bids should be entered on the summary sheet as well.
- Telephone bids from subcontractors should be recorded and filed in some logical order, usually in accordance with the company's standard format or with the sequence developed from the project plans and specifications.
- The total direct cost should be obtained by totalling the columns on the summary sheet for labor, material, equipment, and subcontract costs.
- If the project involves alternates, these should be summarized as well.
- Once the bid is finalized, all changes should be made on a cut/add sheet, which should be used on bid day to tabulate all last-minute changes in costs as well as new bids received from subcontractors or suppliers.
- At an appropriate time, the estimator should stop accepting phone calls so that the net effect of the adds and deducts on the base bid can be determined.
- If the bid form has already been completed, changes are usually made on the bid envelope and submitted. If the bid form has not been completed, the new bid price is entered as appropriate.
- Before the bid is submitted, it should receive a final check to ensure that it complies with all the bid instructions.
- Finally, plans should be made to submit the bid on time. The bid close-out process is greatly simplified if a contractor uses a computerized bid-preparation system that will accommodate last-minute changes and automatically reflect their impact throughout the bid. It has been said that the "successful low bidder" is the one who has made the most and biggest mistakes. Therefore, the estimator should make sure that simple items such as formulas in spreadsheets are correct and error free, and that nothing is left to chance.

COMPUTER-AIDED ESTIMATING

With the advent of the affordable computer and, more importantly, sophisticated software, the world of estimating is being continually reduced from an art form to more of an applied science. All aspects of estimating are being computerized, and many new applications are being marketed. The following are but a small sampling of the situations in which the computer can help in preparing definitive estimates:

- doing quantity take-offs by using digitizers to "read" the architect/engineer's plans;

- using CAD programs that can automatically generate quantity take-offs and measurements;
- using CAD programs that will integrate the work of various trades to check for completeness and interferences, and that can easily determine the feasibility costs of various options;
- generating and retrieving historical cost databases;
- performing risk analyses; and
- using spreadsheets to compile and generate information, a process that is usually limited only by the user's imagination.

The computer is a cost-effective tool if used properly and with care. Still, since output is totally dependent on the accuracy of the data from which it is derived, caution should be taken not to rely solely on the information generated. Rather, the user should regularly spot-check and validate computer results by hand calculations.

RECOMMENDED READING

The following is an abbreviated list of reference materials that are available to the estimator.

1. **Process Plant Construction Estimating Standards.** Mesa, AZ: Richardson Engineering Services, Inc. 1998.
2. **Contractor's Equipment Cost Guide.** Dataquest—The Associated General Contractors of America (AGC) 1993.
3. Siddens, Scott, ed. **The Building Estimator's Reference Book.** 25th ed. Lisle, IL: Frank R. Walker, Co. 1995.
4. Waier, Phillip. **Means Building Construction Cost Data.** Duxbury, MA: R.S. Means Co. 1998.
5. Atcheson, D. **Estimating Earthwork Quantities.** Lubbock, TX: Norseman Publishing Co. 1983.
6. **Caterpillar Performance Handbook.** 23rd Edition Peoria, IL: Caterpillar, Inc.
7. Waier, Phillip. **Means Man-Hour Standards.** Duxbury, MA: R.S. Means Co. 1998.
8. **Rental Rates & Specifications.** Associated Equipment Distributors.
9. **Rental Rate Blue Book.** New York: Dataquest—The Dun & Bradstreet Corporation. 1993.
10. **Index of the Cost of Industrial.** Aberthaw Co.
11. **Historical Local Cost Indexes.** Cost Engineers Notebook Vol. 1. AACE International.
12. **Engineering News Record.** New York: McGraw-Hill Co.
13. **U.S. Army Engineer's Contract Unit Price Index.** US Army Corps of Engineers

14. **Chemical Engineering Plant Cost Index.** McGraw-Hill Co.
15. **Bureau of Labor Statistics.** US Department of Labor.
16. McMahon, Leonard. **Heavy Construction Costs.** (formerly Dodge). 1995.
17. Societies and Organizations:
    American Concrete Institute (ACI)
    American Institute of Architects (AIA)
    American Institute of Steel Construction (AISC)

American National Standards Institute (ANSI)
American Nuclear Society (ANS)
American Society for Testing and Materials (ASTM)
American Society of Mechanical Engineers (ASME)
American Welding Society (AWS)
Associated Builders and Contractors (ABC)
Associated General Contractors of America (AGC)
Construction Specifications Institute (CSI)
National Constructors Association (NCA)
National Electrical Contractors Association (NECA)
Power Crane and Shovel Association (PCSA)

SAMPLE PROBLEMS

1. What is the labor unit cost for forming a 3-meter high wall, 3-meter long, given the following data:

   - the crew consists of three carpenters and two laborers;
   - it will take the carpenters 4 hours and the laborers 2 hours to complete the task;
   - each carpenter makes $21.00/hr; and
   - each laborer makes $17.00/hr.

2. You are an estimator working on your overhead estimate. List five items you will consider under the following major categories:

   - mobilization;
   - temporary facilities; and
   - professional services.

   Which of the above items could be considered time sensitive?

3. You are the chief estimator, and the accounting department has given you the following information:
   One of the other estimators asked which figures should be used for overhead on an estimate. What figure would you recommend?

4. You are given the following information which was derived from several similar projects:

(a)	annual volume	$58,000,000
(b)	total overhead expense:	
	salaries	1,900,000
	legal and accounting fees	350,000
	insurance	2,200,000
	rents	900,000
	utilities	200,000
	other	500,000
		$6,050,000

ANSWERS TO SAMPLE PROBLEMS

1. Carpenter labor cost = $21/hr x 4 hr x 3   = $252

Steel Erected

Project	Year	Tons	Hours	Notes
"A"	1956	235	2,820	1st project for company
"B"	1960	350	3,675	
"C"	1967	850	11,475	7 day strike at beginning
"D"	1979	1,230	1,316	
"E"	1980	850	9,384	300 ton deducted by C.O.
"F"	1981	3,850	54,265	980 tons added by C.O.

Totals: 7,365   82,935 = 11.26 WH/TONS

Should the estimator use 11.26 WH/TON for a 1992 project to erect 6,800 tons of steel?

Based on the above information, what questions should the estimator ask about the new project and the data from the past projects?

Laborer labor cost   = $17/hr x 2 hr x 2   = $ 68

Cost to form nine square meters   = $320

Cost per square meter   = $\frac{320}{9m^2}$ = $ 35.56/m^2

2. Mobilization—construction permit, site security, laydown area, medical support, waste disposal, environmental regulation.

Temporary Facilities—trailer, telephones, toilets, portable water, fencing, parking lot, safety sign, temporary lighting.

Professional Services—soil test, concrete test, survey, medical staff, ambulance service, optical alignment, paging service.

Temporary facilities such as trailers and toilets are usually considered time sensitive. Some professional services, such as construction management, are also time sensitive. However, professional services such as concrete testing and soil boring test, are generally not time sensitive.

3. Use (b) the total overhead expense
   The total overhead expense to annual volume ratio is
   For each annual volume dollar, there is a 10-cent overhead. If the estimate total project cost is $10,000,000, then the estimated overhead would be $1,000,000.

4.   Calculate unit labor rates of similar projects as follows:

"A" 2,820/235   =   12.0 Hours/Ton
"B" 3,675/350   =   10.5

$$\frac{\$6,050,000}{\$58,000,000} = 0.1$$

"C" 11,475/850   =   13.5
"D" 1,316/1,230   =   1.1
"E" 9,384/850   =   11.0
"F" 54,265/3,850   =   14.1

Note: Project D is about 1/10 of other projects. The project should be removed from the data sheet.

a.)   The estimator should not use the overall average of 11.26 WH/Ton to estimate the new quantity which is 77 percent more than the largest quantity of 3,850 tons performed in 1981. The unit labor rate in 1981 was 14.1 WH/Ton indicating either the company had difficulty in handling large quantity or the job complexity had increased.

b.)   The estimator should look at the breakdown of past and new projects regarding large pieces versus many small pieces such as cross bracing, handrails, etc. In general, small pieces are more labor intensive. The other question is whether the company is capable of handling such a large job.

PRE-BID SITE INVESTIGATION CHECKLIST

The following checklist will serve as a guide in evaluating the variables associated with a project. In addition to completing this checklist, the investigators should make a video tape of the project site, access roads, and any other features of the area that may influence final evaluation of the project. Ideally, this tape should be narrated as shot.

Individuals participating in the site investigation should become very familiar with the bid documents, especially the actual contract and specifications, before beginning their investigation so they can properly relate area conditions to contractual requirements. In taking the actions or responding to the questions on the checklist, the investigators must continually seek to identify and catalog all items that have a cost and time implication for the contractor.

1.   **Geographic Data**
A.   Obtain the following maps and annotate them with responses to questions appearing later in the checklist:
   (1) state maps to show overall highway, railroad, and water networks;
   (2) locate maps to show details of nearby communities and local road networks; and
   (3) topographic (contour) map
B.   Provide the population of each nearby community.

C.   Trace and describe the existing drainage system for the area. Will drainage be an unusual problem?
D.   What is the site altitude?

2.   **Geological and Subsurface Data**

A.   Obtain a geological map of the area.
B.   What are the subsurface conditions at the project site— soils strata and characteristics, water table? Determine if any part of the site is a fill area. If so, show its location and describe the type of fill.
C.   Will dewatering be required?
D.   For excavations, what methods or equipment will be required for soil removal?
E.   Will shoring be needed for ditches and other excavations?
F.   Will the natural ground support construction equipment, both rubber-tired and tracked?
G.   Identify the drainage characteristics of the topsoil following precipitation. How long does it take for the surface to dry out? Will topsoils be particularly dusty when dry, if vegetation is removed?
H.   Will a temporary construction drainage system be needed?
I.   Obtain a plat of all known underground utility and drainage systems, or other underground structures or obstacles.

3.   **Meteorological Data**

A.   Describe temperature and humidity ranges by month. Include record low and high temperatures for each month; if wind-chill or heat-index data is available, include it.
B.   Describe rainfall and snow averages by month. Determine the average number of precipitation days for each month.
C.   What is the susceptibility of the area to and frequency of extreme storm activity—thunderstorms, snow storms, tornadoes, and hurricanes?
D.   What is the frost depth?

4.   **Site Preparation**

A.   Can excess cut material be sold? If so, to whom and at what price? If not, where are disposal areas located? What are the disposal charges involved?
B.   If fill material is required, where are its sources located? What is its cost?
C.   What overhead lines or other structures will limit operations or prove to be a safety hazard in cleaning the site?
D.   Will erosion control structures be required?
E.   What historical structures, graveyards, plantings, or other features must be moved or protected during site preparation or while construction is under way?

5.   **Access and Parking**

A.   Describe existing roads in terms of lanes, surface type and condition, capacity limitations, restrictive features, etc. What must be done to upgrade them for contractor use? Will the contractor have any responsibility for maintaining these roads?

B. What new access roads must be developed and who will develop them? Are existing easements or rights-of-way available for such roads? If not, what must be done to obtain them?

C. Is adequate parking space available on the site? If not, where must workers park and how do they get to the site? What parking space development is still required and who will do it? Is the parking area fenced or must fencing be added?

6. **Unloading and Storage**

A. Can material be received and stockpiled on the site before construction begins? If so, what security will be required and who will provide it? Will the owner provide labor to receive these materials? Will this create union jurisdictional problems?

B. What on-site areas are available for development by the contractor into laydown or other storage/prefabrication areas?

C. What off-site storage sites are available to handle items that cannot be stored on site?

D. What special facilities and equipment will be required for materials handling? Which are existing and which must be developed?

7. **Utilities and Temporary Facilities**

A. Are existing structures available for construction use? If so, describe their potential use. If not, describe any development that is required. Obtain drawings or other dimensional data on these structures.

B. May any of the permanent structures to be constructed be used by the contractor on a temporary basis during construction?

C. Identify locations on the site or in nearby areas that are available for temporary structures. If off-site areas must be used, who provides them?

D. Must the contractor provide temporary facility space for owner personnel or others?

E. Will the owner take over any temporary structures when the project is complete or must the contractor remove them?

F. Who provides office furnishings?

G. Who provides potable water? What is its source and what development is required? Will there be separate water systems for concrete water, dust control, and fire protection? If so, what is their source, who provides them, and what development is required?

H. What sanitary facilities (toilets, washrooms, sewer systems) exist? What must be developed and who provides them?

I. How are heating and air conditioning handled and who provides them? What development is required?

J. What is the availability of electrical power (location, voltage, phases, capacity)? What must be done to provide power and who provides it?

K. Is steam required for construction use? If so, what is its source and who provides it?

L. Is compressed air or other construction gas required for

construction use? If so, what is its source and who provides it?

M. Who provides trash and garbage pickup service?

8. **Local Materials, Services, and Subcontractors**

A. Provide names, addresses and other data with respect to local specialty construction contractors whose services may be required in the performance of the contract.

B. What is the source of ready-mix concrete and what is its price? If the contractor must supply concrete, what is the source of aggregates and cement?

C. What trucking firms maintain offices in nearby communities?

D. Obtain classified sections of telephone directories for nearby communities.

9. **Local Conditions**

A. If the site is within an operating facility, what special requirements exist with respect to gates, restricted areas, etc.? Does the potential exist for union problems between operating personnel and construction personnel?

B. To what extent has the owner coordinated with local governments and agencies concerning this project?

C. Do any political or cultural situations exist that can affect the project? Does the project enjoy public support?

D. Are there any unresolved or incomplete actions (such as owner permits) that could delay the planned start of the project or affect construction progress?

E. Is the project of such a nature and/or so located that adjacent communities are going to be subjected to high levels of construction noise, dust, traffic, or conditions that may precipitate complaints and legal actions or that otherwise adversely affect community relations?

10. **Health, Safety, Environmental, and Security**

A. What medical support will be available? Who provides it?

B. Where are nearby hospitals, dispensaries, and clinics? What services do they have available?

C. How is ambulance service provided? Is air evacuation service available?

D. How will fire protection be provided?

E. What is required to comply with environmental regulations relating to garbage, trash, dust, noise, erosion, hazardous waste, chemical spills, and burning? Who provides these services?

F. Will project personnel be exposed to hazardous fumes, chemicals, or radiation for which special protective equipment and training must be provided?

G. Is a local service available to provide chemical toilets? Are these the portable type or toilet trailers?

H. What nearby commercial firms are licensed to handle and transport hazardous waste to licensed disposal areas?

11. **Security**

A. What law enforcement agencies have jurisdiction over the project site, supporting communities, and transportation networks?

B. If the project is open shop, will local law enforcement agencies provide protection in case of adverse union activity?

C. Is security fencing to be provided? By whom? Who provides the guard force and any surveillance systems?

12. Transportation

A. On a map showing the transportation network, identify:

   (1.) the weight and dimensional limitations of any roads, bridges, and tunnels;
   (2.) railroad lines and receiving docks;
   (3.) available barge waterways and docks; and
   (4.) available airports.

B. For railroad service:

   (1.) What railroad lines serve the area?
   (2.) Will a railroad spur be required? If so, who provides it and what line does it tie into?

C. Identify the commercial air carriers serving the area and the airports from which they operate. List the maximum size aircraft that can use at each airport.

D. For barge service, identify available dockage, any weight and dimensional restrictions, seasonal availability, or other restrictions. Also list other ports on the system.

E. Describe public transportation available for personnel.

13. Labor

A. If this is a union project, identify the names and location of locals whose crafts will be used. Get copies of all agreements and wage scales to be applied. Specifically identify any work rules involving limitations on production, overtime, travel pay and time, showup pay, etc. Note the expiration dates of all agreements and assess the potential for strikes upon expiations. Discuss any conditions relating to the area's union culture that may affect project performance and costs.

B. If this is an open shop project, determine the prevailing wages through state employment agencies, local contractors, or other sources. Identify worker source areas and estimate the availability of each craft over the life of the project. In making these evaluations, consider the demands of other existing or planned projects in the area that may compete for the same personnel.

C. Will any skills training of personnel be required? If so which skills and who will provide the training?

D. Evaluate the local economic situation with respect to its effect on availability, productivity, and wage scales for personnel.

E. Describe any conditions (such as commuting distance or high-crime area) that may limit personnel recruiting potential or contribute to high turnover.

F. Obtain any data available that might show area labor productivity.

G. Is there any potential in this area for government-subsidized job training programs for the work force?

14. Construction Equipment

A. Identify equipment that the owner or other contractors will provide. What is the reimbursement system for this support?

B. Identify special types of equipment the contractor must provide.

C. Will equipment servicing and maintenance be handled in on-site facilities or by contract with local firms?

D. Will there be any impediments to moving equipment onto the job site (such as limited capacity roads and bridges, restrictive tunnels, or overhead wires)?

15. Communications

A. How is telephone service to be provided?

B. Will there be any on-site communications (such as loudspeaker or radio)? Who provides them?

C. Is overnight express mail/parcel service available?

16. Permits, Taxes, and Fees

A. Is the project tax exempt, either locally or federally?

B. What state and local taxes will apply?

C. Is a contractor license required to operate in the area? What are the requirements?

D. What permits will be required of the contractor?

E. What hookup fees will the contractor pay (phone, water, sewer, electrical, etc.)?

17. Professional and Office Staff

A. Is adequate housing available in nearby communities for contractor professional staff?

B. What are the availability and wage scale of local-hire office personnel?

18. Miscellaneous

A. What support or services must the contractor provide to the owner, engineer, subcontractors, or others onsite?

B. Will participation in any special programs (such as substance abuse control) be required of the owner?

Portions of this chapter are from previous editions authored by Dr. Kweku K. Bentil, Donald F. McDonald Jr., PE CCE, Duane R. Meyer, PE CCE, and Charles P. Woodward, PE CCE.

AACE International Recommended Practice No. 11R-88

REQUIRED SKILLS AND KNOWLEDGE
OF COST ENGINEERING

Recommended Practice No. 11R-88
Required Skills and Knowledge of Cost Engineering

January 17, 2006

This recommended practice has the following purposes:

- define what *core* skills and knowledge of cost engineering a person is required to have in order to be considered a professional practitioner, and in doing so,
- establish the emphasis of *core* subjects for AACE International education and certification programs.

It is also hoped that enterprises will find this useful as a reference or guide for developing their own competency models. *Knowledge* is an understanding gained through experience or study, and *skills* are abilities that transform knowledge into use. *Core* subjects are those whose usage is occasional to frequent and are considered by AACE International as being required for professional practitioners of cost engineering to know and be able to use.

This recommended practice lists these core subjects and provides general *performance statements* (i.e., "be able to" describe, perform, etc.) to represent the level of proficiency expected in each subject area. These statements are representative or guiding examples only

This text is an outline that is intended to be the structural foundation for products and services developed by the Educational and Certification Boards. It will continue to be modified as current practice changes.

BACKGROUND AND SCOPE UPDATE

The original recommend practice *Required Skills and Knowledge of a Cost Engineer* was developed by the AACE International Education Board and published in 1988 based on their evaluations of a membership survey. Until that time, AACE International lacked a formal definition of professional cost engineering in terms of skills and knowledge. Based on the recommended practice findings, the Education Board then published the first *Skills and Knowledge of Cost Engineering* text to provide an educational product to elaborate on the core skills and knowledge subjects. The earlier text has been regularly updated by the Education Board.

Since the original publication, the AACE Technical Board was given the charter to define the technology of cost engineering and total cost management. In 2005, the Technical Board completed development of the *Total Cost Management Framework* which describes a systematic process (i.e., TCM process) through which the skills and knowledge of cost engineering are applied. It also provides an integrated structure upon which the Technical Board can organize its development of recommended practices, including this one.

This update of the *Required Skills and Knowledge of a Cost Engineer* retains most of the content of the earlier versions while incorporating those elements of the TCM process that the AACE associate boards (Technical, Education and Certification) determined are required for a professional practitioner of cost engineering to know. It also incorporates a more systematic organization of the subjects, based on TCM developments, to better differentiate between general *supporting knowledge* used in more than one practice or process (e.g., statistics, elements of cost, etc.), and specific *practice knowledge* used in particular functions or processes (e.g., cost estimating, planning and scheduling, etc.)

INTRODUCTION

A professional cost engineering practitioner must first be able to articulate the meaning of the terms *cost engineering* and *total cost management (TCM)*. Practitioners will frequently be asked these questions. Given the importance of this first knowledge requirement to the understanding this recommended practice, the questions are answered here. Elaboration of all other skills and knowledge requirements is left for subsequent Education Board products.

What are Cost Engineering and TCM?

The AACE International *Constitution and Bylaws* defines cost engineering and total cost management as follows:

> **Section 2.** The Association is dedicated to the tenets of furthering the concepts of *Total Cost Management* and *Cost Engineering*. Total Cost Management is the effective application of professional and technical expertise to plan and control resources, costs, profitability and risk. Simply stated, it is a <u>systematic approach to managing cost throughout the life cycle of any enterprise, program, facility, project, product or service</u>. This is accomplished through the application of cost engineering and cost management principles, proven methodologies and the latest technology in support of the management process.

> **Section 3.** Total Cost Management is that area of engineering practice where engineering judgment and experience are utilized in the application of scientific principles and techniques to problems of <u>business and program planning; cost estimating; economic and financial analysis; cost engineering; program and project management; planning and scheduling; and cost and schedule performance measurement and change contro</u>*l*.

In summary, the list of practice areas in Section 3 are collectively called *cost engineering*; while the "process" through which these practices are applied is called *total cost management* or TCM.

How is cost and schedule management an "engineering" function?

Most people would agree that "engineers" and engineering (or more generally, the "application of scientific principles and techniques") are most often responsible for creating functional things (or *strategic assets* as we call them in TCM). However, engineering has multiple dimensions. The most obvious is the dimension of physical design and the calculation and analysis tasks done to support that design (e.g., design a bridge or develop software). However, beyond the physical dimension of design (e.g., the bridge structure), there are other important dimensions of *money, time*, and other *resources* that are invested in the creation of the designed asset. We refer to these investments collectively as *costs*. Using the above example, someone must estimate what the bridge might cost, determine the activities needed to design and build it, estimate how long these activities will take, and so on. Furthermore, someone needs to monitor and assess the progress of the bridge design and construction (in relation to the expenditure of money and time) to ensure that the completed bridge meets the owner's and other stakeholder's requirements. Someone must also monitor and assess the cost of operating and maintaining the bridge during its life cycle.

Returning to the *Constitution and Bylaws* definition, understanding and managing the cost dimensions requires skills and knowledge in "business and program planning; cost estimating; economic and financial analysis; cost engineering; program and project management; planning and scheduling; and cost and schedule performance measurement and change control." No significant asset has ever been built without dealing with these cost dimensions in some way, and the more systematically and professionally these dimensions are addressed, the more successful the asset performance is likely to be. Therefore, cost *engineering* recognizes that cost is a necessary extension of traditional engineering (and other creative functions such as systems analysis, etc.), and that there is an intimate connection between the physical and cost dimensions of the asset.

Do cost engineering practitioners need to have a traditional "engineering" background?

The skills and knowledge required to deal with *costs* (i.e., cost estimating, planning and scheduling, etc.) are quite different from those required to deal with the physical design dimension. From that difference, the field of *cost engineering* was born. Cost engineering practitioners work alongside of and are peers with engineers, software analysts, play producers, architects, and other creative career fields to handle the cost dimension, but they do not necessarily have the same background. Whether they have technical, operations, finance and accounting, or other backgrounds, cost engineering practitioners need to share a common understanding, based on "scientific principles and techniques", with the engineering or other creative career functions.

Do cost engineering practitioners all have the same function?

Cost engineering practitioners tend to be: a) specialized in function (e.g., cost estimating, planning and scheduling, etc.); b) focused on either the asset management or project control side of the TCM process; and c) focused on a particular industry (e.g., engineering and construction, manufacturing, information technology, etc) or asset type (e.g., chemical process, buildings, software, etc.). They may have titles such as cost estimator, quantity surveyor, parametric analyst, strategic planner, planner/scheduler, value engineer, cost/schedule engineer, claims consultant, project manager, or project control lead. They may work for the business that owns and operates the asset (emphasis on economics and analysis), or they may work for the contractor that executes the projects (emphasis on planning and control). But, no matter what their job title or business environment, a general knowledge of, and skills in, all areas of cost engineering are required to perform their job effectively. In summary, the purpose of this document is to define these *required skills and knowledge of professional cost engineering*.

THIS DOCUMENT'S OUTLINE STRUCTURE AND ITS RELATIONSHIP TO PARTICULAR FUNCTIONS AND AACE INTERNATIONAL CERTIFICATIONS

Figure 1 illustrates the hierarchical structure of the Required Skills and Knowledge of Cost Engineering. The first level of the structure differentiates between general *supporting knowledge* used in more than one practice or process, and specific *practice knowledge* used in particular functions or process steps. Succeeding levels further break down the content to whatever level is appropriate for each skills and knowledge area. The location of a skill or knowledge element in the level of the outline does not reflect on its relative importance.

On the process and functional side, the structure is organized in accordance with the plan, do, check, (or measure), and assess (PDCA) process model that serves as the basis for the TCM process through which all the skills and knowledge of cost engineering are applied. It is not structured by a practitioner's work function. For example, cost estimators will not find all of their required skills and knowledge under one heading. Their particular function's required skills and knowledge will include elements of supporting knowledge, as well as elements of planning, measuring, and assessing that are appropriate to their function.

This document includes the required skills and knowledge that certified cost engineers and consultants (CCE/CCCs) must have. Its scope is broad and represents the comprehensive skills and knowledge that business management may expect someone with overarching responsibilities in an organization to have (e.g., supporting overall capital program or project system management).

For specialty certifications [e.g., planning and scheduling professionals (PSP)], the Certification Board will document appropriate skills and knowledge requirements. These will include elements from this overall outline as they apply to the scope of the particular function. They may also include more detailed skills and knowledge than included here. The scope of those requirements will not be as broad, but will be deeper, representing the skills and knowledge that business management may expect from a manager of or expert in the particular function.

common understanding, based on "scientific principles and techniques", with the engineering or other creative career functions.

Do cost engineering practitioners all have the same function?

Cost engineering practitioners tend to be: a) specialized in function (e.g., cost estimating, planning and scheduling, etc.); b) focused on either the asset management or project control side of the TCM process; and c) focused on a particular industry (e.g., engineering and construction, manufacturing, information technology, etc) or asset type (e.g., chemical process, buildings, software, etc.). They may have titles such as cost estimator, quantity surveyor, parametric analyst, strategic planner, planner/scheduler, value engineer, cost/schedule engineer, claims consultant, project manager, or project control lead. They may work for the business that owns and operates the asset (emphasis on economics and analysis), or they may work for the contractor that executes the projects (emphasis on planning and control). But, no matter what their job title or business environment, a general knowledge of, and skills in, all areas of cost engineering are required to perform their job effectively. In summary, the purpose of this document is to define these *required skills and knowledge of professional cost engineering.*

THIS DOCUMENT'S OUTLINE STRUCTURE AND ITS RELATIONSHIP TO PARTICULAR FUNCTIONS AND AACE INTERNATIONAL CERTIFICATIONS

Figure 1 illustrates the hierarchical structure of the Required Skills and Knowledge of Cost Engineering. The first level of the structure differentiates between general *supporting knowledge* used in more than one practice or process, and specific *practice knowledge* used in particular functions or process steps. Succeeding levels further break down the content to whatever level is appropriate for each skills and knowledge area. The location of a skill or knowledge element in the level of the outline does not reflect on its relative importance.

On the process and functional side, the structure is organized in accordance with the plan, do, check, (or measure), and assess (PDCA) process model that serves as the basis for the TCM process through which all the skills and knowledge of cost engineering are applied. It is not structured by a practitioner's work function. For example, cost estimators will not find all of their required skills and knowledge under one heading. Their particular function's required skills and knowledge will include elements of supporting knowledge, as well as elements of planning, measuring, and assessing that are appropriate to their function.

This document includes the required skills and knowledge that certified cost engineers and consultants (CCE/CCCs) must have. Its scope is broad and represents the comprehensive skills and knowledge that business management may expect someone with overarching responsibilities in an organization to have (e.g., supporting overall capital program or project system management).

For specialty certifications [e.g., planning and scheduling professionals (PSP)], the Certification Board will document appropriate skills and knowledge requirements. These will include elements from this overall outline as they apply to the scope of the particular function. They may also include more detailed skills and knowledge than included here. The scope of those requirements will not be as broad, but will be deeper, representing the skills and knowledge that business management may expect from a manager of or expert in the particular function.

Note: In the outline that follows, the **bold** or *italic list* words signify key concepts for which the practitioner should at least be able to provide a basic description. Regular text is for representative performance statements.

I. SUPPORTING SKILLS AND KNOWLEDGE

1. **Elements of Cost**

   a. **Costs**: be able to define/explain these general concepts in relation to each other and to assets and/or activities.
      i. **Resources**
      ii. **Time**
      iii. **Cost**

   b. **Cost Dimensions**:
      i. **Lifecycle**: be able to describe this term and differentiate the life cycle of an *asset* and a *project*
      ii. **Process (product vs. project)**: be able to describe and differentiate the cost characteristics and types (see cost types below) that make up *product* and *project* costs.
         1. be able to distinguish among products, co-products, and byproducts.
      iii. **Responsibility**: be able to describe and differentiate the cost perspectives of an owner and a contractor/supplier
      iv. **Valuation**: be able to describe and differentiate cost from *cash/monetary* versus economic/**opportunity costs** (also see **economic analysis**) perspectives.
      v. **Influence**: be able to explain the concept of the *cost influence curve*
      vi. **Legal**:
         1. be able to explain how cost and schedule analysis practices might differ when applied for *forensic* versus traditional planning and control purposes.
         2. be able to describe some potential legal consequences that may result from using poor or unethical cost management practices (e.g., anti-trust, claims, Sarbanes-Oxley, etc)

   c. **Cost Classifications**: for the following classifications, be able to:
      i. explain the general differences between the ways costs are classified for various cost management purposes
      ii. given a problem with appropriate cost classification inputs (e.g., indirect cost using ABC classification method), be able to calculate how the cost would be accounted for in a *project* or *product* estimate.
         1. **Operating (Production, Manufacturing, Maintenance, etc.) vs. Capital**
         2. **Capital vs. Expense**
            a. *Depreciation*
            b. *Amortization*
            c. *Accrual*
         3. **Fixed vs. Variable**
         4. **Direct vs. Indirect**
            a. *Activity-Based Costing (ABC)*
            b. *Job Costing*

   d. **Cost Types**: for the following cost types, given cost type and classification inputs, be able to apply them in a project or manufacturing estimating application (i.e., for *project* or *product* cost)
      i. **Materials**:
         1. **Materials types**: be able to describe the types and their cost drivers:
            a. *Raw*
            b. *Bulk*
            c. *Fabricated*
            d. *Engineered or designed*

APPENDIX D—R.P. 11R-88

AACE INTERNATIONAL

Required Skills and Knowledge of Cost Engineering

6 of 22

aace
International

January 17, 2006

e. *Consumables*

2. **Purchase costs**: be able to describe these terms/concepts and their influence on the cost of materials:

a. *market pricing (pre-negotiated vs. competitively bid, etc.)*
b. *order quantity*
c. *taxes and duties*
d. *carrying charges*
e. *cancellation charges*
f. *demurrage*
g. *hazardous material regulations*
h. *warranties, maintenance and service*

3. **Materials management costs**: be able to describe these terms/concepts and their influence on the cost of materials:

a. *delivery schedule*
b. *packing*
c. *shipping and freight*
d. *freight forwarding*
e. *handling*
f. *storage and inventory*
g. *agent cost*
h. *surveillance or inspection*
i. *expediting*
j. *losses (shrinkage, waste, theft, damage)*
k. *spare parts (inventory or start-up)*
l. *surplus materials*

4. **Capital Equipment**: (i.e., fabricated or engineered items)

a. **Rent vs. lease vs. purchase**:
    i. be able to explain the mechanics and cost considerations.
    ii. given a problem with useful life, fixed and operating cost, credits, depreciation, taxes, etc., be able to determine the most economical option

b. **Valuation**: be able to explain these concepts:
    i. *reproduction costs*
    ii. *replacement costs*
    iii. *fair value*
    iv. *market value*
    v. *book value*
    vi. *residual or economic value*
    vii. *operating vs. economic life*

5. **Temporary Equipment**: (expensed items for construction, maintenance, etc) be able to explain the cost implications of *rent, operators, maintenance, scheduling, etc.*

ii. **Labor**

1. **Labor Wage Rate or Salary**:

a. be able to describe the differences in mechanics of compensation for wage and salaried employees including the meaning of *exempt* and *non-exempt*.
b. Be able to calculate an effective wage rate allowing for:
    i. *overtime premium*
    ii. *other premium pays*
    iii. *shortened shift time*
    iv. *travel time*
    v. *show-up pay*

2. **Benefits and Burdens (mandated and fringe)**:

a. be able to describe the basic mechanics of benefits and burdens such as:
    i. *retirement (social security),*
    ii. *unemployment insurance*
    iii. *workers compensation*
    iv. *insurance*

AACE International Recommended Practices

AACE INTERNATIONAL

APPENDIX D—R.P. 11R-88

Required Skills and Knowledge of Cost Engineering

7 of 22

aace
International

January 17, 2006

v. *paid time off (sick, vacation, holiday)*
   b. be able to identify typical differences between industrialized and non-industrialized countries and between populated and remote areas.
   3. **Overhead and profit**: be able to describe the basic mechanics of charging various overhead and profit cost elements to direct labor costs such as:
      a. *Indirect labor (home office, administrative and similar costs)*
      b. *small tools*
      c. *profit*
   4. **Union**: be able to explain the cost differences between union and open shop labor
iii. **Subcontract**: be able to explain the cost implications of the following issues:
   1. *reimbursable vs. non-reimbursable costs*
   2. *overhead and profit (including contract administration and legal costs)*
   3. *license, fees or royalties*
   4. *bonds (bid, payment, or performance)*
   5. *retainage*
   6. *performance guarantees*
   7. *liquidated damages*
iv. **Cost of money**: be able to describe these costs:
   1. *escalation*
   2. *inflation*
   3. *currency exchange rates*
v. **Risk and Uncertainty**: be able to describe these costs:
   1. *contingency*
   2. *allowance*
   3. *reserve*

   e. **Pricing**
     i. **Cost vs. Pricing**: be able to explain the difference
     ii. **Price strategy**:
       1. be able to describe how business strategy and market forces may affect pricing.
       2. be able to describe from an owner or buyer perspective concerns about pricing (i.e., risks, competitiveness, cash flow, etc).
       3. be able to describe how profit affects pricing
       4. be able to describe how profit may be determined how the different types of contracts may influence the amount

2. **Elements of Analysis**

   a. **Statistics and Probability**
     i. **Samples and Populations**: be able to describe the relationship of the mean of a sample to the mean of a population, and the general affect of sample randomness, bias and size on the reliability of the sample statistics .
     ii. **Descriptive Statistics**
       1. **Basic Statistics**: given a set of data, be able to determine the arithmetic *mean, median, mode, standard deviation and variance.*
       2. **Normal Distribution**: be able to provide the percent of observations within one and two standard deviations of the mean for a *normally* distributed variable.
       3. **Non-Normal Distributions**: be able to describe the following concepts:
         a. *skewness* (symmetry*)*
         b. *kurtosis* (central tendency relative to normal).
       4. **Histograms, Cumulative Frequency**: given a tabular distribution for a variable that is other than normal, be able to draw a histogram and resultant cumulative frequency curve (frequency distribution), and determine the percent probability of the variable not being less than or more than a given number
     iii. **Inferential Statistics**

1. **Probability:** given a curve of normal distribution and an accompanying table of areas under the curve, be able to determine the probability of a) the variable being between two given numbers, b) not being higher than a given number, or lower than that number, and c) given a confidence interval or range in terms of percentage probability, give the corresponding low and high number of the interval or range.
2. **Regression Analysis:** be able to describe the concept of the methodology as well as diagnostic statistics (*R2, root mean square error (RMSE), and t*)
3. **Statistical Significance:**
   a. Be able to describe the purpose and use of chi-squared and t-tests
   b. Be able to interpret the t-statistic for comparing two sets of normally distributed data.
   c. Be able to interpret of the chi-squared statistic for comparing two sets of data that may not be normally distributed.

b. **Economic and Financial Analysis**
   i. **Economic Cost**: be able to define concepts of **opportunity cost** and assigning monetary value to non-cash values, costs and benefits.
   ii. **Cash Flow Analysis**:
      1. be able to calculate simple and compound interest rates and solve interest problems using the basic single payments, uniform series, and gradient formulas.
      2. given a set of cost and revenue forecasts calculate a cash flow for an asset investment option
   iii. **Internal Rate of Return**: be able to determine discounted rate of return of a cash flow series.
   iv. **Present/Future Value Analysis**: be able to calculate present value, future value, and equivalent uniform annual value of a cash flow series.

c. **Optimization**
   i. **Model**:
      1. be able to describe the concept of a quantitative representational *models* and *parameters*.
      2. given an optimization goal involving a result Y which is a function of X, use graphical or incremental methods to determine the optimum value of Y.
   ii. **Linear Programming**: be able to describe the types of problems amenable to this mathematical optimization technique (i.e., find extreme points of a function given a set of constraints).
   iii. **Simulation:** be able to describe the use of a model for analysis of a cost problem.
   iv. **Sensitivity Analysis**: be able to perform a sensitivity analysis of a modeled problem.

d. **Physical Measurements:** be able to convert basic metric and imperial weight and dimensional measurements.

3. **Enabling Knowledge**

a. **Enterprise in Society**
   i. **Societal Values**: be able to generally describe societal concerns and needs that should be considered in asset and project planning.
   ii. **Decision Policy**: be able to describe how to translate societal values to policy so that an enterprise can consistently address societal values in everyday practice.
   iii. **Ethics**:
      1. be able to explain the need to judge the means and the ends of a practice or process against personal and societal values and rules of conduct.
      2. be familiar with AACE International's ethics policy (Canon of Ethics).

b. **People and Organizations in Enterprises**
   i. **Leadership**: Be able to explain why it is important to obtain team *commitment* and clearly communicate the *purpose* of a task or project, and how this might be done.

AACE International Recommended Practices

1. **Leadership Roles**:
   a. be able to explain why the need for *leading, managing, facilitating, and mentoring* roles may vary by situation.
   b. discuss the meaning and provide examples of "*participative management*."
2. **Motivation/Incentives (Behavioral Science)**:
   a. be able to discuss *motivator/demotivator* affects on labor attitude and performance
   b. given a list, be able to describe the basic themes of two or more generally accepted behavioral science theories:
       i. *McGregor- Theory X and Y*
       ii. *Herzberg-Motivation-Hygiene*
       iii. *Argyris-Effects of organization like on individuals*
       iv. *Likert-Four model systems*
       v. *Mouton-Managerial grid*
       vi. *Other current theories*
3. **Performance/Productivity Management**:
   a. Be able to describe the concept of *productivity* (and its difference from the term *production*).
   b. be able to describe the affect on performance of these factors in terms of *motivation* and *waste/inefficiency*, and how performance could be improved and at what cost (e.g., leadership role, work process change, etc.):
       i. *individual worker skills*
       ii. *crew balance of skills*
       iii. *immediate supervision competence*
       iv. *overall supervision competence*
       v. *worker and supervision attitudes*
       vi. *work force sociological, cultural and demographic characteristics*
       vii. *absenteeism and turnover*
       viii. *overtime*
       ix. *level of technology used*
       x. *learning curve*
       xi. *work area environment*
       xii. *weather*
       xiii. *geographic location*
       xiv. *proximity to other work and contractors*
       xv. *job layout*
       xvi. *work rules*
       xvii. *safety practices*
       xviii. *quality control practices (including quality circles)*
       xix. *materials and tools availability*
       xx. *wages, salaries and benefits.*

ii. **Organization Structure**
   1. **Organizational Design**: be able to describe the issues that organizations must address (*division of labor, unity of command, unity of directions, and span of control*) and how each may affect performance.
   2. **Basic Structures**:
       a. be able to draw and example chart and explain the differences between, and advantages/disadvantages of traditional *functional, divisional, and matrix* structures
   3. **Teams**:
       a. be able to explain how and why teams are used in enterprises and why they are typically used to manage projects.
       b. be able to describe typical team organization (i.e., matrix) and operation and the roles, responsibilities, and methods for its successful performance.
   4. **Typical Organizations in TCM**: be able to generally describe the typical roles of *capital investment management* (business planning), *operations management*, and *project management* in TCM (i.e., where cost engineers usually work).

APPENDIX D—R.P. 11R-88

AACE INTERNATIONAL

Required Skills and Knowledge of Cost Engineering

10 of 22

aace
International

January 17, 2006

c. **Information Management**

    i.**Data, Information, and Knowledge**: be able to explain the difference between these three types of "information"

    ii.**Databases and Database Management**. Be able to define and explain the following concepts:

        1. **History**: the importance of historical and empirical information to most cost engineering practice

        2. **Reference Data**: the need that specific methods and tools for specific processed data

        3. **Lessons Learned**: the need for data that is qualitative in nature.

        4. **Metric**: the need that benchmarking or validation methods have for specific processed quantitative data

        5. **Validation**: the need to assure the reliability and sometimes competitiveness of data

        6. **Basis**: the need to understand the basis of all data and information in a database

        7. **Normalization**: be able to adjust data to a common basis in currency, time, location, etc.

    iii.**Information Technology (IT) and Systems**: be able to explain that information systems are the mechanisms or tools by which knowledge is delivered to the enterprise and those it interacts with (i.e., includes communication).

        1. **Enterprise Resource Planning/Management (ERP/ERM)**: be able to describe the goal of these types of systems (support efficient business processes, including project management, through shared or common databases)

d. **Quality Management**: be able to explain the following concepts:

    i.**Quality**: be able to define this as conformance to *requirements* (which are based on customer needs).

    ii.**Requirements**: (see **Requirements Elicitation and Analysis** practices)

    iii.**Quality Planning**: be able to describe this as an integrated way of planning directed towards satisfying customer needs.

    iv.**Quality Management**: be able to describe this as a process for managing quality and understand that TCM is a quality management process focused on continuous cost performance improvement.

    v.**Quality Assurance**: be able to describe this as actions that provide confidence that the requirements will be fulfilled.

    vi.**Quality Control**: be able to describe this as actions focused on fulfilling requirements

    vii.**Continuous Improvement**: be able to describe this as a common goal of quality management processes (the traditional result of the PDCA process).

    viii.**Plan-Do-Check-Assess (PDCA)**: be able to describe this as the basis model for TCM and many other management processes.

    ix.**Quality Measurement**: be able to explain that in some views, cost is the best single quality measurement because so many measures can be expressed in cost terms.

    x.**Quality Policy**: be able to explain that this as an imposed requirement that is assumed guided by accepted quality management principles

    xi.**Quality Standards**: be able to describe these *imposed requirements*.

        1. **ISO 9000** standard quality management series

        2. **ISO 10006** quality in project management

    xii.**Quality Focused Practices in TCM** be aware that these key practices (covered in later sections) have particular importance to quality management

        1. *Benchmarking*

        2. *Cost of Quality*

        3. *Value Analysis/Engineering*

        4. *Change Management*

e. **Value Management:**

    i. Be able to explain the following general concepts (i.e., not in the context of Value Analysis and Engineering practice):

1. **Value** (i.e., a measure of the worth of a thing in terms of usefulness, desirability, importance, money)
2. **Value Management** (i.e., what an enterprise does to ensure that its assets provide or maintain the usefulness and/or value that the various stakeholders require.)
3. **Value Improving Practices** (i.e., practices that have a specific focus and/or significant effect on getting the most value from a process and meet criteria that set the practice apart from "business as usual".)

ii. Be able to describe the purposes and general approach of these value improving practices (also see the section on Value Analysis and Engineering):
1. **Manufacturability Analysis**
2. **Constructability Analysis**
3. **Reliability, Availability and Maintainability (RAM) Analysis**

f. **Environment, Health, Safety, and Security (EHS)**: be able to explain the following concepts:
i. **Quality Management**. be able to describe why TCM is a quality management process and EHS issues are considered using this process approach (i.e., through establishing EHS *requirements* and managing to them).
ii. **Non-Conformance/Prevention**. be able to explain why it is important, as in quality management, to focus on preventing non-conformance with EHS requirements and improving performance rather than after the fact *appraisal, failure and correction*.
iii. **EHS Standards/Compliance**. be able to explain why compliance with minimum standards and regulations should be the minimum expected.
1. **ISO 14000**: management systems that an organization employs to manage environmental matters.
iv. **Sustainable Development**. be able to explain why enterprises should not use resources in a manner or degree that compromise the ability of future generations to sustain such development.

II. PROCESS AND FUNCTIONAL SKILLS AND KNOWLEDGE

1. **Total Cost Management (TCM) Process**

a. **Overall TCM Process and Terminology**
i. Basic Terminology: be able to explain the following:
1. *Plan-Do-Check-Assess (PDCA):*
2. *Strategic asset*
3. *Project*
4. *Portfolios and Programs*

ii. **TCM Processes:** be able to sketch the **TCM, strategic asset management,** and **project control** processes in basic **PDCA** format and explain the following:
1. the cost management purpose of the overall processes
2. how the two component subprocesses differ, but are related to each other
3. the benefits of an integrated, systematic cost management approach over the life cycle of assets and projects

b. **Strategic Asset Management Process**
i. given a representation of the strategic asset management process map (or some portion of it), be able to describe the basic purpose of each step and how it relates to the other steps in the map.

c. **Project Control Process**
i. given a representation of the project control process map (or some portion of it), be able to describe the basic purpose of each step and how it relates to the other steps in the map.

APPENDIX D—R.P. 11R-88

AACE INTERNATIONAL

Required Skills and Knowledge of Cost Engineering

12 of 22

aace
International

January 17, 2006

ii. be able to describe the ***Earned Value*** management process as a specific way of applying the project control process (i.e., in what ways is it specialized)

2. **Planning**

a. **Requirements Elicitation and Analysis**: be able to describe the following concepts
   i. **Stakeholders/Customers**: be able to describe how to identify these in relation to various business problems
   ii. **Needs, wants, or expectations of stakeholders**: be able describe challenges of eliciting this information from various stakeholders
   iii. **Requirements**: be able to describe the characteristics of a good requirement for use in asset or project control planning
   iv. **Cost requirements**: be able to describe the following asset planning methodologies for which cost may be a requirement
      1. *Target costing (including design-to-cost, and cost as an independent variable)*
      2. *Quality-function deployment*
   v. Other Concepts:
      1. **Asset vs. Project**: be able to explain how requirements for an asset or product might differ from those for a project.

b. **Scope and Execution Strategy Development**: be able to describe the following concepts
   i. **Asset scope**: be able to describe this as the physical, functional and quality characteristics or design basis of the selected asset investment
      1. **Functional decomposition**
   ii. **Project scope**: be able to describe this as the scope of work to deliver the asset
      1. **Project scope breakdown (work decomposition)**
   iii. **Work Breakdown Structure (WBS):** be able to diagram a WBS for a basic scope provided in narrative form
   iv. **Organization Breakdown Structure (OBS)**: be able to diagram an OBS for a basic scope provided in narrative form
   v. **Work package**
   vi. **Deliverables**
   vii. **Execution strategy**

c. **Schedule Planning and Development**: be able to describe the following concepts:
   i. **Schedule Planning**
      1. **Activities**
      2. **Activity Logic and Logic Diagramming**:
         a. given a series of logic statements, be able to draw a *logic diagram*.
         b. given a *soft-logic* work package with no strict activity interrelationships, be able to describe ways to do schedule planning for this work.
         c. be able to describe how schedule planning differs between a *batch and a continuous process*.
         d. Be able to describe the concept of *linear scheduling*
      3. **Activity Duration**
      4. **Critical Path:** be able to define and identify the critical path(s) in a project schedule
      5. **Float**: be able to describe the relationship and significance of *total and free float* in the scheduling of an activity.
      6. **Schedule Models**: Using the PDM method, and given a logic diagram and durations for activities, be able to calculate the early start and finish, late start and finish, and total and free float times for all activities. Identify minimum project completion time.
         a. **Precedence Diagram Method (PDM)**: in using this method include at least on each finish-start, finish-finish, start-finish, and start-start relationships with lags and identify critical path(s)

AACE INTERNATIONAL

APPENDIX D—R.P. 11R-88

Required Skills and Knowledge of Cost Engineering

13 of 22

aace
International

January 17, 2006

     b.   **Bar chart/Gantt chart**:
- i. be able to explain the difference between this and a logic diagram
- ii. given network activity durations, early and late start and finish times, and total float, be able to draw a bar chart based on early start of all activities, and show total float of activities where applicable.

    7.   Historical Data: be able to describe the importance of historical, empirical data and databases to schedule planning and schedule development

ii. **Schedule Development**: describe difference from schedule planning
1. **Milestones**
2. **Resource Loading**
3. **Resource Leveling or Balancing**: for a simple PDM network with resource inputs, be able to resource level the network within early and late start limits, and draw a histogram of worker-loading for early start, late start, and resource leveled configurations.

iii. **Schedule Control Basis**
1. **Schedule Control Baseline**
    a.   Be able to describe the concept of short interval scheduling (SIS) in relation to an overall project schedule control baseline.
2. **Planned Schedule**
3. **Schedule Basis**

iv. Other Concepts:
1. **Programs and Portfolios**: be able to explain these concepts and how schedule planning and development might be handled for groups of projects
2. **Operations/Production**: be able to explain how production scheduling differs from project scheduling
3. **Schedule strategy**
    a.   be able to describe the characteristics and risks of a *fast track* schedule
    b.   be able to describe alternate schedule strategies in regards to potential changes and claims that a contractor may apply in developing a network schedule (e.g., crashing).
    c.   be able describe the characteristics and risks of *just-in-time (JIT)* scheduling.
4. **Schedule Development**:
    a.   be able to describe the concept of development by *schedule level*
    b.   be able to describe the concept of *rolling wave* development.
5. **Schedule Change Management**: be able to describe how schedule changes might be managed.
6. **Critical Chain**: be able to describe the concept
7. **Linear Scheduling**: be able to describe the concept
8. **Schedule Contingency**:
    a.   Be able to define the term including what it is supposed to cover
    b.   Be able to describe several typical ways that it can be assessed

  d.   **Cost Estimating and Budgeting**: be able to describe the following concepts:
    i. General Concepts (must also understand *Elements of Cost and Analysis*):
1. **Cost Estimate Classification**. Be able to describe AACE's recommended practice and its basis on scope definition (also see *project implementation* for discussion of scope development phases).
2. **Uncertainty**.(also see *Risk Management*)
    a.   **Probability**: Be able to describe the *probabilistic* nature of cost estimates and the concept of *ranges* and *accuracy*, and the importance of communicating these to the project team.
    b.   **Accuracy**: Be able to describe asset and project characteristics likely to affect the accuracy of cost estimates, and the relationship of estimate classification to accuracy.
    c.   **Contingency**:

APPENDIX D—R.P. 11R-88

AACE INTERNATIONAL

Required Skills and Knowledge of Cost Engineering

14 of 22

aace
International

January 17, 2006

    i. be able to define the term including what cost it is supposed to cover
    ii. be able to describe several typical ways that it can be estimated

3. **Algorithms and Cost Estimating Relationships (CER).**
    a. **Algorithm types**: Be able to describe the basic characteristics of these algorithm types:
        i. **Stochastic or parametric**
            1.   given the inputs, be able to perform a *"scale of operations"* estimate
            2.   be able to explain why this algorithm type is most often applied in *asset planning.*
        ii. **Deterministic or definitive:** be able to explain why this algorithm type is most often applied in *project control planning.*
    b. **Factors**:
        i. be able to describe some typical uses of *factors, ratios, and indices* in algorithms of various types.
        ii. given a set of project characteristics and associated factors, be able to adjust a cost estimate from one time, location, situation, currency, etc. to another.

4. **Chart or Code of Accounts**: be able to describe the characteristics of a good code account structure and its benefits for estimating and project control

5. **Historical Data**: be able to describe the importance of historical, *empirical* data and databases to cost estimating

ii. Practices: be able to describe the basic mechanics of these estimating steps

1. **Quantification and Take-off**:
    a. be able to describe how the practices vary by level of scope definition and the algorithm type to be used for costing
    b. be able to describe ways that this step is sometimes automated, and considerations for using the results of automated take-off

2. **Costing and Life Cycle Costing** (see algorithms); be able to explain the concept of project versus life cycle costing

3. **Cash Flow and Forecasting**:
    a. be able to discuss the importance of integrating estimating and scheduling practices (incorporating the element of timing in quantification and costing)
    b. be able to discuss the affects on planning and cost estimating when cash flow is restricted
    c. given a schedule and set of cost inputs, be able to develop a *cost flow curve.*

4. **Pricing**:
    a. be able to discuss some business considerations for establishing pricing (risk, competition, desired rate of return, current economic conditions, etc.).
    b. given a basic set of cost inputs and production plans be able to calculate a *break-even product price*

5. **Bidding**
    a. be able to discuss some considerations for using someone else's bid as an input to your cost estimate.
    b. be able to describe the purpose and mechanics of *unbalancing* or *front-end loading* a bid

6. **Budgeting**: be able to describe the mechanics of creating a control budget from a cost estimate

7. **Cost Control Baseline**: be able to describe how cost and schedule control baselines can be integrated

8. **Estimate Basis**: be able to describe the typical content of estimate basis documentation

iii. Other Concepts:

1. **Product vs. Project costs**: be able to explain how estimating *product* (i.e., output of manufacturing) cost differs from *project* cost

AACE INTERNATIONAL

APPENDIX D—R.P. 11R-88

Required Skills and Knowledge of Cost Engineering

15 of 22

aace
International

January 17, 2006

e.   **Resource Management:** be able to describe how this process is tied closely to cost estimating (e.g., quantification) and schedule development (e.g., resource allocation).Also see *performance / productivity management* considerations

   i.**Resource availability**: be able to discuss ways to assess availability and potential consequences of not doing so

   1.   be able to describe the types of resources and their appropriateness to analysis
   2.   be able to discuss potential sources for resources
   3.   be able to discuss methods for validation of initial estimates

   ii.**Resource limits and constraints**: be able to discuss typical limits and constraints that may occur or be imposed

   1.   be able to discuss the role supervision and span of control has on resource limits
   2.   be able to describe how optimal and maximum crew sizing may play a part
   3.   be able to discuss the effects of physical workspace limits

   iii.**Resource allocation**: be able to describe the mechanics of this step in *schedule development*

   1.   forward vs. backward allocation: be able to explain the differences in the methods
   2.   smoothing vs. maximum limits: be able to explain the difference in the terms
   3.   maximum vs. over-maximum allocation: be able to explain the differences in the terms

f. **Value Analysis and Engineering**: be able to describe the following concepts:

   i.General Concepts:

   1.   **Purpose**:

   a.   be able define the concept (i.e., "the systematic application of recognized techniques which identify the functions of the product or service, establish the worth of those functions, and provide the necessary functions to meet the required performance at the lowest overall cost." Where overall cost is usually life-cycle cost).

   b.   distinguish among the terms "lowest life-cycle cost," "best quality," and "best value."

   c.   be able to describe how value analysis/engineering differs from other cost or scope reduction exercises

   d.   be able to describe how value analysis and engineering differs from other value improving practices such as manufacturability and constructability.

   2.   **Value:** be able to explain the this general concept as well as the meanings, using examples if desired, of these four kinds of value that may be associated with an item:

   a.   Use value
   b.   Esteem value
   c.   Exchange value
   d.   Cost value

   3.   **Functions**

   ii.Process/Practices; be able to describe the purpose and mechanics of these steps:

   1.   **Function Analysis** (*Value Measurement*)
   2.   **Creativity**

   i.   Describe each of the following problem solving techniques:

   1.   Brainstorming
   2.   Checklists
   3.   Morphological analysis
   4.   Attribute listing

   3.   **Value Screening**

g.   **Risk Management**: be able to describe the following concepts:

   i.General Concepts

1. **Risk and Uncertainty**: be able to define risk in terms of opportunities and threats
2. **Risk Factors** (or drivers) and *Risk Factor Properties*
3. **Risk Management Plan**
4. **Contingency Action Plans**
5. **Contingency** (see cost estimating and schedule development)
   a. Be able to describe the appropriate level of authority for managing contingency
   b. Be able to describe typical criteria for its use (i.e., as opposed to a slush fund).

ii. Practices: be able to describe the purpose and mechanics of these risk management process steps:
   1. **Risk Assessment**
   2. **Risk Analysis**
   3. **Risk Factor Screening**
   4. **Risk Mitigation or Acceptance**
   5. **Risk Control**

h. **Procurement Planning and Contract Management**
   i. **Contract types**: be able to explain the advantage and disadvantages of these types of contracts from the owner and contractor viewpoints:
   1. *Fixed price (with fixed, incentive, or award fees)*
   2. *Unit price*
   3. *Cost-plus (with fixed, incentive, or award fees)*
   4. *Time and materials (T&M)*

   ii. **Risk Allocation**: be able to explain how each contract type above allocates risks between the contracting parties.
   iii. **Contract Documents:**
   1. be able to describe the general contents and purposes of the following elements of bidding and contract documents:
      a. invitation to bid or request for proposal
      b. bid form
      c. agreement
      d. general conditions
      e. supplementary or special conditions
      f. technical specifications
      g. drawings
      h. addenda
      i. modifications
      j. bid bond and contract (performance) bond
      k. performance guarantee
      l. warranties
   2. be able to explain the role of contract documents in avoiding and resolving disputes, changes and claims (also see Change Management).
   3. be able to describe the various types of insurance that may be required as part of a contract
   4. be able to explain the term "*retention*" and be able to calculate its effective cost given the terms of the contract and time-value of money.
   5. be able to distinguish between "Job (project) overhead" and "general overhead' and provide examples of each.
   6. be able to explain what is meant by a contract payment term such as "2/15 net 30", and given a payment timing and time value of money scenario, be able to determine the method of payment that is economically most advantageous under these terms.
   iv. **Integrated Project Control:**

1. be able to explain the basic mechanics of how the project control process might be integrated between parties to each type of contract. (e.g., how to *measure and report progress, integrate schedules*, etc.).

2. be able to explain the role of contract documents in avoiding and resolving disputes, changes and claims (also see *Change Management*).

v. **Changes and Claims:** (see *Change Management* and *Forensic Performance Assessment*)

vi. Other Concepts:

1. **Supply chain:** be able to explain this concept and how it might affect procurement planning.

2. **Supplier relationships:** be able to explain this concept and how it might affect procurement planning (e.g., initial price versus life cycle cost)

3. **Schedule of values:** be able to explain this concept in regards to contracts, change management, and project control for contracted work.

i. **Investment Decision Making**

i. General Concepts:

1. be able explain the concepts and perform the analyses covered previously in the *Economic and Financial Analysis* section.

2. **Decision Policy / Criteria:**

a. be able to describe the role of decision policy in consistent asset *investment strategy deployment*

b. be able to explain why decision policy for most corporations establishes *net present value and return on investments* (or equivalent) as primary decision criteria.

ii. **Decision Analysis:**

1. **Decision Model:**

a. be able to able to explain the benefits of using a cost-based, quantitative decision model that addresses probabilities

b. be able to describe the mechanics of addressing non-cash value and risk considerations in a monetary decision model.

c. be able to evaluate and select the best alternative from several alternatives using these methods.

i. **Net Present Value**

ii. **Decision Tree** (probability weighted present value):

iii. **Discounted Rate of Return** (breakeven)

iv. **Cost/Benefit Ratio**

2. **Sensitivity Analysis and Monte Carlo Simulation**: be able to discuss mechanics of using a decision model to assess probable outcomes.

iii. **Business Decision Basis or Business Case**: be able to describe the information (e.g., objectives, assumptions, constraints, etc) that should be communicated to the project team.

iv. **Capital Budgeting**. be able to describe the mechanics of investment decision making in a typical enterprise capital budgeting process.

v. **Portfolio Management**. be able to describe the affect of portfolio considerations (multiple and often competing assets and projects) on investment decision making and capital budgeting processes.

3. **Implementation**

a. **Project Implementation**: be able to explain the following concepts:

i. **Phases and Gates Process**: be able to describe the typical stages in respect to project planning and funding authorization and the benefits of an established process

1. **Front-end loading (FEL):** be able to describe this concept and its benefits in terms of risk management and project control planning

APPENDIX D—R.P. 11R-88

AACE INTERNATIONAL

Required Skills and Knowledge of Cost Engineering

18 of 22

aace
International

January 17, 2006

ii.**Project Implementation Basis** or **Scope Statement**: be able to describe the typical information in this deliverable at project initiation and the importance of business and project team agreement and communicating this information to all stakeholders.

b. **Project control plan implementation**: be able to explain the following concepts:
  i.**Control Accounts**: describe this concept and its content in relation to WBS and earned value application
  ii.**Project Control Plan and Basis**: be able to describe the typical information in this deliverable at the start of project execution and the importance of integrating, agreeing on and communicating this information to the project team.

c. **Validation**: be able to describe how the quality and competitiveness of plans might be assessed before implementation and why the process is important. Also explain the value of historical, empirical information.

4. **Performance Measurement**

a. **Cost Accounting**: be able to describe the interface of the accounting process with cost engineering practice
  i.**Cash and Accrual Accounting**. Be able to describe these concepts
  ii.**Control and Cost Accounts**: be able to discuss the role of the **chart or code of accounts** with integrating project control
    1. **initiation/closure**: be able to discuss the importance of timely management of cost accounts
    2. **review/correct**: be able to discuss ways to deal with and the affects on project control of mischarges.
  iii.**Classify and account**: be able to explain the role of the cost engineer in assuring that cost accounting information is accounted for so as to align with the control basis. Be able to describe these cost accounting concepts:
    1. **Expenditures** (i.e., cash disbursements)
    2. **Incurred Costs** (i.e., expended plus cost of work performed but not paid for yet)
    3. **Commitments** (i.e., including expended costs and financial obligations)
    4. **Cost Allocation**
    5. **Activity-Based Costing (ABC)**
  iv.**Capitalization and Depreciation**: be able to explain these concepts and the typical role of the cost engineer in working with the finance function to assure it is done effectively
  v.**Asset vs. Project Accounting**:
    1. be able to describe how traditional asset operation and finance focused accounting differs from that needed for project control
    2. be able to describe how legacy or contractor cost accounting system accounts are often not consistent with project control needs, and how the inconsistency may be addressed.

b. **Project Performance Measurement**
  i.General Concepts
    1. **Earned Value:** be able to explain the general concept and the importance of and reliable control basis and objective, quantitative physical progress measures
  ii.Practices
    1. **Physical Progress**: be able to explain the general concept and the following methods, and, given input information, be able to calculate percent complete.
      a. *units completed*
      b. *incremental milestone*
      c. *weighted or equivalent units completed*
      d. *resource expenditure*
      e. *judgment*
    2. **Track Resources**

AACE INTERNATIONAL

APPENDIX D—R.P. 11R-88

Required Skills and Knowledge of Cost Engineering

19 of 22

aace
International

January 17, 2006

    a.   **Labor hours**: be able to explain the advantages and disadvantages of tracking labor hours instead of cost as the basis for earned value

    b.   **Material management and fabrication**: be able to discuss how material progress/status can be measured

3. **Measure Performance** (how work is being done)

    a.   be able to discuss why earned value measures alone have limited value in finding ways to improve performance.

    b.   be able to discuss the mechanics of the following methods, how they can help find ways to improve performance, and their strengths and weaknesses:

        i. *Work sampling*

        ii. *Time and motion studies*

        iii. *Time lapse photography and video monitoring*

        iv. *Expediting*

        v. *Inspection*

4. **Status Schedule**: be able to discuss the mechanics of statusing and updating a schedule

  c.   **Asset Performance Measurement**: be able to explain how earned value methods do not apply for operations and performance is measured against metrics established by the *requirements*.

     i. **Functional Performance**: be able to explain how measures capture what an asset does and how it does it including quality control attributes, cycle time, and so on.

     ii. **Utility measures:** be able to discuss ways to capture user or customer perceptions of how well the asset meets their wants and needs.

     iii. **Measure Activity Factors**: be able to explain how if ABC/M methods are used, *cost assignment network tracing* ties expenses to activities whose performance must be measured.

     iv. **Track Resources**: be able to explain how *ERP systems* increasingly handle these measures in operation facilities

5.   **Performance Assessment**

    a.   **Project Performance Assessment**: be able to explain the concepts

     i. General Concepts

        1. **Variance**: be able to describe this concept as an empirical difference between actual and planned performance for any aspect of the control plan.

        2. **Trends**: be able to describe the difference between random and non-random variance and how this might influence subsequent control actions and forecasts

     ii. Practices for **control assessment**: be able to describe methods for assessing and reporting performance (variances and trends) against the following baseline plans:

        1. **cost**:

           a.   be able to describe basic earned value methods

           b.   be able to describe and prepare tabular and cumulative distribution charts ("s-curves") for reporting

        2. **schedule**:

           a.   be able to describe methods to identify variance (e.g., calculate slip, earned value methods, etc), assess critical path and remaining float.

           b.   Be able to describe performance reporting methods (e.g., schedule plot showing the planned and actual schedule activity status), tables showing a percentage or factor that expresses the extent that the schedule is ahead or behind at given points in time, lists of activities sorted by early start date or total float, etc.).

        3. **resources**

           a. **labor**

             i. be able to describe basic earned value methods

APPENDIX D—R.P. 11R-88

AACE INTERNATIONAL

Required Skills and Knowledge of Cost Engineering

aace
International

20 of 22

January 17, 2006

    ii. be able to describe and prepare tabular and *cumulative distribution charts* (*"s-curves"*) for reporting

    b. **material and fabrication**: be able to describe the use earned value, schedule assessment, material management reports, and so on.

    4. **risk**: be able to explain the monitoring and assessment of risk factors in accordance with a risk a management plan

iii. Practices for **integrated earned value (Earned Value Management System or EVMS) assessment**

    1. be able to explain and calculate all the basic *earned value measures and indices (Planned and/or Budget [was BCWS], Earned [was BCWP], and Actual [was ACWP], SV, CV, SPI, CPI)*

    2. be able to describe the advantages and disadvantages of a fully integrated EVMS assessment using costs

iv. Practices for **work process and productivity improvement**

    1. **Productivity assessment**

    a. **Labor productivity factor**: be able to calculate this using earned value and explain its significance

    2. **Work process improvement**.

    a. **Work sampling**: be able to describe the mechanics of the method and how it can be used to eliminate *wasted effort* and improve the work process

    b. be able to describe other methods such as *informal sampling, manpower surveys, time card notations, quality circles, inspection observations*, etc.

b. **Asset Performance Assessment**: be able to explain how for operations, earned value methods do not apply and performance is measured against metrics established by the requirements.

    i. **Measurement Basis**: be able to describe these concepts for measuring and assessing asset management performance (profitability being the most common metric):

    1. **Balanced Scorecard**

    2. **Key Performance Indicators (KPI)**

ii. **Practices**

    1. **Profitability**: see *return on investment*

    2. **Cost of Quality**:

    a. be able to describe the mechanics of the method and *costs of prevention, appraisal and failure*.

    b. be able to explain how the method can lead to corrective actions

    3. **Benchmarking**: be able to describe the purpose and mechanics of a benchmarking study

    4. **Lessons Learned**. be able to explain the purpose and mechanics of capturing and evaluating lessons learned

    5. **Risk Assessment**: be able to explain the monitoring and assessment of risk factors in accordance with a risk a management plan

c. **Forecasting**

    i. **Forecast and Forecasting**.

    1. be able to describe the concepts of forecasts and forecasting

    2. be able to describe how the project control planning concepts (e.g., estimating, scheduling, etc.) are applied in the context of work in progress, performance assessment findings, change management, and corrective actions.

    ii. **Earned Value Methods**:

    1. be able to explain and calculate the basic earned value concepts related to forecasting (*BAC, EAC, labor productivity factor*)

    2. be able to explain why earned value measures alone may not be an appropriate basis for a forecast; explain what else must be considered.

d. **Project Change Management**

AACE INTERNATIONAL

APPENDIX D—R.P. 11R-88

Required Skills and Knowledge of Cost Engineering

21 of 22

aace
International

January 17, 2006

i. Basic Terminology: be able to describe the concepts
1. **Scope:** be able to describe how the meaning of the term "scope" differs in the contexts of owner project funds authorization versus contracting
2. **Deviations**
3. **Trends** (also see *performance assessment*):
4. **Changes:** be able to explain the difference between scope and non-scope changes in an owner funding context
5. **Changes and Contract Types:** be able to explain how the change order process may differ with different contract types.
6. **Disputes and Claims**
7. **Contingency, Allowances, and Reserves** (see *Risk Management*)

ii. Practices: be able to describe the concepts
1. **Variance or trend analysis:** be able to describe the difference between performance variance and a trend
2. **Impact assessment:** be able to describe how the project control planning concepts (e.g., estimating, scheduling, etc.) are applied in change management
   a. Be able to describe the concept of *time impact analysis* related to schedule change
3. **Make and track disposition**
   a. **Corrective action** (also improvement action): be able to describe what these are and why they might be needed.
   b. be able to describe ways that change management findings and dispositions (actions) are recorded, reported, and incorporated in the *project control plans*
4. **Manage contingency and reserves:**
   a. **Draw down:** be able to describe methods for managing contingency
   b. be able to describe ways to assess the need for contingency for work in progress
5. **Resolve contract disputes and claims:** be able to discuss the concept of changes and change management in respect to contract agreements (also see *Forensic Performance Assessment*)

e. **Asset Change (Configuration) Management**
   i. **Requirements:** Be able to explain how managing the scope of the "asset" in respect to its requirements in strategic asset management differs from managing the scope of "work" in project control.
   ii. **Configuration Management:** be able to describe the role of this practice area in managing change in information that defines the asset

f. **Historical Database Management** (see basic concepts in *Information Management*)
   i. **Empirical Data:** be able to explain why empirical information is the most fundamental planning resource available (why is it critical for asset and project planning?)
   ii. **Project Closeout:** be able to describe the mechanics and challenges of closing out a project in respect to project control systems, data and information.

g. **Forensic Performance Assessment**
   i. be able to describe how *forensic* assessment differs from typical project control performance assessments (i.e., the primary purpose is to relate *causation* and *responsibility (or entitlement)* to performance to resolve disputes in a legal context and/or to gain knowledge to support long term performance improvement.
   ii. be able to describe the difference between changes and claims (for *scope, compensation, relief, damages, delay*, or other disagreements)
   iii. be able to describe major reasons for contract changes including the role of *project scope definition*
   iv. be able to describe various types of schedule **delay** in respect to contract changes and claims:
   1. *excusable*

APPENDIX D—R.P. 11R-88

AACE INTERNATIONAL

Required Skills and Knowledge of Cost Engineering

22 of 22

aace
International

January 17, 2006

2. *non-excusable*
3. *compensatory*
4. *concurrent*

v. be able to describe the potential affects of disputes on project performance

vi. be able to discuss role of these costs (see **Elements of Cost**) in context of disputes and claims (*bonds, retainage, performance guarantees, liquidated damages, demurrage, legal costs, etc.*)

vii. be able to discuss means and methods of resolving disputes and claims through *negotiation, mediation, arbitration*, and/or *litigation* (or other forms of *alternative dispute resolution*) including being able to discuss potential good points and bad points of each forum.

viii. Be able to describe the terms *discovery process, depositions* and *interrogatory.*

ix. Be able to describe why it is import to distinguish between *supposition* and *fact.*

AACE International Recommended Practice No. 17R-97

COST ESTIMATE CLASSIFICATION SYSTEM

Acknowledgment:

Peter Christensen CCE, Primary Author
Larry R. Dysert CCC, Primary Author
Jennifer Bates CCE
Dorothy J. Burton
Robert C. Creese PE CCE
John K. Hollmann PE CCE

Kenneth K. Humphreys PE CCE
Donald F. McDonald JR. PE CCE
C. Arthur Miller
Bernard A. Pietlock CCC
Wesley R. Querns CCE
Don L. Short II

Recommended Practice No. 17R-97

Cost Estimate Classification System

August 12, 1997

PURPOSE

As a recommended practice of AACE International, the Cost Estimate Classification System provides guidelines for applying the general principles of estimate classification to asset project cost estimates. Asset project cost estimates typically involve estimates for capital investment, and exclude operating and life-cycle evaluations. The Cost Estimate Classification System maps the phases and stages of asset cost estimating together with a generic maturity and quality matrix that can be applied across a wide variety of industries.

This guideline and its addenda have been developed in a way that:

provides common understanding of the concepts involved with classifying project cost estimates, regardless of the type of enterprise or industry the estimates relate to;
fully defines and correlates the major characteristics used in classifying cost estimates so that enterprises may unambiguously determine how their practices compare to the guidelines;
uses degree of project definition as the primary characteristic to categorize estimate classes; and
reflects generally-accepted practices in the cost engineering profession.

An intent of the guidelines is to improve communication among all of the stakeholders involved with preparing, evaluating, and using project cost estimates. The various parties that use project cost estimates often misinterpret the quality and value of the information available to prepare cost estimates, the various methods employed during the estimating process, the accuracy level expected from estimates, and the level of risk associated with estimates.

This classification guideline is intended to help those involved with project estimates to avoid misinterpretation of the various classes of cost estimates and to avoid their misapplication and misrepresentation. Improving communications about estimate classifications reduces business costs and project cycle times by avoiding inappropriate business and financial decisions, actions, delays, or disputes caused by misunderstandings of cost estimates and what they are expected to represent.

This document is intended to provide a guideline, not a standard. It is understood that each enterprise may have its own project and estimating processes and terminology, and may classify estimates in particular ways. This guideline provides a generic and generally-acceptable classification system that can be used as a basis to compare against. If an enterprise or organization has not yet formally documented its own estimate classification scheme, then this guideline may provide an acceptable starting point.

INTRODUCTION

An AACE International guideline for cost estimate classification for the process industries was developed in the late 1960s or early 1970s, and a simplified version was adopted as an ANSI Standard Z94.0 in 1972. Those guidelines and standards enjoy reasonably broad acceptance within the engineering and construction communities and within the process industries. This recommended practice guide and its addenda improves upon these standards by:

1. providing a classification method applicable across all industries; and
2. unambiguously identifying, cross-referencing, benchmarking, and empirically evaluating the multiple characteristics related to the class of cost estimate.

This guideline is intended to provide a generic methodology for the classification of project cost estimates in any industry, and will be supplemented with addenda that will provide extensions and additional detail for specific industries.

CLASSIFICATION METHODOLOGY

There are numerous characteristics that can be used to categorize cost estimate types. The most significant of these are degree of project definition, end usage of the estimate, estimating methodology, and the effort and time needed to prepare the estimate. The "primary" characteristic used in this guideline to define the classification category is the degree of project definition. The other characteristics are "secondary."

Categorizing cost estimates by degree of project definition is in keeping with the AACE International philosophy of Total Cost Management, which is a quality-driven process applied during the entire project life cycle. The discrete levels of project definition used for classifying estimates correspond to the typical phases and gates of evaluation, authorization, and execution often used by project stakeholders during a project life cycle.

Five cost estimate classes have been established. While the level of project definition is a continuous spectrum, it was determined from benchmarking industry practices that three to five discrete categories are commonly used. Five categories are established in this guideline as it is easier to simplify by combining categories than it is to arbitrarily split a standard.

The estimate class designations are labeled Class 1, 2, 3, 4, and 5. A Class 5 estimate is based upon the lowest level of project definition, and a Class 1 estimate is closest to full project definition and maturity. This arbitrary "countdown" approach considers that estimating is a process whereby successive estimates are prepared until a final estimate closes the process.

	Primary Characteristic	Secondary Characteristic			
ESTIMATE CLASS	LEVEL OF PROJECT DEFINITION Expressed as % of complete definition	END USAGE Typical purpose of estimate	METHODOLOGY Typical estimating method	EXPECTED ACCURACY RANGE Typical +/- range relative to best index of 1 [a]	PREPARATION EFFORT Typical degree of effort relative to least cost index of 1 [b]
Class 5	0% to 2%	Screening or Feasibility	Stochastic or Judgment	4 to 20	1
Class 4	1% to 15%	Concept Study or Feasibility	Primarily Stochastic	3 to 12	2 to 4
Class 3	10% to 40%	Budget, Authorization, or Control	Mixed, but Primarily Stochastic	2 to 6	3 to 10
Class 2	30% to 70%	Control or Bid/ Tender	Primarily Deterministic	1 to 3	5 to 20
Class 1	50% to 100%	Check Estimate or Bid/Tender	Deterministic	1	10 to 100

Notes: [a] If the range index value of "1" represents +10/-5%, then an index value of 10 represents +100/-50%.
[b] If the cost index value of "1" represents 0.005% of project costs, then an index value of 100 represents 0.5%.

Figure 1 – Generic Cost Estimate Classification Matrix

DEFINITIONS OF COST ESTIMATE CHARACTERISTICS

The following are brief discussions of the various estimate characteristics used in the estimate classification matrix. For the secondary characteristics, the overall trend of how each characteristic varies with the degree of project definition (the primary characteristic) is provided.

Level of Project Definition (Primary Characteristic)

This characteristic is based upon percent complete of project definition (roughly corresponding to percent complete of engineering). The level of project definition defines maturity or the extent and types of input information available to the estimating process. Such inputs include project scope definition, requirements documents, specifications, project plans, drawings, calculations, learnings from past projects, reconnaissance data, and other information that must be developed to define the project. Each industry will have a typical set of deliverables that are used to support the type of estimates used in that industry. The set of deliverables becomes more definitive and complete as the level of project definition (i.e., project engineering) progresses.

End Usage (Secondary Characteristic)

The various classes (or phases) of cost estimates prepared for a project typically have different end uses or purposes. As the level of project definition increases, the end usage of an estimate typically progresses from strategic evaluation and feasibility studies to funding authorization and budgets to project control purposes.

Estimating Methodology (Secondary Characteristic)

Estimating methodologies fall into two broad categories: stochastic and deterministic. In stochastic methods, the independent variable(s) used in the cost estimating algorithms are generally something other than a direct measure of the units of the item being estimated. The cost estimating relationships used in stochastic methods often are somewhat subject to conjecture. With deterministic methods, the independent variable(s) are more or less a definitive measure of the item being estimated. A deterministic methodology is not subject to significant conjecture. As the level of project definition increases, the estimating methodology tends to progress from stochastic to deterministic methods.

Expected Accuracy Range (Secondary Characteristic)

Estimate accuracy range is in indication of the degree to which the final cost outcome for a given project will vary from the estimated cost. Accuracy is traditionally expressed as a +/- percentage range around the point estimate after application of contingency, with a stated level of confidence that the actual cost outcome would fall within this range (+/- measures are a useful simplification, given that actual cost outcomes have different frequency distributions for different types of projects). As the level of project definition increases, the expected accuracy of the estimate tends to improve, as indicated by a tighter +/- range.

Note that in figure 1, the values in the accuracy range column do not represent + or - percentages, but instead represent an index value relative to a best range index value of 1. If, for a particular industry, a Class 1 estimate has an accuracy range of +10/-5 percent, then a Class 5 estimate in that same industry may have an accuracy range of +100/-50 percent.

Effort to Prepare Estimate (Secondary Characteristic)

The level of effort needed to prepare a given estimate is an indication of the cost, time, and resources required. The cost measure of that effort is typically expressed as a percentage of the total project costs for a given project size. As the level of project definition increases, the amount of effort to prepare an estimate increases, as does its cost relative to the total project cost. The effort to develop the project deliverables is not included in the effort metrics; they only cover the cost to prepare the cost estimate itself.

Cost Estimate Classification System   4 of 6

August 12, 1997

RELATIONSHIPS AND VARIATIONS OF CHARACTERISTICS

There are a myriad of complex relationships that may be exhibited among the estimate characteristics within the estimate classifications. The overall trend of how the secondary characteristics vary with the level of project definition was provided above. This section explores those trends in more detail. Typically, there are commonalties in the secondary characteristics between one estimate and the next, but in any given situation there may be wide variations in usage, methodology, accuracy, and effort.

The level of project definition is the "driver" of the other characteristics. Typically, all of the secondary characteristics have the level of project definition as a primary determinant. While the other characteristics are important to categorization, they lack complete consensus. For example, one estimator's "bid" might be another's "budget." Characteristics such as "accuracy" and "methodology" can vary markedly from one industry to another, and even from estimator to estimator within a given industry.

Level of Project Definition

Each project (or industry grouping) will have a typical set of deliverables that are used to support a given class of estimate. The availability of these deliverables is directly related to the level of project definition achieved. The variations in the deliverables required for an estimate are too broad to cover in detail here; however, it is important to understand what drives the variations. Each industry group tends to focus on a defining project element that "drives" the estimate maturity level. For instance, chemical industry projects are "process equipment-centric"—i.e., the level of project definition and subsequent estimate maturity level is significantly determined by how well the equipment is defined. Architectural projects tend to be "structure-centric," software projects tend to be "function-centric," and so on. Understanding these drivers puts the differences that may appear in the more detailed industry addenda into perspective.

End Usage

While there are common end usages of an estimate among different stakeholders, usage is often relative to the stakeholder's identity. For instance, an owner company may use a given class of estimate to support project funding, while a contractor may use the same class of estimate to support a contract bid or tender. It is not at all uncommon to find stakeholders categorizing their estimates by usage-related headings such as "budget," "study," or "bid." Depending on the stakeholder's perspective and needs, it is important to understand that these may actually be all the same class of estimate (based on the primary characteristic of level of project definition achieved).

Estimating Methodology

As stated previously, estimating methodologies fall into two broad categories: stochastic and deterministic. These broad categories encompass scores of individual methodologies. Stochastic methods often involve simple or complex modeling based on inferred or statistical relationships between costs and programmatic and/or technical parameters. Deterministic methods tend to be straightforward counts or measures of units of items multiplied by known unit costs or factors. It is important to realize that any combination of methods may be found in any given class of estimate. For example, if a stochastic method is known to be suitably accurate, it may be used in place of a deterministic method even when there is sufficient input information based on the level of project definition to support a deterministic method. This may be due to the lower level of effort required to prepare an estimate using stochastic methods.

Expected Accuracy Range

The accuracy range of an estimate is dependent upon a number of characteristics of the estimate input information and the estimating process. The extent and the maturity of the input information as measured by percentage completion (and related to level of project definition) is a highly-important determinant of accuracy. However, there are factors besides the available input information that also greatly affect estimate accuracy measures. Primary among these are the state of technology in the project and the quality of reference cost estimating data.

AACE International Recommended Practice No. 18R-97

COST ESTIMATE CLASSIFICATION SYSTEM – AS APPLIED IN ENGINEERING, PROCUREMENT, AND CONSTRUCTION FOR THE PROCESS INDUSTRIES

Acknowledgment:

Peter Christensen CCE, Primary Author
Larry R. Dysert CCC, Primary Author
Jennifer Bates CCE
Dorothy J. Burton
Robert C. Creese PE CCE
John K. Hollmann PE CCE

Kenneth K. Humphreys PE CCE
Donald F. McDonald JR. PE CCE
C. Arthur Miller
Bernard A. Pietlock CCC
Wesley R. Querns CCE
Don L. Short II

Recommended Practice No. 18R-97

Cost Estimate Classification System – As Applied in Engineering, Procurement, and Construction for the Process Industries

February 2, 2005

PURPOSE

As a recommended practice of AACE International, the Cost Estimate Classification System provides guidelines for applying the general principles of estimate classification to project cost estimates (i.e., cost estimates that are used to evaluate, approve, and/or fund projects). The Cost Estimate Classification System maps the phases and stages of project cost estimating together with a generic maturity and quality matrix, which can be applied across a wide variety of industries.

This addendum to the generic recommended practice provides guidelines for applying the principles of estimate classification specifically to project estimates for engineering, procurement, and construction (EPC) work for the process industries. This addendum supplements the generic recommended practice (17R-97) by providing:

- a section that further defines classification concepts as they apply to the process industries;
- charts that compare existing estimate classification practices in the process industry; and
- a chart that maps the extent and maturity of estimate input information (project definition deliverables) against the class of estimate.

As with the generic standard, an intent of this addendum is to improve communications among all of the stakeholders involved with preparing, evaluating, and using project cost estimates specifically for the process industries.

It is understood that each enterprise may have its own project and estimating processes and terminology, and may classify estimates in particular ways. This guideline provides a generic and generally acceptable classification system for process industries that can be used as a basis to compare against. It is hoped that this addendum will allow each user to better assess, define, and communicate their own processes and standards in the light of generally-accepted cost engineering practice.

INTRODUCTION

For the purposes of this addendum, the term process industries is assumed to include firms involved with the manufacturing and production of chemicals, petrochemicals, and hydrocarbon processing. The common thread among these industries (for the purpose of estimate classification) is their reliance on process flow diagrams (PFDs) and piping and instrument diagrams (P&IDs) as primary scope defining documents. These documents are key deliverables in determining the level of project definition, and thus the extent and maturity of estimate input information.

Estimates for process facilities center on mechanical and chemical process equipment, and they have significant amounts of piping, instrumentation, and process controls involved. As such, this addendum may apply to portions of other industries, such as pharmaceutical, utility, metallurgical, converting, and similar industries. Specific addendums addressing these industries may be developed over time.

This addendum specifically does not address cost estimate classification in nonprocess industries such as commercial building construction, environmental remediation, transportation infrastructure, "dry" processes such as assembly and manufacturing, "soft asset" production such as software development, and similar industries. It also does not specifically address estimates for the exploration, production, or transportation of mining or hydrocarbon materials, although it may apply to some of the intermediate processing steps in these systems.

The cost estimates covered by this addendum are for engineering, procurement, and construction (EPC) work only. It does not cover estimates for the products manufactured by the process facilities, or for research and development work in support of the process industries. This guideline does not cover the significant building construction that may be a part of process plants. Building construction will be covered in a separate addendum.

AACE International Recommended Practices

Cost Estimate Classification System – As Applied in Engineering
Procurement, and Construction for the Process Industries

2 of 8

aace
International

February 2, 2005

This guideline reflects generally-accepted cost engineering practices. This addendum was based upon the practices of a wide range of companies in the process industries from around the world, as well as published references and standards. Company and public standards were solicited and reviewed by the AACE International Cost Estimating Committee. The practices were found to have significant commonalities that are conveyed in this addendum.

COST ESTIMATE CLASSIFICATION MATRIX FOR THE PROCESS INDUSTRIES

The five estimate classes are presented in figure 1 in relationship to the identified characteristics. Only the level of project definition determines the estimate class. The other four characteristics are secondary characteristics that are generally correlated with the level of project definition, as discussed in the generic standard. The characteristics are typical for the process industries but may vary from application to application.

This matrix and guideline provide an estimate classification system that is specific to the process industries. Refer to the generic standard for a general matrix that is non-industry specific, or to other addendums for guidelines that will provide more detailed information for application in other specific industries. These will typically provide additional information, such as input deliverable checklists to allow meaningful categorization in those particular industries.

ESTIMATE CLASS	Primary Characteristic	Secondary Characteristic			
	LEVEL OF PROJECT DEFINITION Expressed as % of complete definition	END USAGE Typical purpose of estimate	METHODOLOGY Typical estimating method	EXPECTED ACCURACY RANGE Typical variation in low and high ranges [a]	PREPARATION EFFORT Typical degree of effort relative to least cost index of 1 [b]
Class 5	0% to 2%	Concept Screening	Capacity Factored, Parametric Models, Judgment, or Analogy	L: -20% to -50% H: +30% to +100%	1
Class 4	1% to 15%	Study or Feasibility	Equipment Factored or Parametric Models	L: -15% to -30% H: +20% to +50%	2 to 4
Class 3	10% to 40%	Budget, Authorization, or Control	Semi-Detailed Unit Costs with Assembly Level Line Items	L: -10% to -20% H: +10% to +30%	3 to 10
Class 2	30% to 70%	Control or Bid/ Tender	Detailed Unit Cost with Forced Detailed Take-Off	L: -5% to -15% H: +5% to +20%	4 to 20
Class 1	50% to 100%	Check Estimate or Bid/Tender	Detailed Unit Cost with Detailed Take-Off	L: -3% to -10% H: +3% to +15%	5 to 100

Notes: [a] The state of process technology and availability of applicable reference cost data affect the range markedly. The +/- value represents typical percentage variation of actual costs from the cost estimate after application of contingency (typically at a 50% level of confidence) for given scope.

[b] If the range index value of "1" represents 0.005% of project costs, then an index value of 100 represents 0.5%. Estimate preparation effort is highly dependent upon the size of the project and the quality of estimating data and tools.

Figure 1. – Cost Estimate Classification Matrix for Process Industries

Cost Estimate Classification System – As Applied in Engineering
Procurement, and Construction for the Process Industries

3 of 8

aace
International

February 2, 2005

CHARACTERISTICS OF THE ESTIMATE CLASSES

The following charts (figures 2a through 2e) provide detailed descriptions of the five estimate classifications as applied in the process industries. They are presented in the order of least-defined estimates to the most-defined estimates. These descriptions include brief discussions of each of the estimate characteristics that define an estimate class.

For each chart, the following information is provided:

- **Description:** a short description of the class of estimate, including a brief listing of the expected estimate inputs based on the level of project definition.
- **Level of Project Definition Required:** expressed as a percent of full definition. For the process industries, this correlates with the percent of engineering and design complete.
- **End Usage:** a short discussion of the possible end usage of this class of estimate.
- **Estimating Methods Used:** a listing of the possible estimating methods that may be employed to develop an estimate of this class.
- **Expected Accuracy Range:** typical variation in low and high ranges after the application of contingency (determined at a 50% level of confidence). Typically, this results in a 90% confidence that the actual cost will fall within the bounds of the low and high ranges.
- **Effort to Prepare:** this section provides a typical level of effort (in hours) to produce a complete estimate for a US$20,000,000 plant. Estimate preparation effort is highly dependent on project size, project complexity, estimator skills and knowledge, and on the availability of appropriate estimating cost data and tools.
- **ANSI Standard Reference (1989) Name:** this is a reference to the equivalent estimate class in the existing ANSI standards.
- **Alternate Estimate Names, Terms, Expressions, Synonyms:** this section provides other commonly used names that an estimate of this class might be known by. These alternate names are not endorsed by this Recommended Practice. The user is cautioned that an alternative name may not always be correlated with the class of estimate as identified in the chart.

CLASS 5 ESTIMATE	
Description: Class 5 estimates are generally prepared based on very limited information, and subsequently have wide accuracy ranges. As such, some companies and organizations have elected to determine that due to the inherent inaccuracies, such estimates cannot be classified in a conventional and systemic manner. Class 5 estimates, due to the requirements of end use, may be prepared within a very limited amount of time and with little effort expended— sometimes requiring less than an hour to prepare. Often, little more than proposed plant type, location, and capacity are known at the time of estimate preparation. **Level of Project Definition Required:** 0% to 2% of full project definition. **End Usage:** Class 5 estimates are prepared for any number of strategic business planning purposes, such as but not limited to market studies, assessment of initial viability, evaluation of alternate schemes, project screening, project location studies, evaluation of resource needs and budgeting, long-range capital planning, etc.	**Estimating Methods Used:** Class 5 estimates virtually always use stochastic estimating methods such as cost/capacity curves and factors, scale of operations factors, Lang factors, Hand factors, Chilton factors, Peters-Timmerhaus factors, Guthrie factors, and other parametric and modeling techniques. **Expected Accuracy Range:** Typical accuracy ranges for Class 5 estimates are - 20% to -50% on the low side, and +30% to +100% on the high side, depending on the technological complexity of the project, appropriate reference information, and the inclusion of an appropriate contingency determination. Ranges could exceed those shown in unusual circumstances. **Effort to Prepare (for US$20MM project):** As little as 1 hour or less to perhaps more than 200 hours, depending on the project and the estimating methodology used. **ANSI Standard Reference Z94.2-1989 Name:** Order of magnitude estimate (typically -30% to +50%). **Alternate Estimate Names, Terms, Expressions, Synonyms:** Ratio, ballpark, blue sky, seat-of-pants, ROM, idea study, prospect estimate, concession license estimate, guesstimate, rule-of-thumb.

Figure 2a. – Class 5 Estimate

Cost Estimate Classification System – As Applied in Engineering
Procurement, and Construction for the Process Industries

4 of 8

aace
International

February 2, 2005

CLASS 4 ESTIMATE	
Description: Class 4 estimates are generally prepared based on limited information and subsequently have fairly wide accuracy ranges. They are typically used for project screening, determination of feasibility, concept evaluation, and preliminary budget approval. Typically, engineering is from 1% to 15% complete, and would comprise at a minimum the following: plant capacity, block schematics, indicated layout, process flow diagrams (PFDs) for main process systems, and preliminary engineered process and utility equipment lists. **Level of Project Definition Required:** 1% to 15% of full project definition. **End Usage:** Class 4 estimates are prepared for a number of purposes, such as but not limited to, detailed strategic planning, business development, project screening at more developed stages, alternative scheme analysis, confirmation of economic and/or technical feasibility, and preliminary budget approval or approval to proceed to next stage.	**Estimating Methods Used:** Class 4 estimates virtually always use stochastic estimating methods such as equipment factors, Lang factors, Hand factors, Chilton factors, Peters-Timmerhaus factors, Guthrie factors, the Miller method, gross unit costs/ratios, and other parametric and modeling techniques. **Expected Accuracy Range:** Typical accuracy ranges for Class 4 estimates are -15% to -30% on the low side, and +20% to +50% on the high side, depending on the technological complexity of the project, appropriate reference information, and the inclusion of an appropriate contingency determination. Ranges could exceed those shown in unusual circumstances. **Effort to Prepare (for US$20MM project):** Typically, as little as 20 hours or less to perhaps more than 300 hours, depending on the project and the estimating methodology used. **ANSI Standard Reference Z94.2-1989 Name:** Budget estimate (typically -15% to + 30%). **Alternate Estimate Names, Terms, Expressions, Synonyms:** Screening, top-down, feasibility, authorization, factored, pre-design, pre-study.

Figure 2b. – Class 4 Estimate

CLASS 3 ESTIMATE	
Description: Class 3 estimates are generally prepared to form the basis for budget authorization, appropriation, and/or funding. As such, they typically form the initial control estimate against which all actual costs and resources will be monitored. Typically, engineering is from 10% to 40% complete, and would comprise at a minimum the following: process flow diagrams, utility flow diagrams, preliminary piping and instrument diagrams, plot plan, developed layout drawings, and essentially complete engineered process and utility equipment lists. **Level of Project Definition Required:** 10% to 40% of full project definition. **End Usage:** Class 3 estimates are typically prepared to support full project funding requests, and become the first of the project phase "control estimates" against which all actual costs and resources will be monitored for variations to the budget. They are used as the project budget until replaced by more detailed estimates. In many owner organizations, a Class 3 estimate may be the last estimate required and could well form the only basis for cost/schedule control.	**Estimating Methods Used:** Class 3 estimates usually involve more deterministic estimating methods than stochastic methods. They usually involve a high degree of unit cost line items, although these may be at an assembly level of detail rather than individual components. Factoring and other stochastic methods may be used to estimate less-significant areas of the project. **Expected Accuracy Range:** Typical accuracy ranges for Class 3 estimates are -10% to -20% on the low side, and +10% to +30% on the high side, depending on the technological complexity of the project, appropriate reference information, and the inclusion of an appropriate contingency determination. Ranges could exceed those shown in unusual circumstances. **Effort to Prepare (for US$20MM project):** Typically, as little as 150 hours or less to perhaps more than 1,500 hours, depending on the project and the estimating methodology used. **ANSI Standard Reference Z94.2-1989 Name:** Budget estimate (typically -15% to + 30%). **Alternate Estimate Names, Terms, Expressions, Synonyms:** Budget, scope, sanction, semi-detailed, authorization, preliminary control, concept study, development, basic engineering phase estimate, target estimate.

Figure 2c. – Class 3 Estimate

AACE INTERNATIONAL

APPENDIX F—R.P. 18R-97

Cost Estimate Classification System – As Applied in Engineering
Procurement, and Construction for the Process Industries

5 of 8

aace
International

February 2, 2005

CLASS 2 ESTIMATE

Description:
Class 2 estimates are generally prepared to form a detailed control baseline against which all project work is monitored in terms of cost and progress control. For contractors, this class of estimate is often used as the "bid" estimate to establish contract value. Typically, engineering is from 30% to 70% complete, and would comprise at a minimum the following: process flow diagrams, utility flow diagrams, piping and instrument diagrams, heat and material balances, final plot plan, final layout drawings, complete engineered process and utility equipment lists, single line diagrams for electrical, electrical equipment and motor schedules, vendor quotations, detailed project execution plans, resourcing and work force plans, etc.

Level of Project Definition Required:
30% to 70% of full project definition.

End Usage:
Class 2 estimates are typically prepared as the detailed control baseline against which all actual costs and resources will now be monitored for variations to the budget, and form a part of the change/variation control program.

Estimating Methods Used:
Class 2 estimates always involve a high degree of deterministic estimating methods. Class 2 estimates are prepared in great detail, and often involve tens of thousands of unit cost line items. For those areas of the project still undefined, an assumed level of detail takeoff (forced detail) may be developed to use as line items in the estimate instead of relying on factoring methods.

Expected Accuracy Range:
Typical accuracy ranges for Class 2 estimates are -5% to -15% on the low side, and +5% to +20% on the high side, depending on the technological complexity of the project, appropriate reference information, and the inclusion of an appropriate contingency determination. Ranges could exceed those shown in unusual circumstances.

Effort to Prepare (for US$20MM project):
Typically, as little as 300 hours or less to perhaps more than 3,000 hours, depending on the project and the estimating methodology used. Bid estimates typically require more effort than estimates used for funding or control purposes.

ANSI Standard Reference Z94.2-1989 Name:
Definitive estimate (typically -5% to + 15%).

Alternate Estimate Names, Terms, Expressions, Synonyms:
Detailed control, forced detail, execution phase, master control, engineering, bid, tender, change order estimate.

Figure 2d. – Class 2 Estimate

CLASS 1 ESTIMATE

Description:
Class 1 estimates are generally prepared for discrete parts or sections of the total project rather than generating this level of detail for the entire project. The parts of the project estimated at this level of detail will typically be used by subcontractors for bids, or by owners for check estimates. The updated estimate is often referred to as the current control estimate and becomes the new baseline for cost/schedule control of the project. Class 1 estimates may be prepared for parts of the project to comprise a fair price estimate or bid check estimate to compare against a contractor's bid estimate, or to evaluate/dispute claims. Typically, engineering is from 50% to 100% complete, and would comprise virtually all engineering and design documentation of the project, and complete project execution and commissioning plans.

Level of Project Definition Required:
50% to 100% of full project definition.

End Usage:
Class 1 estimates are typically prepared to form a current control estimate to be used as the final control baseline against which all actual costs and resources will now be monitored for variations to the budget, and form a part of the change/variation control program. They may be used to evaluate bid checking, to support vendor/contractor negotiations, or for claim evaluations and dispute resolution.

Estimating Methods Used:
Class 1 estimates involve the highest degree of deterministic estimating methods, and require a great amount of effort. Class 1 estimates are prepared in great detail, and thus are usually performed on only the most important or critical areas of the project. All items in the estimate are usually unit cost line items based on actual design quantities.

Expected Accuracy Range:
Typical accuracy ranges for Class 1 estimates are -3% to -10% on the low side, and +3% to +15% on the high side, depending on the technological complexity of the project, appropriate reference information, and the inclusion of an appropriate contingency determination. Ranges could exceed those shown in unusual circumstances.

Effort to Prepare (for US$20MM project):
Class 1 estimates require the most effort to create, and as such are generally developed for only selected areas of the project, or for bidding purposes. A complete Class 1 estimate may involve as little as 600 hours or less, to perhaps more than 6,000 hours, depending on the project and the estimating methodology used. Bid estimates typically require more effort than estimates used for funding or control purposes.

ANSI Standard Reference Z94.2 Name:
Definitive estimate (typically -5% to + 15%).

Alternate Estimate Names, Terms, Expressions, Synonyms:
Full detail, release, fall-out, tender, firm price, bottoms-up, final, detailed control, forced detail, execution phase, master control, fair price, definitive, change order estimate.

Figure 2e. – Class 1 Estimate

AACE International Recommended Practices

Cost Estimate Classification System – As Applied in Engineering
Procurement, and Construction for the Process Industries

aace
International

COMPARISON OF CLASSIFICATION PRACTICES

Figures 3a through 3c provide a comparison of the estimate classification practices of various firms, organizations, and published sources against one another and against the guideline classifications. These tables permits users to benchmark their own classification practices.

AACE Classification Standard	ANSI Standard Z94.0	AACE Pre-1972	Association of Cost Engineers (UK) ACostE	Norwegian Project Management Association (NFP)	American Society of Professional Estimators (ASPE)
Class 5	Order of Magnitude Estimate -30/+50	Order of Magnitude Estimate	Order of Magnitude Estimate Class IV -30/+30	Concession Estimate / Exploration Estimate / Feasibility Estimate	Level 1
Class 4	Budget Estimate -15/+30	Study Estimate	Study Estimate Class III -20/+20	Authorization Estimate	Level 2
Class 3		Preliminary Estimate	Budget Estimate Class II -10/+10	Master Control Estimate	Level 3
Class 2	Definitive Estimate -5/+15	Definitive Estimate	Definitive Estimate Class I -5/+5	Current Control Estimate	Level 4
Class 1		Detailed Estimate			Level 5 / Level 6

INCREASING PROJECT DEFINITION

Figure 3a. – Comparison of Classification Practices

Cost Estimate Classification System – As Applied in Engineering
Procurement, and Construction for the Process Industries

aace
International

February 2, 2005

AACE Classification Standard	Major Consumer Products Company (Confidential)	Major Oil Company (Confidential)	Major Oil Company (Confidential)	Major Oil Company (Confidential)
Class 5	Class S Strategic Estimate	Class V Order of Magnitude Estimate	Class A Prospect Estimate / Class B Evaluation Estimate	Class V
Class 4	Class 1 Conceptual Estimate	Class IV Screening Estimate	Class C Feasibility Estimate / Class D Development Estimate	Class IV
Class 3	Class 2 Semi-Detailed Estimate	Class III Primary Control Estimate	Class E Preliminary Estimate	Class III
Class 2	Class 3 Detailed Estimate	Class II Master Control Estimate	Class F Master Control Estimate	Class II
Class 1		Class I Current Control Estimate	Current Control Estimate	Class I

Figure 3b. – Comparison of Classification Practices

AACE Classification Standard	J.R. Heizelman, 1988 AACE Transactions [1]	K.T. Yeo, The Cost Engineer, 1989 [2]	Stevens & Davis, 1988 AACE Transactions [3]	P. Behrenbruck, Journal of Petroleum Technology, 1993 [4]
Class 5	Class V	Class V Order of Magnitude	Class III*	Order of Magnitude
Class 4	Class IV	Class IV Factor Estimate	Class II	Study Estimate
Class 3	Class III	Class III Office Estimate	Class II	Budget Estimate
Class 2	Class II	Class II Definitive Estimate	Class II	Budget Estimate
Class 1	Class I	Class I Final Estimate	Class I	Control Estimate

[1] John R. Heizelman, ARCO Oil & Gas Co., 1988 AACE Transactions, Paper V3.7
[2] K.T. Yeo, The Cost Engineer, Vol. 27, No. 6, 1989
[3] Stevens & Davis, BP International Ltd., 1988 AACE Transactions, Paper B4.1 (* Class III is inferred)
[4] Peter Behrenbruck, BHP Petroleum Pty., Ltd., article in Petroleum Technology, August 1993

Figure 3c. – Comparison of Classification Practices

AACE International Recommended Practices

Cost Estimate Classification System – As Applied in Engineering
Procurement, and Construction for the Process Industries

8 of 8

aace
International

February 2, 2005

ESTIMATE INPUT CHECKLIST AND MATURITY MATRIX

Figure 4 maps the extent and maturity of estimate input information (deliverables) against the five estimate classification levels. This is a checklist of basic deliverables found in common practice in the process industries. The maturity level is an approximation of the degree of completion of the deliverable. The degree of completion is indicated by the following letters.

- None (blank): development of the deliverable has not begun.
- Started (S): work on the deliverable has begun. Development is typically limited to sketches, rough outlines, or similar levels of early completion.
- Preliminary (P): work on the deliverable is advanced. Interim, cross-functional reviews have usually been conducted. Development may be near completion except for final reviews and approvals.
- Complete (C): the deliverable has been reviewed and approved as appropriate.

	ESTIMATE CLASSIFICATION				
General Project Data:	**CLASS 5**	**CLASS 4**	**CLASS 3**	**CLASS 2**	**CLASS 1**
Project Scope Description	General	Preliminary	Defined	Defined	Defined
Plant Production/Facility Capacity	Assumed	Preliminary	Defined	Defined	Defined
Plant Location	General	Approximate	Specific	Specific	Specific
Soils & Hydrology	None	Preliminary	Defined	Defined	Defined
Integrated Project Plan	None	Preliminary	Defined	Defined	Defined
Project Master Schedule	None	Preliminary	Defined	Defined	Defined
Escalation Strategy	None	Preliminary	Defined	Defined	Defined
Work Breakdown Structure	None	Preliminary	Defined	Defined	Defined
Project Code of Accounts	None	Preliminary	Defined	Defined	Defined
Contracting Strategy	Assumed	Assumed	Preliminary	Defined	Defined
Engineering Deliverables:					
Block Flow Diagrams	S/P	P/C	C	C	C
Plot Plans		S	P/C	C	C
Process Flow Diagrams (PFDs)		S/P	P/C	C	C
Utility Flow Diagrams (UFDs)		S/P	P/C	C	C
Piping & Instrument Diagrams (P&IDs)		S	P/C	C	C
Heat & Material Balances		S	P/C	C	C
Process Equipment List		S/P	P/C	C	C
Utility Equipment List		S/P	P/C	C	C
Electrical One-Line Drawings		S/P	P/C	C	C
Specifications & Datasheets		S	P/C	C	C
General Equipment Arrangement Drawings		S	P/C	C	C
Spare Parts Listings			S/P	P	C
Mechanical Discipline Drawings			S	P	P/C
Electrical Discipline Drawings			S	P	P/C
Instrumentation/Control System Discipline Drawings			S	P	P/C
Civil/Structural/Site Discipline Drawings			S	P	P/C

Figure 4. – Estimate Input Checklist and Maturity Matrix

REFERENCES

ANSI Standard Z94.2-1989. **Industrial Engineering Terminology: Cost Engineering**.
AACE International Recommended Practice No.17R-97, **Cost Estimate Classification System**.

Recommended Practice No. 21R-98

Project Code of Accounts – As Applied in Engineering, Procurement, and Construction for the Process Industries

January 27, 2003

INTRODUCTION

This guideline is an industry-specific addendum to AACE International's generic guideline for project code of accounts (Recommended Practice No. 20R-98). This document describes recommended practices for codes of accounts (COA) as applied to engineering, procurement, and construction (EPC) projects in the process industries. "Process industries" are those with facilities whose main function is to perform a process. This includes chemical, petrochemical, hydrocarbon, pulp and paper, pharmaceutical, power generation, thermal, metallurgical, assembly, fabrication, and other processing. The primary characteristic of these industries, as it relates to codes of accounts, is that process or manufacturing <u>equipment</u> is the core or primary physical component of the facility. Equipment differentiates these projects from commercial construction and infrastructure where the core component is a structure, from software development projects where the core component is programming code, and so on.

COAs are applicable to all phases of the asset life cycle, but this guideline specifically addresses the EPC for creation, modification, or termination of a process facility. This guideline does not apply to code of accounts to support ongoing operations of process facilities. Properly defining a work breakdown structure (WBS), and other project structures, and deciding how they should be structured are outside the scope of this document.

A project code of accounts is a coded index of project cost, resource, and activity categories. A complete COA includes definitions of the content of each account code and is methodically structured to facilitate finding, sorting, compiling, summarizing, defining and otherwise managing the project information that is linked to the code. The information is used to support total cost management practices such as cost estimating, cost reporting, cost accounting, planning, and scheduling. Refer to 20R-98 for a more complete description of the principles of COAs.

PURPOSE

The purpose of this guideline is to establish a common understanding of the attributes of project COAs in the process industries so that communication is improved among all process industry project stakeholders. These guidelines are intended to help cost management practitioners create or modify a COA in a way that maximizes its value.

Common understanding is important because all projects are the product of team endeavors in which the timely and accurate flow of project cost, resource, progress, and other information is essential to project success. Industry experience has shown that a large amount of time and resources are wasted in the effort to reconcile disparate project records, and project failures are often traced to poor communication. The practice of benchmarking process industry project costs at a meaningful level of detail is a daunting task because of the lack of cost coding commonality.

A "standard" fully-defined, process industry code of accounts that meets every user's requirements is beyond the scope of this guideline, but, a basic guideline COA structure is provided. The basic guideline COA establishes a minimal level of cost information organization that a process industry COA should follow to achieve the objective of establishing common understanding.

GUIDELINE METHODOLOGY AND BACKGROUND

This guideline was developed using a practical approach rather than a theoretical one. Real COAs were gathered and dissected to identify core COA principles, prevailing attributes and characteristics of COAs

Recommended Practice No. 21R-98

Project Code of Accounts – As Applied in Engineering, Procurement, and Construction for the Process Industries

January 27, 2003

INTRODUCTION

This guideline is an industry-specific addendum to AACE International's generic guideline for project code of accounts (Recommended Practice No. 20R-98). This document describes recommended practices for codes of accounts (COA) as applied to engineering, procurement, and construction (EPC) projects in the process industries. "Process industries" are those with facilities whose main function is to perform a process. This includes chemical, petrochemical, hydrocarbon, pulp and paper, pharmaceutical, power generation, thermal, metallurgical, assembly, fabrication, and other processing. The primary characteristic of these industries, as it relates to codes of accounts, is that process or manufacturing <u>equipment</u> is the core or primary physical component of the facility. Equipment differentiates these projects from commercial construction and infrastructure where the core component is a structure, from software development projects where the core component is programming code, and so on.

COAs are applicable to all phases of the asset life cycle, but this guideline specifically addresses the EPC for creation, modification, or termination of a process facility. This guideline does not apply to code of accounts to support ongoing operations of process facilities. Properly defining a work breakdown structure (WBS), and other project structures, and deciding how they should be structured are outside the scope of this document.

A project code of accounts is a coded index of project cost, resource, and activity categories. A complete COA includes definitions of the content of each account code and is methodically structured to facilitate finding, sorting, compiling, summarizing, defining and otherwise managing the project information that is linked to the code. The information is used to support total cost management practices such as cost estimating, cost reporting, cost accounting, planning, and scheduling. Refer to 20R-98 for a more complete description of the principles of COAs.

PURPOSE

The purpose of this guideline is to establish a common understanding of the attributes of project COAs in the process industries so that communication is improved among all process industry project stakeholders. These guidelines are intended to help cost management practitioners create or modify a COA in a way that maximizes its value.

Common understanding is important because all projects are the product of team endeavors in which the timely and accurate flow of project cost, resource, progress, and other information is essential to project success. Industry experience has shown that a large amount of time and resources are wasted in the effort to reconcile disparate project records, and project failures are often traced to poor communication. The practice of benchmarking process industry project costs at a meaningful level of detail is a daunting task because of the lack of cost coding commonality.

A "standard" fully-defined, process industry code of accounts that meets every user's requirements is beyond the scope of this guideline, but, a basic guideline COA structure is provided. The basic guideline COA establishes a minimal level of cost information organization that a process industry COA should follow to achieve the objective of establishing common understanding.

GUIDELINE METHODOLOGY AND BACKGROUND

This guideline was developed using a practical approach rather than a theoretical one. Real COAs were gathered and dissected to identify core COA principles, prevailing attributes and characteristics of COAs

as they are applied in process industry EPC projects today. The content characteristics that were most
commonly used were tabulated and compiled into the basic guideline COA.

There are almost as many different codes of accounts as there are companies executing EPC projects in
the process industries. For this guideline, 21 actual COAs were collected, analyzed, and summarized in
table 1. Despite the differences, there is sufficient consistency of approach in the industry to provide
confidence that the COAs collected are an adequate sample.

Process Industry Type	Organization	Type of Projects	Number
Oil & gas	Owner	EPC, maintenance	3
Oil & gas	Standards/professional	EPC, operating	1
Offshore oil & gas	Standards/owners	EPC, operating, maint.	1
Offshore oil & gas	Contractor/owner	EPC	2
Process-general	Contractor	EPC	4
Process-general	Standards/professional	EPC	2
Process-general	Benchmarking	EPC	1
Chemical	Owner	EPC, operating, maint.	1
Chemical	Contractor	EPC	2
Utility	Owner	EPC, maintenance	1
Utility	Contractor	EPC	1
Process - pulp & paper	Contractor	EPC	2
			21

Table 1 – Sample of Process Industry Code of Accounts Used in This Guideline

The detailed contents of the owner and contractor company COAs are confidential. Some of the sample
COAs have been previously published, and a general description of these is included in Appendix A. The
COA from the organization referred to as "benchmarking" is a format that 14 international owner
companies had agreed to use for cost and resource benchmarking and metrics purposes.

After identifying the content characteristics of each COA, these characteristics were listed in tables that
categorize them by their prevalence of use. The most prevalent characteristics were then compiled in a
logical manner into the basic guideline COA. When determining the most prevalent (i.e., primary) content
characteristics, each COA was given equal weight, with the exception of the "benchmarking" COA that
was given double weight because many owner companies had agreed to this format for cost sharing
purposes. Characteristics were categorized or ranked by prevalence of use as shown in table 2.

Characteristic Group	Percent Occurrence in the Sample COAs
Primary	Equal to or greater than 75 percent
Secondary	50 to 74 percent
Tertiary	25 to 49 percent
Other	Less than 25 percent

Table 2 – COA Characteristic Ranking Categories

While the practical approach described above is not specifically forward-looking, the core COA practices
identified are expected to have lasting value. This and related guidelines will serve as a documented
basis for AACE's cooperation with other industry COA initiatives (particularly those of vendors and users
of computer-aided engineering and design, enterprise and project planning systems, and accounting
systems as they attempt to further integrate their products).

Project Code of Accounts – As Applied in Engineering, Procurement, and Construction for the   3 of 13
Process Industries

aace
International

January 27, 2003

ATTRIBUTES OF PROCESS INDUSTRY CODES OF ACCOUNTS

The four basic attributes of a code of accounts as described in RPS-20R98 include:

> usage;
> content;
> structure and format; and
> standardization.

When evaluating a COA, these attributes should be considered within the context of the project system's circumstances and requirements. In the case of this guideline, the general requirements of the process industries are considered. Each of these four attributes is discussed in the sections that follow.

Usage

There are three primary groups who use project code of accounts in the process industries: asset owners, contractors, and consultants.

Asset Owner Companies
The primary use of COAs by process industry owner companies is for allocation of costs for financial budgeting and close-out reporting. Asset classifications such as cost center, area/unit, authorization for expenditure, and location, are frequently used by owners. Most owners contract out their construction work, detailed engineering, and bulk material procurement, and therefore, the owners perceive less immediate need for activity-based accounts as used for project control during execution. In many cases, owners do not have a COA that allows effective project control of their own internal activities, such as front-end engineering. Activity-based cost data is critical to owners for understanding their own long-term project cost performance and developing their own conceptual cost estimating and benchmarking capabilities, but many owners do not adequately understand its value.

Over 80 percent of process industry owners segregate capital, expense, and suspense cost types. Suspense costs are temporary holding accounts for items such as project material stock, contractor retention, and so on, which are cleared-out prior to closing the project. Expense costs are those that are written-off in the year they are incurred, while capital costs are those that depreciate over more than one year. About 70 percent of process industry owners have a code to classify capital cost of assets for taxation, capital cost allowance, and fixed asset accounting depreciation.

EPC Contractors
The primary use of COAs by process industry contractors is the allocation of costs for project control. Cost and resource data need to be captured by discipline/commodity and area/unit so that work progress can be planned and assessed. Asset classification and capitalization are minor issues (except to the extent that owners request this data). A special code that is often used by contractors, but not owners, is the billing code that indicates whether the relevant cost can be charged or billed to the client. General contractors and construction managers need to separate subcontractor costs from their own (they are also sometimes asked by owners to maintain overall project cost records, including owner costs).

Standards Groups, Benchmarking Consultants, and Others
The use of COAs by groups other than owners and EPC contractors depends on what role they are assuming in a project. However, consultants are often asked to assess or benchmark past cost performance or to predict, estimate, or validate future project costs. Performance evaluation and estimation both require an understanding of activities that comes from the discipline/commodity project control information collected by EPC contractors for execution. Standards groups tend to also focus on these same uses. Asset classification, capitalization, and taxation issues are usually secondary uses to these groups.

AACE International Recommended Practices

aace
International

January 27, 2003

Content

In table 3 below, all of the content characteristics found in the process industry COA sample are classified into the primary categories as defined in the generic COA guidelines (see RPS-20R98 for further definitions of general content attributes).

Accounting and special	Geographical (where)	Physical (deliverable)	Resource (who and what)	Activity (how)	Timing (when)
Cost group	Location	Area/unit	Prime account	WCS/SAB	Phase
Project #	Country	System	Commodity	WBS	Budget year
Cost center	State/province	Project type	Discipline	Activity	Shutdown/non-shutdown phase
Capital/expense	City/town	Facility	Cost type	Work type	
Billing code	Plant	Commodity	Trade	Phase	
Asset class	Area	Process	Organization	Process step	
Tax jurisdiction	ISBL/OSBL	Component	Company	Sub-phase	
Change #	Site	WBS	Department	Discipline	
Contract #	Office	Direct/indirect	Material	Activity type	
AFE #			Contractor		
			Service		

Table 3 - Classification of Process Industry COA Content Characteristics

Table 4 ranks the process industry content attributes in terms of their prevalence of occurrence by organization type.

Type of Organization	Primary (75% +)	Secondary (50%-74%)	Tertiary (25%-49%)	Other (24% or less)
Owners	Capital/expense	Prime account Detail account Cost center Cost type Project number Plant/site location	Project type Area/unit Cost group Company Sub-account	WCS/SAB WBS Trade Fund Responsibility
Contractors	Prime account	Sub-account Detail account Cost type Cost group Area	WCS/SAB WBS System Billing status Commodity Project number Unit	Phase Customer job # Plant/site location Change # Responsibility
Standards and others	Cost type Prime account Sub account	Area Detail account Cost group	Project no. Project type System Unit Trade Plant/site location	Phase WCS/SAB Cost center Company WBS

Table 4 - Characteristics by Organization Type

Project Code of Accounts – As Applied in Engineering, Procurement, and Construction for the   5 of 13
Process Industries

aace
International

January 27, 2003

Table 5 ranks the above process industry content attributes in terms of their prevalence of occurrence in the COA sample for all organization types combined.

Type of Organization	Primary (75% +)	Secondary (50%-74%)	Tertiary (25%-49%)	Other (24% or less)
All	Prime account	Cost type Area/unit Cost group Sub account Detail account	Project number WCS/SAB WBS Cost center Plant/site location	Work type/activity Trade System Project type Billing status Phase Company Asset class

Table 5 – Characteristics Ranked by Prevalence of Usage (All End Users Combined)

DEFINITIONS OF CONTENT CHARACTERISTICS

The text that follows provides definitions of the most prevalent content characteristics. Users should also refer the generic guidelines (RPS-20R98) for further definition.

Accounting and Special Codes

Cost Group (Secondary)
As the title implies, a cost group represents a high-level summarization used for general cost reporting as opposed to project control or asset accounting. A cost group may be a combination of cost type and direct/indirect characteristics (e.g., direct material, direct labor, and so on). Another cost grouping is field versus home office costs (field and home office are typically not geographic or organizational characteristics because they are general groupings that do not specify actual location or organization). Table 6 shows how different organization types tend to group or summarize costs at a high level.

Generic Group Name	Owners	Contractors	Standards/Benchmarks
Direct costs	Capital directs	Directs	Directs
Indirect costs	Capital indirects	Field indirects Home office	Field indirects Project management and administration Engineering
Expense costs	Expense		
Suspense costs	Suspense		
Other costs		Other costs	Other costs

Table 6 - Typical Primary Group Categories Used by Organization Type

Project Number (Tertiary)
The project number is rarely included as part of a COA dictionary but is normally included in the coding format. This allows organizations involved with more than one project to keep the costs of each project separate.

Cost Center (Tertiary)
A location, a machine, or an organization may be cost centers. Cost centers are also used in activity-based costing to allocate costs to a process-step or activity. This attribute is used more for accounting or cost analysis purposes rather than project planning and controls.

AACE International Recommended Practices

aace
International

Product/Deliverable

In the process industries, the deliverable is a physical product such as a petrochemical plant, refinery, or one of the major parts of the facility. Equipment, materials, and labor are not products in this context. They are resources used to arrive at the final product. Equipment is easily related to the final product because it is the primary focus of the permanent installation. Bulk materials are more difficult but may be related to the final product. Labor may be allocated to the final product if the cost coding system is designed properly.

Direct/Indirect (Secondary)

Direct costs are those which are readily or directly attributable to, or become an identifiable part of, the final product (e.g., piping labor, and material). Indirect costs are all costs that cannot be attributed readily to a part of the final product (e.g., costs for managing the project). Indirect costs are sometimes called prorates or distributives because they are often allocated to direct cost categories to determine the total costs of a product or asset class. Indirect costs are occasionally called overheads, but overheads are generally considered a sub-type of indirect costs. This characteristic is often combined with cost type to form a cost group (e.g., direct materials, indirect labor, and so on). Owners and contractors commonly account for indirects differently. For instance, a contractor may account for employee salary as a direct cost and benefits as an indirect cost, but the owner is billed for total labor cost (i.e., all-in rate including contractor direct and indirect labor items), all of which the owner considers a direct cost.

Unit (Secondary)

Unit is more commonly known as process unit, but the word *process* is dropped to minimize field descriptors in software programs. A process unit is comprised of equipment, piping, process control devices, support structures, and associated materials. There may be several systems or a single system in a unit that make it a functional whole. A process unit typically changes the physical properties of whatever enters it, or it can be a utility process that enhances or improves the efficiency of the processing function. A unit code is commonly used in combination with an area code.

Work Breakdown Structures (WBS - Tertiary)

A WBS can be described as a hierarchical division of work scope divided into manageable parts that correspond to key deliverables, phases, or milestones. Work breakdown structures may be product-oriented (e.g., bridge section, building foundation, software program, aircraft wing), process-oriented (e.g., phase, step, activity), organization-oriented (e.g., contractor, department, team), or combined product/process/organizational hierarchies. Some organizations use WBSs only to divide work scope into manageable parts while others use WBSs as a replacement for COAs. Labels or identifier codes for WBS elements are commonly called cost codes because it is possible to predefine a dictionary of WBS elements in the same manner as for codes of accounts. Conversely, several organizations refer to their code of accounts as a WBS because the project breakdown is incorporated into the cost coding. Many organizations executing projects have some form of both. When an extensive WBS exists, there is reduced need for a fully detailed code of accounts. For example, if the WBS is broken down by discipline (e.g., civil, electrical), cost codes for discipline become redundant if costs are being charged to the WBS.

Resource

Prime Account of Discipline (Primary)

Prime account is the most common characteristic of all process industry COAs and is also applicable to the product and work type dimensions. Discipline, commodity, major account, work classification, header account, code of resource (COR), and activity type are other names used for this category. In project controls for EPC projects in the process industries, engineering is driven by discipline, procurement is driven by commodities, and construction is driven by discipline or type of work. The material and equipment costs for process industry projects range roughly between 40 and 80 percent of the total cost. That being the case, it becomes prudent to further break commodities down into major categories. Commodities are simply classes of common materials. Several commodity items are normally required to result in a product that is functional. In this context, a commodity also can be considered a resource because it is a resource required for installation. Discipline is a type of work, craft, profession, or trade. Each discipline will employ a somewhat unique set of skills and knowledge and will tend to work with different types of materials (i.e., commodities) and resources.

Cost Type (Secondary)

Cost type generally refers to the type of resources such as labor, material (i.e., equipment and bulk materials), or subcontract (i.e., a combination of labor and material). This account type also may be used for organizational and accounting breakdowns. In organizational usage it may segregate owner costs from contractor costs and may further identify contract type (subcontract, service, turnkey supply and install, design, labor, and so on). In accounting usage it may segregate rental and lease costs from purchases. Also, asset owners need to separate capital costs from expense costs (e.g., demolition and software development are often expensed) because they affect depreciation, taxation, and ultimately profitability.

Some COAs have combined cost type and direct/indirect designations such that an account may be defined as "direct labor" for example. This means there are two distinct elements. One part is the designation of direct versus indirect cost, which is actually a grouping of prime accounts, and the other part indicates the type of resource (e.g., labor, material, contracts, or general costs). Not every organization uses both types of characteristics. Benchmarking analysis indicated that approximately 60 percent of the COAs separate cost type and the direct/indirect categories. It is therefore recommended that the two characteristics be separate rather than used together. This also allows for separate computerized sorting, selecting, summarization, and analysis (i.e., "slice and dice"). The combined cost type and direct/indirect indictor was referred to as "group code" in some COAs.

Organization

Organization refers to responsibility for a cost category. Formal organizational breakdown structures (OBS) are not often part of a project COA; however, contractors routinely make provision to accommodate external organizations' cost categories, such as owner or subcontractor costs. Owner versus contractor costs is the highest level of organizational breakdown. If more than one contractor is involved, a separate code would be required for each contractor. Organizational codes may be used on timecards to record the discipline or trade involved. A similar approach is used for other organizational attributes such as coding of contractor invoices. Organizational attributes are often combined with cost type to achieve a hybrid cost type and eliminate extra coding requirements. Responsibility, company, department, trade, discipline, and internal/external are examples of organizational attributes.

Activity

Work Classification Structure (WCS), Standard Activity Breakdown (SAB), and Phase (Tertiary)

WCS and SAB represent the actions or types of activities required to execute the work scope (e.g., review drawing, fabricate equipment, erect pipe, and so on). Activity types for engineering work are commonly categorized by discipline. This account is a basic attribute of project control and activity-based costing. Phases are stages of project development and represent the highest level of summarized work process steps and activities. Tracking costs against phases can provide summary expenditure profiles and related cost performance indices when timing of the phases is known.

Location

Area (Secondary)

Area is a geographical location with a defined boundary and may include several process units and non-process parts of a plant. Non-process refers to roads, walkways, rail spurs, docks, ponds, landscaping, office buildings, and so on. For example, a "white oils area" in a lubricant plant may contain a hydrotreater unit, a hydrogen unit, dewax units, and some roads and walkways. "Area" is often used in combination with "unit".

January 27, 2003

Plant/Site (Tertiary)

Projects that encompass multiple sites use a plant or site indicator to collect costs for each location. A plant is related to a location. Sometimes the term *plant* is used to describe an area within a plant complex. For example, the asphalt production of a refinery is often referred to as the asphalt plant even though it is part of the refinery. Facility is a generic term for plant. A facility could be larger or smaller than a plant or it also could be a building. In the process industries, a plant is a functional entity used to produce a sellable product as opposed to being used for shelter.

Timing

No timing attributes were found to be primary, secondary, or tertiary.

BASIC PRINCIPLES FOR COA'S APPLIED TO EPC IN THE PROCESS INDUSTRIES

A brief summary of basic principles is provided as a reference for the basic coding structure.

A code of accounts should have no more or less detail than needed to meet stated requirements. Fewer account codes are required if a WBS exists that covers the product, activity, and/or organizational dimensions.

The highest level of summarization below total project level should fit easily on one page.

There are significant benefits to using multi-dimensional, hierarchical coding structures regardless of whether intelligence is built into the codes or not. A well-designed COA allows costs to be summarized, selected, and sorted by resource, prime account, cost type, end product, phase, etc.

Each cost code item requires a clear definition of what is included and what is excluded. Three or four-word descriptions are only acceptable for summary-level codes when the full definition can be found by referring to the detailed items.

It is acceptable to use either alpha or numeric or combined alpha/numeric characters for cost codes. There are some advantages to using alpha codes.

On projects where a cost engineering or "project controls" function exists, this function is usually responsible for determining and maintaining the code of accounts. The project manager approves the project COA and any changes to it.

BASIC CODING STRUCTURE

Two tables are provided in this section. The two tables are often shown as a matrix (as in a spreadsheet) with the primary accounts and cost groups on the vertical axis and the cost types across the horizontal axis.

Primary Accounts and Cost Groups

Table 7 lists the prime accounts and groupings most frequently used in the sample COAs.

aace
International

Primary Category	Brief Description and Comments
Direct Field Costs *(Cost Group)*	
Civil and Marine	Includes sitework, earthwork, clearing, excavation and backfill, fencing, landscaping. Marine is considered a separate prime category only in offshore work.
Concrete	Includes cast-in-place concrete as well as pre-cast items.
Structural Steel	Includes steel and other metal supports, ladders and platforms. May also include specialty structural materials such as plastics.
Buildings and Architectural	Includes buildings with all foundations, structure, HVAC, etc., where buildings are an incidental part of the project (i.e., control sheds, etc.). If the project includes a major building, building costs are best accounted for with a nonprocess COA.
Equipment	Includes process and mechanical equipment. This is commonly broken down into more categories. Includes refractory linings.
Piping and Process Air Ductwork	Includes pipe, valves, fittings, hangers, etc. Process air ductwork is considered a separate prime category in industries with extensive drying, combustion, and similar processes.
Electrical	Includes power, lighting, raceway, telecommunication, etc.
Instrumentation/Process Controls	Includes field instrumentation, control valves, control panels, instrument air tubing, instrument wiring. Raceway is usually included in electrical.
Protective Coatings	Insulation, paint, and fireproofing.
Indirect Field Costs	
Temporary Construction Facilities and Utilities	Includes temporary trailers, camps, roads, fencing, field fabrication shops, temporary power, water.
Construction Services and Supplies	Consumables, fuel, janitorial, medical, security, clean-up.
Construction Tools and Equipment	Cranes, hoists, trucks, welding machines, hand tools.
Construction Management Staff and Administration	Supervision, clerical, stationery, reprographics, furniture.
General Construction Overheads	Construction permits, duty, transportation, mob/demob, insurance.
	Note: when managing direct hire work, it is common to account for craft labor benefits and burdens as an indirect.
Commissioning & Start-Up	Direct labor and material for post-mechanical completion work until steady state production is achieved. Includes vendor reps and first fill catalysts and filter charges.
	Note: raw process materials are generally not a project cost.
General Project Indirects	
Project Management and Administration	Includes PM, project engr., cost, schedule, accounting, procurement, clerical, office stationery, travel, staff relocation.
Engineering and Design	All disciplines including process and models, travel, royalties, studies, staff relocation, as-builts. Includes engineering management (unless they also serve as project manager) and follow-up engineering support after release of drawings.
Special Project Costs	Project financing, permits, taxes, insurance, legal, fees, etc.
Contingency and Escalation	Estimate contingency, escalation & other estimate allowances.
	Note: no actual costs are charged to these but they hold budget costs that are allocated via a change management process.

Table 7 - Basic Coding Structure - Primary Accounts for EPC Projects in the Process Industries

aace
International

Cost Types

Table 8 shows a cost type structure with a second tier that allows more detail.

Cost-Type - Level 1	Cost Type - Level 2
Labor	Internal
	External (contract)
Material/Equipment	Process equipment (may need 3rd level)
	Packaged units
	Nonprocess equipment
	Bulk material
	Construction consumables
Contracts	Supply & install (directs)
	Leasing and rentals
	Construction services (indirects)
General costs/overheads	Financing, contractor fees/penalty, taxes, permits, regulatory, bonds, insurance, etc.
Expense	Noncapital costs as defined by legislation and/or owner requirements
Suspense	Contingency, unallocated estimate allowances and escalation, backcharges, project stock, contract retention

Table 8 - Cost Type Hierarchy

Coding Format and Structure Characteristics

Coding Formats
A cost code usually contains a series or set of cost code elements. COAs for projects should include a key to the overall coding format which explain how the various code parts fit into the structure. Figure 1 illustrates a typical method used to illustrate this in COA documents.

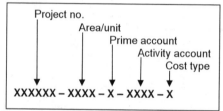

Figure 1 - Example of a Coding Format Definition Key

Alpha or Numeric Characters in Coding
In the COA samples evaluated for this guideline, there are about the same number of COAs with combined alpha/numeric codes as there are with pure numeric codes. Detail accounts tend to be numeric. Numeric codes are constraining because each character can only represent 10 breakdown categories (9 if zero is not used). More than 10 breakdowns requires the use of letters (i.e., alphas) or alpha-numeric combinations. Using only letters allows 26 categories (English alphabet) in a single character field. A combination of both numbers and letters yields 36 categories. One drawback of using alpha-numeric codes is potential confusion because of the visual similarity of some characters. (letter I vs number 1 or letter O vs number 0) Refer to Table 9 for the number of combinations per digit used. Alpha-numeric can reduce data processing and storage costs because increasing the number of fields or code categories increases database size. "Intelligence" is commonly designed into the coding to facilitate understanding learning and accuracy. For instance, ENG may stand for engineering, L for labor and so on.

Project Code of Accounts – As Applied in Engineering, Procurement, and Construction for the   11 of 13
Process Industries

January 27, 2003

# of Digits	Numbers only	Letters Only	Alpha-numeric
1	10	26	36
2	100	676	1296
3	1000	17576	46656

Table 9 – Number of combinations available by type of character

AACE International Recommended Practices

Project Code of Accounts – As Applied in Engineering, Procurement, and Construction for the   12 of 13
Process Industries

January 27, 2003

APPENDIX A: EXISTING STANDARDS

Existing standards included in the benchmarking analysis of process industry codes of accounts are described below.

The Association of Cost Engineers (UK) has produced a standard code of accounts as recently as 1994, which is intended to cover a variety of industries. It is very suitable for use in the process industries. The code structure is hierarchical and minimizes the volume of accounts required.

Norwegian petroleum industry operators have developed a coding guideline called Standard Cost Coding System (SCCS) in concert with the Norwegian Petroleum Directorate (NPD). The SCCS is an extensive three-dimensional model of hierarchical coding structures that covers resources, activity types, and physical components for both offshore and land-based installations. The NPD requires all companies operating on the Norwegian continental shelf to report costs prior to or with submission of a development plan and also report actual costs upon completion of each development project. There are specific statutory reporting requirements under the jurisdiction of the NPD. Both of the above-mentioned standards are included with the benchmarking and analysis of North American organizations.

In Canada, all oil and gas exploration and production organizations exchange project and operating cost information using the Petroleum Accounting Society of Canada (PASC) standard. Exchanging cost information is required because joint ventures are common practice in this industry. It is more of an accounting standard than a project standard so it is used on multiple small projects more often than on medium and larger-sized EPC projects.

Construction Specifications Institute's (CSI) MasterFormat is a widely used standard among the industrial/commercial/buildings/architectural construction and government contracting industries. Consequently, several estimating software packages use this format as well. It is a comprehensive, commodity-based specification format for bidding and administration of construction contracts, so engineering and some other indirect costs are not key considerations. For these reasons, it was not included in the benchmarking of COAs for EPC projects in the process industry. MasterFormat is occasionally used to form part of a COA by organizations in the process and utility industries. Most process industry projects could only effectively use three or four of the 16 primary MasterFormat divisions. The remaining categories would have negligible use (e.g., wood and plastics). Building costs typically make up about 15 percent of process industry project costs. However, as shown in table 9, the building industry could effectively use all of the categories commonly used in the process industries.

Process Industry Guideline	Suitability for Building Industry
Earthworks/civil	Primary equivalent
Concrete	Primary equivalent
Structural steel	Secondary (part of metals)
Buildings/architectural	Covers several primary equivalents
Equipment	Primary equivalent
Ductwork	Secondary
Piping and process air ductwork	Secondary
Electrical	Primary equivalent
Instrumentation/controls	Secondary
Protective coatings	Secondary - close to thermal & moisture protection
Construction indirects	Primary equivalent
Project management & administration	Secondary
Engineering and design	Not included
General project overheads	Secondary

Table 10- Suitability of Process Industry Prime Accounts for Use in the Building Industry

aace
International

January 27, 2003

REFERENCES

A **Guide to the Project Management Body of Knowledge**, Project Management Institute, 1996.

A New Look at Work Breakdown Structure, Robert Youker, PMI Seminar, Oct '90.

Accounting: The Basis for Business Decisions - Meigs, Mosich, Johnson, and Blazouske.

Applied Cost Engineering - 2nd edition - Clarke & Lorenzoni.

Construction Industry Institute Publication 6-3, *Model Planning and Controlling System for EPC of Industrial Projects*, April 1987.

Conducting Technical and Economic Evaluations in the Process and Utility Industries - AACE Recommended Practices and Standards, November 1990.

Cost and Optimization Engineering, 2nd edition, Jelen and Black.

Cost and Schedule Workshop, J. A. Bent, Chinook-Calgary Section of AACE-Canada Inc. "Back to Basics" seminar, 1992.

Cost Estimate Classification System - AACE Recommended Practices, 1997.

MasterFormat - The Construction Specifications Institute, May 1995.

Project and Cost Engineer's Handbook, 1979, American Association of Cost Engineers.

Project Management A Systems Approach to Planning, Scheduling and Controlling, 3rd edition - Harold Kerzner.

Standard Code of Accounts - The Association of Cost Engineers (UK), 1994.

Standard Cost Coding System - Statoil, Saga Petroleum, Norsk Hydro, Norwegian Petroleum Directorate, May 1992.

Uniformat - The Construction Specifications Institute, 1992 Interim edition for building construction.

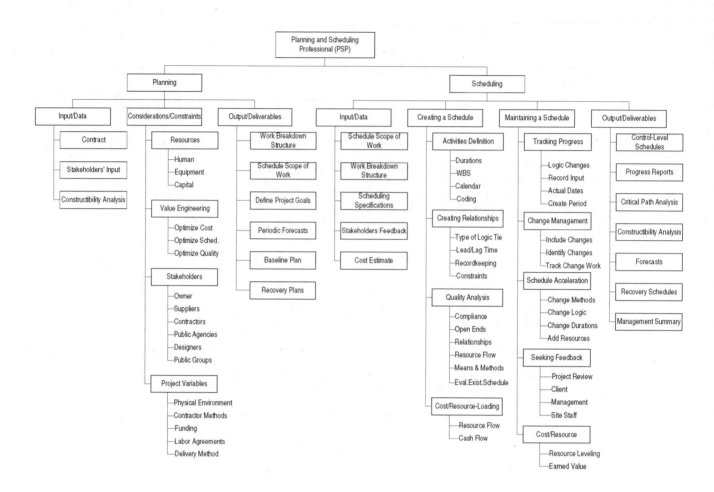

Welcome to AACE International

Promoting the Planning and Management of Cost and Schedules

AACE International is a non-profit professional association comprised of thousands of cost and schedule practitioners worldwide. The Association is dedicated to the advancement of planning and management of costs and schedules through education and certification, programs and technical products. AACE is the only technical association concerned with the entire spectrum of project costs.

As a member of AACE, your professional connections and resources will allow immediate opportunities for skill development and networking; access to the latest methods and information in the field of cost management; and the chance to be recognized in the community through certification. Explore what AACE International has to offer you and your company.

THE AACE International Advantage

Cost Engineering Journal - AACE International's monthly publication features cost estimating, project control, economic and financial analysis, planning and scheduling, cost engineering, and project management technical articles for cost professionals around the world. Through the mail or via the AACE International website, the *Cost Engineering* Journal is a great resource for members.

AACE Website - Visit AACE's website, www.aacei.org, and locate thousands of technical papers and publications at the Online Bookstore. AACE's database is keyword searchable for quickly locating appropriate reference articles. Enjoy full access to current member benefits. Check out our AACE section website links, upcoming events, certification news and forms, and AACE's E-ployment page (where members can post resumes at no additional cost).

Education - AACE offers courses to educate anyone who wishes to advance their professional capabilities. AACE offers numerous distance learning courses on estimating and project management. The AACE AEP (Approved Educational Provider) Program helps identify high quality development courses and providers. In addition to these learning tools, AACE holds many seminars throughout the year and an annual scholarship competition for college and graduate students.

AACE's Virtual Library - The Virtual Library (VL) is a fully searchable database that contains over 40 years of the Association's full-text technical articles available electronically in Adobe Acrobat (PDF) format. AACE offers two versions of

this member's only benefit -- one for our Corporate Sponsors and one for our individual members. The VL will continue to expand as newly published articles /are scanned and added to the library.

Technical Development - Increase your knowledge and expertise by joining one of AACE International's many technical committees, subcommittees, and Special Interest Groups (SIG's) at no additional cost to members. Discuss problems with your peers or help experts develop of new and improved techniques and practices for the profession.

Annual Meeting - Join cost and management practitioners from around the world to learn, network, and expand your career at AACE International's Annual Meeting. With over 100 technical presentations and seminars by global leaders in the cost and management field as well as networking and social events, the Annual Meeting is an experience you won't want to miss.

Certification - AACE's Certified Cost Consultant (CCC), Certified Cost Engineer (CCE), or Interim Cost Consultant (ICC) Programs are third-party credentials that are recognized as signifying specialized cost and management capabilities. AACE's programs are accredited by both the Council of Engineering and Scientific Specialty Boards and the International Cost Engineering Council, and are internationally recognized certifications in the cost management field. AACE's latest cutting-edge program is our new Planning and Scheduling Professional (PSP)

certification, a first-of-its-kind program for identifying professional planners and schedulers.

The Bookstore -You can purchase all the leading estimating and cost management books and CD's, as well as Professional Practice Guides and Annual Meeting Transactions online 24 hours a day.

Networking & Contacts - Expand your contacts through AACE International. Attend AACE local section or Annual Meetings for interesting speakers, informational tours, social dinners and much more. The annual Membership Directory and Resource Guide is an excellent source for a list of contact information of thousands of members. Another great resource is to join one of our many technical committees and their listservs.

Member Benefits & Affinity Partners - As a member, you get exceptional discounts on AACE International publications, educational seminars, certification and the Annual Meeting as well as medical and life insurance coverage at group rates, GlobalPhone International calling card, ExtraTouch Florists, car rentals and hotel services.

AACE International membership is a great value for all professionals who work in the cost and management disciplines. Whether you are a member or a prospective member, you will find AACE has many notable programs to offer!

Would you like to know more?

Contact AACE International Headquarters at 209 Prairie Avenue, Suite 100, Morgantown, WV 26501 USA
Phone: 304.296.8444 or 800.858.COST / Fax: 304.291.5728 / Email: info@aacei.org
Internet: http://www.aacei.org

aace International   *Membership Application*

To apply for membership:
- Complete this application, providing **all** information requested on both sides.
- Send completed application along with a check, money order, or credit card information to **AACE International, 209 Prairie Avenue, Suite 100, Morgantown, WV 26501, USA.** Canadian checks or money orders must include the currency differential between US and Canadian dollars.
- Upon membership approval you will receive a member packet with membership card, certificate, information on other member benefits, and your first issue of **Cost Engineering** journal.

Mail to the address listed above, or fax credit card payments to 304.291.5728. If you have any questions, call 800.858.COST or 304.296.8444.

MEMBERSHIP CLASSIFICATION

Application is for:
- ❐ Member
- ❐ Associate Member
- ❐ Student Member (Complete line at right, and include documentation of full-time student status.)
- ❐ PrePaid Life Member (See description on reverse)
- ❐ Reinstatement
- ❐ Change of Membership Grade

Member–A professional in cost management or cost engineering who has a minimum of six (6) years of related work experience, which may include up to four (4) years of full-time studies in a relevant degree program.

Associate Member–An individual interested in AACE membership, who does not specifically qualify as a member.

Student Member–An individual enrolled in a curriculum relevant to cost engineering or management (i.e., engineering, construction management, quantity surveying, architecture, mathematics, business, etc.) as a full-time student in a college or university.

Degree/Program _____ Projected Graduation Date _____

GENERAL INFORMATION

NAME _____
First   Middle   Last (Family)

BUSINESS (OR SCHOOL) ADDRESS:

Company Name   Title

Street Address

City   State/Province   Postal Code   Country

Phone   Fax

E-mail Address

HOME ADDRESS:

Street Address

City   State/Province   Postal Code   Country

Phone   Fax

E-mail Address

PREFERRED ADDRESSES:	Business	Home	Publish in Directory	DEMOGRAPHIC INFORMATION:
Mail	❐	❐	Yes ❐ No ❐	
Phone	❐	❐	Yes ❐ No ❐	Date of Birth
Fax	❐	❐	Yes ❐ No ❐	❐ Male ❐ Female
E-mail	❐	❐	Yes ❐ No ❐	

BACKGROUND INFORMATION

EDUCATION INFORMATION:

College/University _____

City, State or Province, Country _____

Degree and Major _____

Date Received _____

College/University _____

City, State or Province, Country _____

Degree and Major _____

Date Received _____

WORK EXPERIENCE:

From: _____ To: _____
Title: _____
Company Name: _____
Supervisor: _____
Job Duties: _____

From: _____ To: _____
Title: _____
Company Name: _____
Supervisor: _____
Job Duties: _____

By signing this application, I agree to abide by the Constitution and Bylaws, and Canon of Ethics of AACE International.

Signature: _____   Date: _____

rev 9/06

PAYMENT INFORMATION

See Chart Below for Dues Amount

Dues *Please see dues charts below.*
(Includes 1 complimentary section membership.) ....US$ _____
Change of Membership Grade (US$10) ....US$ _____
Application Fee ....US$ **10.00**
International Air Mail (US$99)...US$ _____
Membership Plaque* ....US$ _____
 Total Amount Due ....**US$** _____

*An attractive walnut-finished plaque is available for an additional: US—$30.00, Canada—$35.00, and non—US/Canada $55.00 (all prices US$).

❏ Check or money order made payable to **AACE International** enclosed

❏ Visa ❏ Mastercard ❏ American Express
❏ Eurocard ❏ Access

Credit Card Number _____

Card Expiration Date_____
 (Credit Card Charges in US$.)

Name on Card_____

Full Signature _____

AACE DUES

AACE's dues are invoiced annually. At the end of the subscription year, you will be billed for the next year at the annual rate.
The dues structure is based on the World Bank's income classifications, your national origin, and whether you are working AND residing in that country.
You must be a national living and working in your home country to qualify for a dues rate other than US$130.00. To determine your dues rate, see the tables below.

Group A — Annual Dues $115.00

Australia	Cyprus	Hong Kong	Kuwait	Singapore	United Kingdom
Bahamas	Finland	Ireland	Netherlands	Spain	
Belgium	France	Israel	New Zealand	Switzerland	
Bermuda	Germany	Italy	Portugal	Taiwan	
Cayman Islands	Greece	Japan	Qatar	United Arab Emirates	

Group B — Annual Dues $93.00

Argentina	China	Ghana	Mexico	Phillippines	Thailand
Bahrain	Columbia	Grenada	Morocco	Poland	Turkey
Bangladesh	Czech Republic	India	Nigeria	Republic of Korea	Uganda
Bosnia & Herzegovina	Dominican Republic	Indonesia	Oman	Russia	Ukraine
Brazil	Egypt	Jordan	Pakistan	South Africa	Venezuela
Chile	Ethiopia	Malaysia	Papua New Guinea	Sri Lanka	Vietnam

Group C — Annual Dues $130.00

Canada	Norway	St. Vincent & the Grenadines	United States
Jamaica	Saudi Arabia	Trinidad & Tobago	Virgin Islands (British)

Student Membership (regardless of country) — Annual Dues $25.00

Prepaid Life Membership Program

Prepaid Life Membership is available to anyone wishing to lock in their dues rate at today's rate, and thus be exempt from futher dues increases. This rate table is adjusted when any general dues increase occurs, but is only applicable to new enrollees. Just check the appropriate box on the dues form and include your first payment as determined by the table. In just four more years, your dues will be paid for life and you will be protected from any future dues increases. **This program does not exempt a member from paying annual section dues.*** Students, graduating students, and members paying the reduced international rates will be charged the full rate if they choose to select this option.

age <=45 - 5 payments of $345 = $1725 total	age 51 - 5 payments of $280 = $1400 total	age 57 - 5 payments of $185 = $925 total
age 46 - 5 payments of $335 = $1675 total	age 52 - 5 payments of $265 = $1325 total	age 58 - 5 payments of $170 = $850 total
age 47 - 5 payments of $325 = $1625 total	age 53 - 5 payments of $250 = $1250 total	age 59 - 5 payments of $150 = $750 total
age 48 - 5 payments of $315 = $1575 total	age 54 - 5 payments of $235 = $1175 total	age >=60 - 5 payments of $130 = $650 total
age 49 - 5 payments of $305 = $1525 total	age 55 - 5 payments of $220 = $1100 total	*Members outside the US, Canada, Norway, Saudi Arabia, and Trinidad & Tobago deduct $15 from the amount shown, and pay section dues locally.
age 50 - 5 payments of $290 = $1450 total	age 56 - 5 payments of $205 = $1025 total	

AACE SECTIONS

(please check off the section you wish to join. If you wish to join more than one, each additional is $15)

UNITED STATES
 Alabama
❏ Alabama
❏ Alaska
❏ Arizona
California
❏ San Francisco Bay Area
❏ South Central California
❏ Southern California
❏ Colorado (Rocky Mountain)
❏ Connecticut (Nutmeg)
❏ Delaware (Delaware Valley)
District of Columbia
❏ Baltimore Metro
❏ National Capital
Florida
❏ Emerald Coast
❏ Greater Miami
❏ North Florida

Georgia
❏ Atlanta Area
❏ Central Savannah River
❏ Hawaii
❏ Idaho (Snake River)
❏ Illinois (Chicago-Midwest)
❏ Kansas City
❏ Kentucky (Tri-States)
❏ Louisiana (Greater New Orleans)
Maryland
❏ Baltimore Metro
❏ National Capital
❏ Massachusetts (New England-Boston)
❏ Michigan Great Lakes
Missouri
❏ Kansas City
❏ St. Louis

❏ Nevada (Las Vegas)
❏ New Jersey
❏ New Jersey (Delaware Valley)
❏ New Mexico
❏ New Mexico (Valle Grande)
New York
❏ Genesee Valley
❏ Metropolitan New York
❏ Niagara Frontier
North Carolina
❏ Catawba Valley (Charlotte)
❏ Raleigh-Durham
Ohio
❏ Northeast Ohio
❏ Southwestern Ohio
❏ Tri-States
❏ Oklahoma (Northeast)
❏ Oregon (Cascade)

Pennsylvania
❏ Central Pennsylvania
❏ Delaware Valley
❏ Pittsburgh
❏ South Carolina
❏ South Carolina (Central Savannah River Area)
Tennessee
❏ East Tennessee
❏ Tennessee Valley
❏ University of Tennessee
Texas
❏ Central Texas
❏ Dallas-Ft. Worth
❏ Houston Gulf Coast
❏ Palo Duro Canyon
Virginia
❏ Central Virginia
❏ National Capital

Washington
❏ Rattlesnake Mountain
❏ Seattle
❏ Spokane
❏ University Of Washington
West Virginia
❏ Northern West Virginia
❏ Tri-States
❏ Wisconsin

CANADA
Alberta
❏ Aurora-Edmonton
❏ Chinook-Calgary
❏ British Columbia
❏ University of Calgary
Ontario
❏ Bluewater (Sarnia)
❏ Toronto
❏ Quebec Montreal

INTERNATIONAL
❏ Caribbean
❏ Norway
❏ Puerto Rico
❏ Saudi Arabia - Arabian Gulf

INTERNATIONAL
Pay Locallly
❏ Australia - Victoria
❏ Egypt - Greater Cairo
❏ Japan
❏ Kuwait
❏ Malaysia
❏ Nigeria
❏ Russia
❏ Ukraine - Chornobyl

OTHER
❏ Cybersection

Note: If you are unsure about which section to join, please contact AACE Headquarters at 800.858.COST or 304.296.8444.

AACE International Canon of Ethics

Introduction

The AACE member, to uphold and advance the honor and dignity of Cost Engineering and the Cost Management profession and in keeping with the high standards of ethical conduct will (1) be honest and impartial and will serve employer, clients, and the public with devotion; (2) strive to increase the competence and prestige of their profession; and (3) will apply knowledge and skill to advance human welfare.

I. Relations With the Public
   A. Members will hold paramount the safety, health, and welfare of the public, including that of future generations.
   B. Members will endeavor to extend public knowledge and appreciation of cost engineering and cost management and its achievements, and will oppose any untrue, unsupported, or exaggerated statements regarding cost engineering and cost management.
   C. Members will be dignified and modest, ever upholding the honor and dignity of their profession, and will refrain from self-laudatory advertising.
   D. Members will express an opinion on a cost engineering or cost management subject only when it is founded on adequate knowledge and honest conviction.
   E. On cost engineering or cost management matters, members will issue no statements, criticisms, or arguments that are inspired or paid for by an interested party or parties, unless they preface their comments by identifying themselves, by disclosing the identities of the party or parties on whose behalf they are speaking, and by revealing the existence of any pecuniary interest they may have in matters under discussion.
   F. Members will approve or seal only those documents, reviewed or prepared by them, which are determined to be safe for public health and welfare in conformity with accepted cost engineering, cost management and economic standards.
   G. Members whose judgment is overruled under circumstances where the safety, health, and welfare of the public are endangered shall inform their clients or employers of the possible consequences.
   H. Members will work through professional societies to encourage and support others who follow these concepts.
   I. Members will work only with those who follow these concepts.
   J. Members shall be objective and truthful in professional reports, statements, or testimony. They shall include all relevant and pertinent information in such reports, statements, and testimony.

II. Relations With Employers and Clients
   A. Members will act in all matters as a faithful agent or trustee for each employer or client.
   B. Members will act fairly and justly toward vendors and contractors and will not accept any commissions or allowances from vendors or contractors, directly or indirectly.
   C. Members will inform their employer or client of financial interest in any potential vendor or contractor, or in any invention, machine, or apparatus that is involved in a project or work for either employer or client. Members will not allow such interest to affect any decisions regarding cost engineering or cost management services that they may be called upon to perform.
   D. When, as a result of their studies, members believe a project(s) will not be successful, or if their cost engineering and cost management or economic judgment is overruled, they shall so advise their employer or client.
   E. Members will undertake only those cost engineering and cost management assignments for which they are qualified. Members will engage or advise their employers or clients to engage specialists whenever their employer's or client's interests are served best by such an arrangement. Members will cooperate fully with specialists so engaged.
   F. Members shall treat information coming to them in the course of their assignments as confidential and shall not use such information as a means of making personal profit if such action is adverse to the interests of their clients, their employers, or the public.
      1. Members will not disclose confidential information concerning the business affairs or technical processes of any present or former employer or client or bidder under evaluation, without consent, unless required by law.
      2. Members shall not reveal confidential information or finding of any commission or board of which they are members, unless required by law.
      3. Members shall not duplicate for others, without express permission of the client(s), designs, calculations, sketches, etc., supplied to them by clients.
      4. Members shall not use confidential information coming to them in the course of their assignments as a means of making personal profit if such action is adverse to the interests of their clients, employers, or the public.
   G. Members will not accept compensation—financial or otherwise—from more than one party for the same service, or for other services pertaining to the same work, without the consent of all interested parties.

H. Employed members will engage in supplementary employment or consulting practice only with the consent of their employer.

I. Members shall not use equipment, supplies, laboratory, or office facilities of their employers to carry on outside private practice without the consent of their employers.

J. Members shall not solicit a contract from a governmental body on which a principal officer or employee of their organization serves as a member.

K. The member shall act with fairness and justice to all parties when administering a construction (or other) contract.

L. Before undertaking work for others in which the member may make improvements, plans, designs, inventions, or records that may justify copyrights or patents, the member shall enter into a positive agreement regarding the rights of respective parties.

M. Members shall admit and accept their own errors when proven wrong and refrain from distorting or altering the facts to justify their decisions.

N. Members shall not attempt to attract an employee from another employer by false or misleading representations.

O. Members shall act in professional matters for each employer or client as faithful agents or trustees and shall avoid conflicts of interest.
    1. Members shall avoid all known or potential conflicts of interest with their employers or clients and shall promptly inform their employers or clients of any business association, interests, or circumstances that could influence their judgment or the quality of their services.
    2. Members shall not solicit or accept gratuities, directly or indirectly, from contractors, their agents, or other parties dealing with their clients or employers in connection with work for which they are responsible.

III. Relations With Other Professionals
    A. Members will take care that credit for cost engineering and cost management work is given to those to whom credit is properly due.
    B. Members will provide prospective employees with complete information on working conditions and their proposed status of employment. After employment begins, they will keep the employee informed of any changes in status and working conditions.
    C. Members will uphold the principle of appropriate and adequate compensation for those engaged in cost engineering and cost management work, including those in subordinate capacities.
    D. Members will endeavor to provide opportunity for the professional development and advancement of individuals in their employ or under their supervision.
    E. Members will not attempt to supplant other cost engineers or cost management professionals in a particular employment after becoming aware that definite steps have been taken toward the others' employment or after they have been employed.
    F. Members shall not maliciously or falsely, directly or indirectly, injure the professional reputation, prospects, practice, or employment of another, nor shall they indiscriminately criticize another's work. Proof that another cost professional has been unethical, illegal, or unfair in his/her practice shall be cause for advising the proper authority.

G. Members will not compete unfairly with other cost professionals.

H. Members will cooperate in advancing the cost engineering and cost management profession by interchanging information and experience with other cost professionals and students, by contributing to public communication media and to cost engineering, cost management and scientific societies and schools.

I. Members will not request, propose, or accept professional commissions on a contingent basis under circumstances that compromise their professional judgments.

J. Members will not falsify or permit misrepresentation of their own or their associates' academic or professional qualifications. They shall not misrepresent or exaggerate their degrees or responsibility in or for the subject matter of prior assignments. Brochures or other presentations incident to the solicitation of employment shall not misrepresent pertinent facts concerning employers, employees, associates, joint ventures, accomplishments, or membership in technical societies.

K. Members will prepare articles for the lay or technical press that are only factual, dignified, and free from ostentatious or laudatory implications. Such articles shall not imply credit to the cost professionals for other than their direct participation in the work described unless credit is given to others for their share of the work.

L. Members will not campaign, solicit support, or otherwise coerce other cost professionals to support their candidacy or the candidacy of a colleague for elective office in a technical association.

IV. Standards of Professional Performance
    A. Members shall be dignified and modest in explaining their work and merit and will avoid any act tending to promote their own interests at the expense of the integrity, honor, and dignity of the profession.
    B. Members, when serving as expert witnesses, shall express a cost engineering and cost management opinion only when it is founded upon adequate knowledge of the facts, upon a background of technical competence, and upon honest conviction.
    C. Members shall continue their professional development throughout their careers and shall provide opportunities for the professional development of those cost professionals under their supervision.
        1. Members should keep current in their specialty fields by engaging in professional practice, participating in continuing education courses, reading in the technical literature, and attending professional meetings and seminars.
        2. Members should encourage their cost engineering and cost management employees to become certified at the earliest possible date.
        3. Members should encourage their cost engineering and cost management employees to attend and present papers at professional and technical society meetings.
        4. Members shall uphold the principle of mutually satisfying relationships between employers and employees with respect to terms of employment including professional grade descriptions, salary ranges, and fringe benefits.

AUTHOR INDEX